WHAT'S WHO?

New edition, revised and enlarged

WHAT'S WHO?

A Dictionary of things named after people and the
people they are named after

FIG. 265.—*Aldini's Battery*,
Formed of the heads of recently decapitated oxen, A, B, C.

Roger Jones and Mike Ware

Matador
5 Weir Road
Kibworth Beauchamp
Leicester LE8 0LQ, UK
Tel: (+44) 116 279 2299
Fax: (+44) 116 279 2277
Email: books@troubador.co.uk
Web: www.troubador.co.uk/matador

ISBN 978 1848765 214

British Library Cataloguing in Publication Data.
A catalogue record for this book is available from the British Library.

Typeset in 11pt Garamond by Troubador Publishing Ltd, Leicester, UK

Matador is an imprint of Troubador Publishing Ltd

Printed in Great Britain by the MPG Books Group, Bodmin and King's Lynn

This book is dedicated to all those who believe, with the authors,
that there is no such thing as a useless fact.

CONTENTS

INTRODUCTION

What's Who? has been planned and written with a dual aim in view: to provide a reliable work of reference and, at the same time, a book that can be read - or at least dipped into - for pleasure.

Its subject matter is also two-sided. On the one hand (the *What?*) it is concerned with the meanings and origins of words and phrases formed on the name of a person; and on the other (the *Who?*) with the identity and biography, however brief, of the person in question.

Eponymy, the naming of things after people, is not a mere linguistic oddity, but a historical record of discoveries, ideas and inventions. It is a verbal memorial to those men and women, both famous and forgotten, who found, imagined or created such innovations, and even, in some cases, to those who bear credit for innovations that were not theirs. A brief glance through this book will suffice to show that virtually every field of human activity has left these nuggets of history embedded in our language. We make no claim, however, to have exhausted our subject. Because the aim has been to produce a book that can be held in the hand for reading (rather than a comprehensive tome requiring a lectern) we have had to be selective, and in some areas the selection has been frankly arbitrary. To rectify our omissions by completing a Massive Tome may well be a task for our successors.

Philological note

Formally, eponyms can be grouped into two broad categories which we may call Unitary and Compound. In the first case, the name of a person simply becomes the name of a thing as in *cardigan, hoover,* or *zeppelin*. In the second case, the name of a person is added to the name of a thing as an adjectival qualifier to distinguish that thing from other things of the same general type. Thus a *petri dish* is a dish, but it isn't a pie dish. These formations may be likened to Linnaean binomials (*q.v.*). We might, in addition, admit of a third, hybrid category in which the person's name is slightly altered by the addition of a suffix. Examples are, in the case of plant genera, the addition of *-ia* (*Aubrietia, Fuchsia*); in other cases, of *-ise* to make a verb (*grangerise, mithridatise*), or of an *-ism* (*sadism, lysenkoism*), and so on. In compiling *What's Who?*, we have regarded all three categories as admissible, together with a fourth category, technically known as *antonomasia*, by which an individual's name becomes that of a type figure, as when we refer to someone as a *Jezebel*, a *Scrooge*, or a *Lothario*.

Contributors

Roger Jones's entries are unsigned, Mike Ware's are signed MW. Other expert and very welcome contributions have come from Richard Staszynski (RS), Paul Pignon (PP), Gareth Jones (GJ), Jasna Pignon (JP), Ben Sorgiovanni (BS), Gerry Beswick (GB), and Rob Cameron (RC).

Comments, corrections, complaints, and contributions to a possible future Massive Tome can be addressed to us by e-mail at rwj@andover.co.uk, or mike@mikeware.co.uk. Meanwhile, for all omissions, mistakes, lapses from Political Correctness, mischievous opinions, and assorted infelicities, the authors take full responsibility.

Roger Jones
Mike Ware

A

[1] ABBE REFRACTOMETER

The bending of a ray of light passing obliquely into a translucent substance is determined by its refractive index. (For an explanation of refraction, see FERMAT'S PRINCIPLE OF LEAST TIME.) Refractive index can be simply measured with great precision thanks to the ABBE REFRACTOMETER, invented in 1869. This is a microscope-like instrument with the substance under investigation smeared on a prism which is rotatable to determine the *critical angle* beyond which no light is seen to be refracted. The refractive index is then calculated from this angle by SNELL'S LAW. Refractive index is an intrinsic physico-chemical property and has therefore provided a key for identifying substances before the advent of modern spectrometric methods of analysis. With an ABBE REFRACTOMETER, you can tell real butter from margarine, without relying on the taste buds. ERNST KARL ABBE (1840-1905) – his name is often erroneously Gallicised with an acute accent (é) – was a German optical physicist, born in Eisenach, who studied at the Universities of Göttingen and Jena, where he joined the faculty, becoming professor in 1870. In 1866 he was appointed as research director for CARL ZEISS (1816-1888), the optical instrument maker from nearby Wetzlar. In 1876 Abbe was made a partner in the firm and, on Zeiss's death, inherited it. He proved to be a humane and philanthropic employer. By developing the mathematical theory of lens design with ABBE'S SINE CONDITION, he greatly improved the correction of optical aberrations, which was furthered by a collaboration with Dr Otto Schott, glass-chemist of Jena. The researches of these three men placed the ZEISS OPTICAL WORKS in a league of its own, and Zeiss microscopes, employing the ABBE CONDENSER system of illumination, became a byword for optical excellence. (MW)

[2] ABEGG'S RULE

It has long since disappeared from the chemistry textbooks, but Abegg and Bodländer's "Rule of Eight" dating from 1899 still retains a certain usefulness: later known as the *Octet Rule*, it refers to the "magic number", eight, that governs the length of the second and third rows of MENDELEEV'S PERIODIC TABLE of the elements (the first row has just two members: hydrogen and helium). ABEGG'S RULE states that *an element shows a minimum valence* and a maximum valence which sum to 8. E.g.* phosphorus in Group Five: 3 and 5; sulphur in Group Six: 2 and 6; chlorine in Group Seven: 1 and 7; etc. We now know that the inert gases which terminate each successive row of the periodic table (neon, argon, krypton, xenon and radon) each have eight electrons in their outermost shells (the first, helium, has only two). Eight electrons form a particularly stable arrangement or *configuration* that atoms of the other elements strive to achieve by sharing their electrons in chemical combination** (to understand why it's exactly eight, one must take a long journey with Professors **SCHRÖDINGER** and **PAULI**). So chemistry is governed by the redistribution and sharing of electrons. An atom of an element in the nth vertical Group of the Periodic Table has n valence electrons in its outer shell, and tends to combine either by losing those n electrons so that it achieves the electron configuration of the previous inert gas, or by gaining $(8-n)$ more electrons giving the configuration of the next inert gas. The sum of the minimum and maximum valencies inevitably is $n + (8-n) = 8$. Nature ain't always quite so simple, or chemists would be out of a job. German chemist **RICHARD WILHELM EINRICH ABEGG** (1869-1910) graduated at Kiel, worked under Hofmann at Berlin, **OSTWALD** at Leipzig, Nernst at Göttingen, and **ARRHENIUS** at Stockholm, before becoming professor at Breslau. His colleague Guido Bodländer (1855-1904) was a graduate of Breslau and became professor in Braunschweig. Abegg died young in a ballooning accident before his vision of chemical reactions as exchanges of electrons could be fully appreciated and further developed. (MW)

*The valence or valency of an element is a number defining its combining ability – *i.e.* the number of attachments or bonds it can make to other elements. Hydrogen always has a valence of one, and oxygen two (hence H_2O) but most elements are more varied: *e.g.* nitrogen has valencies of three and five, so ammonia is NH_3 and nitrogen pentoxide is N_2O_5.

**Obviously the inert (or noble) gases have little inclination to share their electrons by entering into chemical combination, which is why they are so named.

[3] ABELIA

A genus of flowering shrubs named after **DR CLARKE ABEL** (1780-1826) its discoverer. Abel was a physician and naturalist in the Maturin mould (see **ADANSONIA**). In 1816-17 he accompanied Lord Amherst's disastrous embassy to China, a founding moment in the Great Wall of mutual misunderstanding which has bedevilled Europe's relations with China ever since. His account of the expedition, which involved shipwreck on the return journey and a small-boat voyage of the survivors to Batavia, was published in 1819 under the title *Narrative of a journey in the interior of China and voyage to and from that country*. The official account of the mission was written by Amherst's secretary Henry Ellis and entitled *Journal of the proceedings of the late embassy to China* (1817; 2nd ed. 2 vols 1818) (See also **LADY AMHERST'S PHEASANT**.)

[4] ABERNETHY

A biscuit for the upper crust tea party, plain and semi-sweet, said to be Scottish, and named after London-born, Edinburgh-trained medic, **DR. JOHN ABERNETHY** (1764-1831), who achieved celebrity by the eccentricity of his lecturing style on anatomy and physiology at the College of Surgeons. Elected FRS in 1796, he became chief surgeon at Bart's Hospital in 1815, was a vigorous proponent of the "Life Force" in the "Vitalism" debate (see **FRANKENSTEIN**), treated Coleridge for opium addiction,* and denounced the cruelty involved in animal experimentation.** Legend has it that while lunching on traditional "captain's biscuits" at the local baker's, Abernethy suggested the addition of sugar and caraway to the recipe. The outcome can still be purchased in a supermarket near you – tho' the caraway seems no longer in evidence. (MW)

* Poor Coleridge was alarmed by Abernethy's brusque manner and severe methods and referred to him as "an old bear". (Holmes: Coleridge: darker reflections 1998).

** His opposition to animal cruelty was tinged with xenophobia: he held that it was foreigners who took a particular and sadistic delight in tormenting our fellow-creatures in the name of science.

[5] ABNEY LEVEL

A surveying instrument for measuring slopes and vertical angles invented by **SIR WILLIAM DE WIVELESLIE ABNEY** (1843-1920). Born in Derby, Abney began his career as a junior officer in the Royal Engineers in 1861. After service in India, he was appointed instructor in chemistry and photography at the School of Military Engineering, Chatham. In 1877 he left the army for the civil service in the Department of Science and Art. He became an influential figure in the field of photographic technology and education, authoring many instructional books, and building the photographic collection at South Kensington Museum – to become the Science Museum. His chief discovery was the use of hydroquinone as a developer in 1880, and he made important contributions to astronomical photography and spectrography. The **ABNEY EFFECT** in the perception of colour is also named after him. He was elected FRS in 1876 and knighted in 1900. (MW)

[6] ABRAMS TANK

The **M1 ABRAMS** has been the United States' main battle tank since it came into service in 1980 in place of the M60 Patton. Following the US custom of naming tanks after generals (*cf.* **SHERMAN TANK**), its name honours **General CREIGHTON W. ABRAMS** (1914-1974). Abrams performed with distinction as a commander of armoured forces in WWII and held staff appointments in the Korean war. In 1968 he took over command of American forces in Vietnam in succession to the unspeakable General Westmoreland and served there until 1972. Abrams' recipe for success in this conflict – "clear and hold" (as opposed to "search and destroy") tactics, plus greatly increased emphasis on improving the efficiency of the South Vietnamese army (ARVN) – bear a remarkable similarity to what is currently being touted as the war-winning strategy for Afghanistan. This might mean that the Americans have learnt something from their Vietnam experience, but it might equally mean they have learnt nothing.*

* On the eve of "Desert Storm", President Bush Snr. gave a public address in which he assured his countrymen, "We have learnt the lesson of Vietnam – this time we won't be fighting with one hand tied behind our backs." A truly chilling utterance.

[7] ACHILLEA

The chief medicinal use of the wild plant *Achillea millefolium*, which we know as yarrow, is, and always has been, to heal open wounds, especially those made with metal tools or weapons. Hence its dialect names: soldier's herb, staunch-grass, carpenter's plant, woundwort, etc. What is less clear is why it should be named after the legendary Greek hero ACHILLES. Though he was certainly a military man, he was invulnerable – thanks to the preventive measures taken by his mother Thetis – to edged weapons (except in one place – his ACHILLES HEEL). However, Geoffrey Grigson* quotes the explanation given in an Anglo-Saxon version of the *Herbarium* of Apuleius Platonicus** to the effect that Achilles was the discoverer of the plant's virtues and used it to heal his soldiers' wounds. The active principle in yarrow is thought to be one of its constituent alkaloids, achilleine. In Chinese tradition, the stiff, straight stalks are used in divination to interpret the *I Ching*.

* The Englishman's flora 1958, 1975

** The philosopher Lucius Apuleius Platonicus was a Romanised North African who flourished around 150 AD. He is perhaps better known as the author of *The Golden Ass*. The book on plants attributed to him drew heavily on Dioscorides and Pliny and is the first to which the word herbarium was applied. It was apparently compiled from his miscellaneous writings in the 4th or 5th century AD. Regarding the Anglo-Saxon version, the lovingly-executed product of a Dark-Age monkish scriptorium, Anna Pavord in a fine book entitled *The naming of names: the search for order in the world of plants* (2005), says harsh things. But she is judging content and not context. Though the illustrations in the manuscript look nothing like the real thing, and though the real thing was probably growing within yards of where the scribe was sitting, there is nevertheless something touchingly human and in its way admirable about the mediaeval scholars' assumption that the ancients knew more, and better, than they.

[8] ADA

Computer programming language named after British mathematician ADA AUGUSTA, COUNTESS OF LOVELACE (1815-1852), daughter of Lord Byron, whose collaboration with Charles Babbage (see BABBAGE'S DIFFERENCE ENGINE) has earned her the generally-accorded distinction of being the world's first computer programmer. In an Internet poll in March 2110, Ada Lovelace headed the list of contenders for "the world's most inspiring woman in technology" ahead of MARIE

CURIE, mathematician-turned-actress Hedy Lamar, and Stieg Larsson's repellent fictional anti-heroine and ace hacker Lisbeth Salander. (RC)

[9] ADANSONIA

The baobab or monkey-bread tree *Adansonia digitata* was named by LINNAEUS in honour of the French botantist MICHEL ADANSON (1717-1806), who sailed to West Africa in the employ of the E. India Company and wrote (*inter alia*) *Histoire naturelle du Sénégal* (1757, English trans. 1759). His name is further remembered in the title of a modern French journal of plant biology, **"ADANSONIA"**. Adanson belongs among the travelling physician-naturalists who, between the second half of the 18th century and the first half of the 19th contributed so largely to the foundations of modern systematic biology and who figure elsewhere in this dictionary.* The late Patrick O'Brian's brilliant fictional creation Stephen Maturin is an archetype of the breed and testifies to O'Brian's admiration for these far-faring pioneers of scientific exploration. As witness the encomium of Adanson he puts into Maturin's mouth in *The Reverse of the Medal* (1993).

* See for example ABEL, JUSSIEU, KALM, NATTERER, PALLAS, PARROT, PUSCHKIN, SAUSSURE, STELLER, TOURNEFORT.

[10] ADDISON'S DISEASE

The condition also known as "adrenal insufficiency" is an insidious disorder of the adrenal glands. Symptoms include: changes in skin pigmentation, severe asthenia, anaemia, gastro-intestinal irritation, weak and irregular heart action, and death. It was first described by Edinburgh-trained DR THOMAS ADDISON (1793-1860) of Guy's Hospital in 1855, though it was French physician Armand Trousseau (1801-1867) who applied Addison's name to the condition. Modern treatment is with hydrocortisone. (See also BRIGHT'S DISEASE.)

[11] AETHERIUS SOCIETY

DR. GEORGE KING (1919-1997), the founder of the quasi-religious organisation called the AETHERIUS SOCIETY was a taxi-driver, former fire-fighter, yoga adept, psychic, and spiritual healer. In 1954 he was unexpectedly contacted by an extra-terrestrial named AETHERIUS, who told him he, King, had been chosen as the intermediary or "Primary Terrestrial Mental Channel" between our world and a race of spiritually advanced super-beings living on other planets. This unsought evangelical mission King sought manfully to fulfil and the outcome was the Aetherius Society with its headquarters in the United States, where King took up residence from 1959, and a branch office in London.* After leaving England for the States, King was awarded a doctorate of divinity by an American religious organisation (perhaps the same one that conferred a like distinction on Ian Paisley?). Though viewed by some as merely another UFO cult, the Aetherius Society does claim the status of a religion, aiming at the spiritual improvement of those who believe its message and follow its methods. As with all fringe religions, the question inevitably arises as to whether the founder's enlightenment was a delusion (pointing to psychological instability), a deliberate deception (pointing to criminal liability), or plain and sober truth, which would make King eminently deserving of the gratitude and respect we owe to anyone working, under divine direction or otherwise, to make the world a better place and us better people.

* Where further enlightenment may be had as to the organisation's aims and methods. Tel. 0207 736 4187, or try Mental Channels.

[12] AIRY'S DISC

When light from a point source is shone through a small circular aperture the projected beam forms, on any surface at right angles, a circular image which is called AIRY'S DISC. While that may seem trivial and obvious, there is a bit more to it than meets the eye: a careful inspection of the image reveals faint, narrow, concentric rings of light surrounding the bright central disc. This AIRY PATTERN is an interference pattern due to the diffraction of light waves at the edge of the aperture (see FERMAT'S PRINCIPLE OF LEAST TIME). Accounting for this phenomenon quantitatively is a rather difficult mathematical problem, involving BESSEL FUNCTIONS,* which was first solved in 1834 by English mathematician SIR GEORGE BIDDELL AIRY (1801-1892). Born in Alnwick, he graduated from Cambridge as Senior Wrangler in 1823, was elected Fellow of Trinity College in 1824, and appointed Lucasian Professor of Mathematics in 1828, and Astronomer Royal from 1835 to 1881. He reorganised Greenwich Observatory and established Greenwich Mean Time as Britain's legal time in 1880. The importance of the AIRY PATTERN is that it sets a limit on the resolving power of telescopes and other optical instruments. (MW)

*After German mathematician and astronomer, FRIEDRICH WILHELM BESSEL (1784-1846) who made the first accurate measurement of an interstellar distance.

[13] AK-47 – see KALASHNIKOV

[14] ALBRIGHT'S QUESTION

In a recent study of American foreign policy under the Bush régime*, the academic historian Andrew Bacevich coined the phrase "Albright's question" to refer to a casual but highly significant utterance by MADELEINE ALBRIGHT (b. 1937), America's intercontinental horror weapon in the Clinton era. "What's the point," she asked of General Colin Powell, the man who was to succeed her as Secretary of State, "of having this superb military you're always talking about if we can't use it?"** Of course, the real meat of the question is in the part that comes before the word "if". And that really *is* the question.

* *The new American militarism* 2005

** Powell *My American journey* 1995

[15] ALDINE TYPE

Name given to any one of several elegant fonts designed by **ALDUS MANUTIUS**, the Latinised name of Italian classical scholar and printer **ALDO MANUCCI** or **MANUZIO** (ca. 1450-1515), originator of "italic" type and first printer of works in Greek. He founded the famous Aldine press at Venice and produced editions of classical Greek and Latin authors including Aristotle, Aristophanes, Demosthenes, Herodotus, Plato and Virgil. His son **PAULUS MANUTIUS** (1511-1574) and grandson **ALDUS MANUTIUS "THE YOUNGER"** (1547-1597) continued the family tradition of scholarship and publishing.

[16] ALDINI'S BATTERY

An 18th century example of a renewable electric power source, calling for the heads of three freshly-decapitated oxen. The right ear of each ox-head, well-moistened with salty water, is connected in series by silver wire to the tongue of the next. The conducting wires from this bovine battery may be used to energise convulsions in a pair of frog's legs. **GIOVANNI ALDINI** (1762-1834), from Bologna, Italy, was a nephew of **LUIGI GALVANI**, whose work he edited; he became professor of physics at the University in 1798. His interest in "muscular electricity" culminated in 1803 at the Royal College of Surgeons, London, with an attempt to re-animate electrically the corpse of one George Forster, recently hanged at Newgate. (MW)

[17] ALDIS LAMP

Signalling lamp specifically designed for transmitting messages in **MORSE CODE**, named after English inventor **A.C.W. ALDIS** (1878-1953). It worked by opening and closing a shutter resembling a venetian blind in front of the lens. Aldis lamps were in general use in the Royal Navy for ship-to-ship or ship-to-shore signalling throughout most of the 20th century, being finally phased out in 1997. (See: R.S. Pomphrey *Marine signalling methods* 1966.)

[18] ALEXANDERS

The common name of the umbellifer *Smyrnium olustratum*, formerly *Petroselinum alexandrinum* or "Alexandrian parsley", named not after Alexander himself but after Alexander's city. A native of the Mediterranean, once grown in this country as a pot-herb, it has since been displaced from our vegetable plots by celery and is now naturalised as a hedgerow plant, mainly in seaside locations. Aficionados of wild food may still be willing to include it in their gleanings. Grigson (*The Englishman's Flora* 1958) asserts that the young shoots, boiled, have "a pleasant taste to begin with, though the aftertaste is decidedly bitter and forbidding". Richard Mabey, the doyen of hedge-cuisine (*Food for Free* 1972), speaks only of their "wonderfully delicate texture, and a pleasantly aromatic taste". However, in a later work (the beautiful *Flora Britannica* 1996), Mabey concedes that the "pungent" savour "is probably too pronounced for it to make a comeback as a vegetable".

[19] ALEXANDER'S DARK BAND

Also known as **ALEXANDER'S DARK SPACE**, the name is given to the darkened area of sky which separates the twin arcs of a double rainbow. It is named after the Peripatetic philosopher **ALEXANDER OF APHRODISIAS***, the first person to describe the phenomenon. Alexander taught in the Athens Lyceum around the end of the 2nd century AD. He is chiefly remembered for his commentaries on Aristotle, which earned him the title Ὁ Ἐξηγητής (= "The Explainer"), and for his denial of the immortality of the soul. Gavin Pretor-Pinney** in his *Cloud-spotter's guide* (2006), a delightful and authoritative account of what is going on daily over our heads, hastens to reassure us that Alexander's Dark Band is not the name of "a goth group from Middlesborough". It turns out, however, that it *is* the name of a goth group from somewhere or other since it appears that a combo of this name has enriched our musical culture with a CD entitled *Dobutsu Bancho*, notable, according to one reviewer, for its "sleek electro stabs and lardy beats" and featuring such titles as "Farmyard battle weapon", "Space donkeys on crack", and "Scratch the pussy".

* Aphrodisias – a town in Caria, a region of what is now south-western Turkey.

** In 2110 Pretor-Pinney, as head of the Cloud Appreciation Society, campaigned to have a new (if rare) type of cloud formation which he called "asperatus" officially recognised by the World Meteorological Association of Geneva.

[20] ALEXANDRIA

ALEXANDER THE GREAT, King of Macedon, (356-323 BC), is remembered for his whirlwind creation of an empire stretching from the Adriatic to the Indus. Alexander's empire, as is the way of empires created in a hurry by aggressive militarism, disintegrated on his death like those of Napoleon, Hitler, Attila the Hun, Shih Huang-Ti, Charlemagne, and Genghis Khan. But among Alexander's longer-lasting legacies was a string of cities in locations as far distant from Alexander's starting-point as Tajikistan, founded by him and named after him.

Most of these have changed their names or vanished from the pages of history. Among the notable survivors (disregarding parvenu American examples) are Kandahar in Afghanistan, and above all Egyptian **ALEXANDRIA**, home in its day to such wonders as the Pharos and the Ptolemaic Library, the world's greatest repository of classical learning and literature until the Arab conquerors of Egypt in 640 AD found a better use for the library's contents – stoking the boilers which heated the city's numerous bathhouses, thus satisfying at a stroke the requirements of both cleanliness and godliness. Under the **OTTOMAN** Empire (a multi-cultural society of ever there was one) and until the middle of the last century when it fell victim to resurgent Egyptian nationalism, Alexandria must have been one of the world's most fascinating examples of a truly cosmopolitan city.

> *"Say goodbye to her, to Alexandria,*
> *the city you are losing."*
>
> – Kavafis

[21] ALEXANDRINE

In prosody, a 12-syllable line of six iambic feet – an iamb consisting of an unstressed followed by a stressed syllable (*e.g.* "a-way").* Thus James Thomson in *The Castle of Indolence* (1748):

And mù-/ sic lènt / new glàd-/ ness tò / the mòr-/ ning air

Though it has a stately rhythmic quality, it never gained much ground in English poetry where the pentameter (5-foot line) is generally preferred for epic and tragedy, but in the 17th century the **ALEXANDRINE** found a congenial home with the consciously classicising French verse dramatists Racine and Corneille whose poetry is shaped by Greek and Latin models and whose plots by the "unities" of time, place and action which supposely governed Greek tragedy. The name "Alexandrine" is thought to derive from the fact that this was the metre employed in a 12th-century collection of French verse romances recounting the (mythologised) deeds of **ALEXANDER THE GREAT**.

* Virgil's *Aeneid* is also written in hexameters but his are a mixture of *dactyls* (a long followed by two short syllables *e.g.* "won-der-ful) and *spondees* (two long syllables, *e.g.* "top hat"). These two types of foot are regarded as of equal weight on the ground that two short syllables equal one long one. (See **VIRGILIAN METRE**.)

[22] ALEXANDRITE

One of the three naturally-occurring forms of the gemstone chrysoberyl. **ALEXANDRITE** was discovered in the Urals in 1830 and named in honour of the future Czar Alexander II by the Swedish traveller and mineralogist Nils Gustav Nordenskiöld, father of the Arctic explorer Nils Adolf Erik Nordenskiöld (after whom several bits of boreal geography are named). In jewellery-making, alexandrite is prized for its famous ability to change colour dramatically from dark green to bright red with changes in light (*e.g.* from sunlight to candle-light).

[23] ALGORITHM

A word beloved of IT experts to denote a step-by-step procedure for computation or problem-solving; it often takes the form of a sequence of questions whose yes/no answers determine the logical flow towards the solution. Surprisingly, the word derives from the name of a 9th Century Persian mathematician, **ABU JA'FAR MUHAMMAD IBN MUSA AL-KHWARIZMI**, (*ca.* 800-850) who studied in Baghdad, but hailed toponymically from ancient Khwarezm (spellings vary considerably), now Uzbekistan. His is the credit for introducing sophisticated mathematics to the West, including the Hindu – or so-called "Arabic" – system of numeration: 1,2,3,4, etc. A mediaeval mistransliteration of **AL-KHWARIZMI** into Latin as *algorismus*, compounded with *arithmos*, the Greek word for "number", is responsible for this mangled eponym **ALGORITHM**. Modern use of the word dates from 1881. It is an anagram of "logarithm". **AL-KHWARIZMI** also provided us with the word "algebra" in the title of his famous treatise on equations, *Kitab al-Jabr w'al-Muqabala,* "Rules of Re-integration and Reduction." (MW)

[24] ALLEN KEY

Also known as "hex key". An L-shaped rod of hexagonal section used to tighten screws and bolts which have a hexagonal indentation of corresponding diameter in the head. The name derives from the **ALLEN MANUFACTURING CO.** of Hartford Connecticut and dates back to the 1940s. Outside of its engineering uses, it has become widely familiar to purchasers of "self-assembly" furniture where this simple tool obviates the need for spanners and screwdrivers. It doesn't, however, compensate purchasers of these items for their chagrin on discovering that the furniture doesn't actually assemble itself.

[25] ALLEN'S OLINGO

The olingo (*Bassaricyon alleni*), a South American arboreal mammal, belongs to the family Procyonidae and is therefore a relative of the panda, the kinkajou, the coati and the cacomistle. It takes its name from zoologist **JOEL ASAPH ALLEN** (1838-1921), who headed the department of birds and mammals at the American Museum of Natural History from 1885-1921. Also named after Allen are a number of other mammals – **ALLEN'S BUSHBABY** (*Galago alleni*), **ALLEN'S MONKEY** (*Allenopithecus nigroviridis*), **ALLEN'S BIG-EARED BAT** (*Idionycteris phyllotis*), **ALLEN'S BAEODON** (another bat – *Baeodon alleni*), and **ALLEN'S WOOD RAT** (*Hodomys alleni*) – as well as a South African water fowl, **ALLEN'S GALLINULE** (*Porphyrula alleni*). For the record, the African snail *Gulella alleni*, a resident of the Usambara mountains in Tanzania, is named after a different J.A. Allen, the current head of the Biological Sciences Department at Southampton University.

[26] ALZHEIMER'S DISEASE

Incurable progressive dementia of unknown aetiology. First identified by German physician and psychiatrist **ALOIS ALZHEIMER** (1864-1915) in 1906.

[27] AMBROTYPE

All the published histories of photography attribute the name of this 19th century process for cased photographs to that of its American inventor, **JAMES AMBROSE CUTTING** (1813-1867), born in Worcester, New Hampshire, who patented it without a title in 1854, but reissued the patent in 1856 under the title **AMBROTYPE**. However, it transpires that he was actually christened **JAMES ANSON CUTTING** and must therefore have adopted **AMBROSE** as his middle name *after* the invention – a rare case of *reverse eponymy*, which he also used for his sailing yacht, *The Ambrotype*. He subsequently established a marine aquarium as a public attraction in Boston, but over-extended himself, lost all his money, and died in the Insane Asylum at Worcester. *Ambrotos* in Greek means "imperishable": Marcus Aurelius Root (1808-1888), a Philadelphia daguerreotypist, claimed that the name originated from his studio, but spiritualist newspapers preferred to credit Cutting's partner, Isaac A. Rehn (1815-1853), a noted spiritualist, for the invention of these "everlasting" images. In truth it matters not: Cutting himself had stolen the idea, with a trivial modification, from the British photographic inventor, Frederick Scott Archer, who developed the process with Peter Fry in 1851 but omitted to patent it. When an underexposed collodion negative on glass is backed with black felt or lacquer, and viewed under reflected light, the negative image is magically transformed into a softly-toned positive. The process was much used for portraiture by itinerant photographers, offering a "finished while you wait" service. **AMBROTYPES** are sealed in a decorative surround of **PINCHBECK**, but can be distinguished from that other popular cased image, the **DAGUERREOTYPE**, by their lack of its shiny metallic surface. When a black-enamelled plate of sheet-iron is used as the image support, the process is called tintype, ferrotype, or melainotype. It was used by 19th century street photographers – the cheap and cheerful "one-off Polaroid" of its day. (MW)

[28] AMERICA – see WALDSEEMÜLLER MAP

[29] AMPÈRE

This basic SI unit* of electric current, commonly abbreviated to AMP, symbol A, corresponds to the flow of one COULOMB of electricity per second. Measured by a GALVANOMETER, or latterly an ammeter, it can be formally defined by the force exerted between electrically conducting wires. In absolute terms one AMPÈRE is equal to 6.24×10^{18} electron charges per second. It celebrates the French mathematician and physicist ANDRÉ MARIE AMPÈRE (1775-1836), who was born in Lyon, was a child prodigy in mathematics, and taught at the University of Paris, laying the foundations of electromagnetism (or "electrodynamics" as he called it), following the work of the Dane, HANS CHRISTIAN OERSTED (1777-1851). (MW)

* The SI (Système International) units of scientific measurement replace the earlier c.g.s. (centimetre-gram-second) system, as well as earlier, purely local systems (goodbye, pound – goodbye, foot!)

[30] ANDERSON SHELTER

The ANDERSON SHELTER, was named after SIR JOHN ANDERSON, later VISCOUNT WAVERLEY (1882-1958), Lord Privy Seal and minister responsible for air-raid precautions prior to the outbreak of war. It was designed to protect individual families from Goering's bombers, and consisted of a pre-formed corrugated steel shell (cf. NISSEN HUT) resembling a large dog-kennel, capable of holding up to six people. It was installed by burying it to half its height in the garden and shovelling a 15-inch layer of earth over the protruding roof. Families not blessed with the amenity of a garden could have recourse to a different device, the MORRISON SHELTER. This took the form of a strongly-built metal table to the sides of which could be bolted weld-mesh panels, transforming it into a kind of people-sized rabbit hutch. The idea was that in case of the house collapsing, the metal box would act as a survival capsule, protecting those inside from falling debris until they could be dug out by the emergency services, and it did, in fact, perform as intended. The "table shelter", as it was sometimes called, took its name from HERBERT MORRISON (1888-1965), wartime Minister for Home Security. Over 2 million Anderson shelters were issued (free to low-income families) but many citizens made their own arrangements, taking refuge in London Underground stations, or sleeping rough in the countryside outside towns that were heavily targeted by night-bombers. In the present writer's own home, there was no formal air-raid shelter. The custom was for the family to take refuge in the cupboard under the stairs, one of those pointy arrangements where people keep their vacuum cleaners. From this the dog – a large beast – had first to be extracted and he would then repair to the nearest thing he could find to a Morrison shelter, the space under the grand piano – where he was probably better off.

[31] ANDRADITE – see SCHEELITE

[32] ANGEL FALLS

The world's highest waterfall, located at 5°49'N, 62°19'W, was discovered in 1933 by an American bush pilot JIMMY ANGEL (1899-1956). It was a clear case of serendipity ("the art of making happy chance discoveries") since he was looking for something else at the time, specifically, a rumoured "mountain of gold" supposedly located in that part of the jungle-clad Venezuelan interior (*cf.* ELDORADO).

[33] ÅNGSTRÖM

A non-SI unit of length, symbol Å; it is now eclipsed by the SI nanometer, nm, which is one billionth (US) of a meter, and equal to 10 Å. It was a measurement much used by crystallographers and spectroscopists to describe things conveniently at the atomic scale: molecular dimensions, (a water molecule is about 2 Å across); the wavelengths of X-rays (typically 1 to 10 Å – see RÖNTGEN) and of visible light (roughly 4000 to 7000 Å). The name derives from the Swedish physicist ANDERS JONAS ÅNGSTRÖM (1814-74) who was born in Lödgö and became professor of physics at Uppsala. (MW)

[34] ANTIDOTUM MITHRIDATICUM – see MITHRIDATIZE

[35] APGAR SCORE

A test devised in 1952 and first published in 1953 by American anaesthesiologist and paediatrician VIRGINIA APGAR (1909-1974) as a rapid method of assessing, immediately after their birth, the health of new-born infants. Points, either 2, 1 or 0, are awarded for five aspects of physical condition: heart-rate, respiration, muscle tone, response to stimulation and skin coloration. The result is a score out of ten. The test may be repeated after intervals of five and ten minutes. Apgar's system won rapid acceptance and has become a standard procedure world-wide. In her later career, Apgar did important work in the field of birth defects and congenital malformations.

[36] APPLETON LAYER – see HEAVISIDE LAYER

[37] ARAGO POINT

Anyone donning a pair of trendy shades – if they're Polaroid – will notice that skylight is polarized (see RAYLEIGH SCATTERING and NICOL PRISM) but the degree of its polarization from a given point in the sky depends on the angular displacement from the sun; there are three *neutral points* in the cloudless sky where the polarization is zero.* The ARAGO POINT is one of these, lying at *ca.*

20° vertically above the *antisolar point*, which is diametrically opposite the sun. This phenomenon should not be confused with the **ARAGO SPOT**, (also called Poisson's spot or **FRESNEL'S** spot) which is the bright spot of light at the centre of the shadow of a perfectly circular object illuminated by a point source – it was the evidence obtained by **ARAGO** to confirm the prediction by Siméon Denis Poisson (1781-1840) based on the wave theory of light advanced by Jean Augustin Fresnel (1788-1827) – see **AIRY'S DISC**. The French-Catalan man of science and politician, **FRANÇOIS JEAN DOMINIQUE ARAGO** (1786-1853) was born in Estagel near Perpignan, educated at the École Polytechnique, Paris, and became an astronomer at the Observatory.** In 1806 he travelled with Jean Baptiste Biot (1774-1862) on a geodetic mission to Spain to measure a degree of the meridian (like several other Frenchmen sent abroad in the service of the Nation to define the size of the meter – see **BEER-LAMBERT LAW**) and was absent for three years owing to various misadventures. On his return in 1809 he was elected member of the *Académie des Sciences* and to a mathematical chair at the Polytechnique. He then devoted two decades to productive scientific work, particularly in magnetism and optics, before becoming embroiled in politics. Arago was prominent in the July revolution of 1830, when he was elected member of the Chamber of Deputies, and in the same year he was appointed Director of the Observatory, and perpetual secretary of the *Académie des Sciences*. He became an *eminence grise* of the French scientific establishment, for instance, supporting **DAGUERRE** as the inventor of photography. In 1848 he joined the provisional government, running several ministries and acting briefly as Head of State, but after the *coup d'etat* of 1852 he refused to take the oath of allegiance to Napoleon III. (MW)

* The others are the Babinet point and the Brewster point, located 15-20° above and below the sun respectively.

** Arago's brother, Jacques Étienne Victor Arago (1719-1855) served as draughtsman on the scientific circumnavigation of 1817-1819 in the corvettes *Uranie* and *Physicienne* under Louis Claude de Saulces de Freycinet, and left an account of the voyage (English ed. London 1823).

[38] ARCHBOLD

The standard work of reference for the conduct of criminal trials in the Crown Court. It was first published in 1822 by Dublin-born barrister and legal writer **JOHN FREDERICK ARCHBOLD** (1785-1870), and Archbold's *Criminal pleading, evidence and practice* is still going strong fifty-eight editions later, currently published by Messrs. Sweet & Maxwell, specialists in legal literature. A separate volume deals with procedure in Magistrates' Courts. In the title sequence of the television series *Pie in the Sky* concerning the adventures of a policeman who runs a gourmet restaurant (a likely tale) the camera pans across the chef-copper's bookshelf where **ARCHBOLD** rubs shoulders with Mrs Beeton.

[39] ARCHIMEDES' PRINCIPLE

Greatest of the Greek mathematicians, **ARCHIMEDES** (c. 287-219 BC) was born in Syracuse, Sicily, then part of *Graecia Magna*. He studied in **ALEXANDRIA**, a worthy successor to the mighty geometer **EUCLID**, before returning to Syracuse, where he put his mechanical ingenuity at the service of the military for repelling the besieging Romans. More importantly, he discovered the chief principle of hydrostatics, equating the upthrust on an immersed body with the weight of fluid it displaced. Whence, his legendary cry of "Eureka!" (Greek: "I have found it"), as he leapt apocryphally from his tub. More important still were his formulae for finding the area of the circle and the surface areas and volumes of the sphere, cylinder and cone. He evaluated the transcendental number π to a fair approximation, thus anticipating mathematical methods of infinitesimal calculus, not fully developed for another 1800 years. **ARCHIMEDES' SCREW** is a useful device for lifting water or powders; its shape can be seen in the species of pasta known as fusilli. The **ARCHIMEDEAN** or **ARITHMETIC SPIRAL** is observed in the growth of plant seed heads by spiral phyllotaxis and is also present on every antique vinyl disc. The thirteen semi-regular **ARCHIMEDEAN SOLIDS** constitute a family of polyhedra, inscribable in a sphere, but having two or three different kinds of regular face. Most important of these is the cuboctahedron – with faces square and triangular – fundamental to the world-system of **BUCKMINSTER FULLER** and a crystallographic icon for common salt. The **TRAMMEL OF ARCHIMEDES** is a mechanically-linked device to guide the drawing of ellipses. On the fall of Syracuse, Archimedes was murdered by a conquering Roman soldier, violating the order that his life should be spared. Small wonder that Roman science achieved so little. (MW)

[40] ARGAND BURNER

In 1782 or thereabouts the Swiss chemist **FRANÇOIS PIERRE AIMÉ ARGAND** (1750-1803) invented a new kind of burner for oil lamps. It consisted of a cylindrical wick sandwiched between two metal cylinders. Oil from a reservoir reached the wick through a tube which connected with the outer metal cylinder. At the bottom was an opening which allowed air to pass by convection up the inner cylinder to the incandescent part of the wick. Convection was further improved by the addition of a tall glass chimney, an integral part of the design. The result, thanks to the increased oxygen supply, was a cleaner, brighter light (*cf.* **BUNSEN BURNER**). Argand's contribution to lighting technology seems at first sight relatively trivial, but looked at in a historical context, it is anything but. To him goes the credit for the first actual technical advance on the oil lamps used by the Romans and – together with candles and rush-lights – by everyone else for the next two millennia. It was rapidly adopted not only for domestic lighting but also for stage lighting in the theatre, for signalling lamps, and in lighthouses such as Robert Stevenson's* Bell Rock Lighthouse (1807-1812) where argand burners were used in conjunction with FRESNEL LENSES. In Switzerland's neighbour France, the name of Argand is virtually unknown, though Argand both studied and worked there. The reason being that his invention was stolen by an unprincipled co-worker, ANTOINE ARNAULT QUINQUET (1745-1807), who gave it his own name.

* Grandfather of Robert Louis Stevenson.

[41] ARGAND DIAGRAM

JEAN-ROBERT ARGAND (1768-1822)* was born in Geneva of French parentage; little is known of his early life, except that he became a bookseller in Paris. Without evident formal training in mathematics, he took up the study, and distinguished himself by devising the ARGAND DIAGRAM to represent complex numbers as points in the 2-dimensional plane.** He published his *Essai sur une manière de représenter les quantités imaginaires dans les constructions géométriques* anonymously in 1806, unaware that the idea had already been mooted in 1797 by a Scandinavian surveyor and cartographer, Caspar Wessel (1745-1818), but had passed largely unnoticed because it was published only in Danish. The Argand diagram finds use for describing *vector* quantities, which have both magnitude and direction. The idea was developed in 1828 by John Warren, and taken up in the 1830s by the front-rank mathematicians, HAMILTON and GAUSS. The two-dimensional space of the Argand diagram is now called the *complex plane*; it provides the space for plotting those amazing fractal "objects", the *julia set* and the MANDELBROT SET. (MW)

* Sometimes confused with Aimé Argand (1750-1803), inventor of the ARGAND BURNER though the two were not, as far as is known, related.

** Complex numbers take the form (a+ib), where i stands for the *imaginary* number $\sqrt{-1}$. In a Cartesian coordinate system, the value of the real part of the number, a, is plotted along the x axis (called the abscissa), and the value of the imaginary part, b, along the y axis (called the ordinate) at right angles to it.

[42] ARIAN HERESY

Following the adoption of Christianity as the official religion of the Roman Empire, the task of establishing a common orthodoxy among the various competing versions of Christian belief and practice then current became a matter of political as well as doctrinal urgency. Most of the unresolved difficulties centred on differing ideas about the nature of the Trinity. Obviously, once you've floated the idea of a God composed of three separate entities who are nevertheless all one entity and therefore not separable, logical complications are going to ensue and differing solutions are going to be reached. Was Jesus, for example, simultaneously both human and divine or only human like the rest of us? And if divine was he God in person or was his a secondary and subordinate divinity? Teasing questions, indeed, the more so when one considers that there is absolutely no way of deciding between competing supra-logical theories *on merit*. However, when the Emperor Constantine in 325 AD convened a council of leading churchmen at Nicaea (modern Isnik, Turkey, famous for its pottery), the nature of Christ's relation to God was high on the agenda as a serious split on this very topic was currently dividing the ranks of the faithful. At the heart of the dispute was an Alexandrian cleric ("presbyter") by the name of **ARIUS** (*ca.*. 256-336) whose views on the subject had already earned him and his followers excommunication for heresy from a provincial synod at Alexandria. At Nicaea, however, the Council, after prolonged debate, fudged the issue. Though Arius was duly banished to Illyria and his doctrines condemned, no firm alternative doctrine was asserted. Instead, the Council contented itself with issuing a slightly amended version of a Creed which had already gained general acceptance before Arius came on the scene and contained no specific refutation of his views beyond the inclusion of the word ὁμοούσιος ("of the same substance") to describe the relationship between Father and Son. This formula left virtually untouched Arius' denial of Christ's parity with the Father, a doctrine that remained influential, especially in the Eastern church after Arius' death.*

* For full technical details of Arius' heterodox opinions, the reader is commended to the account given in the *Encyclopaedia Britannica* (11th ed.) under "Arius" with the warning that these are deep and murky waters, theologically speaking, in which the amateur enquirer might rapidly, like the present writer (alas!), find himself in danger of drowning.

[43] ARRHENIUS' RATE LAW

Boiling an egg conveys an intuitive sense that the rate of a chemical reaction increases with temperature: to transform things more rapidly, we heat them. A goodish rule of thumb is that the rate of many reactions doubles for each 10 degree (**CELSIUS**) rise in temperature. Readers who recognise this as an example of exponential behaviour will not be averse to learning the actual mathematical form of this dependence: the rate is proportional to $\exp(-E/RT)$ where T is the temperature in **KELVINS** and E represents the concept of "activation energy". This expression due to **ARRHENIUS** has become a corner-stone of chemical kinetics. "Arrhenius testing" or "accelerated ageing" is used in conservation science: if we want to know how much our wedding photos are going to fade in the next 100 years at room temperature, we can cook one at an elevated temperature for a few hours and then extrapolate the result mathematically. **SVANTE AUGUST ARRHENIUS** (1859-1927) was a distinguished Swedish scientist and one of the founding fathers of physical chemistry. He attended the Universities of Uppsala and Stockholm, and studied with **OSTWALD**, **KOHLRAUSCH** and **BOLTZMANN**. He is famed for his theory of ionic dissociation in solution, and his prophetic recognition of the global "greenhouse effect" due to CO_2 in the atmosphere. In 1903 he was the first Swede to receive the **NOBEL PRIZE** in chemistry; and was subsequently appointed rector of the Nobel Institute. (MW)

[44] ASHMOLEAN MUSEUM

The original museum was opened in 1683 to display the collection given to the University of Oxford by **ELIAS ASHMOLE** (1617-1692). This collection was universal in scope, containing anything considered worth collecting and this included coins, medals, antiquities, natural history specimens, books, manuscripts, prints, engravings and portraits. In the following centuries the museum acquired many more exhibits, but some displays were moved to the new university museums in the nineteenth century leaving the Ashmolean as a museum of Art and Architecture, today among the most important in the country. Ashmole was a man of many parts and interests: an English antiquary, a politician, an astrologer and alchemist, lawyer and royalist excise commissioner. He was a man on the make and he loved to collect. In 1659 he acquired the renowned accumulation of "curiosities" assembled by the Tradescant family (see **TRADESCANTIA**) and this, plus the material Ashmole had collected independently, he donated to the University in 1677 on condition that a suitable home be built to house the exhibits and make them available to the public. The building, designed by Christopher Wren, was completed in 1682. There would have been more artefacts, but, in the meantime, a large part of Ashmole's own collection, destined for the museum, was destroyed in a disastrous fire in the Middle Temple on January 26th, 1679. Ashmole should also be remembered for his own writings. That which perhaps had greatest contemporary impact was a history of the Order of the Garter (1672), in which he consciously used his antiquarian researches to highlight a traditionalist, hierarchical view of society. Another significant work was his *Theatrum chemicum Britannicum* (1652), perhaps the most important of all English alchemical publications, and one which reveals a hierarchical view of the universe that mirrors his political views. (RS)

[45] ASIMOV'S LAWS OF ROBOTICS

For 30 years or more Russian-born American **ISAAC ASIMOV** (1920-1992) virtually personified the literary genre of Science Fiction.* A full-time academic biochemist by profession, he was enormously prolific as an author. It was he who in a story of 1941 coined the term "robotics" and laid down the First Law of robotics, later expanded to 3. They are:

A robot may not injure a human being or, through inaction, allow a human being to come to harm.

A robot must obey orders given it by human beings except where such orders would conflict with the First Law.
A robot must protect its own existence as long as such protection does not conflict with the First or Second Law.

The Three Laws provided a conceptual framework for many of Asimov's own novels and stories, plot lines often being derived from problems or contradictions in the Laws' application. They were also accepted implicitly by other science fiction writers of the fifties and sixties. Not so however the "defence" industries of certain countries which currently are spending billions of dollars on robot killing machines of one kind or another, some of which are already in use. Asimov was also a scientific populariser of a very high order, and among his non-fiction works special mention must be made of his *Biographical encyclopedia of science and technology* (1964, 1972), which alone would have constituted a satisfying life's work for most people.

* Note that whereas the abbreviation "SF" is acceptable, insiders, whether readers or writers, never use the term "Sci Fi", just as no builder speaks of a "breeze block", and no ornithologist of a "seagull". Shibboleths.

[46] ASPERGER'S SYNDROME

A developmental disorder characterized by impaired social interactions and repetitive behaviour patterns. It is named after Austrian paediatrician HANS ASPERGER (1906–1980), who in 1944 first noticed that a number of children referred to his Viennese clinic had similar personality characteristics and behaviour. He suggested that the term *Autistische Psychopathen im Kindesalter* (juvenile autistic psychopathy) be used to cover such cases – i.e. a personality disorder rather than a mental illness. He observed that the children's social maturity and social reasoning was delayed and that some aspects of their social abilities were quite unusual. The condition also includes difficulties in making friends; impaired verbal and non-verbal communication; egocentric preoccupations with a specific topic or interest; conspicuous clumsiness and lack of co-ordination; rigid adherence to routines; misunderstanding of jokes and figurative language; inappropriate facial gestures or expressions and an extreme sensitivity to particular sounds, smells, textures and touch. The condition is now regarded as part of the autistic spectrum of disorders, with the problems in interacting with others frequently continuing into adult life. Asperger's is often undiagnosed and may affect as many as 1 in 300 people, mostly males. In 1944, after the publication of his landmark paper describing autistic symptoms, Asperger secured a permanent tenured post at the at the University in Vienna. Shortly after the war ended, he became director of a children's clinic in the city. He died before his identification of this behaviour-pattern gained wide recognition. The first person to use the term "Asperger's Syndrome" was British researcher Lorna Wing in 1981, in a paper that challenged the previously accepted orthodoxy regarding autism as promulgated by Leo Kanner. Nowadays Asperger's Syndrome is a widely recognised condition that has entered the public consciousness partly through best-selling works of fiction such as Mark Haddon's *The Curious Incident of the Dog in the Night-Time*, and perhaps also by the institution of an International Asperger's Day on February 18th, marking the man's birthday. (RS)

[47] ASTORIA

Astoria, at the mouth of the Columbia River, proudly claims to be the first American settlement west of the Rockies. The river was given its name by Robert Grey (1755-1866), captain of the first American ship to enter the estuary (1782). Gray was a New England mariner and merchant who pioneered the sea-borne fur trade of the Pacific coast. (With true Yankee commercial acumen, he loaded his vessel with cheap ironmongery and traded it to the Coast Indians in exchange for furs, which he then sold in China, returning with a cargo of tea.) In 1805 the area was visited by Lewis and Clark's Corps of Discovery, but it wasn't until 1811 that the settlement of Astoria was founded, and named after **JOHN JACOB ASTOR** (1763-1848) who, taking a leaf from Gray's book, intended to use it as a port from which furs gathered by the trappers of his American Fur Company could be shipped to China. In 1810 Astor had sent out two parties, one by sea and one by land. The ship-borne party arrived first and began building the fort/trading post that was to become the town of Astoria. Later, the overland expedition, known collectively in the history of the American north-west as "the **ASTORIANS**", reached the scene, thus establishing a presence in the area for Astor's already wide-ranging commercial ventures. Astor was a German immigrant, born at Waldorf (properly *Walldorf*) in Baden-Württemberg, who, operating out of New York, became a major player in the fur trade of the Upper Missouri and northern Rockies.* Though he failed in his object of eliminating competitors and establishing a total monopoly in the region, his commercial activities nevertheless earned him a large fortune, much of which he cannily invested in New York real estate and then no less cannily got out of the fur trade before the boom in beaver pelts for hat-making turned to bust. In the 1890's, two of Astor's descendants, William Waldorf Astor (1848-1919) and his cousin John Jacob Astor (1864-1912), built twin hotels in New York, which later merged into the **WALDORF-ASTORIA**. There is an eponymic connection between this famous pairing and the **WALDORF SCHOOLS**, otherwise known as **STEINER SCHOOLS**: the first school with a teaching regime based on the ideas of **RUDOLF STEINER**, which opened in Stuttgart in 1919, was set up at the behest of the Director of the German Waldorf-Astoria Cigarette Company to educate the children of his workers.

* It would be difficult to overestimate the influence of the Rocky Mountain fur trade on the course

of North American history in the first hundred years of the United States' existence. It played a huge part, for good or ill, in the exploration and settlement of the lands west of the Mississippi, on US relations with Spain/Mexico and with Britain/Canada (boundary settlements), and on the miserable history of the White Man's dealings with the continent's aboriginal population. Moreover, and not incidentally, it set the pattern of reckless, greedy and destructive exploitation of America's natural resources which continues almost unchecked today. It might even be said that the entire history of the United States up to the moment when America became a fully-fledged actor in the international states-system (an event which we can date to America's entry into the First World War) could be written in terms of just three commodities: fur, cattle, and cotton. For later developments we would have to add a fourth – oil.

[48] AUBRIETIA

Genus of hardy evergreen trailing rock plants belonging to the *brassica* (cabbage) family, native to the eastern Mediterranean. It carries the name of CLAUDE AUBRIET (1665-1742), French botanical illustrator, who worked mainly with botanists associated with the Jardin des Plantes in Paris. Foremost among these was Joseph Pitton de Tournefort (see TOURNEFORTIA) for whose *Elemens de Botanique* of 1694, a pre-LINNAEAN attempt at botanical systemisation, Aubriet made the original paintings. In 1700-1702 he and Tournefort toured the Levant, travelling through Greece, Turkey, Armenia and Georgia. Aubriet's presence on this trip was the earliest instance of a botanical illustrator being included in a scientific expedition. In 1706 or 1707 he was appointed botanical painter to the royal court, a post created by Henri IV (1553-1610). He illustrated Vaillant's *Botanicon parisiense*, published in 1727. Aubriet specialised in painting on vellum and the originals of his meticulous and beautiful studies are today both rare and sought after.

[49] AUJESKY'S DISEASE

A notifiable viral infection of (mainly) pigs, affecting the central nervous system, also known as Pseudorabies or Mad Itch and first identified by the Hungarian ALADAR AUJESKY (1869-1933). There is no treatment, hence the importance of vaccination. The virus can also cause a fatal form of pneumonia in lambs.

[50] AVOGADRO'S HYPOTHESIS

LORENZO ROMANO AMEDEO CARLO AVOGADRO, (1776–1856) was born in Turin, of noble Piedmontese family, and became professor of physics at the University in 1820. He was removed from his chair in 1823 for revolutionary political activity, but later re-instated. His famous hypothesis, sometimes dignified as a "law", was published in 1811. It states: *Equal volumes of gases, at the same temperature and pressure, contain the same number of molecules.* This implies that the weights of equal volumes of different gases correspond to the respective relative weights of their molecules, and thus provides chemists with a means of finding relative molecular masses. The full significance and value of Avogadro's hypothesis was only recognized after his death. **AVOGADRO'S NUMBER** is the most important number in the whole of chemical science: it represents the scaling factor between the sub-microscopic realm of atoms and molecules, and the everyday world of human senses. A generous tablespoonful of water (about 18 grams) contains roughly an Avogadro's number of water molecules. This number is unimaginably huge, having 24 digits: 602,214,199,000,000,000,000,000 (all those 0s are not zero – simply unknown digits, due to the limited accuracy of measurement.) Six hundred thousand, million, million, million is an awesome lot of molecules. Popularists of science try to tame this monster by calculating useless analogies, such as: every cup of beverage we drink contains about 600 of the original water molecules in Socrates' terminal cup of hemlock – supposing it to have become uniformly mingled with all the waters of the Earth. An Avogadro's number of molecules constitutes a "mole" of any substance – the chemist's unit of quantity – an amount equal to the relative molecular mass, in grams. Amedeo Avogadro himself never attempted to calculate "his" number; the proposal to name it in his honour came in 1909 from Jean Baptiste Perrin, and is now widely accepted – except by those who prefer **LOSCHMIDT'S NUMBER**. (MW)

[51] AYERS ROCK

The celebrated 1100-foot-high-and-five-miles-round sandstone monolith situated near Alice Springs in Australia is known as Uluru in one local dialect and Ayers Rock in another. The first European to set eyes on it was the explorer Ernest Giles in 1872. A year later it was named in honour of **SIR HENRY AYERS** (1821-1897), the Chief Secretary of South Australia, by the surveyor William Gosse. Sticklers for linguistic accuracy will want to know that the "r" in "Uluru" is retroflexive – i.e. pronounced with the tip of the tongue pointing backwards. Just try it. Then send up a prayer of thanks to Mr. Gosse.

B

[52] BABBAGE'S DIFFERENCE ENGINE

CHARLES BABBAGE (1792-1871) was a mathematician, inventor, statistician, campaigner for official recognition of science, and (a personal peculiarity) inveterate enemy of organ-grinders. He is best remembered, however, for his attempted construction of devices that would perform mathematical calculations by mechanical means. His first effort in this direction (for which, rather surprisingly, he received a hefty government grant) was the so-called **DIFFERENCE ENGINE**. It was intended to produce the mathematical tables which at the time were compiled by specialist human operators known as "computers" and which were all too prone, as a result, to human error. The first Difference Engine, containing some 25 thousand separate parts – cogs, rods, and levers – and weighing nearly 15 tons, was never finished. Babbage simply abandoned it in favour of a bigger and better machine known as **BABBAGE NO. 2**, which had an additional feature in the form of a printer to record the results. This, too, remained unfinished until 1991 when the London Science Museum constructed a replica machine, following Babbage's designs and the engineering methods of the period. It worked perfectly and could handle expressions of up to 31 digits. Babbage next turned his mind to yet another device, known as the **ANALYTICAL ENGINE**, intended to perform more complex calculations and which was designed to be programmable by means of punched cards (*cf.* **JACQUARD LOOM, HOLLERITH TABULATOR**). For this venture he had a collaborator in the mathematician **ADA** Augusta, Countess of Lovelace (1815-1852), the only legitimate offspring of mad, bad Lord Byron* and the only person in England, so it was said, capable of fully understanding Babbage's ideas. It was she who worked out the mathematics of the machine's operating system, by virtue of which she is today generally recognised as the first ever computer programmer. The government had by this time withdrawn its support but Babbage worked on for the remainder of his life, the machine growing ever more complex in design and, with each planned refinement, ever further from realisation. In fact it never left the drawing board. Babbage may well have deserved his title of grandfather of the modern computer, but his dream of an infallible machine remains a dream, as everyone who has been seriously tempted to take a hammer to a balky PC will testify. Babbage fathered 8 children, the first of whom was named Benjamin Herschel in honour of Babbage's fellow Cambridge mathematician **SIR JOHN HERSCHEL**.

* Byron, arguably, did just three admirable things in a life otherwise frittered away with womanising and mediocre poetry: he fathered one of the finest mathematical minds of 19th century England, he wrote one perfect poem ("So we'll go no more a-roving"), and he died for Greece.

[53] BACH FLOWER REMEDIES

Alternative medicines* named after their inventor **EDWARD BACH**** (1886-1936).
Bach was born in Birmingham and studied at University College Hospital, London.
Although he practised as a homeopath, the **FLOWER REMEDIES** are not formulated
according to homeopathic principles and, at least in their original form, actually
contained no plant material or extract whatever, consisting merely of water
(originally dew) that had been in contact with certain plants and was then mixed
with equal parts of alcohol (originally brandy). The plants employed were selected
by Bach according to a system of his own devising whereby he was able to detect
the beneficent energies of this or that plant simply by holding his hand over it and
noting its effect (or not) on how well it made him feel. Today, Bach's decoctions
are mainly resorted to by sufferers from mood disorders – nervousness, depression,
irritability, sleeplessnes, and so on. This accords with Bach's belief that disease
originates at the level of the psyche. It can at least be said of the Flower Remedies
that, unlike many conventional medicines, they are completely harmless as, aside
from an expected placebo effect, no one to date has been able to detect any
physiological effect whatever attributable to their use. From 1934 Bach lived in the
Oxfordshire village of Brightwell-cum-Sotwell near Wallingford where his home,
Mount Vernon, today houses the Bach Centre, named in his memory.

* "Alternative", a cynic might say, in so far as they represent an alternative to medicine rather than an
alternative form of medicine.

** Pronounced "batch".

[54] BACH TRUMPET

A modern form of valve-less trumpet which aims to reproduce the range and
timbre of the instruments used in Bach's day and which today is favoured by
early-music groups. The name is not intended to suggest that the mighty **J.S. BACH**
(1685-1750) actually invented the instrument. In any case, it's difficult to imagine
where he would have found the time.

[55] BACONIAN THEORY

Usually applies to the theory that Sir Francis Bacon (1561-1626) wrote dramatic
works (*Hamlet, Macbeth, Romeo & Juliet*, etc.) under the pseudonym "William
Shakespeare". However, the word "Baconian" in this instance applies not to the
supposed author of the plays but to a doughty though mentally unstable American
lady, **MISS DELIA SALTER BACON** (1791-1859), author of *The philosophy of the plays
of Shakespeare unfolded* (1857).* What started as an idea, became for her an
obsession, and finally a full-blown mania. This sad outcome could have been
avoided if someone had taken the trouble to point out to the good lady that her
thesis was invalidated from the word go by a fatal logical flaw: she started from the

question-begging assumption that Shakespeare *could not* have written the plays because he was merely an ignorant, second-rate actor. There is a clear corollary to this which apparently never occurred to her: that if Shakespeare *had* written the plays, then he was not merely a second-rate actor. Interestingly, Miss Bacon never asserted that her namesake was the sole author of the plays. Rather they were (in her view) the work of a sort of underground literary cabal consisting of Bacon, Spenser and Raleigh, who used the plays as a vehicle for subversive political opinions to which they dared not publicly attach their names – a somewhat over-subtle approach to the agitprop business, some might say.

* Publication was funded by Nathaniel Hawthorne as an act of kindness – he didn't share Miss Bacon's convictions but admired the fervour with which she advanced them.

[56] BAGNOLD SUN COMPASS

The sun compass, pioneered by Dr. J. Ball, was perfected as an aid to desert travel and surveying by **MAJOR RALPH ALGER BAGNOLD, R.E., F.R.S.** (1896-1990) in the course of his explorations by motor car in the Sinai, Transjordan and Libyan deserts between the wars. Detailed instructions for its use will be found in *Hints to travellers Vol.II* (11th ed. 1938) published by the Royal Geographical Society. Its main advantage is its immunity to perturbations of the magnetic compass caused by the metal in the vehicle itself and by the violent motion involved in travel over rough ground. Bagnold's experience in desert travel and Bagnold himself were instrumental in the formation of the buccaneering Long Range Desert Group in the North African campaign in WWII. Bagnold's sister was the novelist Enid Bagnold (1889-1981) author of numerous works including *The chalk garden* (1955). Bagnold's own publications, in addition to his reports to the R.G.S., include *Libyan sands: travel in a dead world* (1935, 1941) and – a technical work on Bagnold's special subject – *The physics of blown sand and desert dunes* (1941).

[57] BAILEY BRIDGE

The **BAILEY BRIDGING SYSTEM** was developed during WWII following the designs of **DONALD COLEMAN BAILEY** (1901-1985), a civil engineer working for the War Office and a man for whom "tinkering" was a spare-time hobby. The outcome was a system based on pre-fabricated parts, any one of which could be hand-carried (though not without some grunting) by a party of six men, and which would fit in a 3-ton lorry. The chief desiderata were flexibility, and speed of erection. The use of standardised parts simplified damage-repair and meant that bridges of different lengths and strengths could be put together from the same basic elements. For river-crossings, pontoons were added. Bailey's design worked brilliantly. Field-Marshal Montgomery is said to have said, "Without the Bailey bridge we would not have won the war" – an obvious exaggeration but a nice compliment. (See also **HIGGINS BOAT**.)   Bailey was knighted in 1946. After the war, the Bailey system continued to evolve and its underlying principles still govern the design of the system that has replaced it with the British Army, the Logistical Support Bridge (LSB) made by the firm of Mabey & Johnson.

[58] BAIN-MARIE

Known as a *double boiler* in the USA, this cooking vessel surrounded by a bath of hot or boiling water is used for preparing and holding the most delicate sauces and dishes. Also found in any chemical laboratory as the *water-bath*, its origins are indeed alchemical: the *Balneum Mariae*, as it is known in Medieval Latin, is an invention attributed to **MARY THE JEWESS** – a mysterious founding-figure of Western alchemy dating from the 1st or 2nd century AD. Sometimes referred to as *Maria Prophetissa*, she was a keen proponent of the "alchemical marriage", and has been anachronistically identified by some as Miriam, the sister of Moses. (MW)

[59] BAKELITE

Bakelite was the first synthetic thermosetting resin and so may be said to be the substance on which the entire structure of today's all-devouring plastics industry is based. Its name drives from that of its inventor **LEO HENDRIK BAEKELAND** (1863-1944). He was born in Ghent, Belgium, studying there and at other Belgian universities until becoming Professor of Physics and Chemistry at Bruges in 1885. He emigrated to the USA in 1889 after taking a shine to the place during his honeymoon, and founded a chemical company to manufacture one of his inventions, "Velox" photographic printing paper, selling out to Kodak in 1899. The substance which made him famous, produced by the condensation of cresol or phenol with formaldehyde, was patented in 1907 and marketed under the trade name **BAKELITE** through the Bakelite Corporation, set up in 1910. Bakelite rapidly found uses as an electrical insulator and as a substitute for items previously moulded from hard rubber. It could be produced in a range of rather muddy colours and in the 1920's and 30's became almost an icon of stylish modernity. It was used in the manufacture not only of such humble artefacts as ashtrays and pencil boxes but perhaps most famously in the GPO's standard black telephone*, while products like Raymond Loewy's restyled Gestetner duplicating machine (1929) and Wells Coates's Ekco radio (1934) helped to make bakelite a household name. The most extraordinary item to be moulded from bakelite was a coffin, though sadly, when the manufacturer of this piece died, he never got to use it. Nowadays, since bakelite has been almost entirely superseded, bakelite products are eagerly sought after by collectors who greedily lap up such cultural detritus as buttons, napkin rings, children's toys and games, lamps, jewellery, TV sets, thermos flasks, picnic plates, dresser sets, and (inevitably) telephones. (RS)

* A few years after the war, the GPO proudly announced that henceforth its customers were to be allowed to own coloured telephones. Following the announcement, a GPO spokesman was asked in a BBC interview why coloured telephones cost more than black ones. He replied that this was a necessary precaution since otherwise everybody might want one.

[60] BALDWIN'S PHOSPHORUS

Not phosphorus at all, but an oxide of calcium that happens to be phosphorescent, *i.e.* after exposure to sunlight, it glows in the dark. In 1602, a cobbler and amateur alchemist of Bologna, one Vincenzo Casciarolo was fossicking around Monte Paderno, when he came across a rock, "Bolognian Stone", that felt unusually dense: unbeknown to him, it was actually "heavy spar" (a.k.a. barytes, barium sulphate, $BaSO_4$, Gk: *barus* = "heavy") but Vincenzo hoped its weightiness might conceal gold, so he popped it into his alchemical furnace, which converted the barium sulphate to barium sulphide (BaS). The rest is history: the discovery of the luminous powder, then called *lapis solaris*, which created a sensation among alchemists of the day because it showed a visible connection between matter and "golden" sunlight. Thereafter, anything that glowed in the dark was called a **PHOSPHORUS** (Gk: "light-bearing") and the names of various *phosphori* honour their discoverers: **BALDWIN** is the Englished name of Saxon alchemist **CHRISTIAN ADOLF BALDEWEIN** (1632-1682) – also Latinised as Balduinus – born at Doebeln, near Meissen, who made his "phosphorus" in 1673 by heating calcium nitrate; it earned him an FRS. In 1761 John Canton obtained his "phosphorus" by heating oyster shells with sulphur. In 1669 real, honest-to-god phosphorus – the non-metallic element, symbol P – had been accidentally prepared by German alchemist Hennig Brandt (*ca.* 1630-1710) while trying to isolate a "life force" by distilling copious amounts of his own stale urine. Ironically, the glow of real phosphorus is not true phosphorescence (as a physical chemist would define it) but a chemiluminescent reaction due to oxidation by the air. (MW)

[61] BALFOUR DECLARATION

In November 1917, while Britain was still at war, the then Foreign Secretary **ARTHUR JAMES BALFOUR** (1848-1930) wrote to the British Zionist leader Lord Rothschild* stating that this country would support the project of a Jewish "national home" in Palestine. And he kept his word. When the **OTTOMAN** Empire was carved up by the French and British following the end of WWI, Britain secured the "mandate" for Palestine from the League of Nations under terms which incorporated the provisions of Balfour's letter. However, as the Zionist movement was already growing steadily in numbers, vociferousness and influence when Balfour chose to put his oar in, it is likely that the project of a Jewish homeland ("a land without a people for a people without a land") would have come to fruition at much the same time and in much the same way with or without Balfour's support and that he is, therefore, not really to blame for what has followed.

* The zoologist Walter Rothschild, 2nd Baron. See ROTHSCHILD'S MARSUPIAL NEW GUINEA MOUSE.

[62] BALMER SERIES

The simplest of all possible atoms, hydrogen, emits a characteristic glow when excited electrically in a gas discharge, *e.g.* in a GEISSLER TUBE. If this light is analysed spectroscopically – by dispersing it with a prism into its component colours – bright lines are discovered at definite measurable wavelengths which bear a simple numerical relationship to each other. The pattern looks like a ladder with converging rungs (an icon previously adopted by GALILEO). This observable regularity in the very essence of Dame Nature's prototypical substance cries out to the scientific mind that *something must be going on here*. In 1885 Swiss mathematician JOHANN JAKOB BALMER (1825-1898) was the first to quantify, in a simple mathematical formula, such a series of lines in the hydrogen emission spectrum, using the measurements made by ÅNGSTRÖM; he was followed by Theodore Lymann (1906), Friedrich Paschen (1908), Fredrick Sumner Brackett (1922), August Herman Pfund (1924), and Curtis J. Humphreys (1952), each detecting a new series of lines lurking in distant regions of the hydrogen spectrum, like supermarket barcodes. All these precise empirical observations can be encapsulated in a single simple formula due to RYDBERG (1888), which ultimately found an explanation in the values for the energy levels of the hydrogen atom that emerged from the theories of BOHR (1913) and SCHRÖDINGER (1926). (MW)

[63] BALTHAZAR – see JEROBOAM

[64] BANKSIA

A genus of 70+ species (the exact number, as so often, is still under discussion) of Australian flowering plants, recognisable by their woody-centred flower spikes. The name is that of Sir JOSEPH BANKS (1743-1820), who accompanied Cook on his *Endeavour* expedition of 1768-1771, in the course of which he made extensive and important natural history collections. Banks's long presidency of the Royal Society (1778-1820) made him, in terms of influence and prestige, a sort of Grand Panjandrum of English science during a period of intensive research and discovery.

[65] BANT

In Ford Madox Ford's *Return to yesterday* (1931), we read: "The King asked Lady Londonderry if he might touch the bell and ask the footman for some very dry toast as he was banting." The now obsolete verb "to bant" meaning "to diet" is a back-formation on the name of a London cabinet-maker **WILLIAM BANTING** (1797-1878), who achieved a certain notoriety in the 1860's by suggesting in his *Letter on corpulence* (1863) that by not eating fats, sugars and carbohydrates one could become thinner. By an odd coincidence, Swedish uses the verb *att banta* and its derived noun *bantning* with the meaning "to diet with the intention of losing weight".

[66] BARBAROSSA

Standard military doctrine requires that code-names for operations should be semantically empty – *i.e.* they should give no clue as to the nature of the operation in question. This was normal practice with the Allies in WWII, but the Germans, occasionally at least, were unable to resist adding a touch of pazazz to operational code names with the result that these might contain at least a broad hint of what was afoot. Thus "*Frühlingserwachen*" (Spring Awakening) fairly obviously denoted a spring offensive, and "*Seelöwe*" (Sealion) a naval or amphibious operation, while "*Nordlicht*", the Northern Army Group's planned assault on Leningrad, would have been unlikely to refer to an operation in, say, Libya. Among the best-remembered examples of the Germans' tendency to romanticise their code-names was **BARBAROSSA**, the plan for the invasion of Russia, originally code-named "*Fritz*" but changed on Hitler's orders. **FREDERICK THE FIRST** (1123-1190), popularly known as "**BARBAROSSA**" (= "Red Beard"), the German emperor who brought Lombardy, Poland, Denmark and Burgundy under his sway, was a hero as dear to the Teutonic heart as was the crusade against bolshevism to Hitler's. After a career of almost Napoleonic political and military aggrandisement, Barbarossa drowned in a small river in Anatolia* while leading the Third Crusade. (The proximate cause was the weight of his no-doubt-splendid armour.) His body was taken to Antioch for burial in a vat filled with vinegar, which unfortunately failed to prevent its falling to bits.** However, in German legend, the Emperor is not dead but sleeping – in a mountain cave in central Germany, awaiting, like King Arthur, his country's call. In our own time, and following Hitler's lead so to speak, military code-names have become the very opposite of semantically neutral. Instead they have been pressed into service, notably by the Americans, as a form of propaganda designed to highlight the noble purposes underlying a given operation or exercise. A random sample: Enduring Freedom, Liberty Shield, Constant Vigil, Keen Sword, Uphold Democracy, Provide Hope, Desert Thunder, and – surreally – Flexible Anvil.*** The style of these childish and meretricious confections was neatly satirised in a recent edition of *The Simpsons*, where "Operation Speedy Resolution" was proposed as a code-name for the Hundred Years' War.

* Ever the ironist, Gibbon called it "a petty torrent" to point up the insignifance of the stream as compared to the grandeur of its victim. He went on to compare it to the cold bath that did for

Alexander the Great. He might also have mentioned the ill-judged swim in the Nile which did for the Emperor Hadrian's special friend Antinous. And no doubt Gibbon would have been delighted by the idea of Napoleon's death at the hands of his wallpaper. (See SCHEELE'S GREEN)

** Messy, but not as undignified as what befell William the Conqueror whose corpse swelled like a balloon as it putrefied and blew the lid off his coffin.

*** William M. Arkin's *Code Names* (2005) is a massively comprehensive guide to the language (and, by extension, the mindset) of the Pentagon and its myrmidons.

[67] BARNARD'S STAR

These days almost any Tom, Dick or Harry can have a crater on the moon named after him, but to have a star with your name attached is something quite out of the ordinary, rarely seen since the Greeks, and after them the Arabs, peopled the night sky with gods, heroes and monsters. American astronomer and pioneering astronomical photographer **EDWARD EMERSON BARNARD** (1857-1923) earned this special distinction* following measurements he made of the proper motion** of a faint red-dwarf star in the constellation Ophiucus in 1916. Its displacement, measured in seconds of arc per year was larger than that of any other known star in our galaxy and the conclusion is that **BARNARD'S STAR** is heading our way at a rate of knots, or, not to mince words, 90 kilometers a second. This means that the star, which at present is 6 light years distant from our sun, will some nine thousand years from now, be only 3.8 light years distant from us, almost a whole light year nearer than our present nearest neighbour the Alpha Centauri system at 4.37 light years. That's something to look forward to, but that, unfortunately, is as exciting as it gets as, after that, Barnard's Star will start to recede from us.

* Special but not unique. Hathaway (*The friendly guide to the Universe* 1994) mentions among other eponymous stars those of Van Biesbroeck ("famous for being dim"), Van Maanen ("known for being small") and Plaskett ("thought to be the most massive star in the galaxy").

** Proper motion: motion along our line of sight, as a change of position relative to the sun.

[68] BARTLETT CHILDERS – see FLYING CHILDERS

[69] BARTLETT PEAR

Variety of pear developed by a 17th century English horticulturalist named **WILLIAMS**, who obtained the original cuttings from Berkshire schoolmaster John Stair after whom the pear was first named. Transported to America and further developed by Massachusetts nurseryman **ENOCH BARTLETT** (1779-1860), the pear underwent a further name change, though retaining its Williams identity this side of the Pond. The French call it "*poire william*" and make a very acceptable fruit brandy from it.

[70] BATESIAN MIMICRY

In biology, a form of protective camouflage by which an organism secures a selective advantage through an evolved resemblance to a different organism that would be considered harmful or unpalatable by a potential predator. A number of harmless New World snake species, for example, have evolved a pattern of coloration which mimics that of the deadly coral snake. Most examples, however, are found in the insect world, quite commonly in butterflies. The phenomenon was first described in a paper on the insect fauna of the Amazon published by the Linnaean Society in 1862. Its author was the English naturalist and entomologist **HENRY WALTER BATES** (1825-1892). As a young man, Bates spent eleven years exploring the Amazon rain forest, the first two in company with **ALFRED RUSSEL WALLACE.** Among the fruits of his travels and researches were some 8000 new insect species and *The Naturalist on the River Amazons* (1863), written at **DARWIN'S** urging and described as "one of the most delightful books of travel in the English language" (*EB* 11th ed.). As Assistant-Secretary to the Royal Geographical Society, a post he held from 1864 until his death, Bates encouraged and supported, among others, Livingstone, Stanley and the Arctic explorer Nares. At the same time he used the Society's growing influence to promote the teaching of scientific geography as an academic subject in schools and at Oxford and Cambridge universities, and he may be said to have launched the career of Halford Mackinder whose *Geographical Pivot of History*, a paper read to the RGS in 1904, has remained a powerful influence in the field of geopolitics and international relations to this day. Bates held honorary fellowships in the Zoological, Entomological and Linnaean Societies and was elected FRS in 1881. He died of 'flu. His grave and monument are in Marylebone cemetery.

[71] BATH OLIVER

Another biscuit for the discerning (see **ABERNETHY**), originally created as a dietary item around 1750 by the physician to the Bath Mineral Water Hospital, Cornishman **DR. WILLIAM OLIVER** (1695-1764). Oliver was educated at Pembroke College, Cambridge, elected FRS in 1730, appointed to the Hospital in 1740, and published an essay on gout in 1751. His biscuit is plain, flat, oval, hard, and crisp, and preferred today as an accompaniment to cheese. The genuine item bears an imprint of Dr. Oliver's likeness – the next best thing, perhaps, to having your face on a banknote. The recipe, which Oliver willed on his death to his coachman Atkins, is still supposedly a secret, but this is, like his biscuit, hard to swallow. (MW)

[72] BATTENBERG CAKE

A four-square sponge cake alternately chequered pink and yellow, adhered with apricot jam, and coated with almond paste. (Its cross-section resembles the maritime signal flag for letter U: "*You are running into danger*".) The cake was allegedly contrived in honour of the marriage in 1884 of Princess Victoria of Hesse-Darmstadt, a granddaughter of Queen Victoria, to Austrian-born **PRINCE LOUIS ALEXANDER OF BATTENBERG** (1854-1921). The Prince had adopted British nationality in 1868 and served with distinction in the Royal Navy, rising to First Sea Lord. In 1917 by command of George V, but also reflecting the national prejudice, he relinquished his Hunnish titles and Anglicised – or at least partially de-Germanised – his family name to **MOUNTBATTEN**, becoming Marquis of Milford Haven. His younger son, Louis (1900-1979), held high command during WWII, was made Earl Mountbatten of Burma, presided over the disastrously bungled partition of India, and was killed by an IRA bomb on his holiday boat in County Sligo. (MW)

[73] BAUHINIA

A large genus (200-300 species) of thorny, leguminous tropical and sub-tropical trees, shrubs and (in China) lianas. The flowers of some – particularly S.E. Asian – species give rise to the common name "orchid tree". The genus is named after the Swiss-French **BAUHIN** brothers, physician **JEAN** (1541-1613) and botanist **GASPARD** (1560-1624). Jean dedicated his *Encyclopédie botanique* to his employer the Duke of Wurtemburg. Gaspard, professor of medicine at the University of Basel, is remembered for an early attempt to provide a rational method of plant classification in his *Pinax theatri botanici* of 1623 which contains descriptions of some 6000 plants.

[74] BAUMÉ SCALE

A hydrometer scale (in fact, ambiguously, two scales) for measuring specific gravity (or relative density) of liquids by comparison with standard aqueous solutions of common salt. "Degrees Baumé" are abbreviated as °Bé. The scale is long obsolete in any circles that might be deemed remotely scientific but, with that perverse resistance to rationality that persists elsewhere, it is still used in the printing trade for designating the strength of solutions of gum Arabic, and in the solution processing of sugar beet, and in brewing (*cf.* **BRIX**). **ANTOINE BAUMÉ** (1728-1804) born at Senlis, France, studied at the École de Pharmacie and devoted himself to aspects of commercial chemistry. (MW)

[75] BEAUFORT SCALE

The Beaufort scale of wind-speeds is numbered from 0 (calm) to 12 (hurricane)* and is based on the effect of the wind on such things as wave-height, ship's sails, tree branches, or chimney smoke. It is unusual in that its application doesn't require any kind of measuring instrument beyond a good eye. Its deviser, **sir FRANCIS BEAUFORT** (1774-1857), was a naval surveyor, map-maker and hydrographer. The scale dates from 1805 but it wasn't until 1906 that the

Meteorological Office allotted anemometer-measured wind-speeds to Beaufort's numbers. Beaufort also made an important contribution to the science of cryptography, specifically to the construction and decipherment of codes based on the key-word principle. The **BEAUFORT SEA**, a part of the Arctic Ocean likely to loom large in world affairs in the near future, is named in his honour. (For the history of naval surveying and biographies of major players: Capt. L.S. Dawson, RN *Memoirs of hydrography*, 1885.)

* Recently extended to 17.

[76] BÉCHAMEL SAUCE

BÉCHAMEL SAUCE, or "white sauce" in the language of any Good Plain Cook, is named after **LOUIS DE BÉCHAMEIL, MARQUIS DE NOINTEL** (1630-1703) a French financier and member of the court of Louis XIV. Its first mention in print is in La Varenne's cook-book *Le Cuisinier François* (1651), the founding document of French gastronomy. Its offspring, **MORNAY SAUCE** simply adds cheese (normally gruyère or parmesan or a mixture of both). *Sauce Mornay* was introduced as such in the menu of *Le Grand Véfour* a top Parisian foodies' hangout in the 19th century (and still today). As to which Mornay is the eponymous godfather of this excellent confection, there are several possibilities, including at least two bearers of the name among the Parisian *beau monde* of the period with either or both of whom the proprietors of the restaurant may have wished to ingratiate themselves.

[77] BECQUEREL

Next to a **NOBEL PRIZE**, the mark of supreme distinction in physical science is to have a unit of measurement named after you. It is very rare to enjoy both honours, but this is an instance. The **BECQUEREL** is a unit of radioactivity: it corresponds to the disintegration of one nucleus per second. This is a very low level of radioactivity: for practical purposes, kilo- or mega-becquerels are employed. For instance, every human adult has accumulated in their body – quite inescapably – sufficient of the naturally-occurring radioactive isotope, potassium-40, to generate 3.7 kilobecquerels. **ANTOINE HENRI BECQUEREL** (1852-1908) was born in Paris into a family of scientists. By 1892, he was occupying the physics chair at the Paris Museum. Here in 1896 he discovered the phenomenon of radioactivity, by placing a uranium salt on an opaquely-wrapped photographic plate, and observing that the developed plate bore a fogged image of the uranium salt, presumably caused by some invisible penetrating radiation. He showed that it could be stopped by metal, and differed from the X-rays of **WILHELM RÖNTGEN** (*q.v.*). Becquerel shared a Nobel Prize in 1903 with Pierre and Marie **CURIE,** who also gave their name to a unit of radioactivity (see **CURIE**). (MW)

[78] BEDDGELERT

A touching Welsh legend tells how the dog GELERT belonging to Prince Llewelyn of Gwynedd was killed in a hasty moment by his owner who returned from a hunting trip to find the dog blood-spattered and the baby, whom the dog had been left at home to protect, nowhere in sight. In fact, the baby was concealed in rumpled bed-clothes and the blood on the dog was the product of a desperate fight he had had with a wolf intent on harming the infant. When Llewelyn found the body of the wolf, he realised his mistake and was properly contrite. This sad event supposedly occurred in the North Welsh village of BEDDGELERT (= "Gelert's grave") where the actual tomb of the faithful hound may be visited. In sober truth, both the naming of the village and the erection of Gelert's supposed last resting place are pure invention, stimulated by the locals' desire to take advantage of the increasing popularity of North Wales as a nineteenth-century tourist destination. Rather than judge this harmless – indeed, charming – mendacity too harshly, we should remember Dr. Johnson's charitable observation: "In lapidary inscriptions [*sc.* on tombstones] a man is not upon oath." But anyone inclined to doubt the purely mythical nature of Gelert's story should consider that exactly the same story is told of a dog named Guinefort in mediaeval France, or more correctly, Burgundy. The only points of difference are (1) that in Guinefort's case the threat to the infant came from a large snake, and (2) that after his death, Guinefort was canonised, and women undergoing difficult pregnancies, or no pregnancy at all, used to visit his tomb to pray for his intercession. Unfortunately, Guinefort's sainthood didn't last very long. He was purged from the calendar – presumably by people with no sense of poetry. Meanwhile, Beddgelert remains the only place in the British isles named after a dog (but see also TALBOT).

[79] BEECHAM'S PILLS

In Victorian and Edwardian times it was the custom to ascribe many or most forms of mild internal disorder to malfunction of the liver. Anyone feeling off-colour would be likely to describe themselves as "a bit liverish". In fact what the sufferer in many cases was feeling was the effects of constipation caused by poor diet, and the remedy of choice was BEECHAM'S PILLS, a laxative composed of aloe, ginger and soap, sold under the slogan "Worth a guinea a box". This nostrum, it was claimed, would relieve "nervous and bilious disorders such as wind and pain in the stomach, sick headache, giddiness, fullness and swelling after meals, dizziness and drowsiness, cold chills, flushings of heat, loss of appetite, shortness of breath, costiveness, scurvy, blotches on the skin, disturbed sleep, frightful dreams, and all nervous and trembling sensations, etc." As a clincher, they were said to be "invaluable for females of all ages". Unsurprisingly, a medicine that could cure virtually any condition short of actual death proved enormously popular and led to the creation of a pharmaceutical empire for

THOMAS BEECHAM (1820-1907)* a talented businessman who started life as an Oxfordshire farm worker. In our day, the fashion for liver ailments has somewhat subsided. The word "liverish" has fallen into disuse and most English people, if asked to point to their liver, couldn't, though the French and Italians, by contrast, can unerringly put a finger on the very spot. Even so, as late as 1996 Beecham's Pills were still listed in the British National Formulary under "stimulant laxatives" (active ingredient *aloin*) as a drug on sale to the public but "not prescribable on the NHS". (See also COCKLE'S PILLS.)

* Grandfather of the conductor.

[80] BEEF WELLINGTON – see WELLINGTON BOOT

[81] BEER-LAMBERT LAW

This relationship is used in chemical analysis: it quantifies the absorption of a beam of light by a coloured solution, using a simple equation that involves the concentration of the absorbing substance multiplied by the optical path length of the light. This product is proportional to the *absorbance* (or *optical density*). This law is, however, yet another historical misattribution. It was not discovered by the German physicist AUGUST BEER (1825-1863) of Trier, in 1852, nor by the Swiss mathematician JOHANN HEINRICH LAMBERT (1728-177) of Mulhouse, in 1760 (after whom is named the c.g.s unit of photometric luminance, the LAMBERT, a brightness of one lumen per square centimeter). The origins of the so-called BEER-LAMBERT LAW can be traced to a more interesting person who usually misses out on any credit: French hydrographer and geodesist, PIERRE BOUGUER (1698-1758). He was born at Croisic in Brittany and succeeded his father as professor of hydrography. His *Essai d'optique sur la gradation de la lumière* (1729) laid the foundations of photometry. In 1735 he sailed with French explorer and geographer, Charles Marie de la Condamine (1701-1774) to South America on a scientific expedition (which included Don Antonio de Ulloa – see MERENSKY REEF) to measure a degree of the meridian at the equator, as a basis for determining that French standard of length, the meter (see also ARAGO). For ten years in the South Americas, the expedition conducted measurements in geodesy, gravity, meteorology and astronomy, which were published by Bouguer in 1749. His *Traité du Navire* of 1746 also identifies him as a founder of naval architecture and the theory of navigation. He invented the heliometer in 1748. (MW)

[82] BEGONIA

A genus of tender perennials grown as bedding plants and native to central and South America. It comprises over 20 species and numberless cultivars. The name was authored by the French botanist Father Charles Plumier in honour of MICHEL

BEGON (1638-1710), governor of Haïti and backer of Plumier's botanical explorations.

[83] BELGRANO – see GENERAL BELGRANO

[84] BELISHA BEACON
A black and white striped post with a flashing orange globe on top to mark a pedestrian crossing. Named after English politician LESLIE HORE-BELISHA (1893-1957), Minister of Transport from 1934-37, who introduced a number of road safety measures and worked to improve Britain's arterial road network.

[85] BELL'S *COMET*
No heavenly body shooting across our skies but equally wondrous in its day – the first commercially operated steamship in British waters. *Comet* was the creation of Scottish engineer and entrepreneur HENRY BELL (1797-1869), born at Linlithgow. Rated at 29 tons burden, propelled by paddle-wheels and powered by a 4hp engine (about enough these days for a large lawn-mower) *Comet*, launched on the river Clyde in 1812, offered a regular passenger service between Glasgow and Greenock. Though the first such vessel to see commercial service in British waters, Bell's was not, of course, the first successful steam-powered vessel. Priority in this respect is traditionally accorded to the American painter turned mechanical engineer Robert Fulton (1765-1815), who was experimenting with small steam-powered boats (on the river Seine) as early as 1803 and whose *Clermont*, launched on the Hudson in 1807, showed herself capable of covering the 150 miles between New York and Albany in just 32 hours. Like other pioneers of steam navigation, Bell had no maritime background, but his interest in engineering was put to the service of a number of commercial projects for which he had more inclination than talent. The *Comet* venture was financed by mortgaging the spa hotel he had built at Helensborough to take advantage of the supposed therapeutic properties of the local water. A later venture involving a rebuild for *Comet* and an ambitious extension of her services northwards to the Highlands and Islands was a commercial failure and ended with *Comet's* sinking in the Sound of Jura in 1820.

[86] BELL'S PALSY
An illness which affects the nerve controlling the facial muscles, producing the characteristic drooping appearance which is one of the main visible symptoms. It is named after Edinburgh surgeon and anatomist Sir CHARLES BELL (1774-1882), one of a positive gaggle of Scottish medical men with the same surname. He should not, for example, be confused with Dr. Joseph Bell (1837-1911), also of Edinburgh, considered the founding father of forensic pathology and the mentor

of Arthur Conan Doyle, who used Bell as the model for his famous consulting detective.

[87] BENESH MOVEMENT NOTATION – see LABANOTATION

[88] BENTHAM'S PANOPTICON

JEREMY BENTHAM (1748-1842), writer on jurisprudence and ethics, champion of Utilitarianism, wrote among other works a series of letters outlining a scheme for a model prison which he christened the "PANOPTICON". It was so designed as to subject the inmates to constant scrutiny by the guards, but in such a way as to ensure that the observers remained invisible. It was thus not possible for the convicts to know whether or not they were actually under observation at any given moment. They would therefore, like the citizens who lived under Orwell's Big Brother, have to assume that they were. To achieve this Bentham envisaged a circular multi-storied building with twin walls, the cells being so arranged that each ran from the outer to the inner wall, with windows on the outside and the inside to ensure proper illumination. The guards were housed in a central tower, honeycombed with observation ports but so arranged that the convicts could not tell where in the tower – if anywhere – the guards were at any particular time. By this means, Bentham supposed, the psychological pressure of the guard's all-seeing but unseen presence would make it easy to maintain order with small forces. This would make the prison cheap to run and further economies could be achieved by obliging the inmates to perform useful tasks such as walking treadmills to power various kinds of productive enterprise. It is likely that the original idea came from Bentham's brother Sir Samuel Bentham (1757-1831) naval architect and engineer, who certainly helped with the details of the design. Bentham's proposal met with official approval but in the end the Panopticon was never built because when it came to the pinch the government was unwilling to stump up the necessary funds, though Bentham was awarded a sum in compensation for the time and effort he had spent on the project over nearly 25 years. While Bentham never saw his ideal become reality, the ideas behind the Panopticon live on and have influenced the design of numerous modern prisons in various parts of the world. Today, however, Bentham is probably less remembered for his interest in penal architecture than for his macabre bequest of his mummified body to University College, London, where it still has iconic status, though after a century and a half of restorations and replacements it now mimics the condition of grandpa's hammer.

[89] BESSEL FUNCTIONS – see AIRY'S DISC

[90] BESSEMER CONVERTER

Iron, as usually obtained by the smelting of its oxide ores with coke in a blast-

furnace, contains a substantial amount of carbon, 2.2 to 4.5%, and is called cast-
or pig-iron. The more desirable metal, steel, is iron incorporating only between
0.15 and 1.5% of combined carbon, which confers great strength on the metal.
During the Crimean war of 1853-56, the call for more guns made the manufacture
of steel in bulk a priority. One method of decreasing the amount of carbon in
pig-iron, is to blow air through the molten metal, whereupon the carbon is
oxidised to carbon monoxide which bubbles out and burns off. The BESSEMER
CONVERTER is a pear-shaped furnace, tilting on trunnions, designed to facilitate
this reaction. It was invented, and the process patented in 1855, by SIR HENRY
BESSEMER (1813-1898) an English engineer born in Charlton, Hertfordshire, who
taught himself metallurgy in his father's type-foundry. In 1859 he established a
steel works at Sheffield specialising in gun-making and, later, steel rails. He was
elected FRS and knighted in 1879. (MW)

[91] BESSONNEAU HANGAR

The Bessoneau aircraft hangar was a light, easily-erected structure of wood and
canvas widely used by the Allied air forces in France during the first World War. It
was named after its French inventor and manufacturer JULIEN BESSONNEAU who
originally ran a small family business of rope-makers at Angers, in the hemp-
growing area of Anjou. By 1901 he had built up the business to the point where
he was employing over 4000 persons and by 1910 had diversified into manufacture
of the hangars which bear his name. They were produced in various sizes, the
commonest measuring 20 x 24 metres. A few still survive as museum pieces. It is
worth noting that at one period during the war, the size of hangar commonly
available dictated the size of new aircraft designs, imposing a maximum wing-
span.

[92] BESTUSCHEFF'S NERVINE TINCTURE

In 1725, COUNT ALEXIUS PETROVICH BESTUSCHEFF-RYUMIN (1693-1766), the
Lord High Chancellor of Russia, devised a nostrum rejoicing in the name of
Tinctura tonico-nervina. He kept the formula secret, but intimated that it contained
gold – presumably in order to justify its exorbitant price. He was probably trading
on the public's distant recollection of *aurum potabile*, "drinkable gold", whose
virtues as a panacea had been widely promoted by the iatro-chemists of the
previous century. The secret of the tincture's composition was finally revealed by
the Empress Catherine the Great, who purchased the formula from Bestuscheff's
heirs*. It turned out to be no more precious than a solution of iron chloride in
alcohol, which had been decolourised by exposure to sunlight. Gold was
conspicuously absent from the formulation. Despite the unmasking of its
commonplace nature, the tonic continued to enjoy a long-lived commercial

success as **BESTUSCHEFF'S NERVINE TINCTURE**, although we cannot be sure whether it was the iron, or perhaps the alcohol, that contributed most to the patient's sense of well-being. (As late as 1853, the tincture was still listed in the pharmacopoeias as *Spiritus Sulphurico Etherus Martiatus*, or as *Ferruginated Sulphuric Ether*, having undergone in 1782 a modification due to the chemist Martin Klaproth, who replaced the ethyl alcohol with diethyl ether – making an altogether headier elixir.) (MW)

* The formula had already been purloined, or perhaps merely guessed, by a certain Brigadier (later General) Lamotte who introduced it at the French court under the title *Elixir d'Or*. Louis XIV granted him an annual pension of 4000 *livres* to manufacture his "drops". As the elixir made his fortune it may be said to have lived up to the promise of its name.

[93] BEWICK'S SWAN
Named in honour of **THOMAS BEWICK** (1753-1828), founding father of the British wood-engraving tradition, now remembered largely for his natural history illustrations. **BEWICK'S SWAN** (*Cygnus columbianus bewickii*) breeds in the Arctic tundra and is a winter visitor to Britain. It resembles the Whooper Swan (*Cygnus cygnus*) in the distinctive yellow base to its bill (as opposed to orange), but is much smaller.

[94] BiC – see BIRO

[95] BIG BERTHA
Western Civilization's near-successful attempts at self-destruction in two world wars would have been gravely impeded without the enthusiastic collaboration of the German family Krupp of Essen, proprietors since 1810 of a vast industrial empire of coal, steel and armaments, which became the largest private company in the world. The speciality of the house was bigger and better guns. In WWI the 42-cm howitzer **DICKE BERTHA** (Ger: *dicke* = "thick" or "fat") was unflatteringly so-named after **BERTHA KRUPP** (1886-1957) heiress to the family business since 1902. In 1906 she married nobleman Gustav von Holen und Halbach, who thereby became Company Chairman in 1909. A howitzer is a short, fat artillery piece with a high trajectory, that stands between the field-gun and the mortar. A male counterpart to **BIG BERTHA** was **LANGER MAX** (Ger: *lang* = "long" or "tall"), a railway-mounted supergun of 38-cm calibre, originally designed for German battleships. Which **MAX** the sobriquet commemorates, and whether his personal endowment was in length or height, we shall never be sure. For WWII the Family prepared a railway-mounted artillery-piece of 80-cm calibre capable of firing a seven-ton concrete- and armour-piercing projectile at targets over twenty miles distant – the forts of the Maginot line for example. It was named **SCHWERER GUSTAV** (Ger: *schwer* = "heavy" or "hard"), after the Herr Direktor. Heavy Gustav

was also given a consort when a second gun was built, named **DORA** after the boss's wife – which might in Germany pass for a subtle compliment. These monsters were not completed in time for the invasion of France but were used in anger during operation **BARBAROSSA**. In 1945 both father Gustav and eldest son Alfried Krupp von Holen und Halbach (1907-1967), who had inherited the firm in 1943, were indicted at Nuremberg for war crimes (not the manufacture of lethal weaponry, which was ethically respectable, but the employment of slave labour and looting in occupied territories). Gustav's senile dementia saved him from prison, but Alfried was sent down for 12 years. In 1951 he was amnestied and resumed control of the family business. Post-war, Bertha Krupp scored humanitarian brownie points with her charitable works in and around Essen, but mercifully the Krupp dynasty has now died out. (MW)

[96] BILHARZIA

Bilharzia or schistosomiasis is a form of endemic haematuria caused by a water-borne parasitic worm which invades the genito-urinary tract (or, more rarely, the rectum) of unlucky bathers in the Nile. It takes it name from **THEODOR BILHARZ** (1825-1862), a German doctor in the service of the Egyptian government during the 1850s. Treatment with male fern extract has now been superseded by the schistosomicides Praziquantel and Metriphonate, which sound much more businesslike. Bilharz died in Cairo, worn out by the exertions involved in guiding the Duke of Saxe-Coburg Gotha on a tour of the Eastern Sudan.

[97] BIRCHER-MUESLI

Muesli is not a personal name but a Swiss-German dialect word meaning something like "mixture" or "mash". However, its full and correct title **BIRCHER-MUESLI** commemorates the Swiss doctor **MAXIMILIAN BIRCHER-BENNER** (1867-1939), who, around the beginning of the last century, developed the recipe to improve the diet of patients at his Zürich sanatorium. Bircher was a passionate believer in what he called a "natural" diet, that is, one based not on meat-and-potatoes but on foods that would have been available to man in a state of nature and which, therefore, he is physiologically constitued to live on: fruit, vegetables, nuts, grains, all raw for preference. It is difficult to fault the good doctor's reasoning but, despite this, *fondue*, *raclette* and *rösti* somehow retain their appeal . (cf. **KELLOGG'S CORN FLAKES**).

[98] BIRD'S EYE FISH FINGERS

CLARENCE BIRDSEYE (1886-1956), is widely considered the founder of the modern frozen food industry. He was born in Brooklyn, New York but it was in

Labrador, Canada between 1912 and 1915 that he hit upon his life-changing idea. Whilst working as a field naturalist for the U.S government (a job he had taken on to pay for his biology degree studies at Amherst College), he was ice fishing in Labrador when the temperature had fallen to –30 degrees. When he picked up his day's catch and threw it over his shoulder, the fish froze solid within minutes. A few weeks later, when he thawed them out and cooked them, he noticed they tasted surprisingly fresh. He had discovered the secret of flash-freezing. In 1922 Birdseye conducted fish-freezing experiments at the Clothel Refrigerating Company, then established his own company, Birdseye Seafoods Inc., to freeze fish fillets via chilled air. In 1924, however, the company went bankrupt thanks to lack of consumer interest. But that same year he developed an entirely new process for commercially viable quick-freezing: pack fish in cartons, then freeze the contents between two refrigerated surfaces under pressure. A new company, General Seafood Corporation, was formed to promote this new technique which led in 1925 to Birdseye's newest invention, the double belt freezer, in which cold brine chilled a pair of stainless steel belts carrying packaged fish so the fish froze extremely quickly. Birdseye then began to take out a series of patents on quick-freezing techniques, whereby foods are frozen so quickly that only small ice crystals can form and cell walls are not damaged. In 1927 he began to extend the process to meat, poultry, fruit, and vegetables. In 1929 the company was bought by the Postum Company (later the General Foods Corp.) for $22 million. GFC in turn founded the **BIRDS EYE FROSTED FOOD COMPANY** which in 1930 conducted marketing trials in and around Springfield, Massachusetts. In total 26 items were produced ranging from frozen meat to peas and of course fish fillets. By 1949, Birdseye had perfected the anhydrous freezing process, reducing the time needed for the operation from 18 hours to 1 1/2 . The famous **FISH FINGERS** were let loose on the world in 1955, since when children in western countries have never looked back. (The well-known story that Fish Fingers were originally intended to be marketed under the name "Cod Pieces" has proved impossible to authenticate.) (RS)

[99] BIRO

LÁSZLÓ BÍRÓ (1899-1985) was a Hungarian Jew who patented his ball-point pen in Paris in 1938, whither he had fled to escape persecution in Hungary. Its advantage over existing pens was that it exploited the quick-drying properties of printer's ink, which would not flow in fountain-pens. In 1943 Bíró and his brother turned up in Argentina. Here he took out another patent and formed a company to market his invention under the name "Birome". It caught the eye of the British authorities who realised the value of a pen that would write reliably at high altitudes (which a fountain-pen would not) and began producing it under licence for issue to the Air Force. It did not become generally available for civilian use in this country till after the war. In 1950 the patent was sold to the Frenchman **MARCEL BICH** (1914-1994), who began making and selling cheap ball-point pens under the name **BiC** — so successfully that his company now has a virtual world monopoly, at least at the lower end of the price range, and is said to sell pens at the rate of 20 million a day. The use of the eponym **"BIRO"** to mean "ball-point pen" is mainly confined to the UK and Europe.

[100] BISMARCK ARCHIPELAGO

The name of **Prince OTTO EDWARD LEOPOLD VON BISMARCK** (1815-1898), German statesman and principal architect of the Prusso-German Empire, also known as the "Iron Chancellor", is preserved in a group of some 200 islands in the South Pacific (where Germany once had imperial ambitions), as well as in an ill-fated warship, pride of Hitler's high seas fleet*, seven towns in the USA and one in Canada, a dark brown synthetic dye, and a dish of marinated herring, which, like revenge, is eaten cold.

* *Cf.* **GENERAL BELGRANO**

[101] BLACKSTONE'S MANUALS – see **MORIARTY'S POLICE LAW**

[102] BLANCHARD'S PARACHUTE

The French aeronaut **JEAN-PIERRE BLANCHARD** (1753-1809) takes the credit for the first working parachute (Leonardo, as far as is known, never tested his version). In 1789, Blanchard was in Warsaw to demonstrate a new supersize **MONTGOLFIÈRE** he had constructed for the occasion. No expense was spared — the envelope being made not of paper but of silk. The flight-crew consisted of Blanchard himself, the Polish count Jan Potocki, and Ibrahim, a large Turkish manservant of Potocki's who fell into the gondola by accident as the balloon was leaving the ground. Despite the violence done to Blanchard's calculations of the vehicle's lifting capacity, the flight was a success and, as an extra treat for the onlookers, while triumphantly airborne over Warsaw, Blanchard proceeded to demonstrate his life-saving invention by hurling his pet dog from the gondola with a parachute attached. It landed unhurt.

[103] BLOOMERS

The fact that women have legs was a well-kept secret until around the year 1848 when the American do-gooder **Mrs. AMELIA JENKS BLOOMER** (1818-1894) suggested that for the sake of hygiene, comfort, and equality between the sexes, women might exchange their heavy floor-length skirts and multiple petticoats for a bifurcated garment based on Turkish harem trousers. Even in America, recently the site of a successful revolution and possessed of a desire to make all things new, Mrs. Bloomer's ensembles – ankle-length trousers worn under a short skirt – never really caught on except among the advocates of Rational Dress. When the trousers shrank to above the knee and the skirt re-descended to the ankles, **BLOOMERS** became the baggy women's undergarments that until only recently were a stock theme of music-hall jokes and smutty seaside postcards. If the word is no longer current, it is because bloomers are no longer worn. Brevity is now the order of the day. (See also **KNICKERS**).

[104] BLUETOOTH TECHNOLOGY

BLUETOOTH was the code-name under which a new communication technology for electronic devices was developed. The choice of name supposedly embodies a reference to **HARALD BLUETOOTH*** **GORMSON** (*ca.* 910-*ca.* 985), King of Denmark, whose territories then included southern Sweden (where the Bluetooth technology was developed) and Norway. King Harald is best known in Nordic history for the unification of warring tribes – a very apt model for the process of agreeing a new industrial specification. The code-name stuck and the widely-employed Bluetooth wireless standard and communication protocol is used for simple communication by wireless means between a variety of electronic devices over short ranges (commonly 10, maximum 100 metres). (GJ)

* Blåtand in Danish

[105] BOBBY – see PEELER

[106] BODE'S LAW

On the whole, what in science are called "laws" are not so in any prescriptive sense. Rather they are what might better be termed "observed regularities". So much is certainly true of **BODE'S LAW**, an observed mathematical regularity in the distances of the different planets in the Solar System from the Sun. And in Bode's case the appellation is doubly inappropriate since the original discovery was made by Johann Daniel Titius of Wittenberg in 1766. **JOHANN ELERT BODE** (1747-1826) was Director of the Berlin observatory when in 1772 he published Titius' idea without mentioning Titius' name. Titius had noted that if one took a series of numbers of which the first two were 0 and 3 and the remainder doubled at each step (so: 0-3-6-12-24...), added 4 to each number, and if one then divided each member of the series by 10, the result corresponded with surprising accuracy to the distance, in astronomical units,* of each planet from the sun, starting with Mercury and working outwards:

$$0.4 \quad 0.7 \quad 1 \quad 1.6 \quad 2.8 \quad 5.2 \quad 10 \quad 19.2 \quad 38.4 \quad 76.8$$

The fact that no planet was known in the fifth position (between Mars and Jupiter at 2.8 AU) started a search for the missing object which resulted in the discovery of the asteroid belt. Bode's Law held good until the discovery of the outer planets

URANUS, NEPTUNE and PLUTO in 1781, 1846, and 1930 respectively. Though the first and third of these were found at the predicted distances, Neptune at 30 AU turned out not to fit the pattern.

* An astronomical unit (AU) is the mean distance of the Earth from the Sun: 93 million miles, give or take.

[107] BODLEIAN LIBRARY

The Bodleian Library is the main research library of the University of Oxford. The Bodleian Group now cares for some 8 million items on 117 miles of shelving, and employs a staff of over 400. It is the second largest library in the UK after the British Library. The buildings within the central site include Duke Humfrey's Library above the Divinity School, the Old Schools Quadrangle with its Great Gate and Tower, the Radcliffe Camera – Britain's first circular library – and the Clarendon Building. In addition, the Bodleian has nine "branch" libraries scattered about Oxford in separate locations. The first purpose-built library known to have existed in Oxford was founded in the fourteenth century by Thomas Cobham, Bishop of Worcester. This small collection of chained books was then added to over the years but by the late 16th century it was neglected and in decline, a decline which THOMAS BODLEY (1545-1613), a fellow of Merton College, undertook to reverse. In 1598 his offer to restore the old library was accepted by the university. Bodley not only used his private fortune in this undertaking, but induced many of his friends to make valuable gifts of books. The library was formally re-opened on November 8 1602 as "Bodley's Library". Bodley continued to oversee its growth. In 1610, he made an agreement with the Stationer's Company in London to put a copy of every book registered with them in the library. The Bodleian collection grew so fast that the building was expanded between 1610–1612. Bodley was a prominent diplomat at the court of Elizabeth I, a gifted linguist and scholar, and Merton College's first lecturer in Greek. (RS)

[108] BOHR RADIUS

The BOHR RADIUS simply measures the size of a hydrogen atom, and can serve as a convenient yardstick at the atomic scale of things. Its value of about 53 picometers*, results from the calculations performed in 1913 by Danish physicist NIELS HENRICK DAVID BOHR (1885-1962) the pioneer of modern atomic theory. Bohr envisaged a "classical" model for the hydrogen atom, resembling a miniature solar system, with a negatively-charged electron orbiting around the positively-charged nucleus (a proton). Electrostatic attraction between the two oppositely-charged particles keeps the show on the road, and is just balanced by the centrifugal force of the whirling electron. Unfortunately this setup has a fatal flaw: according to the classical electromagnetic theory of MAXWELL, it should radiate energy and rapidly collapse. Nonetheless hydrogen exists, so Bohr invented an inspired assumption (or fudge) to get over this problem, involving the quantum theory of **MAX PLANCK**. Subsequently Bohr's model was replaced by **SCHRÖDINGER**'s. Bohr worked with J.J. Thomson at Cambridge and **RUTHERFORD** at Manchester. He was awarded the **NOBEL PRIZE** for Physics in 1922, and held the physics chair at Copenhagen from 1916 until 1962, interrupted only by two years in the USA during WWII (see **MAUD COMMITTEE**). Bohr's relations with **HEISENBERG** have been a subject for theatrical speculation. Element number 107, **BOHRIUM**, about which absolutely nothing is known, honours his memory. One of his many *bons mots* ("Your theory is crazy, but it is not crazy enough to be true") epitomises the new thinking in physics, as perhaps does the well-known anecdote concerning a visitor to Bohr's country cottage who found him nailing a lucky horseshoe over a door and remarked, "Surely you don't believe such superstitious nonsense?" Bohr replied, "Whether or not I believe in it has nothing to do with whether or not it works," and went on nailing. (MW)

* There are one million million (10^{12}) picometers in a meter.

[109] BOLIVIA

The country, its currency the **BOLIVIANO,** and the currency of its neighbour Venezuela, the **BOLIVAR**, are named after **SIMÓN BOLIVAR** (1783-1830) who led the fight for independence of Spain's South American colonial possessions between 1811 and 1824. In the process he earned himself the title "El Liberador", though in Chile this title goes to the wonderfully-named Bernardo O'Higgins (1778-1842), bastard son of the Spanish Viceroy (and even more wonderfully-named) Ambrosio O'Higgins (*cf.*1720-1801). Bernardo has also given his name to the Chilean Antarctic research station.

[110] BOLTZMANN'S CONSTANT

Wherever, in chemistry or physics, a temperature needs to be converted into a corresponding energy on the atomic scale of things, this physical constant turns out to be the multiplying factor. **BOLTZMANN'S CONSTANT** is universally given the symbol k, having a value in SI units of 1.38×10^{-23} **JOULES** per **KELVIN** (J/K). Thus, a molecule of a gas at temperature T degrees **KELVIN**, has an average kinetic energy of $^3/_2$kT **JOULES** due to its random translational motion in 3 dimensions. The constant was introduced in 1900 by **MAX PLANCK** who generously named it after the Austrian physicist **LUDWIG EDUARD BOLTZMANN** (1844-1906) who was born in Vienna, where he studied physics at the University, then occupied chairs at Graz, Munich, Leipzig, Berlin, and back to Vienna. He was a founding father of the statistical theory of thermodynamics. Although he never evaluated it, **BOLTZMANN'S CONSTANT** was implicit in his theories from 1877, including the

MAXWELL-BOLTZMANN DISTRIBUTION, the BOLTZMANN EQUATION and the
STEFAN-BOLTZMANN LAW. He was a strong proponent of the atomic theory of
matter at a time when it was still, surprisingly, opposed by some major figures of
the scientific establishment, such as MACH and OSTWALD. BOLTZMANN'S depressive
mood swings suggest that he was probably bipolar, and on vacation in Duino,
near Trieste, in 1906 he hanged himself. His constant was engraved upon his
tombstone, enshrined in his remarkable equation relating the entropy, S, of a
system with its probability, W: $S = k \log W$ – a concept which lies at the core of
statistical thermodynamics and information theory. (MW)

[111] BOOK OF MORMON

The sacred book of the Church of Jesus Christ of Latter-day Saints. Its publishing
history goes back to the year 1830 and concerns the Church's founder, one Joseph
Smith (1805-1844), then living with his family on a small farm near the town of
Palmyra in New York State. Smith's father was a water-diviner and unearther of
hidden treasure, faculties which he evidently passed on to his son. In 1823, Smith
Junior was visited several times by an angel named Moroni who revealed to him
the nearby location of a buried volume of sacred writings. Smith repaired to the
spot indicated and dug up a stone box containing a ring-bound book written in a
previously unknown script on thin plates of gold. Included in the package was a
pair of special spectacles which enabled the wearer to read and understand the
text. (This was fortunate as Smith was only partially literate.) He now set about
translating the contents of the Golden Book. This he did while sitting at a kitchen
table hidden by a curtain so that no profane eye might fall on the plates, and
dictating the translation to a series of amanuenses including a certain Martin
Harris, who eventually paid for the Book's publication in an edition of 5000
copies. The original, its mission accomplished, subsequently disappeared. The text
recounts the history of America following its settlement by Middle-Eastern
refugees from the ethnic confusion which followed the Tower of Babel fiasco.
Internecine warfare among various settler factions culminated in a final battle in
384 AD. Two survivors of the slaughter were MORMON and his son Moroni.
Mormon collected in a single volume the annals of his people and buried them at
a site where he predicted they would later be discovered by a divinely-inspired
prophet. And the rest, as they say, is history. But how Smith managed to enlist
other people in the new religion he founded on the basis of these revelations
remains a profound enigma. What possible motivation could be strong enough to
prevent a person noticing that in Smith the conflict between Fantasy and Reality
had turned out badly for Reality – and strong enough to withstand the vicious
persecution to which his disciples were later subjected? A number of weighty
thinkers from Tertullian to Sir Thomas Browne and beyond have pointed out that
the eye of Faith is blind to the laws of Probability, that between Belief and

Reason there is a great gulf fixed – *Credo quia impossibile*. But that's an observation, not an explanation. On a passing note – there is a surprising congruity between Smith's proceedings and those of the Elizabethan magus Dr. John Dee (1527-1608) and his sinister, earless sidekick Edward Kelley. Both Smith and his father used "spy-stones" to help them find hidden treasures; Dee used "shew-stones". Both Smith and Dee were in regular communication with angels, and both received copious communications in an otherwise unknown language – "Enochian" in Dee's case, "reformed Egyptian" in Smith's. And there are other correspondences in points of detail. It is hard to know what significance if any to ascribe to this echo of Renaissance hermeticism since it is wildly unlikely that Smith had ever so much as heard the name of John Dee or that he was familiar with the methods of the alchemist-astrologers of three centuries before his own time. It is, however, a racing certainty that had Smith lived in an earlier century he would have been in mortal danger from a charge of witchcraft.

[112] BOOLEAN ALGEBRA

A logical calculus developed by the English mathematician and logician, **GEORGE BOOLE** (1815-1864). Boole's calculus was the first to successfully utilise the methods of numeric algebra for the purpose of representing logical forms. The symbols used by the calculus are borrowed from arithmetic as are the majority of its laws. Its operations are logical equivalents of basic numeric operations. For instance, multiplication, xy, is equivalent to Boolean conjunction, x AND y. The calculus is two-valued, *i.e.* its operations have one of two possible values or outcomes, which can be given logically as true/false or arithmetically as 1/0. The influence of Boole's calculus on modern mathematical logic has been incalculable. Indeed, Boole's contribution to symbolic logic in general is considered by many to be comparable in significance to that made by Aristotle. Boolean algebra has practical application also, most notably in electronic circuitry and computer programming. Boole, a polymath whose interests extended to poetry and the classics, was largely self-taught. In 1849 he was appointed professor of mathematics at Queen's College, County Cork, and in 1854 Boole published perhaps his most significant work, *An Investigation into the Laws of Thought*. He died in 1864 aged just 49. (BS)

[113] BORNITE – see SCHEELITE

[114] BORSALINO

The Italian hat company founded in 1857 by **GIUSEPPE BORSALINO** (1834-1900) and his brother **LAZZARO** is known especially for its **FEDORAS** made from felted rabbit fur, and its panamas. The firm's characteristic dated-but-stylish image is reflected in their latest line, a range of motor-cycle helmets which weirdly conjure up Snoopy from *Peanuts* in his Red Baron mode. In 1970 the company produced the French gangster film *Borsalino* starring Alain Delon and Jean-Paul Belmondo, a well-chosen pair of cool hat-pegs. A sequel *Borsalino & Co* followed in 1974.

[115] BOSE-EINSTEIN STATISTICS – see BOSON and EINSTEIN

[116] BOSON

Elementary particles fall into two categories, FERMIONS and BOSONS. Bosons are the particles associated with the transfer of energy, the most familiar one being the photon, or particle of light (but see also HIGGS BOSON). These two sorts of particle are distinguished by the quantization of their "spin" – whether half-integer or integer, respectively (zero is deemed to be an integer). This obscure quantum property (which has really little to do with spinning tops) determines how the particles perform collectively – behaviour which is referred to as their "statistics". Translating into more accessible language: any number of BOSONS within the same space are permitted to enjoy the same quantum state – *i.e.* they are intrinsically indistinguishable. That's just as well, really, or light would be an even funnier thing than it is already. The concept is named after an Indian physicist, the Bengali SATYENDRA NATH BOSE (1894-1974) who was born and educated in Calcutta, where he became a lecturer at the University in 1916, before moving to the University of Dacca in 1921. His unorthodox interpretation of the statistical mechanics of photons in the 1920s was initially rejected by the scientific establishment, but recognised as correct by ALBERT EINSTEIN. In 1925 the two men jointly predicted that a weird new state of matter, called a BOSE-EINSTEIN CONDENSATE, could exist for certain bosonic substances at temperatures close to absolute zero. The superfluid behaviour observed in liquid helium-4 in 1938 had been an indication of this possibility, but the prediction was not fully confirmed experimentally until 1995 when a BOSE GAS (of rubidium-87 atoms) was shown to exhibit exotic quantum phenomena on a macroscopic scale, flowing out of its container against gravity, and slowing a beam of light to walking pace. (MW)

[117] BOUGAINVILLEA

The navigator and maritime explorer LOUIS ANTOINE, COMTE DE BOUGAINVILLE (1729-1811), has been called France's answer to Captain Cook. The genus of tropical climbing plants we know as BOUGAINVILLEA, which he brought back with him from his circumnavigation of 1766-69*, is named, not after Louis Antoine himself, as might be supposed, but in honour of his wife. It is not to be confused with *Bougainvillea fruticosa* a weird marine organism half plant and half jellyfish. Bougainville was, incidentally, involved in a failed attempt to establish a French colony in what later became the FALKLAND ISLANDS, adding one more complication to the tangled history of the islands' ownership.

* See his *Voyage autour du monde* (1771), English trans. by J.R.R.Forster, 1772 (cf. KALMIA).

[118] BOWDLERISE

To edit a text in such a way as to remove all expressions that might be considered offensive or indecent. Refers to the expurgated edition of Shakespeare produced by **THOMAS BOWDLER** (1754-1825). Bowdler's *Family Shakespeare* appeared in 10 volumes in 1818. He subsequently turned his attention to Gibbon's *Decline and fall*, his edition of which was published posthumously in 1828. He settled in Wales and died at Oystermouth, near Swansea. His extensive library, collected by his forebears over 2 centuries, passed to the University College of Wales, Lampeter.

[119] BOWIE KNIFE

A heavy belt knife with a blade up to a foot long. According to legend it was designed by **Colonel JAMES BOWIE** (1796-1836) and forged for him by Arkansas blacksmith James Black. Black is supposed to have modified Bowie's design by adding what became the distinguishing feature of the Bowie knife – the sharpened curve which runs from the point to about a third of way up the back or "blunt" side of the blade. (Black is also credited with the design and manufacture of a throwing weapon, the "Arkansas toothpick", a long heavy dagger which had to be carried in a holster slung over the wearer's back.) Bowie (pronounced *boo-eey*) was, of course, a leading light in the rebellion of the American immigrants in Texas against the Mexican government and died at the Alamo with his co-conspirators Crockett and Travis. (RJ)

[120] BOYCOTT

The verb "to boycott" in its present meaning derives from the "annoyances" (DNB) inflicted by Land League activists on the unpopular agent for Lord Erne's County Mayo estates, **CHARLES CUNNINGHAM BOYCOTT** (1832-1897). Boycott was an early victim of the tactic of social and economic excommunication instigated by the Land League's president and Irish MP Charles Stewart Parnell (1846-1891). Refusal to have any dealings with Boycott meant that he was simply unable to carry out his functions and had to resort to scab labour, protected by a huge force of police and soldiers, to get in the harvest on his employer's estates.

[121] BOYLE'S LAW

One of the fathers of modern physical science, **THE HON. ROBERT BOYLE** (1627-1691) was an Irishman, born at Lismore Castle, a son of the Earl of Cork, and educated at Eton. His achievements in natural philosophy were extensive. He was one of the founders of the Royal Society in 1645 and published *The Skeptical Chymist* in 1661, which revolutionised chemistry, although he still held to the alchemical tenet of transmutation. (As it turns out, modern nuclear physics has proved him right.) His law of gas behaviour, formulated in 1660, seems intuitively reasonable: *For a fixed mass of gas at constant temperature, the pressure and volume are inversely proportional.* This means, for instance, that if you double the pressure then the volume is halved – and so on. In other words: pressure times volume is constant. Experimentally, it's found not to be exactly true, only a useful approximation, but science cleverly gets round this by asserting that it *is* true for a "perfect" or "ideal" gas*, while admitting that all *real* gases are "imperfect" or "non-ideal" – due to attractions between their constituent molecules (see **VAN DER WAALS EQUATION** and **CHARLES'S LAW**). (MW)

* Ideal gas: a purely theoretic concept describing a volume of gas in which the molecules are in perfectly random motion, and are unaffected by intermolecular forces so that on collision they bounce elastically off each other and off the sides of their container.

[122] BOYS ANTI-TANK RIFLE

The "**BOYS**", a British-designed, bolt-action anti-tank rifle of 0.55" calibre was approved for service in 1937. It was named in honour of **CAPT. H.C. BOYS**,* a leading member of the design team at the Royal Small Arms Factory, Enfield, who died in the same year. Its appearance was distinctly odd: a 3-foot-long barrel ending in a cup-shaped muzzle-brake, top-mounted box magazine, T-shaped bipod, and a crutch-like butt equipped with a handle to raise it to the operator's shoulder. However, it proved effective against the relatively lightly-armoured tanks of the period. Its chief disadvantages were its weight – 36lbs, a serious added burden for the modern equivalent of Rome's overloaded legionaries ("Marius's Mules") – and its ferocious recoil. To soften its kick, the weapon featured, in addition to the muzzle-brake, a slide mounting for the barrel operating against a spring-loaded recoil buffer in the stock, and a thick rubber pad fitted to the shoulder-piece. As WWII progressed, improved tank designs and thicker armour rendered the Boys virtually useless and where possible it was replaced by the Americans' 50-calibre Browning machine-gun firing armour-piercing ammunition or, later in the war, by rocket-propelled anti-tank weapons such as the Bazooka. On the German side, the preferred infantry anti-tank weapon was the *Panzerfaust*, ancestor of the Russian-designed RPG which is still in active service today in Afghanistan and elsewhere. (For other products of the Enfield factory, see **LEE-ENFIELD RIFLE** and **STEN GUN**.)

* Often mis-spelt "Boyes".

[123] BOYSENBERRY – see LOGANBERRY

[124] BRADSHAW

When Sherlock Holmes, Consulting Detective, was not being whirled about the streets of foggy London town in a **HANSOM CAB**, he was being rattled across

England to some crisis-ridden rural location in a smoke-belching railway train. The latter expeditions were invariably preceded by a curt instruction to Watson to "Hand me my Bradshaw," and quite possibly (to rack up the tension), "There is not a moment to lose, Watson. I fear we may already be too late." That he never was (late) is partly, therefore, thanks to Lancashire-born printer and engraver **GEORGE BRADSHAW** (1801-1853). Bradshaw was engaged in the 1830s in producing maps of Britain's canals and railways. In 1839 he began publishing *Railway Time Tables*, followed by *Bradshaw's Monthly Railway Guide* from 1842, and later still, *Bradshaw's Continental Railway Guide*. He died of cholera in Oslo.

[125] BRAILLE

Teacher and musician **LOUIS BRAILLE** (1809-1852) became blind at the age of three. In 1828 he obtained a teaching post at the *Institution des Jeunes Aveugles* in Paris where he himself had been an inmate since the age of 10. It was here that he perfected his writing system based on raised dots that could be "read" by touch. Braille's method represented letters and numbers by "cells" each containing two columns of three dots. Each dot in the cell could be raised or not raised and thus constituted a binary coding system with 64 possible permutations – ample for an alphabetic script. Braille's system was not wholly original but was an improved version of a method of "night writing" invented during the Napoleonic wars by French army captain Charles Barbier in reponse to a requirement for soliders to be able to communicate silently in the dark.

[126] BRAUNITE – see SCHEELITE

[127] BRIGHT'S DISEASE

DR. RICHARD BRIGHT (1789-1858) is remembered in medical history as the "father of nephrology". It was he who first made the connection between dropsy and kidney malfunction and gave his name to the condition. However, the term **BRIGHT'S DISEASE**, is no longer current as various forms of kidney disease, chronic or acute, are now divided into different categories each with its own appellation. Bright was born in Bristol and studied medicine at Edinburgh. He taught and practised at Guy's Hospital from 1820-1844 and on retirement set up a successful private practice. Among his patients were Macaulay, Tennyson and Brunel. During Bright's stay at Guy's, the staff included two other medical luminaries, both Edinburgh trained, whose names are eponymously remembered. One was **THOMAS HODGKIN** (1798-1866)* and the other **THOMAS ADDISON** (1795-1860). **HODGKIN'S DISEASE**, now known as **HODGKIN'S LYMPHOMA,** a cancerous condition of the lymph system, was described by Hodgkin in a paper of 1832 but not named after him until some 30 years later. Hodgkin, a Quaker, devoted much of his time and energy to humanitarian causes, taking up the cudgels on behalf of oppressed minorities wherever they might be found: negro slaves in America (he supported the scheme for settling Liberia with freed slaves); Canadian Indians, cheated and mistreated by the Hudson's Bay Company; and Levantine Jews who were having a bad time in certain parts of the Ottoman Empire. Addison, a Geordie, was on the staff of Guy's from 1824 to 1849. His elucidation of the condition for which he is chiefly remembered, **ADDISON'S DISEASE,** originally **ADDISON'S ANAEMIA**, a wasting disease caused by underactivity of the adrenal glands** (called by Addison the "supra-renal capsules") is now regarded as a founding moment in the science of endocrinology. In his later years Addison suffered from depression and died by his own hand. He is buried in the churchyard of Lanercost Priory in Cumbria.

* For note on Hodgkin family see **SOMERVILLE COLLEGE.**

** *Overactivity* of the adrenal glands is known as **CUSHING'S SYNDROME** after American physician **HARVEY CUSHING** (1869-1939). Symptoms include abnormal hair growth, and moon-like swelling of the face so that "the ears are no longer visible when viewed directly from the front" (Green *Introduction to human physiology* 1963).

[128] BRINNELL SCALE

MOH'S HARDNESS SCALE used by field geologists is of little use to engineers wishing to test the hardness of metals (castings, sheet materials, etc.) and the need for an alternative system has produced three principal contenders (and some also-rans) – those of **BRINNELL** (after Swedish engineer **JOHAN AUGUST BRINNELL,** 1849-1925); **ROCKWELL** (after the New England brothers **HUGH M. ROCKWELL,** 1896-1957, and **STANLEY P. ROCKWELL,** 1886-1940); and **VICKERS** after the famous engineering firm which traces its origins to the steel-works founded in Sheffield in 1828 by **EDWARD VICKERS** (1804-1897)). All three systems yield a "hardness number" arrived at, roughly speaking, by bashing a test piece with a heavy weight known as an "indenter" and then measuring the size of the indentation.

[129] BRIX

A scale to measure the sugar content of solutions (symbol °Bx). It is used in the fruit-juice and sugar-manufacturing industries but its main use is in wine-making where a measurement of the sugar content of the must (unfermented grape juice) is used to predict the alcoholic strength of the finished wine (*cf.* **CHAPTALISATION**). Thus a hydrometer reading of, for example, 25°Bx indicates that 100g of water contain 25g of sugar. This figure has to be corrected for temperature and then multiplied by 0.6 since only 60% of the sugar in the must is turned into alcohol by fermentation. This would then yield an approximate figure of 15% alcohol – quite heady. The scale is named after the 19th-century Austrian physicist and mathematician **ANTOINE BRIX** and represents a refinement of an earlier scale devised by German chemist Karl Balling.

[130] BROUGHAM

A light, one-horse, four-wheeled passenger vehicle designed by **HENRY PETER BROUGHAM, Baron BROUGHAM AND VAUX** (1778-1868). The passenger compartment, holding normally two people, was enclosed, with windows facing to the sides and front. The driver sat at the front on an open box seat. It first came into use about 1850. The general design influenced some early forms of motor-car. Brougham trained as a lawyer in Scotland, founded the *Edinburgh Review*, entered Parliament in 1810, supported the anti-slavery movement, interested himself in educational reform, defended early trade unionists including the victims of the Peterloo Massacre, was raised to the peerage and the office of Lord Chancellor in 1830, introduced important reforms of the judicial system, founded London University, served as Rector of Glasgow University and Chancellor of Edinburgh University, was a Fellow of the Royal Society, and authored a number of heavy-duty historical and legal works and a three-volume autobiography. Where he found the time to design horse-drawn carriages, is a mystery.

[131] BROWNIAN MOTION

In 1827 the Scottish botanist **ROBERT BROWN** (1773-1858) observed with a microscope that pollen grains suspended in water exhibit a continuous, haphazard movement. He soon discovered that this random motion is peculiar neither to pollen nor water, but occurs with all sorts of tiny particles suspended in any fluid. The explanation of this universal phenomenon was first suggested by C. Wiener in 1863: the erratic jiggling is due to the continual bombardment of the particle by the invisible molecules in the surrounding fluid, whose impact is slightly unbalanced in a random way. This was direct evidence for the existence of molecules – at that time still widely doubted – and the mathematical analysis provided by the kinetic theory of gases led to a value for **AVOGADRO'S NUMBER**. Brown, meanwhile, had collected about 4000 species of plants in Australia and became first Keeper of the Botanical Department of the British Museum. (MW)

[132] BRUCHMÜLLER'S ORCHESTRA

GEORG BRUCHMÜLLER (1863-1948) was a German artillery officer who revolutionised German gunnery tactics during the World War I and has had a lasting influence on the practice of modern armies. In 1914 Bruchmüller was on the retired list with the rank of Lt. Col. Recalled to the colours, he served with distinction on the Eastern front, organising the artillery complement of a number of victorious German engagements (Riga, Tarnopol). He was moved to the Western front in time to prepare the German artillery – his "orchestra" – for the final, and nearly decisive, German offensive of March 1918. Bruchmüller rejected the doctrine then current, which called for leisurely prolonged bombardments (days or even weeks) designed to destroy the enemy's front-line defences. Instead he opted for "hurricane" tactics: sudden, massive, concentrated and relatively brief artillery assaults on command centres and other key points while continually shifting targets according to an intricate pre-planned scenario in order to sow confusion and achieve maximum surprise. The tactical breakthroughs of the March offensive were backed by a fire plan involving 6,000 pieces deployed against the British line and 3,700 against the French. Back in retirement after the war, Bruchmüller now a full colonel and holder of the prestigious *Pour le Mérite*, wrote a number of books on artillery tactics though, ironically, it was the Russians, not his own country, that took Bruchmüller's teachings to heart and practised them with deadly effect on the Eastern front in WWII.

[133] BÜCHNER FLASK

Yet another piece of chemical laboratory glassware – it's simply an ERLENMEYER FLASK fitted with a short side-arm near the neck. Its purpose is to enable a vacuum to be applied to the interior (by means of a VENTURI PUMP) in order to suck through the contents of a filter funnel (such as a BÜCHNER FUNNEL – a development of HIRSCH'S FUNNEL) fitted into the neck of the BÜCHNER FLASK. The aim is to improve the speed and volume efficiency of the everyday laboratory operation of filtration. This item of equipment were invented in 1885 by German industrial chemist ERNST WILHELM BÜCHNER (1850-1925), who was born in Pfungstadt, studied chemistry at Tübingen, and in 1882 took over running the successful family factory for synthetic ultramarine, in Pfungstadt near Darmstadt, which had been founded by his father WILHELM BÜCHNER (1816-1892).* Unfortunately, due to the discovery of aniline dyes by PERKIN, the bottom dropped out of the ultramarine market, the business was forced to close and the family fell upon hard times. A few days after the death of his second wife, Ernst took his own life. But his flask and funnel live on, in the hands of chemists everywhere. (MW)

* Wilhelm senior was one of four distinguished brothers: the revolutionary dramatist GEORG BÜCHNER (1813-1837) author of the poetical drama *Woyzeck* (1837) used by composer Alban Berg for his 1925 opera *Wozzeck*; the physiologist and philosopher of scientific materialism FRIEDRICH KARL CHRISTIAN LUDWIG BÜCHNER (1824-1899); and the literary historian ALEXANDER KARL LUDWIG BÜCHNER (1827-1904). This quartet should not be confused with a duet of Munich-born Büchner brothers: EDUARD BÜCHNER (1860-1917), zymologist who was awarded the Nobel Prize for chemistry in 1907 for his studies of fermentation, and HANS ERNST AUGUST BÜCHNER (1850-1902) bacteriologist and immunologist. The Büchner clan seems as numerous as the Bachs, and hardly less prestigious.

[134] BUCKMINSTER-FULLERENE

The chemical highlight of 1985 was the jaw-dropping discovery of this completely new allotrope of that common element carbon, which we have for so long known and loved as soot, charcoal, graphite, and diamonds. The deep purple substance called **BUCKMINSTER-FULLERENE** was discovered by Sussex University chemistry professor Sir Harry Kroto and his co-workers Richard Smalley and Robert Curl at Rice University, Texas. The trio was awarded the chemistry nobel prize in 1996. The new carbon molecule has the formula C_{60} reflecting a remarkable polyhedral structure, with sixty vertices of course, known as a symmetrically truncated regular icosahedron. It is now familiar to every football fan as the universal soccer ball logo, and is derived from that twenty-faced **PLATONIC SOLID** the icosahedron, by chopping off all twelve of its corners. Elaborations of this shape were utilised in the 1950s in the geodesic dome structures of American engineer and utopian visionary **RICHARD BUCKMINSTER FULLER** (1895-1983), whose name is thereby more enduringly celebrated in chemistry than in architecture (see **KEKULÉ**). "Buckyballs", as they are now familiarly called, provide a burgeoning new study, named fullerene chemistry. And they turn out to have been present all along – in candle soot. (MW)

[135] BUDDLEIA

The bold, butterfly-attracting, flower-spikes of *Buddleia davidii* brighten a corner of practically every English garden. They commemorate the pleasantly-named **ADAM BUDDLE** (d. 1715), amateur botanist and rector of North Fambridge in Essex, whose garden they would not have brightened as they were not introduced to this country from their native China until about 1890. However, the Rev. Mr. Buddle, we are told by the *DNB*, "possessed a fine collection of mosses and grasses". The species name *davidii* is that of the French missionary **ARMAND DAVID** (1826-1900) who made important botanical and zoological collections in the course of his travels through China, Tibet and Mongolia (see **PÈRE DAVID'S DEER**). The national collection of buddleias is kept at Longstock Park Nursery in Hampshire, a trowel's throw from the desk at which this article is being written.

[136] BUNSEN BURNER

The familiar stock-in-trade of every chemistry lab, this adjustable gas burner controls the mingling of air in the flame, which can be varied from luminous, yellow and sooty, to a quite fierce transparent blue. It is named after the distinguished German physicist and chemist **ROBERT WILHELM BUNSEN** (1811-1899), the co-inventor with **GUSTAV ROBERT KIRCHHOFF** of spectrum analysis in 1859, leading to the discovery of the new elements caesium and rubidium – for which his burner's flame was a prerequisite. Although 1855 was the year the burner was perfected for Bunsen by the Heidelberg instrument maker, Peter Desaga, it was based on a design previously suggested by **MICHAEL FARADAY**.

Also named after Bunsen were a number of inventions including a carbon-zinc cell he used to produce electric arcs, the grease-spot photometer he devised to measure the light they produced, an ice calorimeter, a vapour calorimeter and a filter pump. The **BUNSEN-ROSCOE LAW** of photochemistry states that the total exposure to light is the product of its intensity and the duration of the exposure. Thus an exposure of 50 lux for 10 seconds is the same as one of 500 lux for 1 second, an equivalence also referred to as the Law of Reciprocity. **SIR HENRY ENFIELD ROSCOE** (1833-1915) was a distinguished English inorganic chemist who studied with **BUNSEN** and became professor at **OWENS COLLEGE**. (MW)

[137] BURGESS SHALE

A famously fossiliferous rock formation in the Canadian Rockies 100+ miles west of Calgary. It bears the name of **ALEXANDER MACKINNON BURGESS** (1850-1898), a one time Deputy Minister of the Interior, on account of its proximity to the nearby **BURGESS MOUNTAIN** and **BURGESS PASS**. These features were allotted their names by the engineer and astronomer Otto Klotz (1852-1923) who visited the area in 1886 while surveying a route for Canada's east-west railway. The twin-peaked outline of Mount Burgess is familiar to many Canadians, as in the fifties and sixties it featured on the Canadian ten-dollar note. For zoologists and palaeontologists, however, it is the shale beds which are of special interest on account of the treasure trove of fossilised creatures they have been found to contain. The fossils were first investigated in 1909 by Charles Doolittle Walcott (1885-1927), American palaeontologist and Secretary of the **SMITHSONIAN INSTITUTION**, after whom one of the mountain's two summits has now been named. But the **BURGESS SHALE** only became more widely known following the publication in 1989 of the book *Wonderful life* by biologist and science writer Stephen Jay Gould (1941-2002). The fossils date from the Middle Cambrian period (*ca*. 500 million years BP), when most known groups of animals first appear in the fossil record (the so-called "Cambrian explosion"). They are of especial interest for two reasons: unusually for petrified animals, the soft parts and appendages of the small invertebrates in the shale are preserved, revealing details of their structure normally inaccessible to investigators; secondly, they include a wild diversity of weird-seeming species that it has proved difficult (in the view of some researchers – though this remains controversial) to allot to known phyla, creatures, in other words, which have no known descendants. As a result the Burgess Shale has been regarded by some as a kind of museum of failed experiments, rejected prototypes which never reached the evolutionary production line.

[138] BURKE AND WILLS EXPEDITION

The first crossing of the Australian continent (from south to north) was made in

1860-1861 by an expedition named after its leader **ROBERT O'HARA BURKE** (1821-1861) and second-in-command, the surveyor **WILLIAM JOHN WILLS** (1834-1861).* Its aim was to survey a route for a possible telegraph line linking southern Australia with Europe via Java. The 16-strong expedition left Melbourne on August 20, 1860, lavishly equipped with useless impedimenta loaded on six huge lumbering wagons, and accompanied by 24 Indian camels for whose management a number of Baluchi tribesmen were imported from India, and 23 horses. On November 11 it reached **COOPER'S CREEK**, the last known place on the route north.** Here Burke formed a base camp where the bulk of the party were ordered to remain for 3 months while he and three others – Wills, John King, and Charles Gray – pushed on north, aiming for the Gulf of Carpentaria. They set out on December 16. On February 9, after a terrible journey, the four men reached the coast, or at least the mangrove swamps which lined it, blocking their access to the sea, and turned for home. Gray died on the return journey, but on April 21 1861 Burke, Wills and King made it back to the Cooper, sick, starving and exhausted, to find that the base party had left just nine hours earlier. Too weak to overtake the main body, and too ill-supplied to make the journey unaided, Burke and Wills died at Cooper's Creek. King survived until rescued, being fed and cared for by local aborigines. Hindsight generally regards the expedition as being doomed by poor planning, bad equipment, and faulty leadership. (None of the party had any experience of bush travel, and Burke, a policeman by trade, was an inexplicable choice of leader.) Nevertheless, the courage and dogged endurance of Burke and his companions on the awful 1500-mile walk from the Cooper to the coast and back, must command our deepest respect, and our pity.

* The enterprise was officially known as the Victoria Exploring Expedition, after the state where it was conceived, funded and organised (see also **MACADAMIA NUT**). For a modern account, see Alan Moorehead *Cooper's Creek* (1963).

** First visited by the explorer Charles Sturt in 1845 and named by him after the lawyer and judge **SIR CHARLES COOPER** (1795-1887), who later served as Chief Justice for South Australia (1856-1861).

[139] BURLINGTON HOUSE – see GRAHAM'S LAW

[140] BUTLER ACT – see SCOPES MONKEY TRIAL

[141] BUYS BALLOT'S LAW – see CORIOLIS EFFECT

[142] BYERLEY TURK

All British thoroughbred horses trace their lineage to one or more* of three stallions, the "founding fathers" of the race. They are known as **THE BYERLEY TURK, THE GODOLPHIN ARABIAN**, and **THE DARLEY ARABIAN**. The Turk owes his name to the fact that he was captured from the Turks at the siege of Buda in 1687 by a **Captain** ROBERT BYERLEY (1660-1714) who was serving there as a cavalry officer under the Duke of Lorraine. The next year Byerley and his mount took part in the Battle of the Boyne, after which the Turk retired from military service and got down to the no doubt more congenial and certainly less stressful serving of carefully-chosen mares on Byerley's estate at Middridge Grange in Co. Durham and later at Goldsborough Hall, near Knaresborough. His biography, *The Byerley Turk: the true story of the first thoroughbred* (2005) has been written by Jeremy James.

* See TATTERSALL'S

C

[143] CAESAREAN SECTION

The medical procedure which consists in the surgical removal of a foetus from the mother's womb is named after the Roman general and dictator GAIUS JULIUS CAESAR (102-44 BC) who according to legend was, like Shakespeare's Macduff, "from his mother's womb untimely ripped". The legend may well be true, given that under Roman law such a procedure was obligatory in the event of a woman's dying in a state of advanced pregnancy. But in the words of the *Encyclopaedia Britannica* (11th ed.), "The first recorded instance of its being performed on a living woman occurred about 1500, when a Swiss pig-gelder operated on his own wife." We are not told with what success.

[144] CAMELLIA

Genus of evergreen flowering shrubs native to E. Asia and including the tea plant (*C. theifera*) among other species. It is named in honour of the Moravian Jesuit JOSEPH KEMEL, Latinised as CAMELLUS, (1661-1706), missionary to China, who introduced it to Europe.

[145] CANOPUS

The brightest star in the firmament after the dog-star Sirius, and hence an important point of reference for navigators, CANOPUS takes it name from the steersman of the legendary Greek king Menelaus, brother of Agamemnon and husband of the beautiful two-timing Helen. The same name in classical times was given to a town, first mentioned by Herodotus and later known as Aboukir, situated on one branch (the "Canopic mouth") of the Nile delta. The term "CANOPIC JARS" is applied to the urns decorated with human or animal heads which were used to contain and preserve the internal organs of persons eviscerated as part of the mummification process. The usage reflected a Greek legend that Canopus the pilot was buried in the town which bore his name, and that it was he whose head appeared on the jars, though in fact the heads were originally intended to represent the god Osiris, for whom the town of Canopus was a major cult-centre.

[146] CAPRIVI STRIP

A long, narrow finger of land sticking out from the top right-hand corner of

Namibia and running East to meet the Zambezi just above Victoria Falls. It was created during the imperial carve-up of Africa (Anglo-German agreement of July 1890) and originally intended to give the Germans in their colony of South-West Africa access to the Zambezi. Underlying this arrangement was the Germans' fond supposition that the un-navigable Zambezi would give them a navigable route to the Indian Ocean. The Strip takes its name from **GEORG LEO, Graf VON CAPRIVI DE CAPRERA DE MONTECUCCOLI** (1831-1899), Imperial Chancellor and Prussian Prime Minister from 1890-1894. When German SW Africa became part of British South Africa following World War I, this cartographic anomaly was allowed to persist as there was no particular point in removing it. When South Africa became independent, the apartheid regime sedulously maintained the Strip as a barrier to infiltration from enemies to the north. A glance at the atlas reveals another anomalous aspect of the Caprivi Strip. Its junction with the Zambezi is the only place on the map of the world where four countries meet at a point. A curiously similar finger of land, the Wakhan valley, sticks out from the top right-hand corner of Afghanistan. Its effect (and no doubt its purpose) was to ensure that British India did not share a border with Russia.

[147] CARDAN JOINT

The **CARDAN** or **UNIVERSAL JOINT** enables a shaft (for example the prop shaft of a rear-wheel-drive car) to revolve when its ends are not in alignment. This elegantly simple device is attributed to **GIROLAMO CARDAN** or **CARDANO** (1501-1576), the Italian physician, mathematician and astrologer, who designed it as a means of keeping a ship's compass-card horizontal. Though labouring under the stigma of illegitimate birth, Cardan was educated at the universities of Pavia and Padua and became Professor of Medicine at Padua in 1547. He published important treatises on arithmetic and algebra, and attempted a synthesis of what was then known or guessed about the workings of the physical and natural world in two great works: *De subtilitate rerum* (1551) and *De varietate rerum* (1557). He journeyed to Scotland in 1551 as medical adviser to the asthmatic Archbishop of Saint Andrews, defended the anatomical discoveries of Vesalius, experimented with the *camera obscura*, cast the horoscopes of the English king Edward VI and Martin Luther,* and found time to write poetry. He subsequently fell foul of the Church in the person of the ex-inquisitor Pope Pius V and was forced into retirement, where he occupied his time in composing an autobiography, *De vita propria*, a work which is said to compare favourably with the autobiography of Cardan's contemporary Cellini in that it lacks Cellini's self-promoting bombast while offering valuable insights into European intellectual culture at the dawn of the scientific Renaissance. (for a synopsis, see Henry Morley *Life of G. Cardano* 2 vols. 1854.)

* "Cardan... hated Luther and so changed his birthday in order to give him an unfavourable horoscope." (*Encyclopaedia Britannica* 11th ed.)

[148] CARDIGAN

There is general agreement that the knitted, open-fronted sweater with buttons down the front is named after JAMES THOMAS BRUDENELL, 7TH EARL OF CARDIGAN (1797-1868). It is mildly ironic that whereas the garment – at least as worn by men – has come to symbolise a mild and vaguely donnish domesticity, the man himself has come to personify (thanks to the Light Brigade incident) reckless and lethal courage allied to rocklike stupidity.

[149] CARLEY FLOAT

The unsinkable life raft familiar to all WWII mariners was the invention of an American house-painter, semi-pro musician and seaman HORACE CARLEY (1838-1918).   Carley, who had personal experience of the inadequacies of life-boats in disaster conditions, was looking for an emergency substitute that was cheap to manufacture, easy to handle, and above all could be launched quickly and without the aid of mechanical devices such as davits. His answer was a ring of 35 separate air- and water-tight copper chambers enclosed in cork and canvas, launched by simply dropping it into the sea. Trials of the first prototype in an open competition staged by ship-owners in 1905 proved that Carley's invention had all the advantages he planned for, though it was not a commercial success, only coming into its own in WWII and after Carley's death. However, in wartime on the high seas, the Carley float, from a life-saving point of view, was considered by some sailors to be only marginally preferable to drowning, the problem being that those in the float could neither get nor keep dry, and so rapidly succumbed to exposure in the hostile environment of, for example, the North Atlantic. Survival therefore depended on those who had taken to the raft being rapidly picked up by another vessel. The cause of the problem was that the slatted floor of the raft was attached loosely to the sides by ropes or tapes so that whichever way up the raft landed in the water, the floor would hang down. But the occupiers, who had to sit on the floor for the sake of stability, were thus in water up to their waists. The hanging floor also explained why there were virtually no human support accessories in the raft since no one could predict which way up it was going to float. Thus a cynical view could be taken that the Carley float was a very cheap way of addressing life-saving needs which contributed to delaying the search for more effective life-saving equipment by a good many years. Nevertheless, Carley deserves to be remembered (and better remembered than he usually is) as a true humanitarian deserving of our respect.

[150] CARNOT'S THEOREM

The idealised CARNOT HEAT ENGINE uses a perfect gas (see BOYLE'S LAW) as its working substance, and runs as efficiently as possible in a CARNOT CYCLE of heating, expanding, cooling, and contracting, so the system periodically returns to its original state. Its net effect is to take thermal energy from a hot reservoir and dump some of it into a colder reservoir, having done useful work in between. The nub of this model is Carnot's proof that even such an idealised engine cannot convert all the heat energy it absorbs into mechanical work with 100% efficiency – there is always some residual heat left over to be uselessly dissipated, unless the cold reservoir were at absolute zero, 0 degrees KELVIN – an impossibility. The efficiency depends only on the temperatures of the two heat reservoirs. This theoretical demonstration laid the groundwork for the formulation of the Second Law of Thermodynamics. French physicist NICOLAS LÉONARD SADI CARNOT (1796-1832) published his *Réflexions sur la puissance motrice du feu et sur les machines propres à développer cette puissance* in 1824. Mechanical propulsion systems including the DIESEL, STIRLING, WANKEL and OTTO engines all measure their efficiency in terms of CARNOT'S THEOREM as do other forms of heat engine including the domestic refrigerator, which is essentially running in reverse, using up energy to transfer heat from a colder to a hotter body. (MW)

[151] CARO'S ACID – see MAGNUS' GREEN SALT

[152] CASSINI'S DIVISION

In the year 1610, when GALILEO turned his telescope on Saturn and observed its rings, the instrument wasn't good enough to give him a clear picture and he came away with the impression that the planet was "three-lobed". It was left to HUYGENS, with the aid of better lenses, to see the rings more clearly, though only clearly enough to make them out as a single entity. It wasn't until 1675 that the Italian astronomer GIOVANNI DOMENICO (JEAN DOMINIQUE) CASSINI (1625-1712) observed that Saturn was circled not by a single continuous ring but (apparently) by two rings in the same plane and divided by a dark space subsequently known to astronomers as CASSINI'S DIVISION. Later and more detailed observations, including results from space probes, have revealed that Saturn's rings are a complex system made up of three main rings (christened A, B and C) which in turn are subdivided into thousands of ringlets. Since 2004, the CASSINI SPACECRAFT has been orbiting Saturn and sending back pictures of the giant planet, its rings, and its many moons. As part of the same mission, the HUYGENS PROBE, built and run by the European Space Agency, which had ridden piggy-back on the Cassini spacecraft during the 7-year journey to Saturn, peeled off to investigate Saturn's moon TITAN. Cassini taught astronomy at Bologna until invited to Paris by Louis XIV in 1669. He spent the reminder of his life at the Paris Observatory, becoming a French citizen in 1673. In addition to discovering several of Saturn's moons, Cassini made a ground-breaking contribution to astronomy by measuring the parallax of the planet Mars and hence its distance from Earth. Since the *relative* distances of the planets from the Sun were already known (thanks to **KEPLER**) this single measurement made it possible for the first time to work out the relevant *absolute* values with a fair degree of accuracy. Cassini generated a regular dynasty of French astronomers. His son Jacques (1677-1756) succeeded his father at the Paris observatory, was responsible for measuring an arc of the meridian betwen Dunkirk and Perpignan, and published *Traité de la grandeur et de la figure de la terre* in 1720. Jacques in turn sired César François Cassini de Thury (1714-1784), astronomer and geometer. The fourth member of the dynasty, Jean Dominique, Comte de Cassini (1748-1845), carried on the work of his father César François, completing his father's map of France which became the basis of the *Atlas National* (1791) and carrying out important experiments in methods of determining the longitude at sea (see **HARRISON'S CHRONOMETERS**).

[153] CASTNER-KELLNER CELL

An industrial chemical plant for the electrolytic conversion of brine – a strong solution of common salt (sodium chloride) – into that useful alkali, caustic soda (sodium hydroxide) and chlorine. The latter, a WWI poison gas (see **HABER**) is a powerful bleaching agent used in the manufacture of paper and textiles, for sterilising municipal water supplies and disinfecting swimming pools, and for making chlorinated hydrocarbons, including the egregious CFC's, and PVC. Following the **LEBLANC** and **SOLVAY** processes, the **CASTNER-KELLNER CELL** was the third major development in the vast "chlor-alkali" chemical industry. American industrial chemist **HAMILTON YOUNG CASTNER** (1858-99) from Brooklyn obtained a US patent for the process in 1892, but discovered that Austrian paper chemist **DR KARL KELLNER** (1851-1905) had likewise taken out a similar German patent at about the same time following from his co-invention of the **RITTER-KELLNER SULPHITE-CELLULOSE PROCESS** of 1882, an electrolytic method for bleaching the pulp used in many paper mills. This conflict of interest was resolved by a partnership: the **CASTNER-KELLNER ALKALI COMPANY,** which established profitable plants around Europe and North America. While this "clean" electrolytic process is free from smoking chimneys (it may however transfer them elsewhere – to the electricity generating station) certain environmental problems remain, because the cell uses as its cathode a large pool of metallic mercury. The consequent mercury pollution of the local environments has had some deplorable consequences. While metallic mercury is well-known to be a severe poison, it becomes far more toxic still when converted into methyl mercury compounds by anaerobic micro-organisms in lake and sea silt. Methyl mercury can cross the blood-brain barrier as a neurotoxin, causing insanity, paralysis, coma and death – symptoms now known as Minamata Disease.* Methyl mercury is also a teratogen, causing birth deformities. It accumulates in marine food chains, concentrating especially in shellfish – sushi-lovers beware! – and tuna. A **CASTNER-KELLNER** plant operated by the Dryden Chemical Company in Ontario, Canada, discharged an estimated 9000 kg of mercury into the local river system between

1962 and 1970. The indigenous peoples of the region suffered from the same symptoms, which became known as Ontario Minamata Disease. Appropriately, perchance, **DOKTOR KARL KELLNER** displays a distinctly Jekyll and Hyde character. Born and scientifically trained in Vienna, he became an occultist: a practitioner of Hatha Yoga, Rosicrucian of the Hermetic Brotherhood of Light, Theosophist, and Master Mason; not content with these, he entered the dizzying realms of "irregular" Freemasonry in 1902 to become "*Sovereign Honoured Grand-Master General for Germany and Sovereign Grand Commander of the Ancient and Accepted Scottish 33° Freemasons and the Sovereign Sanctuary of the Ancient and Primitive Rite 95° of Memphis and Misraim.*" Owing to this immersion in the murky depths of occult inner circles, he has been cited as the "spiritual father" of the infamous *Ordo Templi Orientis* which was founded shortly after his sudden death in 1905. This accusation is denied by his descendents and followers, with understandable vehemence, in view of the ensuing subversion of the O.T.O., when it played host to the sex-magic and satanism of the bestial Aleister Crowley. (MW)

* First recognised in 1956 among the population dwelling around the shore of Minamata Bay, Japan, which was directly polluted by methyl mercury compounds in waste discharged from the Chisso Corporation's chemical works between 1932 and 1968. Over 1700 people died of the disease. The lawsuits continue to this day.

[154] CATHERINE WHEEL

The name for this spinning firework is ascribed to **SAINT CATHERINE OF ALEXANDRIA** (3rd-4th century) whose legendary beauty and learning made her a favorite subject of Renaissance painting and iconography, although her historical existence is now in doubt. Supposedly of an illustrious Alexandrian family, Catherine's defence of Christians persecuted by the pagan Roman Emperor Maxentius, and her eloquence in philosophical debate, at first enraged the Emperor, but then he found himself attracted to the pious noblewoman. When Catherine, having converted his wife and her entire retinue to Christianity, refused the Emperor's offer of marriage, his rage was re-kindled. He ordered Catherine to be "broken upon the wheel" which, however, itself broke during her torture – in some versions under a blast of fire from Heaven. *Faute de mieux*, Maxentius then had her beheaded. Catherine's martyrdom ensured subsequent canonization, as the patron saint of wheelwrights, among other more philosophical groups, and her emblem is a spiked wheel. It is ironic that the name of this exemplar of Catholic piety should have been appropriated for the pyrotechnic centrepiece in that annual British anti-Catholic festival, Guy Fawkes' night. (MW)

[155] CATTLEYA

Genus of 40+ species of orchids found in the tropical zone of Central and South

America. The name was given by British botanist John Lindley (1799-1865), author of numerous scientific and popular works on horticulture and botany and a supporter of JUSSIEU'S as opposed LINNAEUS' system of plant taxonomy. Lindley was one of the first botanists to undertake the scientific classification of orchids. CATTLEYA he named in honour of SIR WILLIAM CATTLEY (d. 1832) who "discovered" the species *Cattleya labiata* by growing-on some plant material he had received as packing in a shipment of orchid specimens.

[156] CAVENDISH LABORATORY

Probably the most illustrious physics lab in the world, this is the Department of Physics of the University of Cambridge, UK. It can boast at least 26 Nobel Laureates among its alumni, including such celebrated names as RUTHERFORD, Bragg, Watson, and Crick. The Laboratory was founded in 1874 and named to commemorate the outstanding natural philosopher HENRY CAVENDISH (1731-1810), a grandson of the 2nd Duke of Devonshire. He attended Peterhouse Cambridge, but left without a degree. A reclusive and shy personality, he worked in his private lab in London, where he discovered hydrogen, then called "inflammable air" in 1760. The measurement of its low density made the hydrogen balloon possible (see CHARLES). Cavendish determined the composition of the atmosphere, as consisting of "phlogisticated air" (nitrogen) and "dephlogisticated air" (oxygen), and proved that water was a compound resulting from the union of the two gases, hydrogen and oxygen. He measured the effective density of the Earth by gravitational experiments. Cavendish did not publish many of his discoveries in electrostatics, and therefore they became credited to others, until MAXWELL studied his notes in 1879, and realised that Cavendish had anticipated COULOMB, OHM, and FARADAY in many particulars. (MW)

[157] CELSIUS TEMPERATURE SCALE

ANDERS CELSIUS (1701-1744) was born at Uppsala, Sweden, of professorial forebears, both in mathematics and astronomy. He followed suit, as professor of astronomy at Uppsala in 1730, making important geographical and astronomical measurements. His proposal of a thermometric scale in 1742 displaced the currently competing, but somewhat arbitrary scales of RÉAUMUR and FAHRENHEIT. Celsius's concept of two universal "fixed points" was fundamental to the definition of an international scale of temperature, but his original choice of the freezing point of water as 100 degrees and its boiling point as 0 degrees must have seemed perverse: it was reversed by LINNAEUS after his death. For two centuries the world has referred to this as the "centigrade scale". Celsius was only reinstated as its formal author by an international committee in 1948. (MW)

[158] CERIUM, PROMETHIUM, SAMARIUM

Of the fourteen "rare earth" elements in MENDELEEV'S PERIODIC TABLE, the most abundant is CERIUM, atomic number 58, symbol Ce, which was discovered in 1803 by German apothecary turned chemist, Martin Heinrich Klaproth (1743-1817), and independently in the same year by Swedish chemist Jöns Jakob Berzelius (1779-1848) and Wilhem Hisinger. The metal itself was first extracted in 1875; its pyrophoric property is used in lighter flints. CERIUM shares its name with the largest asteroid (now called a "dwarf planet") CERES, discovered in 1801 by Sicilian astronomer-monk Giuseppi Piazzi (1746-1826). Both derive from the Greek corn-goddess of agriculture or tillage, CERES, also known as Demeter, daughter of the TITANS Cronus and Rhea, and sister of Zeus. The Eleusinian Mysteries were held in her honour. The rarest of the rare earths is certainly PROMETHIUM, because it is quite absent from the earth: all its isotopes are radioactive with half-lives shorter than 18 years, so there is effectively none left since the creation of the solar system. With atomic number 61, symbol Pm, it is entirely a man-made element, predicted in 1902 by Bohuslav Brauner, a prediction supported by MOSELEY'S LAW in 1914. The element was finally obtained at the Oak Ridge National Laboratory, Tennessee, in 1945 as one of the products of URANIUM fission in a nuclear reactor (see MEITNERIUM). Its radioactivity justifies taking the name of another second-generation TITAN, the son of IAPETUS called PROMETHEUS, who stole fire from Mount Olympus, for the benefit of humankind. Allegedly. The next rare earth after PROMETHIUM is SAMARIUM, from the mineral SAMARSKITE, discovered in 1847 in the Southern Urals, which is in turn named after COLONEL VASILI EVGRAFOVICH SAMARSKY-BYKHOVETS (1803-1870) of the Russian Corps of Mining Engineers – arguably the first living person to have an element named after him, and a rare example of "second order" eponymy. The metal, of atomic number 62 and symbol Sm, was isolated from its eponymous mineral in 1879 by Lecoq de Boisbaudron (see GALLIUM). (MW)

[159] CHAGAS DISEASE

A form of trypanosomiasis endemic to Central and South America named after the Brazilan physician CARLOS CHAGAS (1910-2000) who discovered it in 1909 and named the infective parasite *Trypanosoma cruzi* in honour of the Brazilian epidemiologist Oswaldo Cruz (1872-1917). The disease is sometimes called American Trypanosomiasis to distinguish it from the mosquito-borne African form, usually known as Sleeping Sickness. The vector is a nocturnal bloodsucking insect known as a triatomine bug which carries the organism in its faeces and which it deposits in situ after feeding. Chagas disease is also found in areas to which it is not endemic such as the United States but to which it has been carried by population movements. In these areas transmission is more commonly by infected food, mother-to-baby transmission, or blood transfusion. It is a dangerous infection which can have catastrophic effects on the myocardium, central nervous system, or digestive tract, and if untreated may be fatal. Chagas' description of the disease named after him is regarded as a classic of epidemiological research. He was twice nominated for a **NOBEL PRIZE** in medicine but did not receive the award.

[160] CHAPTALISATION

The practice of adding sugar to wine musts in order to increase the alcoholic strength of the finished wine. It is on the whole to be discouraged since it indicates that the grapes were not fully mature to start with, maturity being a function of sugar content. Hence, the subject of chaptalisation is one respectable wine-makers sometimes prefer not to discuss. The process was invented by French industrial chemist and statesman **JEAN ANTOINE CLAUDE CHAPTAL** (1756-1832) on whom Napoleon conferred the title **COMTE DE CHANTELOUP**. Following Bonaparte's downfall, Chaptal necessarily retired from the political arena and devoted himself to scientific popularisation and to promoting the application of chemical discoveries to agriculture and industry. (See also **PARMENTIER.**)

[161] CHARLES'S LAW

Like **BOYLE'S LAW**, **CHARLES'S LAW** applies to a fixed mass of an "ideal" gas: stating that, at constant pressure, its volume is proportional to the absolute temperature (in degrees **KELVIN**). It was formulated *ca.* 1787 by the French scientist and inventor **JACQUES ALEXANDRE CÉSAR CHARLES** (1746-1823) who was born at Beaugency, became Professor of Physics in Paris, and invented several ingenious instruments such as the hydrometer and the goniometer. Charles also constructed the first substantial hydrogen balloon, preparing the gas from iron and sulphuric acid, according to **CAVENDISH'S** method. He modestly dubbed this invention "Globe", but it was honorifically re-named a **CHARLIÈRE**. Its envelope of rubberised silk contained 32 m^3 of hydrogen. It flew, unmanned, on 27 August 1783, but was not well-received at its landing point by the peasantry, who destroyed it as an agency of the devil. Charles himself, accompanied by Marie-Noel Robert, made the first **CHARLIÈRE** ascent on 1st December 1783, only ten days after the first manned flight of the **MONTGOLFIÈRE.** Charles ascended from the Tuileries, watched by a crowd of half a million, and made a 50 km flight to Nesles. On touchdown at sunset, his passenger Robert, in high excitement, immediately leapt out of the basket, with the consequence that Charles swiftly found himself alone at 3,000 m; and thus became the first man to watch the sun set twice on the same day. The disadvantage of the hydrogen balloon was that control of buoyancy was wasteful and irreversible – either by venting gas or dumping ballast. In an attempt to overcome this, the **ROZIÈRE** was invented. (MW)

[162] CHATEAU TALBOT

Serious wine-bibbers will recognise the name of this estate in the St. Julien district of Bordeaux. It takes its name from **JOHN TALBOT** (1388?-1453), Earl of Shrewsbury, Constable of Guienne, who was killed at the battle of Castillon, the battle which finally extinguished England's empire in France. A brilliant military commander, Talbot played a major part in the last stages of the Hundred Years' War (see also **KNOLLYS MITRE**) and though he apparently never owned the Chateau Talbot estate, the name is a fitting reminder of the fact that the only good to come out of England's part in that long sad conflict was an enduring connection between this country and the claret-growing district of southern France. As all serious wine-bibbers will agree. (See also **TALBOT** and **TALBOTYPE**.)

[163] CHATEAUBRIAND STEAK

Refers both to a cut of meat (from the centre of the fillet) and the recipe for cooking it. Compared to that other culinary confection made from fillet steak, the **TOURNEDOS ROSSINI** it is a plain and simple dish, conceived by a chef named Montmirail in the service of **FRANÇOIS RENÉ, VICOMTE DE CHATEAUBRIAND** (1768-1848), French writer and Very Superior Person. Nineteenth-century chefs were much given to the practice of adding a little lustre to their reputations by naming recipes after the celebrities of day – thus Beef Wellington (see **WELLINGTON BOOT**), **PEACH MELBA**, etc. Though in some cases the currency of the dish may outlive the renown of the person it was named for. **EGGS BENEDICT** and Bananas Foster, for example, have both been wrongly identified as underworld characters in the stories of Damon Runyon.

[164] CHAUVINISM

NICOLAS CHAUVIN was a veteran of the Revolutionary and Napoleonic wars and a man of exaggerated loyalties who distinguished himself by a fanatical devotion to the ex-Emperor's cause even after that dreadful little pest had been put where he could do no further damage. It is doubtful whether or to what extent Chauvin is an actual historical figure rather than a stereotype, a sort of "Colonel Blimp" with a bad case of jingoism, or perhaps, like Robin Hood, merely a name around which legends collect.

[165] CHESTERFIELD

The word is applied (a) to a long, tailored overcoat with a velvet collar*, and (b) to a sofa. Both are "presumably" (Onions: *Oxford Dictionary of English Etymology*) named after a 19th-century **EARL OF CHESTERFIELD**, but which earl and why remain unclear to this writer and to any authority he has been able to consult. If it is any consolation, the word "sofa" has a clearly-established etymology – from Arabic via Turkish, meaning a bench or raised portion of a floor on which to recline (see **OTTOMAN**).

* See **TEDDY BOY**.

[166] CHEYNE-STOKES BREATHING

A form of abnormal respiration in which periods of rapid shallow breathing alternate with periods of apnoea. The condition may occur in patients with heart failure and in sufferers from altitude sickness, but most commonly in comatose patients when near death. The condition was first described by **JOHN CHEYNE** (1777-1836) and **WILLIAM STOKES** (1763-1825). Cheyne was Scottish and Stokes Irish, but both men did the majority of their work in Ireland, where they stand as founding fathers of Irish medicine. Cheyne served for a time as an army surgeon in Ireland and was present at the battle of Vinegar Hill (1798). Later he held, among other posts, that of Surgeon General to the forces in Ireland. Stokes, son of a distinguished physician, had, despite a lifelong involvement in medicine, a somewhat unorthodox professional education, only graduating MD (from Edinburgh) in 1825. He is particularly remembered for his work as a clinical diagnostician.

[167] CHILD'S BALLADS

Not a collection of nursery rhymes* but the most important 19th-century collection of British folk poetry. The monumental *English and Scottish Popular Ballads* was published between 1883 and 1898, the work of American philologist **FRANCIS JAMES CHILD** (1825-1896). Apart from its value to historians of literature, it remains a primary source for modern singers of traditional songs. Over a period of nearly 25 years Child collected 305 traditional ballads, primarily from such printed sources as Bishop Percy's *Reliques of Ancient English Poetry* (1767). In fact, the antiquity of the material is difficult to establish. The majority of the ballads, at least in the form in which Child collected and transcribed them, date only from the 17th and 18th centuries, although some at least are certainly based on far more ancient originals. However, only a handful can be traced to a period before 1600. Some songs were excluded on the grounds of "indecency"` and others edited to emphasize their poetic aspects. Child was the son of a sail-maker who became a brilliant literary scholar. He graduated from Harvard, continued his studies in Germany, and at the age of twenty-six returned to Harvard to take up the chair of Rhetoric and Oratory. He continued there as Professor of English from 1876 to 1896, in which capacity he was responsible for training an entire generation of American philologists. Apart from his ballad collection, his publications included an important edition of the works of the Edmund Spenser (1855) and *Observations on the Language of Chaucer's "Canterbury Tales"* (1863). (RS)

* This requirement is superbly met by Iona and Peter Opie's *Oxford dictionary of nursery rhymes*, which first appeared in 1952.

[168] CLARIDGE'S

A nice hotel in London which still, despite changes and chances, bears the names of its creators **WILLIAM CLARIDGE** (1814-1882) and his wife **MARIANNE.** It has the distinction of being the only hotel in London, indeed, the only place in the world, where the present writer has had his scruffy little roll-up lighted for him by a bewigged footman with a silver lighter the size of a tea-pot. Needless to say, this incident took place before the criminalisation of cigarette-lighters.

[169] CLEOPATRA'S NEEDLES

The twin granite obelisks commonly known by this name were erected at Heliopolis in Egypt by the Pharaoh Thothmes II in about 1475 BC and moved two centuries later to Alexandria by Rameses II ("The Great"). One of the pair was presented to Britain and erected on the Thames Embankment in 1878. The other went to New York in 1881 and today stands in Central Park. **CLEOPATRA** (51-30 BC) had nothing to do with the needles at any stage in their career, so why name them after her? The answer can only be that until the discovery of Tutankhamen's tomb in 1922, Cleopatra was the only "ancient Egyptian" the average Briton or American could put a name to. Much less was it generally understood that Cleopatra was not even, genetically speaking, an Egyptian but a Greek, descended from Ptolemy, one of Alexander the Great's generals who inherited part of his Empire on its dissolution. In addition to the New York and London obelisks, two others pitched up in Rome and one in Paris. George Sarton in his history of ancient science (Harvard U.P. 1952) views this diaspora as a way of proclaiming to the wider world the brilliance of Egypt's engineers. He writes, "Modern Egyptians should not regret that so many obelisks were taken away from their native country. Each one of the exiled obelisks is an almost imperishable monument to the glory of ancient Egypt." A thought of relevance to the vexed question of the **ELGIN MARBLES**.

[170] CLERIHEW

A verse form consisting of 2 rhyming couplets, usually humorous or satirical, sometimes scabrous, but always pithy. The lines may be irregular in length but are usually short. It is named after its inventor, the writer **EDMUND CLERIHEW BENTLEY** (1875-1956). One of his best known productions in this line, though not perhaps the best adapted to modern Semitic sensibilities, is:

How odd
of God
to choose
the Jews.

Miltonic it isn't. Which perhaps explains why Bentley never made it to Poet Laureate. Whence -

E.C. Bentley
frowned as he murmured gently
"Could it possibly be that my verse
is getting worse?"

Bentley also wrote detective stories of which the best known is *Trent's last case* (1913). A collected edition of his verses appeared in 1951 under the title *Clerihews complete*.

[171] COCKLE'S PILLS

There was a time when no English traveller, explorer, or colonial administrator would have dreamed of venturing into the Gobi Desert, the Congo Rain Forest, or, indeed, anywhere further than Boulogne, without a plentiful supply of **COCKLE'S ANTI-BILIOUS PILLS**, sovereign against "bile, liver, headache, heartburn, etc.". The main ingredient was aloe, a plant-based laxative (*cf.* **BEECHAM'S PILLS**). They were the invention of **JAMES COCKLE** (*fl.* 1830)*, a doctor who manufactured and sold his own medicines. Later versions carried an endorsement from Capt. Fred Burnaby, author of *A ride to Khiva* (1876) and *On horseback through Asia Minor* (1877), who called them "... a most invaluable medicine, and one which I have used on the natives of Central Africa. In fact, the marvellous effects produced upon the mind and body of an Arab sheik... when I administered him five will never fade from my memory." Burnaby was unfortunately killed by "Fuzzy-Wuzzies" (Beja tribesmen) in the Sudan while taking part in the attempted relief of Gordon at Khartoum. Cockle's Pills were the subject of a cautionary tale in verse entitled "Cockle *vs.* Cackle" by the humorist Thomas Hood (1799-1845). It begins

Those who much read advertisements and bills
Must have seen puffs of Cockle's Pills,
Call'd Anti-bilious -
Which some Physicians sneer at, supercilious,
But which we are assured, if timely taken,
May save your liver and your bacon...

---

* Father of the lawyer and mathematician Sir James Cockle (1819-1895), first Chief Justice of Queensland.

[172] CODY WAR KITE

A large and powerful re-design of the classic box kite originally devised by Australian, Lawrence Hargrave.* The **CODY WAR-KITE** is double-celled with vestigial wings for added stability and lift; when joined in a train of 5 or 6, it provided the classic 'man-lifter' system, patented in 1901, which found some military applications for artillery spotting in the Anglo-Boer War (1899-1902) and naval reconnaissance in WWI. The kite was designed by American-born **SAMUEL FRANKLIN CODY,** (1867-1913) *né* **COWDERY**, from Davenport, Iowa,** self-adopted namesake of the theatrical American bison hunter and showman, William Frederick Cody (1846-1917), widely known as "Buffalo Bill", with whom Samuel F. is often confused – as, indeed, he intended. Samuel Cowdery's youthful history is largely anecdotal but, like his namesake, he toured a successful "Wild West" show during the 1890s. Financed by this, he demonstrated his kites in Europe at the first Meteorological Kite Competition of the Royal Aeronautical Society on the Sussex Downs in 1903, and in the same year successfully crossed the English Channel in a Berthon boat towed by kites (for earlier, land-based applications of kite-traction see **POCOCK'S CHAR-VOLANT**). Following trials at Portsmouth and at sea in 1903, the British Admiralty, in the person of the Director of Naval Intelligence, Prince Louis of **BATTENBERG**, expressed interest in his kites, both for lifting men and aerials for wireless telegraphy. In 1905 Cody was employed by the British War Office, with officer status, as Kite Instructor at the Royal Engineers' Balloon School in Aldershot. His aviatorial ambitions then progressed in 1905 via a man-carrying kite-glider and a motorized pilotless kite in 1907, to work on the Army's first dirigible balloon, the airship *Nulli Secundus*, which made a flight around London. He soon returned to heavier-than-air machines, however, designing *British Army Aeroplane No. 1A* at Farnborough, which in 1908 made the first powered flight in Britain, lasting 27 seconds. Cody became a British citizen in 1909, but that was also the year in which the British War Office terminated his contract, having decided in its collective wisdom that there was no future in aeroplanes. Thereafter, Cody worked independently without government or military support, and the resulting Cody aircraft won several trophies for endurance and distance. When his latest and largest machine, the *Cody VI* broke up in the air in 1913, he died a public hero and was buried at Aldershot with full military honours. There is a distant echo of this dedicated pioneer aviator to be found in RAF banter, where the vernacular term for an aircraft is a "kite", while to crash one, or indeed wreak destruction with one, is conveyed by the verb "to prang" (etymology uncertain). (MW)

* The Hargrave kite of 1893 was also the precursor to the Wright Brothers' first powered aeroplane of 1903.

** Revered by jazz lovers as the birthplace of the great Bix Beiderbecke (1903-1931).

[173] COLIN ARCHER

A boat built by, or built according to the designs of, Norwegian boat-builder and naval architect **COLIN ARCHER** (1832-1921). Archer, whose parents had come to Norway from Scotland, specialised in wooden vessels in which strength and sea-worthiness were the primary desiderata. Perhaps the best-known vessel built in Archer's shipyard was *Fram*, which took Nansen to the Arctic in 1893-6 and Amundsen to the Antarctic in 1910-12. Archer's name was originally applied as the name of a boat-type to the sailing rescue vessel he designed for the Norwegian Lifeboat Institution. The prototype, *Colin Archer No. 1* (length overall 13.95m, beam 4.65m, displacement 30 tonnes) still exists as a floating museum. In the 20th century, Archer's double-ended hull designs were adapted to pleasure yachts and notably to the *Westsail* cruising boats. A sail race from Holland to Larvik in Norway takes place every other year and is named in Colin Archer's honour.

[174] COMET SWIFT-TUTTLE – see **PERSEID SHOWER**

[175] COMPTON SCATTERING

When energetic electromagnetic radiation (X-rays or gamma rays) is scattered by matter, it may eject electrons from the atoms, and then proceed on its way with diminished energy – which also corresponds to a longer wavelength, according to **PLANCK'S LAW**. The energy balance is made up by the ejected electron. This is the **COMPTON EFFECT** of 1923 which provides important evidence that electromagnetic radiation ("light") can behave as a stream of particles – *quanta* with energy proportional to its frequency – rather than as a wave. American physicist **ARTHUR HOLLY COMPTON** (1892-1962) was born in Wooster, Ohio, into an academic family and studied at Princeton and Cambridge (UK), taking up a post at Washington University in St. Louis, and later becoming its Chancellor. He was awarded the 1927 Nobel prize for physics jointly with **C.T.R. WILSON**. In 1941 **COMPTON** was appointed to oversee the production of plutonium for the Manhatten project (see **GRAHAM'S LAW**), and in 1942 at the University of Chicago he was director of the euphemistically-named "Metallurgical Laboratory" where **ENRICO FERMI** and his team built the first nuclear reactor, or "atomic pile", for that production. (MW)

[176] CONGREVE ROCKETS

Sir WILLIAM CONGREVE (1772-1828), pioneer of military rocketry, began experimenting with war rockets in 1804. In promoting the use of these novel weapons he was aided by the support of the Prince of Wales and the Duke of York, by the fact that his father, the 1st Baronet, was Comptroller of the Royal Laboratory at Woolwich, and by his own talent for self-promotion. His early experiments impressed the Prime Minister, William Pitt, and rockets of various calibres went into production at Woolwich. They were employed against the French in the naval attacks on Boulogne in 1805 and 1806 and, directed by Congreve in person, in the bombardment of Copenhagen in 1807. Not all members of the military establishment, however, were convinced of their destructive potential – Wellington for one remained sceptical. Nevertheless a Rocket Brigade of the Royal Artillery was formed, though not commanded by Congreve as he held no rank in the British army. Rockets were again employed in the American war of 1812 and Congreve was present with Wellington's army in southern France in 1814. In 1811 he was elected FRS and was commissioned Lt. Col. in the Hanoverian Artillery. In 1814 he inherited his father's title and posts and continued his experiments at Woolwich, which he now headed. Though Congreve was known in his own day as "the rocket man", rocketry by no means occupied all his time or creative energies. He engaged, though with little success, in a number of industrial enterprises, and from 1820 till his death served as MP for Plymouth. Meanwhile inventions poured from him in wild profusion. These included, as well as improvements to artillery and new uses for rockets, a device for operating canal locks, paper for unforgeable banknotes, a new type of steam engine, a clock operated by a ball-bearing on a tilting plane, a smoke-reduction device, a method of colour printing, an improved method of gunpowder manufacture, a gas meter, and (surprisingly) a perpetual motion machine.* He died and was buried in Toulouse. The baronetcy passed to his son William Augustus Congreve (b. 1827) who disappeared without trace (and without an heir) in Australia some time after 1860.

* Congreve's proposal was for a machine operated by the capillary action of water. For details, see *Encyclopaedia Britannica* (11th ed.) under "Perpetual Motion". (See also **ORFFYREUS' WHEEL**)

[177] CONWAY'S GAME OF LIFE

"Life" is an example of a *cellular automaton*: imagine an unlimited grid of square cells like a sheet of graph paper. Any cell can be either live (filled with a blob) or dead (empty). Every cell, of course, has eight adjacent cells, any of which may be filled – its neighbours. We may draw any pattern of live cells as a starting point or "seed". The rules of "Life" are simple:

> *1) A live cell survives to the next generation only if it has two or three neighbours; if less than two or more than three, it dies – becomes empty in the next generation.*
> *2) An empty cell with just three neighbours becomes live in the next generation: it gives birth.*

These rules are applied to all cells simultaneously to determine the pattern for the next generation. The process is totally deterministic (a "zero-player" game) yet the results are very surprising, and are best run on a personal computer.* Some simple patterns quickly vanish; others become stable and unchanging; patterns which repeat themselves over a short period of generations are known as "oscillators";

mobile "gliders" and "spaceships" can skitter diagonally across the page; long-lived patterns – "Methuselahs" – wax and wane for thousands of generations, leaving piles of assorted residues. Other rules and cellular grids are also possible. Liverpudlian **JOHN HORTON CONWAY** (b. 1937) a Cambridge mathematician, is now Professor of Mathematics at Princeton and one of the liveliest and most unorthodox creative minds at the cutting edge of modern mathematical research. He has made significant and prize-winning contributions to the fields of group theory (he is lead author of the biblical *Atlas of Finite Groups*), topology and knot theory, number theory, game theory, and is especially renowned for his excursions into "recreational mathematics". He invented the **GAME OF LIFE** in 1970, but even this entertainment has found a serious purpose for investigating machine intelligence (see **TURING**). (MW)

* Software for running the game can be freely downloaded from the WWW.

[178] COOK'S TOURS

THOMAS COOK (1808-1892) left school at the age of ten and was apprenticed to a wood-turner. Later he entered a printing and publishing firm in Loughborough and by the age of 19 was travelling from village to village through the Midland counties as a Baptist missionary and Temperance activist. It was in connection with the latter activity that he organised the first publicly-advertised railway excursion. On 5 July 1841 he did a deal with the Midland Railway Company to take 570 Temperance campaigners from Leicester to Loughborough and back to attend a rally for a shilling a head, food included. In 1845, having won a reputation as an entrepreneur who could obtain cheap rates from the railway companies for large parties, he undertook his first profit-making excursion – to Liverpool, Caernarfon, and Mount Snowdon. He began publishing handbooks for tourists and, from 1846, a regular monthly publication *The Excursionist*. In 1846 he organised a tour of Scotland which went disastrously wrong but he bounced back and with the encouragement of Joseph Paxton he set up an office in London, and, exploiting the new rail links, began sending parties to France and Switzerland. The **"COOK'S TOUR"** rapidly became a byword and its originator was hailed as the "Napoleon of Excursions". With the end of the American Civil War he organised successful tours of the U.S.A. which included visits to the battlefields, as well as group outings to Italy, Egypt and the Holy Land. The first organised tourist trip around the world took place in 1872-3. In 1865 he made his son John Mason Cook (1834 -1899) a partner in the firm henceforth known as Thomas Cook and Son. Thomas was edged out and retired in 1878 and his son engaged in even more ambitious ventures which included the opening of a luxury hotel in (appropriately) Luxor and, even more spectacularly, undertook in 1884 to transport an expeditionary force of 18,000 men up the Nile on the abortive mission to rescue General Gordon, besieged in Khartoum. (RS)

[179] COOPER'S CREEK – see BURKE & WILLS EXPEDITION

[180] COPERNICAN SYSTEM

NICOLAUS COPERNICUS (1473-1543), is the Latinised name of Polish astronomer Mikolaj Koppernigk (spellings vary), who was born in Torun, Pomerania, possibly of Germanic descent, which inclines the Germans to claim him as their own, Nikolaus Kopernikus. He studied mathematics at the University of Cracow, law at Bologna, astronomy at Ferrara, and medicine at Padua. Following this protracted education he lived mostly in Frauenburg, West Prussia, occupying the office of canon at the cathedral, and fulfilling many civic duties and administrative roles, but also engaged in scholarly pursuits, especially observational astronomy – *sans* telescope, of course (see GALILEO). His major work *De revolutionibus orbium coelestium* was completed in 1530, but only published with reluctance in the year of his death. Copernicus posited that the earth rotates daily about its own axis, and annually in an orbit around the sun, which is stationary at the centre of the universe. This rather knocked on the head the prevailing PTOLEMAIC SYSTEM derived from the geocentric ideas of PLATO and Aristotle, and supported by Holy Scripture. A truth that forever displaced man – God's putative look-alike – from his pre-eminent seat at the centre of the universe, was unlikely to win rapid acceptance. Despite Copernicus' dedication of his work to Pope Pius III, it was firmly consigned to the *Index librorum prohibitorum* in 1616, and there remained for the next two centuries. Catholics were finally permitted by the Roman Church to learn the truth of the COPERNICAN SYSTEM in 1822. Meanwhile, the earth spun on, and bore witness to the scientific revolution – initiated largely by the ideas of Copernicus. In 2009 the synthetic element of atomic number 112 was formally named COPERNICIUM, symbol Cn. (MW)

[181] COPLEY MEDAL

Awarded annually by the Royal Society of London for outstanding work by any scientist in any area of science. It is the Society's highest award and came into being thanks to a bequest from one of its Fellows, Yorkshire landowner and Member of Parliament Sir GODFREY COPLEY (d. 1709). It was first awarded in 1731 to Stephen Gray (d. 1736) for his work in electricity. The list of recipients since that date can be said to read like a roster of famous names in the history of science, including many of those who figure in this dictionary. In 2006 it went to Stephen Hawking.

[182] CORDIERITE – see SCHEELITE

[183] CORIOLIS EFFECT

In the northern hemisphere of planet Earth we are rotating counterclockwise about the North Pole, and the closer we get to the Pole the slower the speed of our easterly travel, because we cover less distance in a day. Now, if we project an object in a northerly direction over the surface of the Earth (without friction) it will appear to us to deviate to the east, because the object retains its initial easterly speed of rotation but the earth beneath it moves more slowly the further north it goes. And if we throw it south it will appear to deviate to the west, for the opposite reason – so in either case the object appears to deviate to the *right* of its intended path, due to the change in its distance from the Earth's axis of rotation. Contrariwise, folk in the southern hemisphere are rotating clockwise about the South Pole, so there the deviation of a moving object is always to the *left* of the intended track. This is the **CORIOLIS EFFECT**.* It is important for ballistics: in WWI, long range naval guns on battleships deployed in the southern hemisphere frequently missed their targets because their sights had been compensated for the **CORIOLIS EFFECT** in the northern hemisphere. French mathematician and mechanical engineer, **GUSTAVE-GASPARD DE CORIOLIS** (1792-1843) was born in Paris and taught at the École Polytechnique, succeeding to the Directorship in 1838. He was interested in the transfer of energy in rotating systems like waterwheels, and formulated the **CORIOLIS EFFECT** in 1835 to apply to any object travelling within a rotating frame of reference: it is subject to a transverse acceleration (a "fictitious force") at right angles both to the direction of travel and to the axis of rotation. After his death, over 50 years elapsed before the effect named for him began to be associated with the global phenomenon of meteorology: the **CORIOLIS EFFECT** causes the wind circulation pattern to blow *along* the isobars, called *geostrophic flow*, rather than at right angles to them thus quickly filling in the pressure difference, as we might intuitively have expected. Cyclones therefore rotate counterclockwise about low pressure areas in the northen hemisphere and *mutandis mutandis:* this was already known, both as **FERREL'S LAW** of 1856 and as **BUYS BALLOT'S LAW** of 1857.** Ocean currents are also subject to the Coriolis effect, which can be seen in the drift of icebergs – see **EKMAN LAYER**. Even the urban myth that the direction of the water vortex flowing out of a bathtub is opposite in the two hemispheres was attributed to the Coriolis effect: this issue was settled experimentally by Ascher Schapiro in 1962: the Coriolis effect does have this weak influence, but it only determines the drainage through the plug-hole when all other disturbances are eliminated. (MW)

* Only if the object is projected exactly along a line of latitude will there be no deviation at all, but the object will change weight! See **EÖTVÖS EFFECT**. The magnitude of the Coriolis effect can be calculated by vector algebra, and depends on the sine of the angle of latitude.

** American meteorologist, **WILLIAM FERREL** (1817-1891), and Dutch chemist and meteorologist **CHRISTOPHORUS HENRICUS DIDERICUS BUYS BALLOT** (1817-1890) also famous for testing the **DOPPLER EFFECT**.

[184] COTTONIAN LIBRARY

The Elizabethan antiquarian **Sir ROBERT BRUCE COTTON** (1571-1631) collected a notable manuscript library which he made available to scholars including Bacon, Camden, Speed, and Raleigh, and in 1601 he made a gift of manuscripts to the newly-founded **BODLEIAN LIBRARY**. His son **SIR THOMAS COTTON** (1594-1662) enlarged the collection, and in 1702 the entire library was presented to the nation by **SIR JOHN COTTON** (1679-1731), ending up, after some adventures (and misadventures, alas), in the British Museum. A peculiarity of the Cotton manuscripts is that they are catalogued under the names of the Roman emperors whose busts ornamented the library bays in which the manuscripts were originally housed. So, for example, the Anglo-Saxon herbarium mentioned above under **ACHILLEA** is still known in the British Library as "MS Cotton Vitellius C iii", C being the shelf letter and iii the volume number allotted to it by Cotton's librarian.

[185] COULOMB

CHARLES AUGUSTIN DE COULOMB (1736-1806) was born in Angoulême, France. He attended a military academy and made expeditions to the French colonies, studying aspects of geotechnical engineering and the mechanics of friction. On return to Paris, he invented the torsion balance and used it for measuring electrical and magnetic forces, which led him to the formulation of **COULOMB'S LAW** of electrostatic attraction and repulsion, which states that the force is proportional to the product of the charges, and inversely to the square of the distance between them. The **COULOMB** is the SI unit for a quantity of electricity, symbol C, (see **AMPÈRE**, **OHM**, and **VOLT**). It is approximately equal to 6.24×10^{18} times the "natural" unit of electric charge, borne by a single electron. There is currently a proposal to define it exactly as 6,241,509,479,607,717,888 electron charges. (MW)

[186] CRAPPER

The popular notion that **THOMAS CRAPPER** (1836-1910), plumber and supplier of toff-quality sanitary porcelain to the carriage trade, invented the flush toilet is too good to be true. And it isn't (true). That honour is more generally accorded to Sir John Harington (1561-1612), wit, author, and godson to Queen Elizabeth. On the other hand, the extraordinarily apposite concordance of Crapper's name and profession does provide a splendid example of what is now known as *Nominative Determinism*.* The term is of recent coinage and dates back to a 1996 article in the *New Scientist* reporting a paper in *The Psychologist* by Jen Hunt and entitled "The psychology of reference hunting" (1994). The paper's author suggested, among other things, that people might be drawn by their names to particular fields of research. How else to explain, for example an article on incontinence in the *British Journal of Urology* by J.W. Splatt and D. Weedon? While further instances of the phenomenon poured in from readers of the *New Scientist*, serious psychologists were seriously studying the question: Random coincidence (God playing dice)? Or subconscious motivation (impelling Hunt to choose "hunting" as the subject/title of her paper)? We may have to wait some time for the answer as the question has been on the table since the phenomenon was first noticed and the question first posed by C.J. Jung in his 1952 essay "Synchronicity – an acausal connecting principle" (*Collected Works* Vol. 8). Meanwhile etymologists are still worrying away at the history and origins of the word "crap" as a colloquial term for faeces, tentatively identifying it with a Middle English word meaning "chaff" or "residue", cognate with the Dutch *krappe* (verb *krappen* = "discard"). This may not be the last word on the subject.

* "Nominative determinism" is not a well-chosen term but begs the question by its assumption that the phenomenon under discussion is in fact determined and not purely a matter of chance. A better term (because neutral on this point) might be SPLATT-WEEDON EFFECT.

[187] CRÈME DU BARRY

This delicious soup is undoubtedly the best employment for that unpromising vegetable, the cauliflower. According to the *Larousse Gastronomique* a garnish "*à la dubarry*" consists of small florets of cauliflower in a MORNAY sauce. Lacking any substantiated gastrohistory, the attribution of this *potage* may derive from its resemblance to the blonde bouffant hairpieces sported by MARIE-JEANNE, COMTESSE DU BARRY, (1741-1793), née Bécu, a Parisian shopgirl turned professional courtesan who succeeded in becoming the last mistress of Louis XV in 1768 and was conveniently married off by the King to his elderly courtier, Comte Guillaume du Barry. Her legendary profligacy brought her before the Revolutionary Tribunal to anwer a charge of wasting public money. She was found guilty and sent to the GUILLOTINE. (MW)

[188] CROCKFORD, CROCKFORD'S

CROCKFORD'S CLERICAL DIRECTORY, known simply as CROCKFORD, is the *Who's Who* of current Anglican clergy. It was first published in 1858 by JOHN CROCKFORD, printer and son of a clergyman and is now published every two years by the Archbishops' Council of the Church of England. The 2007 edition is the 100th in the series. Clerical Crockford is not – Heaven forfend! – to be confused with the fishmonger WILLIAM CROCKFORD (1773-1844), founder of the famous gambling club named after him.

[189] CROOKE'S TUBE

This is an advance on the GEISSLER TUBE – a device for investigating the passage of electricity through gases at low pressure. Two electrodes are sealed into opposite ends of a cylindrical glass tube which can be evacuated. A high voltage from a **RUHMKORFF COIL** is applied across the electrodes but nothing happens until the pressure is reduced by a vacuum pump, when a gas discharge lights up the tube, as in a "neon" sign. The behaviour of this luminous "plasma" – for instance its deflection by a magnetic field – provides clues to the electrical nature of matter. As the gas pressure is further reduced, the glowing cloud is seen to separate from the cathode (negative electrode) leaving **CROOKES' DARK SPACE**, a significant void which, it turns out, is not empty at all, but full of streaming invisible particles of negative electricity heading for the anode (positive electrode). Observation of this important phenomenon led to the discovery and characterisation of the electron (from the Greek for amber, which readily displays static electricity) as the particle of negative electricity. Crookes' particular contribution was to interpose a metallic plate, shaped as a Maltese cross, within the tube, and observe that its exact shadow was thrown onto a fluorescent screen – implying that the rays of electricity travel in straight lines. Crookes thought they constituted a fourth state of matter, and called them "cathode rays" – a name which has stuck to the tube rather more indelibly than his own. This invention of the cathode ray tube is therefore the precursor to the TV set, computer monitor, oscilloscope, and radar screen. **SIR WILLIAM CROOKES** (1832-1919) was born in London, the eldest son of a tailor, and educated chiefly at the Royal College of Chemistry, where he also taught until 1854. He became an excellent experimentalist, and a leading figure in British science, receiving a knighthood in 1897 and the OM in 1910. In 1861 he discovered the element thallium (Greek "thallos" = green shoot) by its characteristic green line showing up in spectroscopic analysis and he is also credited with the invention of **CROOKES' RADIOMETER** and **CROOKES' SPINTHARISCOPE.** Unfortunately in 1870 his open-mindedness regarding physical phenomena seduced him into investigating psychical manifestations – always a disastrous mistake for any honest observer, who lacks the skill to deceive of a professional conjuror or stage magician. Like some other eminent but incautious Victorian scientists, Crookes was duped by spiritualist mediums. Despite the damage to his reputation, he retained a faith in spiritualism until his death, but has not been reliably heard from since. (MW)

[190] CRUDEN

To Bible students, the name **CRUDEN** is shorthand for **CRUDEN'S COMPLETE CONCORDANCE TO THE OLD AND NEW TESTAMENTS AND THE APOCRYPHA.** The product of mind-boggling labour, it lists in alphabetical order every noun, verb, adjective, adverb and proper name in the **KING JAMES BIBLE** and identifies each occurrence of the word in question by relevant citations. It is, in effect, a massively inclusive dictionary of Biblical quotations. The first edition appeared in 1737, followed by further editions in 1761 and 1769. Its author, **ALEXANDER CRUDEN** (1701-1770) was a native of Aberdeen, where he received his MA. He lived for a time in the Isle of Man and later became a bookseller in London. He suffered throughout his life from recurrent bouts of insanity, though these in no way detracted from the value of his work, which was greeted in academic circles with proper respect.* However, his lexicographical labours brought him little pecuniary recompense and he died poor. His monument is the fact that his *Concordance* is still in print.

* *Cf.* the case of W.C. Minor (see under **MacNAGHTEN RULES**).

[191] CRUFT'S

Annual jamboree at which hairdressers compete to show off their tonsorial skills as applied to dogs, and dog-breeders foregather to demonstrate the extent to which perfectly good animals can be physically wrecked by studiously breeding-out any suspect tinge of hybrid vigour while breeding-in heritable weaknesses and deformities like hip dysplasia. This public orgy of bad taste and bad judgement was inaugurated in 1886 by **CHARLES CRUFT** (1852-1939), who worked as a shop-assistant for the firm of James Spratt, dog-biscuit manufacturers, later rising to General Manager. It shot to the heights of fashionable respectability when Queen Victoria entered three Pomeranians and a collie in 1891. Since then, there has been no stopping it. The show is now run by the Kennel Club, an organisation devoted to "improving" dogs.

[192] CRUMP'S MOUSE

Diomys crumpi (Thomas 1917) is an inhabitant of the Indian sub-continent named after the biological specimen collector **C.A. CRUMP**. Crump arrived by chance in Bombay in 1910 and was promptly taken on as collector for a proposed survey of Indian mammals on the initiative of W.S. Millard, a wine merchant and keen amateur naturalist, editor of the Bombay Natural History Society's *Journal* from 1906-1920. The survey lasted 12 years and resulted in the two volumes of *Mammalia* edited by R.I. Pocock in the monumental *Fauna of British India* series.

[193] CULLINAN DIAMOND

The largest gem-quality rough diamond in the world was found in 1905 at the Premier Diamond Mine in Gauteng, South Africa and named after the mine's owner **Sir THOMAS CULLINAN**. It was cut into 11 stones, the largest of which, known as **CULLINAN I** (or, less prosaically, the Great Star of Africa), was presented to King Edward VII and now forms part of the Crown Jewels housed in the Tower of London, as does **CULLINAN II** or the Lesser Star of Africa. The Great Star was the largest polished diamond in the world until an even bigger sparkler, the Golden Jubilee Diamond, was discovered at the same mine in 1985.

[194] CURIE

PIERRE CURIE (1859-1906), born in Paris, was a French physicist at the Sorbonne who developed a particular interest in the study of piezoelectricity and magnetism, which remembers him by CURIE'S LAW, the CURIE CONSTANT, and the CURIE POINT – phenomena a trifle too recherché for description here. However, it is for the study of radioactivity, jointly with his Polish-born wife, Maria Sklodowska-Curie, known as MARIE CURIE, that his name is best-known; the couple were jointly awarded the 1903 NOBEL PRIZE for physics, shared with HENRI BECQUEREL, for elucidating the phenomena of radioactive emissions. In 1906, Pierre suffered a tragic accidental death, being run over by a carriage while crossing a Paris street. The Radiology Congress of 1910 honoured his memory by adopting his name for the first proposed unit of radioactivity, the CURIE, defined as the radioactivity of one gram of radium (an element discovered in 1898 by Marie and Pierre and isolated by Marie in 1911). One curie corresponds to 37 billion nuclear disintegrations per second. This large unit, most appropriate for describing quite lethal levels of radioactivity, was recently replaced by a much smaller one – the BECQUEREL. (MW)

[195] CURIUM

MANYA SKLODOWSKA (1867-1934) was born in Warsaw, Poland, but moved to Paris in 1891 for her higher education in chemistry and physics at the Sorbonne. She became a naturalised French citizen, and married physicist PIERRE CURIE in 1895, becoming known as MARIE CURIE. The couple worked together on radioactivity and were jointly awarded the NOBEL PRIZE for physics in 1903, shared with HENRI BECQUEREL, the discoverer of the phenomenon. Following the untimely death of Pierre in 1906, Marie's continuing dedication to her work, often under conditions of great difficulty, was recognised by the Nobel Prize for chemistry in 1911, nominating her discovery of the elements: polonium (named after her native land), and radium, whose medical uses were so important to her that her name is almost synonymous with radiotherapy today. As a consequence of her devotion to her experimental work and the neglect of her personal safety, Marie Curie was no stranger to large doses of radiation, which were almost certainly responsible for her death. CURIUM, the transuranic chemical element of atomic number 96, symbol Cm, is named in her honour, and was first prepared by SEABORG, James, and GHIORSO in 1944 by the bombardment of PLUTONIUM with helium ions in the Berkeley cyclotron (see LAWRENCIUM). The isotope curium-244 generates three watts of heat-energy per gram by virtue of its radioactivity, and has some application as an isolated thermoelectric power source in space vehicles. It is exceedingly radiotoxic. (MW)

[196] CUSHING'S SYNDROME – see BRIGHT'S DISEASE

[197] CUVIER'S BEAKED WHALE

Ziphius cavirostris belongs to the family Ziphidae or Beaked Whales, of which there are 14 species, most of them named after an individual scientist. That named after French zoologist, anatomist and geologist BARON GEORGES CUVIER (1769-1832) has been chosen to represent the entire family as bearing the name of the most famous of these individuals.* Cuvier was an opponent of LAMARCK, an important precursor of Darwin, and a founding father of modern zoology. He pioneered the systematic classification of animals on the basis of their anatomy and, by including fossil creatures in his survey, proved the existence of disappeared species and simultaneously brought into being the science of palaeontology.

* For the sake of completeness, the names of the omitted persons are: Arnoux, Baird, Blainville (pupil of Cuvier), Gervais, Gray, Longman, Sowerby, Stejneger, and True.

[198] CYRILLIC ALPHABET

The writing system known as Cyrillic commemorates one of two Greek brothers, SAINT CYRIL (827-869) and Saint Methodius (825-884), known as "the apostles of the Slavs", who in the course of their mission to Christianise the peoples of the Bulgarian Empire in the 9th century AD are jointly credited with the creation of an alphabet known as Glagolitic, which enabled liturgical texts and the translated Bible to be written in the local language. From this alphabet, the Cyrillic alphabet developed. The letter forms are based on the Greek alphabet but there are also Latin and Hebrew influences. The Cyrillic alphabet is today used, with local variations, for twenty or more languages, not all of them Slavic. With the accession of Bulgaria in 2007, the EU acquired Cyrillic as its third official alphabet. (JP)

D

[199] DAGUERREOTYPE

The French artist and theatrical scene painter, LOUIS JACQUES MANDÉ DAGUERRE (1789-1851) enjoys the credit for this photographic innovation, made *ca.* 1835 but not published until 1839. It was the outcome of a partnership he entered into in 1829 with the chemist and pioneer of photography, JOSEPH NICÉPHORE NIÉPCE (1775-1833), whose untimely death left Daguerre with the sole rights to the discovery: a presumption that was hotly contested by the son, Isidore Niépce. A polished, silvered metal plate was treated with iodine vapour in order to deposit a surface layer of light-sensitive silver iodide. After exposure in a camera, the latent image was "developed" by the vapour of hot metallic mercury, which formed a silver amalgam in the light-struck areas. The image was fixed by treatment with sodium thiosulphate ("hypo"), and usually "gilded" with a gold-toning solution. The optical effect of the DAGUERREOTYPE is subtle: the image can appear as either positive or negative, depending on the orientation of the viewing light. Aptly called "the mirror with a memory", it provided exquisite portraits, sometimes hand-tinted, and its commercial use rapidly put miniature-painting out of business. The image surface is very delicate, so daguerreotypes are always protected by glass, mounted in PINCHBECK, and encased. Since mercury vapour is a significant neurotoxin, mental disorder was an occupational hazard of daguerreotypy. *See also* AMBROTYPE, HILLOTYPE, NIEPCEOTYPE and TALBOTYPE. (MW)

[200] DAHLIA

Genus of perennial flowering Mexican plants named for DR ANDERS DAHL (1751-1789), Swedish botanist and pupil of LINNAEUS at the University of Uppsala. Linnaeus, in addition to his massive contribution to botanical and zoological taxonomy, was the inspiration of a brilliant group of students who were drawn to Uppsala from all over Europe and who, both before and after his death, travelled the world collecting, describing and classifying the plants and animals they found. Their names include KALM, Löfling, Solander (who accompanied BANKS on Cook's 1st voyage, 1768-1771), Foersskål, THUNBERG, Koenig... There are 331 entries in Weinstock's *Biographia discipuli Linnaei* (Copenhagen 1985). Seventeen of the best known are treated exhaustively in *The Linnaeus apostles* published by the IK Foundation (2007).

[201] DALTON

Cumbrian-born Quaker, JOHN DALTON (1766-1844) is celebrated principally as the father of the atomic theory of modern chemistry. He was dedicated to scientific pursuits, including extensive meteorological observations. He never married, and earned his modest living by elementary teaching. In 1793 Dalton moved to Manchester, continuing with private tuition (see JOULE), where he progressed within the Manchester Literary & Philosophical Society, becoming Secretary, then President. He was granted an Honorary Degree by Oxford University, and a state pension in 1833. His *New System of Chemical Philosophy*, published in 1808, set chemistry – until then merely a collection of disconnected facts – firmly upon the rational, quantitative foundations of atomic and molecular theory that underpin it today.   A DALTON is the unit of relative atomic mass, (previously called atomic weight), i.e. one twelfth of the mass in grams of a mole (see AVOGADRO) of atoms of the isotope Carbon 12. DALTONISM is colour-blindness – first clearly described in 1794 by the sufferer Dalton himself (how could it have taken civilized thought so long to recognise and articulate this not uncommon malfunction in the human male?). DALTON'S LAW OF PARTIAL PRESSURES is of significant use in the study of the gaseous state. (MW)

[202] DANIELL CELL

An early (1836) form of "wet" electric battery employing electrodes of metallic zinc and copper, each plate immersed in a solution of its salt, zinc sulphate and copper sulphate respectively, the two solutions being interfaced so as to allow the passage of electric current but without much mixing, e.g. by a porous pot or a gelatinised barrier (a "salt bridge"). On completion of an external circuit between the electrodes, an electric current flows and the zinc anode dissolves while copper is deposited at the cathode. The potential of this cell is 1.1 VOLTS. It was a considerable improvement on the original VOLTA'S PILE. JOHN FREDERIC DANIELL (1790-1845) was a British meteorologist and chemist born in London, who became in 1831 the first professor of chemistry at King's College, London. His *Introduction to the study of chemical philosophy* (1839) was a seminal work at the time. (MW)

[203] DANNERT WIRE

(Properly DANAERT) a variant form of barbed or razor wire for mainly military uses and made of spring steel. Named after its 20th-century German inventor. Also known as "concertina wire" as it is packed flat in coils which can be extended longitudinally to form a barrier.

[204] DARLEY ARABIAN

This famous stallion, one of the three founders of the race of British Thoroughbred horses (see also **BYERLEY TURK** and **GODOLPHIN ARABIAN)** was born around the year 1700 and acquired by **THOMAS DARLEY**, merchant and British Consul at Aleppo, and in 1704 sent by him to his father at Aldby Park in East Yorkshire where he (the Arabian) remained until his death 30 years later. He was the sire of **FLYING CHILDERS**, called "the first really great racehorse".*

* Mortimer, Onslow & Willet *Biographical encyclopaedia of British flat-racing* 1978.

[205] DARRIEUS ROTOR

A form of wind-powered generator formed from curved aerofoils, vertically mounted and attached top and bottom to a central spindle.* The design was patented in 1931 by French aeronautical engineer **GEORGES JEAN MARIE DARRIEUS** (1888-1979). Though it has the advantage of not being dependent on wind-direction, it has its own technical disadvantages and, overall, is considered less efficient than the now-familiar aeroplane-propeller type of wind turbine.**

* An alternative version exists with three blades twisted into a helical configuration.

** There is a school of thought which regards these machines as blots on the landscape. The present writer, by contrast, finds them rather beautiful. As a landscape-blotter, the ubiquitous electricity pylon wins hands down.

[206] DARWIN MEDAL

Awarded annually in commemoration of **CHARLES DARWIN** (1809-1882) by the Royal Society for outstanding work "in the broad area of biology in which Darwin worked". The first and highly appropriate recipient, in 1890, was Alfred Russel Wallace (see **WALLACE LINE**). Other laureates include Hooker, Haeckel, Galton, D'Arcy Thompson, and both Huxleys. (*Cf.* **COPLEY MEDAL, FIELDS MEDAL, RUMFORD MEDAL, RICHARDSON MEDAL.**)

[207] DARWINISM

The theory of evolution by means of "natural selection", which **CHARLES ROBERT DARWIN** (1808-1882) expounded in his *Origin of Species* (1859) was an idea whose time had come. Others had investigated the question of how and why species had varied over time, and one – **LAMARCK** – had hit on almost the right answer. So it is fair to assume that if Darwin had not proposed the idea, someone else would have. In fact someone else did – **ALFRED RUSSEL WALLACE** (1823-1913), who arrived independently and simultaneously at broadly the same conclusions. Despite this, and despite the fact that Darwin's proposed solution to the problem of differential evolution was incomplete and in some respects actually misleading, his name, together with that of

ISAAC NEWTON, stands very high on the list of those Britons who have contributed most profoundly to the world's understanding of itself. This might explain why, a hundred and fifty years after the intellectual earthquake produced by Darwin's book, aftershocks are still being felt. Evolutionary theory is currently a hot topic thanks on the one hand to the efforts of the lunatic Right in America to have Hebrew creation myths taught in schools in place of science, and on the other the strident atheism of Prof. Dawkins and his like. While it is true that we have as yet no more notion of how the universe came into being than did the authors of the Book of Genesis,* we do, thanks in large part to Darwin and his successors, have a rather more convincing account of the history of the cosmos and its inhabitants *since* the moment of its creation. Perhaps the real trouble with Darwinism as far as the anti-evolutionists are concerned is not merely that it knocks on the head the belief that each species is a special creation, nor that it does away with the idea of a universe created in seven days** and only a few thousand years old – by Darwin's time no thinking person seriously held the Genesis account to be factual – nor even that it substitutes blind chance for the Divine Plan. All these can be explained, argued, or wished away. Blind Chance, for example, might *be* the Divine Plan. But there is another problem, and one that just won't go away: namely that Darwin's world, the world that we inhabit, has no place in it for a benevolent Creator, since a system whereby God's creatures can only maintain themselves on the face of the earth by killing and eating each other is surely very far from qualifying as benevolent. Indeed, it appears to be expressly designed to ensure that as many as possible of His creatures shall live in fear and die in agony. And if a human being had devised such an arrangement he would be deemed a sadistic maniac and removed from circulation. Darwin explicitly recognised this difficulty when, in a letter to Hooker, he penned his famous remark: "What a book a Devil's chaplain might write on the clumsy, wasteful, blundering, low and horribly cruel works of Nature." Perhaps after all the MANICHAEANS are in the right of it: our world is the Devil's creation and God's is elsewhere. (See also SCOPES MONKEY TRIAL.)

* The Big Bang Theory, though it enables us to trace the evolution of the cosmos back through time to Ground Zero, tells us nothing about its ultimate origin. If the universe as we currently see it is the product of an exploding lump of incredibly dense matter, we still need to be told (1) where that matter came from, (2) why it exploded, and (3) why it exploded when it did. Of course, in a world as far removed from everyday commonsensical reality as that of the theoretical nuclear physicist, such questions would doubtless seem hopelessly naive and simplistic. But for the ordinary thinking person they still demand answers.

** And why so long? Why not seven minutes?

[208] DAUBENTON'S BAT

Or "Water Bat" after its habit of hunting insects over water. A bat of Europe and Asia (including Britain), one of 71 species of *Myotis**. *M. daubentonii* takes its name from the French naturalist **LOUIS JEAN MARIE DAUBENTON** (1716-1800), born at Montbard in Burgundy. His wide-ranging interests and activities included collaboration with his fellow-Montbardian Buffon in the latter's great multi-volume *Histoire Naturelle* (1749-1789) as well as work in comparative anatomy, palaeontology, mineralogy, plant physiology, and agriculture (he introduced the Merino sheep to France).

* See also **NATTERER'S BAT**.

[209] DAVIDIA – see PÈRE DAVID'S DEER

[210] DAVY LAMP

Since 1815 this humble device has saved the lives of countless coal-miners: it is a simple oil lamp in which the flame is enclosed by a cylinder of iron wire gauze, so inhibiting the ignition of any inflammable gas in the surrounding atmosphere, usually methane (also known as "firedamp") – a perpetual danger in mines. It is a memorial to that esteemed man of science, **SIR HUMPHRY DAVY** (1778-1829), perhaps the most famous of Cornishmen. His main contribution came in 1807 with an early application of the **VOLTAIC BATTERY** to liberate by electrolysis the highly reactive alkali metals, sodium and potassium, and the alkaline earth metals, magnesium, calcium, strontium and barium. In 1810 he established that chlorine, first discovered by **SCHEELE**, was an element and so named it (from the Greek "chloros" meaning "pale green" – an improvement on its previous name of "oxymuriatic acid"). At the Royal Institution, Davy was the mentor of **MICHAEL FARADAY,** whose achievements ultimately transcended his own. It is unlikely that Davy's memory will ever be able to shake off the first-ever **CLERIHEW**:

> *Sir Humphry Davy*
> *Abominated gravy.*
> *He lived in the odium*
> *Of having discovered sodium.*

(MW)

[211] DE BRAZZA'S MONKEY

PIERRE SAVORGNAN DE BRAZZA (1852-1905), was born in Italy, naturalised French (1874), and trained as a naval officer. Explorer and coloniser, he played an important part in the "Scramble for Africa" which took place in the last quarter of the nineteenth century. His expeditions to West-Central Africa took him as far as the Congo and led to the creation of the French (as opposed to Belgian) Congo and the foundation of the town named after him – Brazzaville. "His" monkey has the scientific name *Cercopithecus neglectus*. Neglected is probably what most African primates would prefer to be these days.

[212] DE BROGLIE'S HYPOTHESIS

Matter at the sub-atomic scale does not behave in quite the everyday manner we are accustomed to by our rather gross sense-perceptions. We distinguish between the behaviour of "particles" – balls on a billiard table – and "waves" – splashing around in a pool. But electrons, those minute particles of electric charge, can also manifest themselves as waves, depending on what sort of experiment we perform. Contrariwise, light waves can behave as streams of particles, called photons. DE BROGLIE'S HYPOTHESIS of "wave-particle duality" lies at the heart of all modern atomic physics and proposes that the effective wavelength of any moving particle is given by PLANCK'S CONSTANT divided by the particle's momentum. It was first put forward in 1924 in the doctoral thesis of LOUIS-VICTOR PIERRE RAYMOND, 7th DUC DE BROGLIE (1892-1987) a French physicist, born in Dieppe of noble Piedmontese family, who studied at the Sorbonne. His hypothesis has received ample experimental confirmation – the electron microscope is one obvious consequence – and it formed the basis for SCHRÖDINGER'S development of wave mechanics. It also implies the possibility of an electron's being simultaneously present in two different places, calling to mind the divine gift of bilocation said to have been manifested by the highly mobile St. Anthony of Padua. (MW)

[213] DE MOIVRE'S FORMULA

Another pretty connection between trigonometric functions and imaginary numbers, where $i = \sqrt{-1}$:

$$(\cos x + i \sin x)^n = \cos nx + i \sin nx$$

French mathematician ABRAHAM DE MOIVRE (1667-1754) was born at Vitry-le-François in Champagne. During an academy-based education he showed skill in mathematics, but his Calvinist persuasion impeded his higher education in Catholic France, so he came to England in 1687 as a Huguenot exile and remained until his death (the day of which he accurately predicted). He subsisted in London as a private tutor in mathematics, but became friendly with EDMOND HALLEY and ISAAC NEWTON and produced mathematical work of such quality as to earn him an FRS in 1697. His major contribution was in probability theory. His *The Doctrine of Chances: a method of calculating the probabilities of events in play* went through four editions (1711-1756) and contains the DE MOIVRE–LAPLACE THEOREM showing how the binomial distribution for large exponents can approximate to the GAUSSIAN curve of the normal distribution. (MW)

[214] DEBYE

A physical unit (non-SI) that measures the molecular property known as a *dipole* *moment*, which arises when the centres of positive and negative electric charge do not coincide, and the molecule is said to be *polar*. It's an important property in determining a substance's physical properties: *e.g.* water is a liquid because the bent molecule H_2O (see **LEWIS FORMULA**) has a dipole moment causing a strong attraction between water molecules, whereas carbon dioxide is a gas because CO_2 is linear $O=C=O$ and therefore has no dipole moment. **PETER JOSEPH WILLIAM DEBYE** (1884-1966) was a Dutch chemical physicist born in Maastricht, who studied first at Aachen then Munich under Sommerfeld, and served thereafter at a succession of Swiss and German Universities, becoming Director (1934-39) of the prestigious Kaiser Wilhelm Institute for Physics in Berlin (rebranded as the Max Planck Institute post-WWII). He was awarded the Nobel Prize for chemistry in 1936 for his contributions to the theory of atomic and molecular structure. His name is attached to several physico-chemical phenomena and theories, notably the **DEBYE-HÜCKEL THEORY** for strong electrolytes. Declining the offer of German citizenship, he left the country in 1940 for the USA, adopted American nationality in 1946 and remained there until his death. In 2006 a previously forgotten letter from 1938 was republished, from Debye to the members of the *Deutsche Physikalische Gesellschaft*, of which he was then President, requiring that, under the Nazi-enacted Nuremberg Laws of 1935, Jewish members must resign from the Society. This official letter was signed by Debye under the salutation *Heil Hitler!* – an obligatory formalism of the day. This recent revelation led to Debye being traduced as a Nazi activist and anti-Semite, and various Dutch Universities were consequently advised to remove the vilified name of **DEBYE** from their Institutional titles and prizes.* The ensuing brouhaha was resolved in 2008 by an official Commission that re-examined all the historical evidence for these allegations and concluded that Debye was substantially apolitical, although maybe a trifle ambivalent in his adopted strategy for survival under the Third Reich, that he was certainly not anti-Semitic, and that his name should be re-habilitated.** Debye Street and Debye Square can still be found in Maastricht. (MW)

* Might this be characterised as a rare instance of *diseponymy?*

** And the Institutions correspondingly were *re-eponymised.*

[215] DECIBEL

Unit of perceived noise level (PNdB). The last syllable derives from the name of the Scottish-born inventor of the telephone and pioneer in the education of the deaf **ALEXANDER GRAHAM BELL** (1846-1922). A related unit is the "Noy" (1 Noy = 40 PNdB), meaning "noisiness" but also, by a pleasant coincidence, suggesting "annoyance". As an alternative to the decibel we have the "Phon" and its related unit the "Sone".

[216] DEGREES GAY-LUSSAC – see **GAY-LUSSAC'S LAW**

[217] DERBY

The **DERBY STAKES**, one of the five British Classic Flat Races (see also **ST. LEGER STAKES**) has been run annually at Epsom since 1780. The first winner was *Diomed*, owned by Sir Charles Bunbury. Bunbury had organised the race together with **EDWARD SMITH-STANLEY, 12TH EARL OF DERBY** (1752-1834), whose career must otherwise have been relatively undistinguished as, unlike other scions of his line, he doesn't make it into the *Dictionary of National Biography*. It is said that the two men flipped a coin to decide who the race should be named after. Derby won the toss but had to wait until 1787 before a horse of his came in first. The original race was run over one mile but the official distance today is 2,650 yards. In America, a **DERBY** (pronounced *durby*) is a bowler hat.

[218] DESMOULINS' WHORLED SNAIL

Vertigo moulinsiana is found throughout Atlantic and Mediterranean Europe – but found only with difficulty as it is tremendously small (under 3 mm). In most locations it is rated as either rare or endangered, but these assessments have to take into account the difficulty of spotting the little fellow in the first place. Its habitat provides another limitation, as it is found (when found) only in marshy or wet locations in chalk-soil areas, where it feeds on sedges and reed-grass. Rarity means that the presence of *V. moulinsiana* leads almost automatically to the locality being declared a Site of Special Scientific Interest (SSSI) – good news for land-owners as there are grants attached. But when the micro-mollusc was detected on the site of the proposed Newbury by-pass, the project had to be halted until the snails could be moved to another location (where, apparently, they died out). The name, dating from 1849, is that of **CHARLES ROBERT ALEXANDRE DES MOULINS** (1798-1875), Franch botanist and malacologist.*

* "Malacology" – branch of zoology concerned with molluscs, from a Greek root meaning "soft" (and by extension "effeminate" – hence its use in modern Greek as a term of abuse corresponding to something like "wanker").

[219] DEVIL'S ARSE –see **POOLE'S CAVERN**

[220] DEWAR VESSEL

The scientist's name for a vacuum flask: a double-walled insulating glass vessel, silvered on the inside to reflect radiant heat, and the air-gap evacuated to minimise conduction through the walls. The commercial product, the everyday "Thermos flask", is protected by a metal can. By minimising the ingress of heat energy, dewar vessels can retain refrigerated liquids having very low boiling points, such as liquid oxygen, nitrogen or even helium, with only slow loss of the substance. By the same token, hot substances like nutritious soups or beverages, will retain their heat in such a container for many hours, thanks to its very low thermal conductivity.

The invention is due to the Scottish physicist and chemist SIR JAMES DEWAR (1842-1923) who was educated at Edinburgh University and appointed Jacksonian professor at Cambridge in 1875, and then Fullerian professor of chemistry at the Royal Institution in 1877, when he was also elected FRS. Assuming the mantle of an earlier incumbent, MICHAEL FARADAY, who had liquefied chlorine and ammonia, Dewar indulged his overriding ambition to achieve low temperatures by setting out to liquefy the so-called "permanent gases" that had defied Faraday's cryogenic endeavours. By making use of the JOULE-THOMSON EFFECT, he succeeded in liquefying nitrogen, oxygen and even hydrogen (at –252 degrees CELSIUS). When it came to liquefying helium, however, (at –268 Celsius, or only 5 degrees KELVIN above absolute zero) he was pipped at the post in 1908 by the Dutch physicist, Heike Kamerlingh Onnes in Leiden, who consequently received the NOBEL PRIZE in 1913 instead of Dewar. He was knighted in 1904, possibly for his invention of cordite, used as a propellant in artillery and small-arms ammunition. (MW)

[221] DEWEY DECIMAL SYSTEM

MELVIL DEWEY (1851-1931) was successively librarian of Columbia College, NYC, where he started the first-ever school of librarianship, and Director of the New York State Library (1888-1905). He founded and edited *The Library Journal* and was a co-founder of the American Library Association. He published his numerical cataloguing system (which embodied elements of earlier systems) in 1876 in a work snappily entitled *A classification and subject index for cataloguing and arranging the books and pamphlets of a library.* Dewey's system allots each book to one of ten main numbered categories (religion, philosophy, art, etc), each of which is further divided into ten sub-categories, which are in turn divided into 10 sub-sub-categories. The system is still widely used but has necessarily undergone considerable amendment since Dewey's day. Dewey was also interested in that perennial crank-magnet Spelling Reform. It is thanks to him that Americans write catalogue as "catalog".

[222] DICKIN MEDAL

An award given to animals for bravery and more especially for actions instrumental in saving human life. The Medal was instituted in 1943 by MARIA DICKIN (1870-1951), a doughty worker for animal welfare who in 1917 founded the People's Dispensary for Sick Animals (PDSA). It was intended as an act of public recognition for animals who had distinguished themselves in war or in civilian rescue operations. It is still being awarded today – recently, for example, to a dog named Apollo belonging to the NYPD on behalf of all the search-and-rescue dogs working in the ruins of the World Trade centre. Other laureates have included carrier pigeons, horses, and a cat named Simon who served aboard HMS

Amethyst during the Yangtse incident, earning promotion from Ordinary Cat to Able Cat by his seamanlike conduct on this occasion.

[223] DIELS-ALDER REACTION – see GRIGNARD REACTION

[224] DIESEL ENGINE

The name of German inventor **RUDOLF DIESEL** (1858-1913) is given to a form of internal combustion engine (German patent 1893) in which the fuel is introduced to the cylinder as an aerosol and ignited by compression. The concept arose from Diesel's work as a heating engineer and was his answer to improving the thermal efficiency of the **OTTO CYCLE** engine (see also **CARNOT'S THEOREM**). Diesel invented various other forms of engine including one that was solar powered and another, fuelled by ammonia vapour, which almost cost him his life when it blew up under test. In 1913 he was lost overboard during a ferry-crossing of the North Sea. Suicide is the most probable interpretation but, according to another theory, he met his end at the hands of the German military who were afraid he was about to sell his invention to the British Navy for use in submarines. In our own day, diesel engines are preferred for military vehicles as requiring lower-volatility fuel than petrol engines.

[225] DIOGENES SYNDROME

is a serious misnomer. It denotes a psychiatric disorder of old age in which the sufferer manifests symptoms of self-neglect and social withdrawal, and accumulates vast quantities of useless rubbish around him- or her-self. More appropriate names for the condition are "senile squalor syndrome", syllogomania, or Plyushkin's* Syndrome. **DIOGENES OF SINOPE** (*ca.* 410-320 BC) – to distinguish him toponymically from several other Greek philosophers of the same name** – is said to have employed a lantern, at noon, to aid his futile attempt "to seek out an honest man". This is read as an early manifestation of the philosophy of Cynicism. He is also reputed to have lived in a barrel: given such an insufficiency of habitable space, anyone less likely to acquire superfluous junk is hard to imagine. (MW)

* After a character in Gogol's *Dead Souls*.

** Such as **DIOGENES OF APOLLONIA** (*fl.* 425 BC) whose name is given to the meteoritic mineral **DIOGENITE**, one of the achondritic stony meteorite groups, **HOWARDITE-EUCHRITE-DIOGENITE** or **HED-METEORITES**, which arrive on Earth as fragments chipped off the brightest asteroid **VESTA**, and are occasionally found lying about on the snow fields of the Antarctic.

[226] DIPPEL'S ANIMAL OIL

JOHANN KONRAD DIPPEL (1673-1734) was born at Castle Frankenstein near Darmstadt, the son of a Lutheran pastor. He became a master theologian, publishing under the name of *Christianus Democritus*, but succumbed to the lure of alchemy, signing himself *Frankensteinensis*. Having failed to make gold, he launched his *elixir vitae* – a medicinal "animal oil" – upon an unsuspecting public in 1700. Dippel's oil was a malodorous distillate of the unconsidered residues of animal carcasses – blood, bones and offal. His predilection for body parts may have later inspired Mary Shelley, when she visited Castle Frankenstein in 1814, on her elopement with Percy (see **FRANKENSTEIN'S MONSTER**). We now know Dippel's oil to consist of a mixture of nitrogenous organic bases such as pyrrole, and several alkyl cyanides. At the time it was hailed as a panacea – presumably sustained by the widely-held belief that anything so obnoxious must be beneficial. In 1704 Dippel supplied the artists' colourmaker, Heinrich Diesbach of Berlin, with an impure sample of alkali that was contaminated with his oil. By chance, this provided the essential ingredient – cyanide – to enable Diesbach's serendipitous discovery of the first synthetic pigment,* Prussian blue or **TURNBULL'S BLUE**. All painters thereafter have reason to be grateful to this unscrupulous alchemist, who, after numerous scrapes with European royalty, died at Castle Wittgenstein, possibly a victim of his own elixir. (MW)

* This title may now be ceded to the recently rediscovered Egyptian blue.

[227] DIRAC'S CONSTANT

Given the same symbol as the alchemists used for the planet Saturn and the metal lead: $\hbar$, (unimaginatively pronounced "h-bar"), today this is simply **PLANCK'S CONSTANT**, h, divided by 2π. It is the quantum of angular momentum, in the same way that Planck's constant is the quantum of energy, providing a convenient unit to measure the mysterious property of particle "spin" (see **BOSON** and **FERMION**). British theoretical physicist **PAUL ADRIAN MAURICE DIRAC** (1902-1984) was born in Bristol and educated at the Universities of Bristol, then Cambridge, where he occupied the Lucasian Chair of Mathematics from 1932 to 1969. He is acknowledged as one of the most outstanding theoreticians of the 20th century. The **DIRAC EQUATION** (1928) united the principles of **EINSTEIN'S** special relativity with those of **HEISENBERG'S** quantum mechanics, to describe the behaviour of any **FERMION**. It explains the "spin" of the electron, the fine structure of the hydrogen spectrum, and predicts the existence of antimatter, such as the positron, subsequently discovered in 1932. Dirac shared the **NOBEL PRIZE** in Physics with **SCHRÖDINGER** in 1933. (MW)

[228] DISSTON SAWS

Before the advent of "hard-point" saws, which cannot be sharpened by their owners and are therefore, like the **BiC RAZOR**, disposable, any craftsman in wood (carpenter, joiner or cabinet-maker) relied on the quality of his saws for the quality of his work, and their upkeep – sharpening and setting – demanded regular and skilled attention. It therefore made sense to own the best saws available, and though the Sheffield toolmakers produced, as they always had done, excellent work, the best saws by common consent came from the DISSTON SAW WORKS in Philadelphia, USA. HENRY DISSTON (1819-1878) was born in Tewkesbury and emigrated to America in 1833 where he set up as a toolmaker, specialising in saws. He established his own foundry and rolling mill, making steel to his own specification and obviating the need for imported tool-steel. Disston was a paternalistic employer who created a "company town" for his workers and ensured that they were able to buy on easy terms the homes he had built for them. During WWII the company diversified into the making of armour-plate for military vehicles. It continued as a family-run business and the largest saw-making facility in the world, until 1955. Now that Sandvik and co. rule the roost, DISSTON SAWS, which exist in a wide variety of patterns for different specialised tasks, are eagerly sought by collectors of woodworking hand-tools, and many, no doubt, are still in use by craftsmen who know a good thing when they see one.

[229] DIXIE – see MASON-DIXON LINE

[230] DÖBEREINER'S TRIADS

Foreshadowing MENDELEEV'S PERIODIC TABLE, this was an early attempt (*ca.* 1817) to systematize the list of known chemical elements by the observation of chemically similar "triads", like the alkali metals: lithium, sodium, potassium; the alkaline earths: calcium, strontium, barium; the chalcogens: sulphur, selenium, tellurium; and the halogens: chlorine, bromine, iodine. In each triad the atomic weight of the middle one is close to the arithmetic mean of the other two. JOHANN WOLFGANG DÖBEREINER (1780-1849) was apprenticed to an apothecary at the age of 14, and although largely self-educated, was nonetheless appointed "extraordinary professor" at the University of Jena in 1810. He published his *An Attempt to Group Elementary Substances according to Their Analogies* in 1829, and a text on platinum chemistry in 1836. His photochemical investigations attracted the attention of SIR JOHN HERSCHEL. He was a founder of the study of catalysis, and was a friend of JOHANN WOLFGANG von GOETHE, whom he advised on chemical matters. DÖBEREINER'S LAMP or *feuerzeug* of 1823 is an early table-lighter: gaseous hydrogen, generated by zinc and acid, is ignited catalytically in air by platinum sponge. (MW)

[231] "DOING A MELBA" – see MELBA TOAST

[232] DOLLOND LENS

A simple convex lens brings differently-coloured rays of light to a focus at different points. Such images are therefore blurred by the *chromatic aberration* which caused NEWTON to resort to mirrors for his telescopes. Around 1730, British lawyer and amateur optician, Chester Moor Hall (1703-1771) from Surrey invented a compound lens called an *achromatic doublet* consisting of two different types of glass (crown and flint) having different refractive indices to correct this aberration internally, and bring both red and blue light to the same focus. Hall was said to have commissioned the first achromatic refracting telescope to be built for him, but he was secretive and did not exploit his discovery publicly. The man who developed the achromatic doublet was the British silk-weaver turned optician, **JOHN DOLLOND** (1706-1761) who was born in London of Huguenot stock. He published his *Account of some experiments concerning the different refrangibility of light* in the *Philosophical Transactions* of 1758, for which he was awarded the **COPLEY MEDAL** of the Royal Society, and a Fellowship. He patented the achromatic doublet in the same year, but his son Peter Dollond (1738-1820) had subsequently to enforce the patent, and defend his father's integrity against accusations of plagiarism by rival opticians. His letters assert that Dollond had known nothing of Hall's "prior art" when he made his re-discovery. With achromatic objectives, refracting telescopes were vastly improved and became items of commerce. The family name survives to the present in the extensive High Street optician business, Dollond & Aitchison – but is now likely to disappear in a recent merger with Boots. (MW)

[233] DOLLY VARDEN

The name of a character in Dickens' *Barnaby Rudge* (1841) is commonly applied to a type of women's hat, wide-brimmed and with profuse floral decoration. However, the hat worn by the original Dolly, as described by Dickens, is not at all in that style. We read: "*As to Dolly, there she was again, the very pink and pattern of good looks, in a smart little cherry-coloured mantle, with a hood of the same drawn over her head, and upon the top of that hood, a little straw hat trimmed with cherry-coloured ribbons, and worn the merest trifle on one side – just enough in short to make it the wickedest and most provoking head-dress that ever malicious milliner devised....*". On this evidence it would seem that the iced bun surmounted with a glacé cherry known in parts of Scotland as a Dolly Varden is nearer the mark. For anglers, however, a Dolly Varden is not to be worn on the head or consumed with a cup of tea but dragged from a river with hook and line, the name having been applied in the past to two species of pink-spotted North American fish: *Salvelinus confluentus* or Bull Trout, and *Salvelinus malma malma* or Arctic Char. This prompts the thought that, given the propensity of late Victorian and Edwardian milliners for constructing hats resembling restaurant sweet trolleys and loaded with wax fruit, stuffed pigeons, etc., a hat featuring an artfully-arranged dead trout on, say, a bed of lettuce, would not be considered altogether over the top.

[234] DOLOMITE

The mineral **DOLOMITE**, composed of calcium and magnesium carbonates, can appear in a crystalline form similar in appearance to calcite, or as a type of rock otherwise known as magnesian limestone. It takes its name from the French geologist **DÉODAT GUY SYLVAIN TANCRÈDE GRATET DE DOLOMIEU** (1750-1801). He led an adventurous life, was a member of the order of the Knights of Malta, narrowly escaped a death sentence for killing a fellow knight in a duel, travelled widely in southern Europe in the course of his geological researches, and in 1799, on his way back from taking part in Bonaparte's scientific expedition to Egypt, was imprisoned in Naples (then at war with France) where he wrote *Sur la philosophie minéralogique* (1801) with a home-made pen in the margins of his Bible. He advanced the remarkably bold theory (for its time) that the materials comprising the earth and its atmosphere were arranged in layers according to their specific gravity and that the central mass beneath the earth's crust was fluid. (For other minerals see **SCHEELITE**.)

[235] DONATION OF CONSTANTINE

Document whereby the Emperor Constantine, in gratitude for his conversion to Christianity, granted Pope Sylvester I and his successors temporal as well as spiritual authority over the Western Empire. Though there were doubters, the document was generally accepted as genuine by both supporters and opponents of the Popes' pretensions to an authority trumping that of the German Emperors. However, in 1440, the humanist scholar Lorenzo Valla (1406-1457) was able to show by an analysis of the text's style, vocabulary and grammar that it could not have been composed in the late Roman Empire and was therefore a mediaeval forgery. Valla's demonstration was a founding moment in the establishment of textual criticism as a tool of scholarship and the basis of an academic discipline. The forgery is now thought to date from the 9th century. Gibbon suggested "the notorious Isidore" (a French cleric based at Metz around 840) as the possible culprit, a view that has prevailed among later historians.

[236] DOPPLER EFFECT

The "...neeeee-yowwww..." as the racing-car speeds by and the rising and falling whistle of a passing train are familiar auditory experiences. But the **DOPPLER EFFECT** is a general characteristic of any moving source of waves – not just sound, but also light, or other electromagnetic radiation – infra-red, ultraviolet, radiowaves or gamma rays. The phenomenon is easily understood: as the source approaches us (the detector), the waves are compressed by its velocity, and arrive more rapidly than it is emitting them; as the source recedes, the waves stretch out and arrive less rapidly. The drop in frequency of the received waves as the source passes is heard as a sudden lowering in pitch of the note – if sound – or seen as a shift to longer wavelengths in the dispersed spectrum if electromagnetic radiation is the source. In 1845 BUYS BALLOT (see CORIOLIS EFFECT) tested Doppler's theory that pitch (wave-length) depended on the relative motion of transmitter and detector by a famous experiment which took place in Holland. It involved a railway engine pulling a flatcar at different speeds past an observation point. On the car were trumpeters playing sustained notes. On the ground were observers endowed with perfect pitch who recorded what they were hearing. The results fully confirmed Doppler's theoretical calculations. Observations of the Doppler effect have had key importance in the history of physical science. The red shift in the lines of stellar spectra is a Doppler shift proving that the universe is expanding (see HUBBLE'S CONSTANT). Recently the effect has been employed in a subtle method of nuclear spectroscopy due to MÖSSBAUER. The "Doppler broadening" of spectral lines can be used to determine the temperatures of stars. The effect also enables acoustic sonar to measure the speed of submarines, and likewise the radar guns toted by traffic cops to nab the speeding motorist. CHRISTIAN JOHANN DOPPLER (1803-1853) was an Austrian physicist born in Salzburg, who studied in Vienna and began his career in Prague. He described the principles of the effect in 1842, and was appointed to a chair at Vienna in 1851. Also named after Doppler is DOPPLERITE, an organic substance occuring as gelatinous masses in peat bogs in Switzerland and Styria (Austria). It contains a high concentration of humic acid, a product of vegetable decomposition. (MW)

[237] DOUBTING THOMAS

In Christian tradition, the disciple Thomas, who demanded tangible proof before he would accept the fact of Jesus' resurrection (*John* Ch. xx, 24-29), is generally regarded as blameworthy – the very type-figure of one who, when faith is called for, is found wanting. In real life, on the other hand, refusal to accept an improbability as true without solid evidence is, most people would think, a valuable survival characteristic.

[238] DOUGLAS FIR

Alternative common name given to the Oregon Pine *Pseudotsuga menziesii* in honour of Scottish botanist DAVID DOUGLAS (1798-1834). Douglas travelled widely in Canada and the USA as a botanical collector for the Horticultural Society of London and was responsible for many introductions including the Giant Fir (*Abies grandis*). Also named after him are a genus of North American rock plants DOUGLASIA, and the DOUGLAS SQUIRREL (*Tamiasciurus douglasii*), a red tree squirrel inhabiting the Pacific Coast region from British Columbia to northern California. Douglas was killed by a wild bull in the SANDWICH ISLANDS.

[239] DOW-JONES INDUSTRIAL AVERAGE

Known to the debonair boulevardiers of Wall Street simply as "The Dow", it records the daily rise and fall of the New York stock market in terms of the share prices of 30 of America's biggest publicly-owned companies. It was devised in 1896 by CHARLES H. DOW (d. 1902), editor of the *Wall Street Journal* and co-founder with financial statistician EDWARD D. JONES (d. 1920) of the Dow Jones Company. The term "industrial" is now something of an anachronism as by no means all of the companies quoted (Wal-Mart, for example) are "industrial" in 19th-century terms. The meanings of words, of course, are not fixed in stone. But a Brunel, say, or an Armstrong would almost certainly have raised an eyebrow to hear prostitution or gambling referred to as "industries", just as they would have on hearing the latest scam cooked up by some dodgy bank or finance company referred to as a "product".

[240] DOWN'S SYNDROME

Developmental disorder caused by a chromosomal abnormality. First described in an 1866 paper by British physician JOHN LANGDON DOWN (1828-1896). The condition was once known as Mongolism on account of certain commonly occurring physical characteristics including epicanthic folds to the eyelids. Down's career was marked by a humane and enlightened attitude to mental disability. In 1868 he established a private asylum at Normansfield, Hampton Wick, where his pioneering techniques of education and training set a standard for best practice in its day.

[241] DR. COLLIS BROWNE'S CHLORODYNE

This wonderful patent nostrum was devised around 1850 by Dr. JOHN COLLIS BROWNE (1819-1894), a British army doctor serving in India, and remained available without prescription until relatively recently (as some seekers after drug-induced heightened awareness found to their delight). The recipe varied over time. The original formula included cannabis and chloroform, and the British pharmacopeia of 1885 mentions peppermint, ether and prussic acid as constituents, but the main ingredient was always tincture of opium – *i.e.* opium dissolved in alcohol, or in other words, laudanum, that *sine qua non* of literary activity in the 19th century. Opium, as every schoolboy knows, causes chronic constipation, hence the use of Chlorodyne to treat cholera and dysentery. And hence the testimonial puffs from grateful users on the printed sheet which came with every bottle of the magic mixture, written by military persons trapped in unhealthy environments during the Boer War and similar excitements. Chlorodyne made Dr. Brown's fortune, enabling him to take an early and comfortable retirement to Ramsgate, where he is buried.

[242] DR. PRICE'S ALPHABET

Apart from a few sketchy references in Caesar, Tacitus and Strabo, absolutely
nothing of any substance is known about the pre-Christian beliefs and religious
practices of the Welsh. Modern Druidry has had to be invented *ab ovo* by human
imagination with little or no help from historical authority.* Most of this outburst
of creativity occurred in the 18th and 19th centuries. It was symptomatic of a
sentimental but perfectly understandable yearning for bygone glories, and intimately
connected on the one hand with the birth of the Romantic movement in art and
literature and on the other with the revival of cultural nationalism in Britain's
Celtic Fringe – Wales, Scotland and Ireland. It was also a powerful crank-magnet.
In Wales, a prime mover of the revival was Edward Williams (1747-1826), who
sailed under the bardic name Iolo Morgannwg (he hailed from Glamorgan).
Williams devoted much of his life and considerable energies to ferreting out
ancient manuscripts in which he hoped to find embodied the lost culture of the
Welsh. His problem then, and since, is that he saw no harm in improving the texts
as and when he saw fit or, when the evidence he sought was lacking, simply
creating it himself, secure in the belief that what he wrote is what the original
author would have written. So to describe Iolo simply as a forger is unduly harsh
– his intentions were good even if his methods were, shall we say, insufficiently
rigorous. The heir to the Archdruidic mantle of Iolo Morgannwg was **DR.
WILLIAM PRICE** (1800-1893), a colourful eccentric who went about in a self-
designed costume featuring a fox's head by way of a hat and who pioneered the
practice of cremation in this country, braving the law (which banned it) to do so.
Among his many innovations, Price claimed to have discovered what he called a
BARDIC ALPHABET, which figured in his ritual outfit – a one-piece garment
resembling combination underwear and made of scarlet merino wool embroidered
in green silk with the letters of his alphabet (which strangely resembled Greek).

* To give a trivial example: the "traditional" costumes worn by modern Welsh druids at national and
local *eisteddfodau* were designed by Queen's Victoria's favourite portrait painter Sir Hubert von
Herkomer.

[243] DRAKE EQUATION

Are we alone? That is the question addressed by American radioastronomer **DR.
FRANK DONALD DRAKE** (b. 1930), professor of astronomy at the University of
California, Santa Cruz, who began his career at Cornell and Harvard. In 1961 he
proposed an equation for estimating the likely number, N, of "communicating
civilizations" at the present time within our "Milky Way" Galaxy of 100 billion
stars. Drake expressed N as the product of seven factors, some of them
scientifically guessable "ballparkwise", such as the likely number of planets capable
of supporting life; but some factors are highly conjectural, such as the probable
duration of any civilization's ability – and, indeed, inclination – to keep transmitting

radio signals into space. Current assessments of N, depending on these assumptions, come out somewhere between N = 1 or less, and N = 100 or thereabouts. These results mean that the answer to the question: "Are we alone?" lies somewhere between: "Definitely yes", (N = 1 = us), and "Effectively yes", (if N = 100, even our nearest neighbours would then be thousands of light years away). It may be significant that the Search for Extra-Terrestrial Intelligence (SETI – an organization founded by Drake) has so far scored a duck. The fact that there are no little green women demanding to be taken to our leaders, or bleeping into our radiotelescopes (this is sometimes called the **FERMI PARADOX**) points to two possible scenarios: the first is that even comfortable planets very seldom evolve intelligent life; and the second is that any "advanced" civilization is bound to destroy itself rather speedily. It's only within the last century that humankind has qualified as a "communicating civilization" so, looking around us today, it's hard to disagree with either conclusion. (See Drake *Intelligent life in space* 1962; Drake and Sobel *Is anyone out there?* 1993.) (MW)

[244] DRAPER'S LAW –see GROTTHUSS-DRAPER LAW

[245] DRECHSEL BOTTLE

A piece of chemical glassware for bubbling a gas through a liquid: the cylindrical bottle has a single, hollow, ground-glass stopper, fitted with a long gas inlet tube dipping below the surface of the liquid, and with an exit tube. By this means, unwanted or noxious volatiles may be "scrubbed" from gas flow systems. The same principle is used in that exotic accessory to recreational smoking, the "hubble-bubble" or water pipe, the Turkish *nargileh*. **HEINRICH FERDINAND EDMUND DRECHSEL** (1843-1897) was born in Leipzig and studied there, became an organic chemist, first working for Kolbe, and later making significant contributions to protein biochemistry. He invented his bottle in 1875 and it remains to this day a useful item of chemists' kit. (MW)

[246] DRUMMOND LIGHT

Also known as "limelight", which was originally invented by a man of many parts, Cornishman Sir Goldsworthy Gurney (1793-1875), and used especially for theatre illumination. A block of quicklime (calcium oxide) heated intensely by an oxy-hydrogen flame emits a brilliant light by thermoluminescence, see **WELSBACH**. In 1826 Scottish engineeer **CAPTAIN THOMAS DRUMMOND** (1797-1840) used this extremely intense light with a surveyor's heliotrope to be visible at a great distance for trigonometric surveying when the sun wasn't shining. Born and educated in Edinburgh, Drummond entered the Royal Engineers in 1815 and joined the Ordnance Survey in 1820. He became under-secretary for Ireland in 1835, a post in which he gained the affectionate respect of many. (MW)

[247] DRYDEN'S ROCK

in the State of Victoria, Australia, was officially named Mount Diogenes in 1844 by pioneer surveyor Robert Hoddle, in line with the classical Greek names bestowed by explorer Major Thomas Mitchell in 1836 on those other central Victorian peaks, Mt. Alexander and Mt. Macedon. Displaying a spectacularly eroded array of pinnacles, Mt. Diogenes rises to 105 meters above the surrounding plain: it is not a true volcanic plug, the geologists tell us, but a *mamelon* (Fr: "nipple") arising from an unusually viscous soda-rich lava called *solvsbergite*, found elsewhere only in Scandinavia. By 1839 the formation was being called after **EDWARD DRYDEN,** a grazier who founded the nearby township called Newham because, it is said, he came from Oldham, near Manchester (there are alternative etymologies). The Rock was also the hideout of a notorious bushranger, "**MAD DAN**" MORGAN, whose name is perpetuated at **MORGAN'S LOOKOUT** and the colourful **MORGAN'S BLOOD WATERFALL.** By 1859 the outcrop had become colloquially known as *Hanging Rock*, owing to a supported boulder that overarches the path. In 1886 the State Government purchased the surrounding land as a Recreational Reserve for horse racing and other delights. Global fame came in 1975 as the setting for Peter Weir's celebrated film *Picnic at Hanging Rock*, after Joan Lindsay's mysterious fictional narrative of the same title (1967). The indigenous peoples of this region were the Wurundjeri and Dja Dja Wurrung clans who lived here for 26,000 years, until displaced into reserves by the incoming white land-claimants. The Rock was undoubtedly a sacred place in their culture, comparable with Uluru (see **AYERS ROCK),** but its Aboriginal name, like the picnicking schoolgirls of Lindsay's story, seems to have disappeared entirely from the oral and written records. (MW)

[248] DUKE OF MARLBOROUGH EFFECT

In zoology it was found that a male cricket is both more ardent and more successful in courting females if he has recently won a fight against another male. Further research has demonstrated that this finding extends to other species as well. This effect has been named after **JOHN CHURCHILL, 1ST DUKE OF MARLBOROUGH** (1650-1722), on the strength of the following entry in the diary of the first Duchess of Marlborough: "*His Grace returned from the wars today and pleasured me twice in his top-boots.*" (JP)

[249] DULONG AND PETIT'S LAW

This "law" of 1819 is a generalised observation that all metals have the same relative capability for taking up heat – in the dignified chemspeak of classical thermodynamics: the molar heat capacity of any metal is a constant. The law was once useful for the evaluation of relative atomic masses. However, tests of the law at low temperatures showed it to be invalid. This was first explained by EINSTEIN using PLANCK's quantum theory, and later refined by the formula due to DEBYE. French scientist ALEXIS THÉRÈSE PETIT (1791-1820) was born in Vesoul, and was a colleague of SADI CARNOT with whom he studied heat engines. His co-discoverer PIERRE LOUIS DULONG (1735-1838) was born in Rouen and educated at the École Polytechnique, where he succeeded Petit as Professor of Physics, although most of his contributions were in chemistry. Dulong's chief notoriety is for the discovery in 1812 of that interestingly ferocious explosive, nitrogen trichloride, and for losing an eye and two fingers to it. While investigating the same substance in the same year, HUMPHRY DAVY was temporarily blinded by the explosion – so he prudently handed the research over to his faithful assistant MICHAEL FARADAY. (MW)

[250] DUNBAR'S NUMBER

Oxford anthropologist and evolutionary biologist ROBIN DUNBAR (b. 1947) in a recently-published book entitled *How many friends does one person need?* (2010) examines the degree to which human behaviour is determined by our evolutionary inheritance. A key and obvious element in this inheritance is the fact that Man, like his ape ancestors, is a social animal. We have no choice in the matter. Each of us is born, brought up, and can only survive, as a member of a group. How big a group? asks Dunbar. He concludes that there is a maximum number of people with whom an individual can maintain direct personal relations, and that number is one hundred and fifty. DUNBAR'S NUMBER as it has been christened tells us that anyone claiming, on Facebook or elsewhere, to have more than that number of friends is either deluded or a liar. (What kind of person gets more than a hundred and fifty Christmas cards?) Nowadays, perforce, the majority of our relationships are maintained at a distance – by letter, phone, e-mail or the like. The reason for this is simple: the experience of living as a member of a community, an experience which has been the norm for most people throughout most of our history, has now virtually disappeared from the menu of possible life-styles, at least in "advanced" societies.* This may seem an odd thing to say at a time when the word "community" is bandied about as freely and as frequently as terms like "digital" and "low-fat". A true community, I suggest, may be defined as a group of people who live in a given location, earn their living in the same location, *and know each other*. If this definition, or something close to it, is accepted, then there is a clear corollary: that the number of people within such a community who can know each other, at least by sight, has an upper limit. I would suggest five hundred (or thereabouts). I propose, modestly, to call this JONES'S NUMBER.

* Most surviving exceptions would have to be sought in *closed* communities – monasteries, prisons, Oxbridge colleges, regular army regiments, small islands, ethnic ghettoes, and boys' boarding schools. A prime instrument in the destruction of communities has been, and continues to be, the pernicious planning doctrine which dictates that people shall not work where they live.

[251] DUNCE

One might reasonably wonder how the word "dunce", meaning a hopeless thicko, could be derived from the name of the man once known as the "Subtle Doctor" and who in our own day has been called "the greatest philosopher ever to have taught at Oxford University"*. The damage was done in the 16th century when humanist adepts of the "New Learning", to emphasise their contemptuous rejection of mediaeval scholastic philosophy, took to referring to the followers of the Franciscan theologian **JOHN DUNS SCOTUS** (ca. 1265-1308) as "Dunses" or "Dunsmen". From then on it was downhill all the way for Scotch John, etymologically speaking.

* Anthony Kenny on BBC Radio 4's "In our time" 31.5.07.

[252] DUNLOP TYRE

The pneumatic rubber tyre was the brainchild of Belfast veterinarian **JOHN BOYD DUNLOP** (1840-1921). Originally fitted to bicycles, it enormously increased the comfort of people riding these accursed machines and hence their popularity. It also enormously increased the demand for rubber, a fact which went a long way to promoting the vile and inhuman behaviour of Belgian rubber collectors in the Congo (see, for example, Adam Hochschild *King Leopold's ghost* 1998, *passim*; Tim Jeal *Stanley* 2007, pp. 287, 389). A little later, similar atrocities were being committed in Amazonia. In both instances, the leading whistle-blower was the British consular official, humanitarian, and Irish patriot Roger Casement (1864-1914). Casement was knighted in 1911 and hanged for treason in 1914 after attempting to elicit German support for the Irish rebellion.* (See also **PLIMSOLL** and **VULCANISATION**.)

* See **ZIMMERMANN TELEGRAM**

[253] DURAND LINE

The line marking the boundary between British India and Afghanistan was established in 1893 by a treaty between the Government of India and the ruler of Afghanistan Abdur Rahman Khan. It takes its name from soldier-diplomat **sir MORTIMER DURAND** (1850-1924), the Indian Government's Secretary for Foreign Affairs. In return for Abdur Rahman's agreement, the British agreed to pay him a hefty money subsidy (18 lakhs of rupees per annum) plus arms for his troops and support in case of a foreign invasion of his territory. The British intention was to make of Afghanistan a buffer state against the Russians. (The theory of the buffer state, unfortunately, though it looks fine on the map, is radically unsound since it inevitably involves an attempt to exercise control over the state in question by one or both of the parties it is meant to separate. This is one reason why the Roman Empire kept getting bigger.) Abdur Rahman was delighted with the arrangement since it relieved him of the necessity for governing the totally ungovernable hill tribes ("wily Pathans") who inhabited the mountains on his western border. These then became the responsibility of the British, for whom they were a permanent headache. The solution was to create an "inner frontier" between the tribal areas and the settled areas of the Indus plain. The tribes, divided into five "agencies", were granted virtual autonomy, subject to good behaviour. As the tribesmen were constitutionally unable to observe the latter condition, regular punitive expeditions had to be mounted into the hill country. These constituted a kind of deadly game between the British and the tribesmen, determined and skilful guerrilla warriors who made the invading columns pay dearly for the slightest tactical mistake. On reaching the target village in the offenders' home territory, the troops would dismantle a few houses (which could be rapidly rebuilt since this involved only re-heaping the stones they were made from) and return home, sped on their way by bullets from stolen British rifles, but with honour satisfied on both sides.

E

[254] E. COLI – see ESCHERICHIA

[255] EARL GREY TEA

This fragrant blend of Indian and Ceylonese teas, scented with oil of bergamot, takes its name from the English statesman **CHARLES GREY, 2ND EARL GREY** (1764-1845). As to how the recipe originated or how it came to be associated with Earl Grey, there are various stories, none particularly convincing, since Grey's only connection with the sub-continent was his part in the impeachment of Warren Hastings. It was the firm of Twinings which first put the tea on the market and it remains a leading and very popular Twinings brand to this day. Politically, Grey was an enormously important figure. As MP (1786), Foreign Secretary, Leader of the House of Commons, and Prime Minister (1830), he oversaw the abolition of the African slave trade, the outlawing of slavery in the colonies, and the great Reform Bill of 1832. In between times he found the leisure to father 15 children. For his enlightened legislative measures, we are in his debt. Yet it is with tea that his name remains associated for the mass of people. (RS)

[256] EDDIE THE EAGLE SYNDROME

The phenomenon whereby inglorious British failure is feted in the press and clutched lovingly to the collective bosom of the great British public, who it seems, love a plucky loser as much as the Americans love a winner. The year is 1988, the event the Calgary winter Olympics, and cometh the man in the shape of a dumpy, owlishly-spectacled, 24-year-old plasterer from Cheltenham, **EDDIE** (real name **MICHAEL) EDWARDS** to compete as Britain's only ski jumper. He came 56th out of 57 entrants. (The 57th was disqualified.) At the closing ceremony the President of the Games singled him out for special mention, saying, "At this Games some competitors have won gold, some have broken records, and one has even flown like an eagle." The sleek Finn who came first jumped twice the distance of our Eddie but was not adored and did not become a media sensation. In actual fact, Eddie had made his debut in the 1987 World Championships in Oberstdorf where he had effortlessly secured last place. He went on to consolidate his reputation (and to line his pockets) with a top-50 pop hit "Fly Eddie Fly", and a book *Eddie on the Piste*, and more recently a Hollywood deal was signed to make a feature film with the hero played by actor Martin Freeman. He even, inadvertently, made a more permanent sporting mark when the International Olympic Committee subsequently instituted what is known as the **"EDDIE THE EAGLE RULE"** which requires Olympic hopefuls to finish in the top half of an international competition. (RS)

[257] EDDY KITE

The traditional diamond-shaped kite is aerodynamically unstable, needing a long decorative tail to provide enough drag to keep the shape upright in the air. The **EDDY KITE,** sometimes called the "Eddy-bow", is an advance on this design, based on a Javanese kite, with a bowed cross-strut which imparts a dihedral curvature to the sail, improving stability and obviating the need for a tail, so making it possible to stack a train of these kites for added lift, without entanglement. American **WILLLIAM ABNER EDDY** (1850-1909) was born in New York City and started out as an accountant and journalist in New Jersey, but his inventive streak eventually took over. In 1894 he introduced his new kite design to the U.S. Weather Bureau's Blue Hill Meteorological Observatory, south of Boston. For several years the Bureau used Eddy's kite trains to lift recording instruments to several thousand feet and obtain hitherto inaccessible meteorological data. In 1895 with a kite-borne camera Eddy made the first aerial photograph in the Americas. In 1910, the year following his death, meteorologists at Mount Weather, Virginia, established an altitude record of 23,385 feet (7128 m) with a train of ten Eddy kites. (MW)

[258] EGGS BENEDICT

Not a Damon Runyon character (see **CHATEAUBRIAND STEAK**) but a delicious snack composed of a poached egg (or two) and a slice of grilled ham or bacon on half an English muffin and topped with hollandaise sauce. The origins of the dish, and of its name, are disputed. The contestants include **LEMUEL BENEDICT**, an American stockbroker, **Commodore E.C. BENEDICT**, banker and yachtsman, and a **Mrs. LE GRAND BENEDICT**, a New York socialite. All these 20th-century claims are rendered suspect by the fact that Mrs Beeton in her *Household Management* of 1861 apparently refers to as "benedict" any dish involving hollandaise sauce.

[259] EHRLICH'S "MAGIC BULLET"

PAUL EHRLICH (1854-1915) was a German bacteriologist, born of Jewish family at Strehlen in (then) Prussian Silesia. After studying at Leipzig, he joined the pioneer bacteriologist, Professor Robert Koch, at the Berlin Institute for Infectious Diseases in 1891, where he contributed to the theory of immunology. Following a move to Frankfurt in 1899, at the Royal Institute of Experimental Therapy he undertook a programme of screening many new compounds, prepared by chemist Alfred Bertheim, for antimicrobial activity. Attention was directed particularly towards finding an organo-arsenical compound of diminished toxicity as treatment for the scourge of syphilis. After 606 trials with syphilitic rabbits, conducted by his assistant Sahachiro Hata, they discovered the first effective agent in 1909: it was called arsphenamine, but its precise chemical structure was only elucidated in 2005. At the time, it was better known as "Compound 606" or "EHRLICH'S MAGIC BULLET", because it selectively targeted the causative syphilis micro-organism *Treponema pallidum*. By 1910 the remedy was being manufactured commercially by Hoechst. Marketed as "Salvarsan" specifically for treating syphilis, it became the most widely prescribed drug in the world, despite some serious side-effects, until supplanted by penicillin in 1940. Ehrlich is regarded as the originator of chemotherapy and a founder of the science of antibiotics, and was jointly awarded the NOBEL PRIZE for medicine in 1908. (MW)

[260] EHUX

or **Emiliania huxleyi**, is the LINNAEAN BINOMIAL of Planet Earth's favorite species of *phytoplankton*. It's also possibly the only micro-organism significant enough to enjoy its own dedicated homepage (http://www.soes.soton.ac.uk/staff/tt/) EHUX is a single-celled, ocean-dwelling photosynthesizing plant, a mere 6 micrometers across, so is barely visible under an optical microscope. The advent of electron microscopy in the 1950s revealed that she (for surely – even given the limitations of asexual reproduction – it ought to be a "she") decorates her exterior with beautiful jewel-like calcareous "flowers", called *coccoliths*, whose biological function is not fully understood, but which largely constitute the White Cliffs of Dover, among other geological structures. EHUX is the only earthly creature whose progress can be watched from space, as her pale turquoise algal blooms cover areas of as much as 100,000 square kilometers of our seas. The present global importance of EHUX is at least threefold (see GAIA HYPOTHESIS): her shiny white calcite embellishments raise the albedo of the oceans, diminishing the degree of insolation; they sequester atmospheric carbon dioxide as calcium carbonate, which falls to the seabed; and she provides an abundance of nourishment at the base of the marine foodchain. The genus honours Italian-American scientist CESARE EMILIANI (1922-1995), who was born in Bologna and studied geology at the University there, founding the science of palaeoceanography. In 1948 he relocated to the University of Chicago where he established the cyclic nature of the Ice Ages. In 1957 his interest in *foraminifera* took him to the University of Miami's Institute of Marine Science, where he became Chairman of the division of Geology and Geophysics.* The species also honours Victorian biologist THOMAS HENRY HUXLEY (1825-1895), famously known as "Darwin's bulldog" for preferring to be descended from an ape rather than a dishonest bishop. Huxley was born in Ealing, Middlesex, studied medicine at Charing Cross Hospital and entered the Royal Navy medical service as assistant surgeon – in the Maturin mould (see ADANSONIA). On an expedition to the South

Seas, 1846-50, he collected marine specimens, especially plankton, including EHUX. He became Professor of natural history at the Royal School of Mines (1854-1885), an influential teacher and philosophical writer, who coined the word "agnostic". (MW)

* EMILIANI, something of a Renaissance man, also proposed the calendar modification known as the Holocene Era (HE), obtained by adding 10,000 to the year AD, or subtracting the year BC from 10,001, so avoiding religious prejudices, resolving the anomaly of there being no year 0, and making year dating altogether more sensible.

[261] EIFFEL TOWER

The Tower is the work of French engineer GUSTAVE EIFFEL (1832-1923). It was built in two years (1887-1889) for the Paris Universal Exhibition in the latter year. Structural engineers regard it as an iconic example of trellis-beam construction, in which Eiffel specialised, having already employed this technique in the design of numerous bridges and viaducts. In later life Eiffel became interested in aerodynamics and hence has a place in the early history of aviation. From an aesthetic point of view and seen through the eyes of an inhabitant of Haussmann's Paris, Eiffel's structure must have looked wildly out of place. Indeed, it is hard to imagine any location where it wouldn't look out of place. The same might be said of London's ludicrous and tragic flirtation with avant-garde architecture – The Gherkin, cruelly but accurately described as "a yurt with an erection". But one would have no difficulty in imagining what a Freudian analyst (if there still are such people) would have to say about the men behind either structure: *acute penis anxiety*. The tower is 300 metres in height, not counting the TV and radio aerials which add a further 20 metres. The Gherkin is only 180 metres – nah! Eiffel's own rivet-by-rivet account of the tower's design and construction, *La tour de trois cent mètres*, published in a limited edition of 500 copies in 1900, is now available as a reprint.

[262] EINSTEIN

The most famous name in science is attached to several phenomena and theories – some of them rather difficult, but the best-known eponyms are a physical unit and a chemical element. The EINSTEIN unit is a measure of light energy (see PLANCK), useful in photochemistry; specifically the energy associated with a mole of photons (see AVOGADRO'S NUMBER). A 100 watt light bulb emits one einstein in about 33 hours. EINSTEINIUM is yet another of the non-natural radioactive elements, atomic number 99, symbol Es, discovered by GHIORSO in the debris from the first hydrogen bomb test (see FERMIUM). History does not record Einstein's reaction at being thus immortalised, but when he heard in 1945 of the use of the first atomic bomb, the possibility of which he had drawn to the notice of President Roosevelt in 1939, he is reputed to have said, "If I had known, I would have been a locksmith." **ALBERT EINSTEIN** (1879-1955) was born in Ulm, Germany, of Jewish parentage. He showed a prodigious interest in mathematics and science, but his passage through the educational system was by no means smooth and orthodox. He renounced his German nationality in 1896, being granted Swiss citizenship in 1901, which he retained throughout his life – despite re-assuming German nationality during 1914-33, and becoming a US citizen in 1940. After graduation from the ETH, Zurich in 1901, he eventually found employment at the Swiss Patent Office, Berne. Academic appointments were slow to arrive, but from 1908 on, he held posts at the universities of Berne, Zurich, Prague, Berlin and Leiden, before moving to the Institute for Advanced Study, Princeton, USA in 1934. While still a Patent Examiner, 1905 was Einstein's *Annus Mirabilis*, in which he produced his theory of special relativity, proved the equivalence of matter and energy encapsulated in the iconic equation $E = mc^2$, as well as explaining the theory of **BROWNIAN MOTION** and of the photoelectric effect – any one of which would have sufficed an ordinary mortal for a **NOBEL PRIZE**. He was awarded only one, however, in 1921 for physics, citing the photoelectric effect. Acknowledged as the greatest conceptual thinker in the entire history of science, his later contributions included: the theory of general relativity (1916), the branch of statistical mechanics known as **BOSE-EINSTEIN STATISTICS** (see also **BOSON**), an unsuccessful unified field theory (1950), and light amplification by the stimulated emission of radiation (better known today by the acronym LASER). He is also remembered for his support for the Zionist movement and the foundation of the State of Israel (whose presidency he regretfully declined), and the battle for civil rights in the USA during the McCarthy era. (MW)

[263] EISENSTEIN MONTAGE

SERGEI MIKHAILOVICH EISENSTEIN, (1898–1948) was the pioneering film director and theoretician responsible for the filmic innovation of **MONTAGE**: the skilful cutting and re-cutting to achieve mounting impressionistic effects, as in the famous Odessa steps sequence of the silent film *Battleship Potemkin* (1925). This rapid editing, where images are cut, spliced and juxtaposed in a particular way in order to obtain a desired narrative, or purely aesthetic effect, allowed him to make complex statements visually rather than through dialogue. Another of his films in which he demonstrated the same technique was *October* (1928), in which the raising of a drawbridge was composed of hundreds of shots edited according to his precise instructions. Another of his stylistic innovations was his substitution of the group or crowd for the traditional hero in conformity with strict Marxist-Leninist ideological guidelines, glorifying the Revolution of 1917. Under Stalin's rule he encountered constant difficulties until the time of his death in 1948. In the early 1940s, he was commissioned to direct a three-film epic, *Ivan the Terrible*. The first instalment of 1944 was a critical and commercial success, but the second, *The Boyar's Plot* completed in 1946 (clearly alluding to the Stalin regime), was banned and not shown in Russia until 1957. Sadly, footage from the third film was destroyed. Eisenstein began his creative career as an architect and engineer, but became interested in the theatre and worked as a scene designer and stage director (1920). He began his film career in 1924 with *Strike*, which demonstrates an already well-developed political and aesthetic style. Today his legacy persists and he is viewed as one of the most influential creators of cinematic form despite having completed only six films. (RS)

[264] EKMAN LAYER

The great Norwegian explorer FRIDTJOF WEDEL-JARLSBERG NANSEN (1861-1930)* made the observation that in the northern hemisphere icebergs drift on a course 20-40° to the *right* of the prevailing wind direction. This was first explained by Swedish physicist, turned oceanographer, VAGN WALFRID EKMAN (1874-1954), who was born in Stockholm, studied physics at Uppsala and became professor of mechanics and mathematical physics at the University of Lund from 1910-1939. In his doctoral thesis of 1902, he investigated the fluid mechanics of boundary layers, such as that of of the upper ocean where it meets the atmosphere; he showed mathematically that the interacting forces of wind pressure, friction due to turbulent drag, and the CORIOLIS EFFECT result in the water flow being stratified in layers called EKMAN LAYERS, and as the water layers go deeper the rightward deflection of the direction of flow generates an EKMAN SPIRAL. Experimental confirmation of some details of this hypothesis has proved difficult. (MW)

*There are several islands and mountains named after NANSEN – mostly in the Arctic.

[265] ELDORADO

While New England was being invaded by English Puritans looking for a place to practice their own particular brand of religious intolerance free from government interference, Central and South America were being invaded by impecunious Spaniards looking to get rich without working.* In the latter case, gold was the lure. Gold hunger was fuelled by stories of stunningly auriferous locations in South America where the stuff was simply to be had for the taking by anyone owning a sack to collect it in (hence "Rio de Oro", for example). Among these stories, none was more persistent or more fatally attractive than that of the fabulous "Gilded Man" (*El Dorado* in Spanish). As befits any myth, the origins of the story are not recoverable. In its generally accepted form it concerned the king or high priest of a South American tribe called the Musica who was subjected to a yearly ceremonial coating in gold dust. This supposedly took place on a raft in a lake near a city called Manoa. As part of the ritual, raft-loads of gold ornaments were thrown into the lake at the same time. Both Manoa and its lake have so far eluded discovery despite numerous expeditions led by Spanish explorers who undertook desperate and herculean itineraries over mountains and through jungles in search of an easy living. These include the journeys of Diego de Ordaz (1531), whose lieutenant Martinez claimed actually to have met the Gilded Man on a previous journey; Orellana (1540); the German Philip Von Hutten (1541-45); Ursua and Aguirre (1560); and Jimenez de Quesada (1569). Raleigh, who made two expeditions (1585, 1616) to Guiana with gold in mind, claimed to have located Manoa in or on a lake called Parima, later proved by HUMBOLDT not to exist. The fact that none of these heroes earned a penny by their exertions (Hutten was beheaded by the Spanish for his pains, Raleigh by his own countrymen) ought to have negated the later use of the term ELDORADO to signify any place where wealth may be acquired rapidly and without effort. That it hasn't might be read as teaching us something about the persistence of illusion.

* The degree to which the contrasting motivations and aspirations of South- and North-American settlers have influenced the present condition (social, political, cultural, economic) of their respective regions must be a fruitful field of study.

[266] ELGIN MARBLES

THOMAS BRUCE, 7TH EARL OF ELGIN (1766-1841), British soldier, diplomat, and art-collector was envoy extraordinary to the Sublime Porte between 1799 and 1803. It was during his tour of duty in Constantinople that he organised the removal from the Parthenon at Athens the sculptured frieze which bears his name. The marbles were purchased for the nation in 1816 at a cost of £36,000 (though their acquisition and removal had cost Elgin in the region of £50,000) and they now reside in the British Museum, a treasured national possession. Both at the time and since, the removal of the sculptures was regarded by some as vandalism. In our own day, Britain has been under heavy moral pressure from the Greeks to return the marbles to their rightful home. This pressure, even when exerted by the formidable Melina Mercouri in a starring role as Greek Minister of Culture, has so far been resisted. This is no place to argue the rights and wrongs of Elgin's action or the Greeks' claim for restitution. It must be said, however, that Elgin, recognising the artistic and historic value of the sculptures, and believing, with very good reason, that under Turkish custodianship their future was by no means secure, saw his act as a rescue operation. To vindicate himself, he published a pamphlet in 1810 entitled *Memorandum on the subject of the Earl of Elgin's pursuits in Greece.*

[267] EÖTVÖS EXPERIMENT

The mass of a body – the amount of matter in it – is manifested in two obvious ways: first, by gravitational attraction to planet Earth (usually, unless you happen to be an astronaut) – this is what we commonly call "weight"; and second, by its resistance to a force tending to set it in motion, which is called its "inertial mass". That these two aspects of mass must be identical was first argued by GALILEO and supported, roughly, by his famous experiment of dropping weights from the Leaning Tower of Pisa. Since then there have been constantly more refined tests of the hypothesis, by NEWTON and others. LORÁND EÖTVÖS, BARON DE VASAROSNAMENY (1848-1919) was born a Hungarian nobleman, the son of statesman and novelist, Baron Joseph Eötvös (1813-1871). He studied at Heidelberg and Königsberg and became professor of physics at Budapest. His chief work, first published in 1890, was to confirm the principle of equivalence between gravitational and inertial mass to a precision of 1 part in 20 million in the EÖTVÖS EXPERIMENT using a sensitive torsion instrument known as an EÖTVÖS BALANCE. Later, his students and successors improved this precision to 1 part in 100 billion. The *equivalence principle* became of central importance to EINSTEIN'S theory of general relativity. The EÖTVÖS EFFECT is a correction to gravitational measurements made on board a ship due to its motion relative to the Earth (see CORIOLIS EFFECT). The name EÖTVÖS is also given to a non-SI unit (symbol E) of gravitational gradient. (MW)

[268] EPSTEIN-BARR VIRUS
The virus was discovered in 1964 by Sir MICHAEL EPSTEIN (b. 1921) assisted by YVONNE BARR (b. 1932). It belongs to the family of herpes viruses. Most adults are infected with it and suffer no ill-effects, but when it is roused from its normal dormancy, so to speak, it can cause problems ranging from mononucleosis (glandular fever) to a number of cancers including Burkitt's lymphoma. Its carcinogenic properties derive from its ability to trigger the rapid multiplication of certain cells and, paradoxically, it is this characteristic of the virus which makes it invaluable in genetics research. It has been found that when large amounts of DNA are required for laboratory work, the white blood cells known as B-lymphocytes from a small amount of blood, if deliberately infected with Epstein-Barr, will multiply indefinitely, a procedure known as "immortalising".*

* Luigi Lucca Cavalli-Sforza *Genes, people and languages* 2000 (p. 68).

[269] ERLENMEYER FLASK
This ubiquitous item of chemical lab glassware, otherwise known self-descriptively as a conical flask, has become an icon. As UCL chemist Dr Andrea Sella explains: "Hold one of them up while wearing a lab coat and you are The Scientist. Do the same wearing blue jeans and a T-shirt and you'll be arrested as a crystal meth*

maker." This innocent glass vessel is such a potent enabler of illegal narcotics manufacture, allegedly, that in Texas its unauthorised purchase is forbidden making conical flasks harder to get hold of than Uzi sub-machine guns or rocket-propelled grenade launchers. **RICHARD AUGUST CARL EMIL ERLENMEYER** (1825-1909), born the son of a pastor in Wiesbaden, intended to become a doctor, but, like his contemporary and colleague-to-be, **AUGUST KEKULÉ**, was switched on to chemistry by the lectures of **LIEBIG** at Giessen, so he compromised for some years as a pharmacist. He worked for **BUNSEN** at Heidelberg, inventing his flask in 1861. He was Professor at Munich Polytechnic 1868-1883, and is also remembered for proposing the structural formula for naphthalene, and having supervised the celebrated composer-chemist, Borodin. (MW)

* Methamphetamine: the psychostimulant, and addictive "recreational" drug.

[270] ERSKINE MAY

The name of **THOMAS ERSKINE MAY** (1815-1886) has come to stand for the ultimate authority on Parliamentary practice and procedure. May was a lawyer who became assistant librarian to the House of Commons in 1831 and Clerk to the House of Commons in 1871, retaining the latter post until shortly before his death. His *Practical Treatise on the Law, Privileges, Proceedings and Usage of Parliament* was first published in 1844 and, with frequent updatings, has gone through 22 editions since. May was knighted in 1866, made a Privy Councillor in 1885, and in 1886, the year of his death, created 1st Baron Farnborough.

[271] ESAKI DIODE – see SCHRÖDINGER'S CAT

[272] ESCALLONIA

Genus of South American shrubs and small trees (50-60 species, mostly evergreen). It was named by the Spanish botanist José Celastino Mutis (1732-1808) after his student and co-worker **ANTONIO ESCALLÓN Y FLOREZ** (1739-1819), who travelled and collected plants in Colombia. In Britain certain species of **ESCALLONIA** able to tolerate salt-laden winds are favoured as hedging plants in seaside locations.

[273] ESCHERICHIA

The study of disease-causing organisms, unlike the study of plants or animals, for example, carries the risk of the researcher's name being attached to something disgusting (*cf.* **YERSINIA, LISTERIA**). Such was the fate of the German physician **THEODOR ESCHERICH** (1857-1911) who discovered the genus of rod-like bacteria which bears his name lurking in the guts of a variety of creatures including man. And though not all its member species are pathogenic (some are "friendly"), that named **E. COLI** is inextricably linked in the public's mind with the concept of diarrhoea. However, on the plus side, medical insulin, which used to be extracted from the pancreas of pigs, can now be produced from a genetically-engineered strain of *E. Coli.* As a paediatrician, Escherich devoted his life to the improvement of children's health and was Director from 1902 of a children's hospital in Vienna built according to his own designs. In the field of microbiology, the *E. coli* bacillus, having been intensively studied, is widely used as a research tool, the micro-equivalent of the fruit-fly, the laboratory rat or the planaria worm.

[274] ESCHSCHOLTZIA

JOHANN FRIEDRICH VON ESCHSCHOLTZ (1793-1834) was born at Dorpat in what was then Russia and now is Tartu in Estonia. He joined, as physician and naturalist, the Russian North Pacific exploring expedition of 1815-1818 led by Otto von Kotzebue. In addition to the plant named after him, *Eschscholtzia californica* or California Poppy, his name was attached to a bay off Kotzebue Sound in Alaska, and to what has since become the Bikini atoll.

[275] EUCLIDEAN GEOMETRY

In this muddled world, there is no better demonstration of the triumph of logic than **EUCLID**: starting from a few simple, self-evident truths about points, lines and circles, he derives geometrical theorems that are far from obvious, and even beautiful. Geometry is one of the seven Liberal Arts of classical antiquity, along with arithmetic, astronomy and music, (the *quadrivium*), and grammar, rhetoric, and logic (the *trivium*), which collectively formed the cornerstones of enlightened pedagogy for a millennium. We know little of the Greek mathematician **EUCLEIDES OF ALEXANDRIA** (ca. 330-275 BC) except that he taught at **PLATO'S** Academy in Alexandria. His famous text *Elementorum Geometricorum* has run through more than 2000 editions since it was first printed in 1462 making him in Isaac Asimov's words "the most successful textbook writer of all time". It builds up a logical system in which theorems are proved from axioms or postulates. Informally speaking, Euclid's five postulates are: (1) you can join any two points by a straight line, and (2) extend it, and (3) make circles with the line as radius. (4) Right angles are all the same. (5) Parallel lines never cross. From these axioms, in the course of 13 "books", **EUCLID** presents us with 465 theorems, such as that attributed to **PYTHAGORAS**. It is an essential feature that all **EUCLID'S** geometrical figures can be constructed with only an uncalibrated straight edge and a pair of compasses. His *tour de force* at the conclusion of the work is the construction of that elegant solid, the regular dodecahedron (see **PLATONIC SOLIDS**). Over the years, axiom (5), "the parallel postulate", has aroused misgivings, because no-one has succeeded in deriving it from the other four. It was discovered in the 19th century that it can be replaced by alternative assumptions, to generate perfectly self-consistent systems of **NON-EUCLIDEAN GEOMETRY** in spaces classified by **KLEIN** as hyperbolic and elliptical, rather than the parabolic **EUCLIDEAN SPACE**; to these systems are attached the names of the Hungarian mathematician, János Bolyai (1802-1860), the Russian, Nikolai Ivanovitch Lobachevsky (1792-1856), and the German, Georg Friedrich Bernhard Riemann (1826-1866). Their extensions of geometrical concepts have proved essential to **EINSTEIN'S** theory of general relativity. (MW)

[276] EULER-BERNOUILLI THEOREM

Swiss mathematician **LEONARD EULER**. (1707-1783) published over 800 papers in the course of his working life. His name is attached to many important discoveries. An early, simple, but important example was the theory of bending of bars in which his name is joined to that of his friend and mentor **DANIEL BERNOUILLI** (1700-1782), a member of a regular dynasty of mathematical prodigies. This theory is used today to calculate the stresses and deflections in beams. He further developed this theory to predict the critical buckling load of slender beams under compression. He was the father of thirteen children only five of whom survived infancy. He stated that some of the most important of the huge number of his mathematical insights came to him when he was dandling his children on his knee. There was hardly a field of mathematics he did not develop, including a proof that the famous problem of the "Königsberg Bridges" was actually insoluble, and by showing why, Euler advanced the theory of Topology. In 1727 Bernouilli persuaded Euler to join him in Russia where Euler spent most of the rest of his working life and where he lost the sight of an eye while making observations of the sun.* Later in life he went completely blind but continued to work. He died in St. Petersburg. At the moment of his death he is reported to have said, " I Die!" (GB)

* Another researcher who lost an eye to science was R.W. Bunsen (see **BUNSEN BURNER**)

[277] EUPHUISM

Affected literary style recalling that of **JOHN LYLY** (?1554-1606), English scholar and playwright, who in 1579 published a proto-novel entitled *Euphues, or the anatomy of wit*, followed in 1580 by a second part *Euphues and his England* – Euphues being the name of the eponymous hero, a young Greek gentleman. Lyly's style has been called "peculiar" (*Oxford Companion to English Literature*, ed. Margaret Drabble 1985), by which we may understand both "strange" and "wildly idiosyncratic". *Euphues* enjoyed considerable success in its day. It was felt in fashionable circles that Lyly's pompous and fanciful diction – notably a manic over-use of antithesis – had brought a much-needed refinement to the coarse English vernacular. But since today there are probably not six people alive in this country who have actually read *Euphues* (and the present writer is not one of them), it is conceivable that the word "EUPHUISM" has only survived so that bookish types can give themselves a pat on the back for knowing the difference between that and "euphemism".

F

[278] FABIAN TACTICS

The term describes a strategy of refusing to meet an opponent head-on until one is certain of being able to beat him. It takes its name from the Roman general known to history as **FABIUS "CUNCTATOR"** ("the Delayer"), full name **QUINTUS MAXIMUS VERRUCOSUS FABIUS** (275-203 BC). When Hannibal invaded Italy in 217 BC, he successively annihilated three Roman armies at the battles of the River Trebia, Lake Trasimene, and Cannae – the last of these a text-book operation in which the weaker side surrounded and utterly destroyed a numerically superior opponent, and one which every general for the next two thousand years has aspired to emulate, though none has so far succeeded. The Romans doggedly put together yet another army under the command of Fabius, who was given dictatorial powers. He set about wearing Hannibal down without risking a major engagement, a strategy which was ultimately successful though the campaign dragged on for nearly fifteen years, up and down the Italian peninsula, ending only when Hannibal was recalled to Carthage. Hannibal was finally beaten on his own ground in North Africa by the Roman general Scipio at the decisive battle of Zama in 202 BC. The tactic of continually retreating before a pursuing enemy and then suddenly turning on one's pursuers (as practiced, for example, by Sam Houston and his Texans in 1836, or by the great Stonewall Jackson in the Shenandoah Valley campaign of 1862) does not exactly qualify for the term "Fabian" but deserves a name of its own. On the other hand, the **FABIAN SOCIETY**, a left-leaning but non-Marxist political organisation founded in 1884 by Beatrice and Sidney Webb and which included George Bernard Shaw and H.G. Wells among its members, was well-named. Its aim was to promote peaceful and gradual reform rather than bloody revolution and to employ tactics which consciously avoided an all-or-nothing confrontation.* The Fabian Society is affiliated to the Labour Party and traditionally has been an intellectual powerhouse of left-wing thought in this country. Though where it stands in the current situation of a Labour Party which has tacitly abandoned the last shreds of its socialist ideology and openly committed itself to the policies of Mrs. Thatcher is a bit of a puzzle.

* The drawbacks of a revolutionary, as opposed to a gradualist, approach to reform were neatly summarised by the Polish historian Count Jan Potocki (1761-1815), writing at the time of the French Revolution: "*Il pourrait arriver qu'après s'être donné bien de la peine pour établir un nouvel ordre des choses, les hommes destinés à être heureux dans ce nouvel ordre, seront au contraire vivement frappés de ses inconvénients et faiblement de ses avantages, et ne songeront qu'à le renverser, car tel est l'esprit humain.*"

[279] FAHRENHEIT TEMPERATURE SCALE

This scale was used in the English-speaking countries until the 1970s, and is still preferred as the measure of temperature by the population of the USA, while everyone else in the world has now adopted the metric system scale due to CELSIUS, which is also the scientific scale. DANIEL GABRIEL FAHRENHEIT (1686-1736) was a German physicist and instrument maker born in Danzig (now Gdansk in Poland), who worked in Holland for most of his life. He seems to have got the idea of thermometry from Danish astronomer, Ole Christensen Rømer (1644-1710), who in 1701 had created one of the first thermometers, using red wine as the operating liquid, and had defined a temperature scale with a range from 0, for an ice-salt mixture, to 60 degrees for the boiling point of water. On this scale the melting point of ice fell inconveniently at 7.5 degrees Rømer. In 1709, Fahrenheit made an alcohol thermometer, and in 1714, one with mercury in glass as the thermometric liquid. He put forward his "improved" temperature scale in 1724, in the *Philosophical Transactions of the Royal Society*. Like Rømer, he wanted to avoid negative temperatures, so he took his 0 °F point as the lowest temperature he could achieve – again, that of an ice-salt mixture; but he chose for his upper point, defined as 96 °F for numerical convenience (12x8), the temperature of a healthy adult human body, as sampled at the armpit (we are not told whose). Subsequently Fahrenheit had to modify this average body temperature to 98.6 °F to achieve a more consistent scale, on which ice melts at exactly 32 °F and water boils at 212 °F. Later users take these as the defining lower and upper fixed points, in preference to armpits. US thermodynamicists found that absolute zero falls inconveniently at -491.67 °F, so have made use of an absolute scale proposed in 1859 by William John Macquorn Rankine (1820-1872), on which absolute zero is 0 degrees Rankine, and ice melts at 491.67 degrees Rankine. See also CELSIUS, KELVIN and RÉAUMUR. (Note: *Fahrenheit 451*, the title of a 1953 book by science fiction writer Ray Bradbury, is the temperature at whch paper spontaneously ignites. Bradbury's book became a Hollywood film in 1966.) (MW)

[280] FALKLAND ISLANDS

The names of islands, particularly those situated in distant parts of the world's oceans, can be subject to confusion thanks to the uncertainty of early mariners as to their true position (see HARRISON'S CHRONOMETERS). In the case of the Falkland Islands the confusion arises from another source – the number of times they have been discovered, claimed, or settled. They were probably first sighted in 1592 by John Davis, sailing as part of Cavendish's second and abortive circumnavigation, but he departed without naming or claiming the islands. Next was the Dutchman Sebald de Weert of the Dutch East India Co. in 1598, who modestly named them Sebald Islands. Following him in 1690 came John Strong in

His Majesty's ship *Welfare*. He named the strait between the two main islands Falkland Sound in honour of **ANTHONY CARY, 5TH VISCOUNT FALKLAND**, Commissioner of the Admiralty and later First Sea Lord. This later became the name favoured by the British for the whole group. However, in 1764 a French flotilla under **DE BOUGAINVILLE** (see **BOUGAINVILLEA**) arrived and planted the islands' first settlement, naming them Iles Malouines (Islas Malvinas in Spanish) after his home port of St. Malo. The complex story of the islands' discoverers, visitors and settlers is exhaustively covered by Ricardo Caillet-Bois in his scholarly tome *Las Islas Malvinas* (2nd ed. Buenos Aires 1952).

[281] FARADAY

The abundance of entries under his name is a testament to the scientific contributions of this outstanding experimentalist of all time. **MICHAEL FARADAY** (1791-1867) was born in London into a blacksmith's family of ten children. He served a seven-year apprenticeship to a bookbinder, during which time he appears to have educated himself quite effectively, although mathematics remained inaccessible to him. In 1813 he was appointed as scientific assistant to **SIR HUMPHRY DAVY**, at the Royal Institution, whom he succeeded as Fullerian Professor of Chemistry in 1827, a chair created for him by John "Mad Jack" Fuller (1757-1834).* Faraday discovered electromagnetic induction, and is therefore the spiritual father of every electric motor and dynamo on the planet. Among chemical innovations, he isolated benzene (see **KEKULÉ**), invented the **BUNSEN BURNER**, and identified **PURPLE OF CASSIUS** as colloidal gold. A **FARADAY CAGE** is a conducting mesh enclosing an electrically-isolated, field-free space, offering protection against high-voltage discharges. **FARADAY'S LAWS** quantify the phenomena of electrochemical decomposition, or electrolysis, and lead to a value for the **FARADAY CONSTANT**, a physico-chemical unit, the electric charge on a mole (*i.e* an **AVOGADRO'S NUMBER**) of electrons: *viz.* 96,487 **COULOMBS**. The **FARAD** is another eponymous physical unit, the SI measure of electrical capacitance. The **FARADAY EFFECT** – otherwise known as magneto-optical rotation – is a profoundly important demonstration that light has a magnetic component. The **FARADAY SOCIETY** was a learned body, founded in 1903, dedicated to the study of electrochemistry; it merged in 1980 with the Royal Society of Chemistry. Faraday refused a knighthood and twice declined the Presidency of the Royal Society. His **SANDEMANIAN** religious principles may have influenced these decisions, in a way that they never influenced his science. But he might have been dismayed to foresee his ultimate celebration – on the *verso* of the English £20 note. (MW)

* Squire of Brightling in Sussex, remembered as a philanthropist and as a builder of follies. In addition to his patronage of Faraday, he encouraged **J.M.W. TURNER**, from whom he bought and commissioned numerous paintings.

[282] FARMER'S REDUCER

This is a solution sometimes applied in the processing of black and white silver photographs of the traditional kind, in order to dissolve some of the silver image: either to reduce the density of an overexposed negative, or to brighten the highlights of a positive print. In the pre-digital era, no darkroom could be without **FARMER'S REDUCER** which consists of a dilute mixture of potassium ferricyanide and sodium thiosulphate ("hypo"). It was devised in 1883 by **ERNEST HOWARD FARMER** (1856-1944) second son of Brighton chemist and daguerreotypist, Robert Farmer (1823-1859). Ernest became the first Head of Photography at Regent Street Polytechnic. (MW)

[283] FEA'S MUNTJAC

The muntjac sub-family of deer (*Cervidae*) comprises ten species, all native to China and South-East Asia and nearly all under threat from hunting and the ongoing destruction of their forest habitat. *Muntiacus feae* is one of the rarer species of these miniature deer, otherwise known as barking deer. It is found in China, Laos and Burma. Its name remembers the Turin-born Italian naturalist and explorer **LEONARDO FEA** (1852-1903), who discovered it in Burma in 1885. Fea's travels also took him to West Africa and to the Cape Verde Islands, and his collections, now housed at the museum in Genoa for which he worked, include other species named after him: a petrel (*Pterodroma feae*), a thrush (*Turdus feae*), a viper (*Azemiops feae*), and **FEA'S TREE-RAT**, native to China and rejoicing in the name *Chiromyscus chiropus*. Muntjac enjoy the singular advantage – if it is an advantage – of being able to breed all the year round, rather than being confined like other deer to a single annual rut. On an etymological note, the word "muntjac" is adopted from Sundanese, an Indonesian language with some 26 million speakers. (See also **REEVES' MUNTJAC**)

[284] FEDORA

Type of hat which takes its name from the eponymous heroine of an 1883 play by the French dramatist Victorien Sardou (1831-1908), who specialised in sumptuously-staged historical romances with wildly improbable plots. The hat in question is made of soft felt, with the crown pinched to a point in front and with a dent running front-to-back. The brim should be worn pulled down at the front. In Hollywood films of the 30's and 40's the fedora became, along with a belted raincoat and a dangling cigarette, virtually a badge of office for private eyes and gat-toting gangsters. In England, the same style of hat is known as a **TRILBY**. By a strange coincidence, this too celebrates the heroine of an eponymous work of literature – a novel published in 1894 by the splendidly-named British writer and artist George Louis Palmella Bussom Du Maurier.

[285] FEERTYPE

A method of photographic printing using a diazonium salt, *i.e.* a reactive, light-sensitive organo-nitrogen compound that can be used to form a whole range of possible azo-dyes (highly-coloured stable substances) as the image. The FEERTYPE is also known under the proprietory names Diazotype, or Ozalid. The process was patented in 1889 by German chemist DR ADOLF FEER who took his doctorate in Munich in 1886 and founded a printing company in Brombach. (MW)

[286] FEHLING'S SOLUTION

A chemical reagent used for the detection and quantitative analysis of sugars. Copper(II) sulphate, Rochelle salt (sodium potassium tartrate) and alkali (sodium hydroxide) are mixed to give a blue solution of a copper(II) tartrate complex. Reducing sugars such as glucose, and other aldehydic substances, react with this to form a characteristic red precipitate of copper(I) oxide. The test was used on urine for the detection of diabetes. HERMANN VON FEHLING (1812-1885) was a German chemist born in Lübeck, trained at Heidelberg and Giessen under JUSTUS VON LIEBIG, and became professor at Stuttgart Polytechnic in 1839. (MW)

[287] FENDER STRATOCASTER

Every "axe"-wielder of the rock generation aspired to ownership of a guitar from the Fender Electric Instrument Manufacturing Company founded by CLARENCE LEONIDAS FENDER (1909-1991). Fender was not the first to manufacture electric guitars but he was the most successful and he was the one to create a series of versatile solid-body, good-looking and alluring electric guitars. It was in 1946 that he brought to the market the first mass-produced Spanish-style electric guitar first called the Broadcaster and then renamed the Telecaster. This instant hit was based on a design supplied by his friend Merle Travis. In 1953 Fender designed an all-new solid-body guitar with a contoured shape, 3 pick-ups and a revolutionary tremolo unit that would "bend" strings. In 1954 it was unleashed on an unsuspecting sleepy 1950's world to define the sound of popular music for the next 50 years. The Fender Stratocaster was first popularised by Buddy Holly and his gravestone in Lubbock Texas features the instrument. Later it was taken up by West Coast surfer groups such as The Beach Boys and the Ventures in lurid colour choices such as sunburst. In Britain it was Hank Marvin of The Shadows who introduced the guitar to a new young audience and to a new generation of aspiring musicians. Fender had planned to stop production of the Strat at the end of the 1960's until the extraordinary Jimi Hendrix came along and took the instrument to new heights of sonic abandonment. (RS)

[288] FERMAT'S LAST THEOREM

PIERRE DE FERMAT (1601-1665) was a brilliant and fecund, though not a professional mathematician (he was a local government functionary in Toulouse), who had the annoying habit of announcing his results without bothering to give proofs or show workings, or even of not announcing them at all. He is remembered, among many other things, for the discovery by his son of a note in the margin of Diophantis' *Arithmetica* which stated that he had discovered a truly remarkable proof to a problem he was working on but which the margin of the book was too small to contain. The problem, which came to be known as Fermat's Last Theorem, was an extension of PYTHAGORAS' famous theorem which states that for a right-angled triangle the sum of the squares of the two smaller sides adds up to the square of the hypotenuse. Extending the concept of a right-angled triangle to higher dimensions, he stated that *the answer to the question whether there might be powers other than squares for which Pythagoras' theorem held was: No.* It took three hundred years for his theorem to be proved correct (by Andrew Wiles in 1997). Some view the final validation of Fermat's bald assertion as an achievement equivalent to shaving half a second off the record for solving *The Times* crossword puzzle, but at least one writer has managed to compose what is virtually a history of Western mathematics around the Theorem and its proof.* (GB)

* Simon Singh *Fermat's last theorem* 1997.

[289] FERMAT'S PRINCIPLE

Why do rays of light appear to travel in straight lines? And why are they deflected when light passes obliquely from one medium into another – the phenomenon called refraction? It appears that in getting from A to B, light obeys FERMAT'S PRINCIPLE OF LEAST TIME: the *quickest* route, not the shortest, is evidently preferred, and light has different speeds in different media. The explanation invokes the wave-like nature of light: all possible routes from A to B *can* be explored by rays of light – but the net effect of all the various longer paths is to cancel out each other's waves at the destination by the phenomenon of *interference*, whereby a wave crest and a wave trough arriving simultaneously wash each other out. The quickest route is unique and cannot be cancelled out. FERMAT'S PRINCIPLE dates from 1660 and was subsequently developed into the HUYGENS-FRESNEL PRINCIPLE and leads directly to SNELL'S LAW of refraction; it is also the forerunner of the analogous *extremum* principle of mechanics in 1744 called MAUPERTUIS' PRINCIPLE OF LEAST ACTION. For a biographical note, see FERMAT'S LAST THEOREM. (MW)

[290] FERMI PARADOX – see DRAKE EQUATION

[291] FERMION, FERMI-DIRAC STATISTICS

Elementary particles fall into two categories, BOSONS and FERMIONS. Fermions are the particles that provide the building blocks of matter, the most familiar one being the electron. These two sorts of elementary particle differ according to the quantization of their "spin" – whether integer or half-integer, respectively. This obscure quantum property (which has really little to do with spinning tops) determines how the particles perform collectively – behaviour which is referred to as their "STATISTICS". Translating into more accessible language: no two fermions within the same space can have exactly the same quantum state – *i.e.* they have to be distinguishable by their "quantum labels". An important instance of this is PAULI'S EXCLUSION PRINCIPLE for electrons in an atom, which is responsible for the shape of MENDELEEV'S PERIODIC TABLE. (For the biographical note on this most notable physicist, ENRICO FERMI, see FERMIUM, and for that of the outstanding theoretician, PAUL DIRAC, see DIRAC'S CONSTANT). (MW)

[292] FERMIUM

This radioactive element of atomic number 100, symbol Fm, does not occur naturally but was identified by Californian nuclear scientist, ALBERT GHIORSO *et al.* in the debris from the very first hydrogen bomb test (codenamed the *Mike* shot of *Operation Ivy*) conducted in the inappropriately named Pacific Ocean in 1952, when the number of known Pacific Islands was thereby diminished by one (Elugelab Island, Eniwetok). Seventeen isotopes of fermium are known, none with a half-life longer than 100 days, and all ferociously radioactive. So little fermium has ever been made, that it is largely uninvestigated and has no uses. It is named after Italian-born physicist ENRICO FERMI (1901-1954) a leading force at the heart – or rather, the core – of the development of atomic energy and the atomic bomb. Fermi was awarded the NOBEL PRIZE for physics in 1938 for his discovery, while Professor at the Institute of Physics in Rome, of new radioactive elements by neutron irradiation. He left fascist Italy for the USA shortly thereafter, with his Jewish wife and children, becoming a naturalised US citizen in 1944. In 1942, Fermi co-designed and helped build the first "neutronic reactor", or "atomic pile" (see WIGNER ENERGY) at the University of Chicago, in a squash court under the football field. Russian espionage mistranslated this location as the "pumpkin field", but American scientists heard of his success in guarded, metaphorical terms: "The Italian navigator has landed in the new world." This was indeed a historical landmark on a par with Columbus: the first self-sustaining, controlled nuclear chain reaction. Intentions at that time were less to harness it for civil power, more for weaponry, so Fermi joined the Manhattan Project at Los Alamos to build the first atomic bomb. Besides being an intensely practical scientist, he was a powerful theoretician and made fundamental contributions to quantum mechanics (see FERMION and FERMI-DIRAC STATISTICS). (MW)

[293] FERREL'S LAW – see CORIOLIS EFFECT

[294] FERRIS WHEEL
The original wheel, named after its inventor, the American civil engineer GEORGE WASHINGTON GALE FERRIS (1859-1896), was built for the Chicago Exposition of 1893. It was designed as a counter-attraction to the EIFFEL TOWER, which had caused a sensation at the Paris Exhibition of 1889. Though it stood only 264 feet high as opposed to the Eiffel Tower's 1063 feet (and the London Eye's 443) it was nevertheless an imposing and powerful structure. It carried 36 gondolas, each of which could accommodate up to 60 passengers, paying 50 cents a head for a twenty-minute ride (two revolutions). Power was provided by two 1000-hp steam engines. Its popularity was such that over the duration of the Fair it earned a massive profit of $750,000, the lion's share of which went to the fair's organisers and almost none to Ferris. The wheel was finally dismantled in 1904 after appearing at the St. Louis Exhibition of that year.

[295] FEYNMAN DIAGRAM
American theoretical physicist RICHARD PHILLIPS FEYNMAN (1918-1988) was born in Brooklyn, studied at MIT, and took his PhD at Princeton in 1942. He worked on the Manhatten project at Los Alamos in WWII (see GRAHAM'S LAW), and taught at Cornell University and California Institute of Technology. The FEYNMAN LECTURES IN PHYSICS are a paradigm for instructors of the subject. His was generally acknowledged as the liveliest mind in theoretical physics during much of the latter half of the 20th century, and also enjoyed a reputation as a professorial maverick with numerous "extracurricular" interests; but as a member of the NASA committee that investigated the Space Shuttle Challenger disaster of 1986, he was responsible for identifying the problem. He received the Nobel Prize for Physics in 1965 for his development of quantum electrodynamics (appropriately abbreviated to QED) to evaluate the magnetic properties of the electron with an accuracy of one part in ten billion – probably the most precise piece of predictive theoretical science in all history so far. His famous FEYNMAN DIAGRAM is a schematic method for displaying the interactions of subatomic particles; time is plotted as the vertical axis, and a single spatial dimension plotted as the horizontal axis. By this means are represented the evolution of interactions and interconversions between members of the bewildering array (to the layperson) of the *Standard Model* of particle physics, *viz.*, the twelve fundamental particles (and their corresponding antiparticles) which comprise six lightweight *leptons*: electron, muon, tauon, and their corresponding neutrinos, and six varieties of *quark*, which combine in threes to make the composite, heavyweight *baryons*, such as the proton, neutron, and many others – all these are FERMIONS. On the other hand there are the BOSONS, made of a quark and an antiquark, such as the pi-

meson. All these particles are juggled by the forces of nature – strong, electromagnetic and weak – which are moderated respectively by particles (also **BOSONS**) called: gluons, photons, and sundry intermediate vector bosons. The successful incorporation of the force of gravity into this picture – to yield the Grand Unified Theory, or GUT – still awaits the coming of another genius on a par with Feynman. (MW)

[296] FIBONACCI SERIES

A mathematical sequence in which each integer (whole number) is the sum of the two preceding integers, as in: 1, 1, 2, 3, 5, 8, 13, 21, 34, 55, ...etc. The attribution to **LEONARDO FIBONACCI** (*ca.* 1170 – *ca.* 1230), the son of an Italian merchant family based in Pisa, was first made by French mathematician François Édouard Anatole Lucas (1841-1891). Certain natural phenomena, such as the spiral arrangement of seeds in a sunflower head, conform to a Fibonacci sequence. It also describes the mathematics of rabbit-breeding, a problem studied by Fibonacci. This gives ammunition to those who suppose that the laws of science, and more especially mathematics, are *derived* from Nature by the operation of the human brain. Others contend that these "laws" are conceived in the human brain and *imposed* on Nature. This is a not a question likely to be resolved in the near future. (See, for example, D'Arcy Thompson *On growth and form* 1917, 1969.) Fibonacci has another and greater claim to fame in that his commercial contacts with North Africa and residence there gave him access to Arab mathematics, and his *Liber abaci* ("Book of the abacus" 1202) started the process by which Arabic numerals, the use of zero, and positional notation gradually came to replace the clumsy Roman system of mathematical notation in Europe. In this, Fibonacci was following in the footsteps of the English traveller and scholar Adelard of Bath who had discovered the use of Arabic numerals a century earlier.

[297] FIELDS MEDAL

The **FIELDS MEDAL** is awarded every four years to not less than two and preferably as many as four young (under 40) mathematicians. The awarding body is the International Mathematical Union, whose executive committee chooses the members of the Medal Committee. The award arose from a suggestion by the Canadian mathematician **JOHN CHARLES FIELDS** (1863-1932) and has two main aims. One is to reward early achievement and, perhaps more importantly, encourage future promise.* The other is to counter (by the award of multiple prizes) the politicisation of mathematics which Fields saw in the exclusion of German mathematicians from the 1924 International Mathematical Congress, and to make the point that mathematics is a world-wide collective enterprise and not a contest – a point emphasised by the inscription on the reverse of the medal which translates as: "Awarded for outstanding writings by the mathematicians of the whole world in congress." The prize fund was endowed by a bequest from Fields himself and the medals first awarded in 1936. Among mathematicians, a Fields medal is accorded the same status as a **NOBEL PRIZE.**

* There might be grounds for supposing that there exists a tendency among genius-level mathematicians to have done their best work in their twenties. A question worth investigating?

[298] FILBERT

A cultivated variety of edible hazelnut, *Corylus maxima*, said to ripen around the time of the festival – 20th August – of **SAINT PHILIBERT** (608-684), Gascon founder and abbot of Jumièges Abbey, who was raised in the court of King Dagobert I of the Franks. The Saint's relics are now venerated at the great Romanesque Benedictine Abbey of St. Philibert at Tournus in Burgundy, though the church of Saint Philbert de Grandieu in Brittany also claims to house his mortal remains – perhaps an instance of bi-location? But it is the nut, rather than the Saint, that is immortalised in a music-hall song written by Arthur Wimperis for impresario Herman Finck's 1914 revue at the Palace Theatre, London, called "The Passing Show":

> *I'm Gilbert, the Filbert, the Knut* with a K,*
> *The pride of Piccadilly, the blasé roué;*
> *Oh Hades, the ladies who leave their wooden huts*
> *For Gilbert, the Filbert, the Kernel of the Knuts!*

The dashing character of Gilbert the Filbert was created by popular singer-actor Basil Hallam (1889-1916) who subsequently, in his true persona of Captain Basil Hallam Radford RFC, was tragically killed in WWI when he fell 3000 feet from a breakaway observation kite-balloon, due to parachute failure. (MW)

*"Knut" is Edwardian slang for a fashionable man-about-town, a dandy.

[299] FISCHER PROJECTION -see **GRIGNARD REACTION**

[300] FITZGERALD-LORENTZ CONTRACTION

In 1895, the Dublin-born physicist **GEORGE FRANCIS FITZGERALD** (1851-1901), in order to explain some apparent anomalies in measurements of the speed of light, proposed the theory that objects travelling at high speeds would become shorter. Thus a six-foot estate-agent, say, travelling head-first at 161,000 miles per second would be only three feet long, and at 186,282 miles per second (the speed of light) he would have no length at all and disappear entirely. The same theory was advanced independently by the Dutch physicist **HENDRIK ANTOON LORENTZ** (1853-1928) and the findings of both men were later found to be consistent with

EINSTEIN's Special Theory of Relativity (1905). Fitzgerald's aha!-moment is
enshrined in a limerick which still gets them rolling in the aisles in the physics labs:

> *There was a young fellow called Fisk*
> *Whose fencing was exceedingly brisk.*
> *So fast was his action*
> *The Fitzgerald contraction*
> *Reduced his rapier to a disk.*

[301] FITZROY BAROMETER – see SEA AREA FITZROY

[302] FITZROYA

FITZROYA, a South American evergreen conifer native to Chile and Patagonia, also
known as the Patagonian Cypress, and named after CAPTAIN ROBERT FITZROY of
HMS *Beagle*. (See also SEA AREA FITZROY.)

[303] FIZEAU-FOUCAULT APPARATUS – see FOUCAULT PENDULUM

[304] FLEMING'S RULES

Apply to electric motors or dynamos: a mnemonic device for recalling the relative
directions of the magnetic field, electric current, and consequent motion. The
thumb and first two fingers of one hand are extended – all three mutually at right
angles – representing thus:
- First Finger = Field
- seCond finger = Current
- THuMb = THrust or Motion

If the left hand is used, the directions refer to a motor, if the right, to a generator
or dynamo. British physicist SIR JOHN AMBROSE FLEMING (1849-1945) was born
in Lancaster, studied at the Universities of London and Cambridge and, as first
Professor of Electrical Engineering at London, pursued an academic career and
was knighted in 1929. He forged strong commercial links with the burgeoning
electrical industry, consulting for companies bearing the names of Edison, Ferranti,
Marconi and Swan. In 1904 Fleming invented the vacuum diode, the first
thermionic valve (US: "vacuum tube") which was crucial to the development of
electronics, radio communications and radar, and therefore to the outcome of
WWII. For 50 years radio "valves" reigned supreme until the invention of solid-
state semiconductor technology. (MW)

[305] FLETA GUITAR

What Stradivarius and Amati are to the violin, Érard to the harp, or Broadwood to
the piano, so is the name of Fleta to the classical Spanish guitar. IGNACIO FLETA

(1897-1977) was born in Huesca, son of a cabinet-maker whose two other sons, Bienvenido and Francisco Manuel (the second of whom trained his brother Ignacio), all grew up to be luthiers – makers of bowed instruments and guitars. Ignacio opened his own workshop in Barcelona in 1927 and soon achieved notice by the quality of his work. He specialised at first in bowed instruments, notably the cello, but in 1955, after hearing Segovia play, Ignacio decided to devote himself to the guitar and soon counted among his clients some of the greatest living performers on the classical concert guitar. These included Alexandre Lagoya, John Williams, and Segovia himself. His two sons Francisco and Gabriel carried on the business after his death.

[306] FLETCHERISE

A now almost obsolete word meaning "to chew thoroughly". **HORACE FLETCHER** (1849-1919) was an American nutritionist/health-faddist who travelled, pamphleted and lectured widely in Europe and America promoting the notion that the road to good health ("dietetic righteousness", he called it) was paved with hard-working molars. The idea has a sound factual basis. Chewing not only breaks up the future contents of the stomach into workable bits but actually begins the process of digestion through an enzyme called ptyalin which is found in spittle. In *Fletcherism – What it is, or, How I became young at sixty* (1913) Fletcher perhaps over-stated his case. But he was able to point, in its support, to the example of no less a personage than Mr Gladstone, a well-known advocate of thorough chewing. "The Grand Old Man of Democracy," wrote Fletcher, "will be known to the future of physiological fitness more permanently on account of his glorification of Head Digestion than for his Liberal Statesmanship." A judgement with which it is hard to quarrel. On the other hand, though, the Grand Old Man will, one suspects, be more permanently known to the future of political history for his statesmanship than for his Head Digestion. Even so, within living memory, children were still being told by their nannies to "chew each mouthful thirty-one times like Mr Gladstone." The question, however, remains as to whether Gladstone actually practised what he (or Nanny) preached, since according to at least one report he talked continuously while eating with no observable pauses for mastication.

[307] FLYING CHILDERS

Called "the first truly great racehorse"* **FLYING CHILDERS** (1715-1741) was bred by **LEONARD CHILDERS** of Doncaster and sired by the **DARLEY ARABIAN**, though his pedigree is otherwise a matter of controversy. He took part in only two formal races (1721 and 1722), which he won so convincingly that he was able to spend the rest of his life as a stud horse at the Duke of Devonshire's modest gaff in Derbyshire. Despite his being one of the fastest horses ever to race in this country, the horses he sired were not of the same standard and it was through his brother **BARTLETT CHILDERS** that the line of great racehorses which trace their descent from the Darley Arabian was established.

* Mortimer, Onslow & Willett *Biographical Encyclopaedia of British flat racing* (1978).

[308] FOLEY ARTIST

The member of a film crew whose job it is, working in conjunction with the sound engineer, to add the sound effects and background noises which the action requires and which accompany the separately-recorded dialogue. The name commemorates **JACK DONOVAN FOLEY** (1891-1967) who pioneered the technique and became its leading practitioner, despite having begun his Hollywood career in silent films.

[309] FORSYTHIA

Genus of seven species of spring-flowering deciduous shrubs with yellow, bell-shaped flowers. Named after **WILLIAM FORSYTH** (1737-1804), gardener to the Chelsea Botanical Gardens and later Superintendent of Kensington Royal Gardens.

[310] FORTEANS

Martin Gardner's classic work of debunking, *Fads & Fallacies in the Name of Science* (1952) has more entries on American writer **CHARLES HOY FORT** (1874-1932) than any other, so we must give him his due. Fort was born in Albany, New York and, after a minimal education, discovered his self-appointed mission in life: to celebrate any phenomenon which seemed inexplicable, and to champion any cause that challenged science. Thanks to an inheritance, he was able to dedicate over 30 years of his life to the accumulation of newspaper cuttings and magazine accounts of supposedly paranormal, supernatural, occult, or bizarre happenings. He filled many shoeboxes with such scraps of paper – an archive now known as the **FORTEANA.** By 1931 this prototypical crank-magnet had acquired a cult following, when writer Tiffany Thayer founded the **FORTEAN SOCIETY**, comprising an assortment of flat-earthers, anti-vaccinationists, anti-vivisectionists, chiropractors, spiritualists and astrologers, cheek by jowl. On Thayer's death in 1959, the **FORTEAN SOCIETY** became defunct but was eventually replaced in 1965 by the **INTERNATIONAL FORTEAN ORGANIZATION** (**INFO**) which survives to this day. The Fortean Society magazine, *Doubt,* was likewise replaced by the **FORTEAN TIMES,** a British monthly publication founded in 1973 by "anomalist" and paranormal writer Bob Rickard, to report weird rumours and happenings of all sorts – UFOlogy, cryptozoology, alien abduction, crop circles (see **HECK HYPOTHESIS**), etc. Fort's own writings were published as four books in 1919,

1923, and 1931-2. His two intimate friends, Tiffany Thayer and Theodore Dreiser, insisted that he was simply an irrepressible joker, an anti-authoritarian satirist and parodist, who did not actually believe one word of what he said and wrote. Be that as it may, his credence in the absurdly improbable, coupled with his vehement contempt for proven science, was a combination calculated to render any scientist incandescent with rage, unless s/he maintained a very well-developed sense of humour. When some of Fort's hobby-horses became respectable objects of scientific study (*e.g.* ball-lightning, earthquakes) he was perversely annoyed: "Now there are so many scientists who believe in dowsing that the suspicion comes to me that it may be only a myth after all." (His suspicion is almost certainly correct in this instance – but not for the reason he gives.) Fort was especially derisive about the achievements of astronomy, but his own published "cosmology" reads as pathetically childish, and the much-vaunted "humour" of his grotesque maunderings has not aged well. The usual apologium trotted out for the likes of Fort is that we should welcome such independent-minded critics, because they provide a salutary counterbalance to the arrogance, presumption, and authoritarianism of science. Actually, science is, by and large, a moderate, concensual, and effectively self-regulating international community of milllions, who have collectively evolved a proven worldview on a scale to beggar the imagination. Loonies need not apply. (MW)

[311] FOSBURY FLOP

A high-jumping technique invented by American athlete **DICK FOSBURY** (b.1947), so named by a sports reporter on the local newspaper in Fosbury's home town of Medford, Oregon. It consists essentially in hurling yourself over the bar *backwards and upside down*. He unveiled this eye-bugging evolution at the 1968 Mexico Olympics, setting a new world record of 7 feet 2.5 inches. The result was that other high-jumpers rapidly abandoned previous methods such as the "straddle" and the "western roll" and the new technique now rules, OK.

[312] FOUCAULT PENDULUM

A large, freely-suspended pendulum capable of swinging for long enough to demonstrate the rotation of the Earth beneath it – by the apparent displacement of its plane of swing with respect to a fixed direction on the Earth's surface. If the pendulum were located at one of the Poles, the period of rotation would be one sidereal day;* if located on the Equator, there would be no apparent rotation at all; at locations in between, the period of rotation depends inversely on the sine of the angle of latitude. The pendulum's apparent displacement can be expressed as due to the **CORIOLIS EFFECT**. This first experimental demonstration of the Earth's rotation was devised in 1851 with a pendulum suspended in the Panthéon,

Paris, by French physicist **JEAN BERNARD LÉON FOUCAULT** (1819-1868), who was born in Paris and educated largely at home. With compatriot physicist Armand Hippolyte Louis Fizeau (1819-1896), he obtained an accurate measurement of the velocity of light in 1850 using the **FIZEAU-FOUCAULT APPARATUS**. He employed and named the *gyroscope* in 1852, invented the polarizing **FOUCAULT PRISM** in 1857 and devised the **FOUCAULT TEST** for the sphericity of reflecting telescope mirrors in 1858. Deservedly, he was awarded the **COPLEY MEDAL** of the Royal Society in 1855 for his "very remarkable experimental researches". *FOUCAULT'S PENDULUM*, on the other hand, is the title of a novel (1988) by Italian author and philosopher, Umberto Eco. Its theme is occultist conspiracy – "the thinking person's *Da Vinci Code*". (MW)

*23 hours and 56 minutes – the period of Earth's rotation with respect to the fixed stars.

[313] FOURCADE'S STEREOGONIOMETER

Among the special contributions of aerial photography to terrain mapping and surveying is its ability to create a 3-dimensional picture of the area under study by means of paired stereoscopic images which enable the map-maker accurately to measure and depict, for example, contour lines. Among the pioneers of this technique was the Frenchman **HENRI-GEORGES FOURCADE** (1865-1948) inventor of the stereoscopic measuring machine that bears his name. Born and educated in France, Fourcade moved in 1880 to Cape Colony where he qualified as a surveyor. In 1901 he published a paper entitled "On a stereoscopic method of photographic surveying" in the *Transactions of the South African Philosophical Society* (xiv.5). This was followed by numerous other publications on the same subject. Outside the field of photogrammetry Fourcade had two other major interests. One was forestry, which led to a survey for the government of the forests of Natal. The other was botany. Specialising in the flora of the Southern Cape, he contributed largely to the *Botanical survey of South Africa*, had 35 species of plant named after him, and himself described and named another 20 species including two proteas. Also named after Fourcade is a mountain in Antarctica on the west coast of the Graham Land Peninsula. (See also **SIDCOT SUIT**. For Africa from the air in the 1930's, see Victor Smith *Open cockpit over Africa*, still in print.)

[314] FOURIER ANALYSIS

With the advent of that wonderful electronic instrument the oscilloscope, and its embodiment in every hospital emergency ward drama, we have all become familiar with the idea of waveforms, especially the simple sine wave (Latin: *sinus* = bay, breast, or curve) which presents an idealised breast-like aspect. **FOURIER'S THEOREM** states that any periodic phenomenon can be expressed as a summation of a series of such trigonometric functions, sines and cosines, known as a

FOURIER SERIES. Such a **FOURIER ANALYSIS** can therefore be applied to the harmonic analysis of regular repetitive happenings, as varied as tides, sunspots, sounds of speech and notes of music, electrical circuits, heartbeats (ECG) and brainwaves (EEG). The application of the principle to physical optics has resulted in the powerful techniques of **FOURIER TRANSFORM SEPCTROSCOPY**. French mathematician **JEAN BAPTISTE JOSEPH, Baron DE FOURIER** (1768-1830) was born at Auxerre, and rose to a chair at the École Polytechnique. He accompanied **NAPOLEON** to Egypt in 1798 and acted as governor of Lower Egypt until the French were expelled in 1801. He was created Baron in 1808. Following a sojourn in England, he returned to France to become Permanent Secretary to the *Académie des Sciences* in 1822. His major work, *Théorie analytique de la chaleur* (1822) solved the differential equations expressing heat flow in a solid body by expansion in terms of the trigonometric series that now bears his name. (MW)

[315] FRANGIPANI

Originally a perfume for scenting gloves, named after its inventor the 16th-century Italian nobleman **MUSIO FRANGIPANI**. Later applied (a) to the sweetly-scented flowering tropical and sub-tropical shrubs of the genus *Plumeria;** and (b) on the strength of a supposed aromatic resemblance, to **FRANGIPANE**, a cream-filled pastry flavoured with almonds. An earlier scion of the Frangipani family, **CENCIO FRANGIPANI**, attracted the attention of the great Gibbon. In 1118, following a violently disputed papal election, this "potent and factious baron" beat up, bound and imprisoned the Vicar of Christ, Gelasius II. A "popular insurrection" secured the Pontiff's release but Frangipani, undeterred, returned to the charge. Days later he and his followers attacked poor Gelasius at the very altar where he was officiating. "While [the Pope's] friends and enemies were engaged in a bloody contest he escaped in his sacerdotal garments. In this unworthy flight ... his attendants were scattered or unhorsed; and, in the fields behind the church of St. Peter, his [*sc.* St. Peter's] successor was found alone and half-dead with fear and fatigue." Gibbon adds an etymological note: "The old consular line of the Frangipani discover their name in the generous act of *breaking* or dividing bread in a time of famine."

* Properly *Plumiera*, after the French monk and botanical explorer Charles Plumier (1646-1704).

[316] FRANKENSTEIN'S MONSTER

Mary Shelley's *Frankenstein*, published in 1818, was not the first "Gothic" novel, but took its place in a genre already established in the preceding century by Walpole's *Castle of Otranto* (1765), Beckford's *Vathek* (1786), and Mrs Radcliffe's *Mysteries of Udolpho* (1794).* A common feature of these works is that much of the imagery (cowled figures prowling sinister moonlit ruins located in savage mountain scenery, etc., etc.) drew on an eighteenth-century conception of the Middle Ages, a period viewed by the civilised classes of the Enlightenment with a shudder of refined distaste, the same distaste with which they viewed unimproved Nature, and which yet exercised a not-altogether unpleasant fascination. What Mrs. Shelley added was a very modern warning of the dangers inherent in the irresponsible exercise of the power conferred by Science. The book's subtitle, *The modern Prometheus*, is an unequivocal reference to the TITAN who in Greek legend created the first men out of mud. But it might equally well have been called *The Modern Faustus*. *Frankenstein* is a tragedy, but it isn't VICTOR FRANKENSTEIN's tragedy. Finally, our sympathies are with the monster, assembled by his creator out of mere curiosity from a mixed bag of body parts, and endowed, by means not specified, not only with life but with the capacity for human emotion (love, longing, rage, jealousy, empathy) while at the same time denied access, on account of his super-repellent ugliness, to human society – denied even the dignity of a name. (For the possible original of Victor Frankenstein and his impious experiment, see DIPPEL'S ANIMAL OIL).

*One might perhaps add Potocki's *Saragossa Manuscript*, composed in 1794 but not published until 1804.

[317] FRANKLIN STOVE – see POOR RICHARD'S ALMANACK

[318] FRANKLIN'S GULL

Small black-headed inland gull, *Larus pipixcan*. Frequents marshy areas of North America and central Canada. Recorded only as a vagrant in Britain. Named after the Arctic explorer Sir JOHN FRANKLIN (1786-1847). As a naval officer, Franklin served under Matthew Flinders in the South Pacific and was in *Bellerophon* at Trafalgar. He took part in and led expeditions to the Canadian Arctic in search of the North-West Passage. In 1845 he set out in two ships, *Erebus* and *Terror*, on what was to be his last expedition – and disappeared. Thanks largely to the energy and persistence of Lady Franklin, over a dozen expeditions were mounted in the search for him. It was eventually established that, with his ships hopelessly ice-bound, Franklin and his crews had perished in an attempt to reach safety by travelling overland on foot.

[319] FRASER SPIRAL

An optical illusion by which a series of concentric circles can be drawn in such as way as to appear to form a spiral. First described by Scottish physician and psychologist JAMES FRASER (1863-1936) in an article of 1908 in the *British Journal of Psychology* (2.307-337). The art historian E.H.Gombrich discusses this and other visual fallacies in *Art and illusion: a study in the psychology of pictorial representation* (1960). (See also NECKER CUBE.)

[320] FRAUNHOFER LINES

When the Sun's light is dispersed with a prism into the continuous rainbow-coloured solar spectrum (**NEWTON'S** experiment), one can discern numerous sharp dark lines crossing it if the resolution is high enough. These **FRAUNHOFER LINES** are due to absorption of narrow wavelengths of light from the continuum by gases in the "cooler" outer regions of the Sun. They correspond in wavelength to the bright emission lines seen in the atomic gas discharge spectra of hydrogen (see **BALMER SERIES** and **RYDBERG CONSTANT**) and other elements such as sodium, magnesium, iron, and helium (the last of which was thus observed in the Sun even before it was discovered on Earth). Although the existence of such lines was first noted in 1802 by English chemist William Hyde Wollaston* (1766-1828), their serious investigation was only begun in 1814 by German **JOSEPH VON FRAUNHOFER** (1787-1826) who "mapped" 574 of them. Born in Straubing, Bavaria, Fraunhofer was orphaned at the age of 11 and came up the hard way apprenticed to a glassmaker. Thanks to the patronage of the Elector of Bavaria, Fraunhofer was appointed to the Optical Institute at the secularised Abbey of Benediktbeuern** where he made optical glass of world-beating quality for lenses and prisms, which was crucial to his development of optical spectroscopy (see **BUNSEN** and **KIRCHHOFF**). He was honoured and ennobled for his achievements in optics, but died young at the age of 39. (MW)

* Inventor of the *camera lucida* (a drawing-aid which displays upon the drawing surface a virtual image of the thing being drawn) and discoverer of the element palladium.

** Original home to the codex of 13th Century songs, *Cantiones Profanae*, famously transcribed by Carl Orff for his delicious composition, *Carmina Burana* (1935). The codex now resides in the *Bayerische Staatsbibliothek*, Munich.

[321] FREESIA

Genus of 14 (or more) species of African flowering plants, all but one native to the Cape and grown in this country as a greenhouse plant. Named after German physician **FRIEDRICH HEINRICH THEODOR FREESE** (1795-1876). Not to be confused with **VRIESIA**.

[322] FREMONTIA

The name of **JOHN CHARLES FRÉMONT** (1813-1890) is prominent among the pioneer explorers of America west of the Mississippi. Trained as an army surveyor and map-maker, he is chiefly remembered for the expedition he led in 1842, guided by Kit Carson, to survey the Oregon Trail, and two subsequent expeditions (1843-4 and 1845-7), the last of which brought him into armed conflict with the Mexicans in California and led ultimately to the absorption of California into the United States. A final expedition of 1848-9 seeking a Pacific railroad route through the Rockies was a disaster. The plant named after him, **FREMONTIA** (or **FREMONTODENDRON**) is a 2-species genus of yellow-flowered shrubs or small trees. In addition, Frémont gave his name to **FRÉMONT'S PINE SQUIRREL**, a sub-species of North American red squirrel (*Tamiasciurus*) found in southern Wyoming and the southern Rockies.

[323] FREMY'S SALT – see MAGNUS' GREEN SALT

[324] FRESNEL LENS

French physicist and engineer **AUGUSTIN FRESNEL** (1788-1827) is remembered for his work in optics, both theoretical and practical. He studied in particular the phenomena of diffraction and polarisation. In his lifetime his work was honoured by membership of the Académie des Sciences, and of the Royal Society (whose **RUMFORD MEDAL** he was awarded shortly before his untimely death from TB.) In 1818 he was made Commissioner for Lighthouses and put his knowledge of optics to work on improved systems for focusing, directing, and intensifying the light they emitted. He drew up the specification for optical glass, whose manufacture was at that time virtually a French monopoly, and designed the lens to which his name is attached, comprising a concentric series of ridged annular rings functioning as prisms. Aside from lighthouses, Fresnel Lenses are found attached to towed caravans: aligned with the driver's mirror, they reflect his viewpoint downwards to the caravan's rear bumper and act as an aid to crunch-free reversing.

[325] FRESSON PROCESS – see PONTON'S PROCESS

[326] FRISBEE

The origin of the word **FRISBEE**, now a proprietary trade name, has been traced to the agreeably aerodynamic pie-plates issuing from the bakery of **MR. JOSEPH P. FRISBIE** of Bridgeport, Connecticut, established in 1871. The basic design of the flying plate was later improved on by Walter Frederick Morrison of Los Angeles who patented a plastic version under the name "Pluto Platter" and sold the patent to the Wham-O Toy Company (who also made hula hoops). Wham-O marketed the toy under the name "Frisbee", which they believed, probably correctly, was a catchier appellation. Morrison's claim to priority of invention has been disputed.

[327] FRISCH-PEIERLS MEMORANDUM – see MAUD COMMITTEE

[328] FUCHSIA

The German physician and botanist **LEONHARD FUCHS** (1501-1566) was professor of medicine at the University of Tübingen from 1535 until his death. His *De historia stirpium* (1542), though much of the text was derivative, rehashing once more Dioscorides and Pliny, was remarkable for the beauty and clarity of its illustrations and for its pioneering attempt to describe each plant from life and present each description in a standardised and rational format. His book was a success and he embarked on a more ambitious project, an encyclopaedia of plants for which, by the end of his life, he had amassed over 1,500 descriptions and illustrations. These included such recent exotic introductions as tobacco, tomato, pumpkin, sunflower, "African" marigold, day lily and tulip. Unfortunately no printer could be found to take on such an ambitious project and, as a result, priority for published description of these novelties went to other writers. The genus FUCHSIA, discovered in the Caribbean in the 1690's, was named in Fuchs's honour by the French botanist Charles Plumier (1646-1704).

[329] FULL MONTY

A phrase meaning all that is desired and/or required, the whole hog, the complete thing, which became widely current in the 90's and even more so following the release of the film of the same name in 1997. The origins of the phrase are obscure and contested and range from a nickname given to inhabitants of the Potteries region of England to a comment on the quality of the wartime briefings given by General Montgomery in North Africa. The most widely-accepted derivation is from the tailoring business of **Sir MONTAGUE BURTON** (1885-1952), born Meshe David Osinsky in Kaunas, Lithuania. Burton opened his first shop in Chesterfield, Derbyshire, in 1904. The business flourished and he began building a chain of shops in 1906. For a long time Burton's was known as the "thirty-shilling tailors", that being the price of a finished three-piece suit – the FULL MONTY. (RS)

G

[330] GADOLINIUM

One of the fourteen very similar "rare earth" elements, or "lanthanides", as they are known in the trade (of chemistry – see CERIUM). Having atomic number 64, and symbol Gd, it was discovered spectroscopically in 1880 by the Swiss chemist Jean Charles Galissard de Marignac, but named in honour of the Finnish mineralogist and chemist, JOHAN GADOLIN (1760-1852) who had discovered the rare element *yttrium* in 1792 in the mineral which was subsequently named GADOLINITE in 1800 (see SCHEELITE) but which, disappointingly, contains little or no GADOLINIUM. The oxide was separated in 1886 by Paul Émile Lecoq de Boisbaudron (see GALLIUM). It finds a use for colour phosphors in monitor screens. (MW)

[331] GADSDEN PURCHASE

The Mexican-American war of 1846-8, ended with the treaty of Guadalupe-Hidalgo and with the transfer to the US of the future states of Texas, New Mexico, California, Utah, Nevada, Arizona, and parts of Colorado and Wyoming (a nice day's work).* Though it took American marines to the Halls of Montezuma, it didn't settle for good and all the question of the Mexican-American boundary, the cause of further sporadic troubles. Meanwhile, JAMES GADSDEN (1788-1858), as president of the South Carolina Railroad Company was engaged in an ambitious scheme for tying together the railways of the southern states into a single system. Part of his plan was the creation of a southern trans-continental railway which would tie California into the network. The proposed route would have passed through what was still Mexican territory. Accordingly, Gadsden, appointed minister plenipotentiary to Mexico by President Pierce in 1853, negotiated the purchase of some 45,000 square miles of territory along the southern border of Arizona. The agreed price was ten million dollars, but Congress would authorise only 7 million and when the money arrived in Mexico City one million had gone missing (Baghdad syndrome?). This was not a basis for a stable settlement and it wasn't until 1899 that a joint boundary commission finally published an agreed border between Mexico and the US. Meanwhile the adventurer and soldier of fortune William Walker, outraged by the puny dimensions of Gadsden's acquisition, took matters into his own hands and led an "army" from California into the state of Sonora. He then declared Sonora (in which he included the entire peninsula of Baja California) an independent republic. Walker's adventures didn't end there. In 1856 he contrived to become President of Nicaragua and his freebooting career was only ended when, at the age of 36, he was shot by a firing squad in Honduras.

The Southern Pacific Railway was opened in 1881, but it failed to realise Gadsden's hopes. His bold and truly visionary scheme for tying together the American West and the American South in a single economic unit with access to both oceans might have made the southern states better able to resist the growing economic dominance of the north and, in all likelihood, radically changed the subsequent course of American history. But history, as they say, declared otherwise. (RS)

* This squalid and nakedly imperialistic caper may be said to have set to this day the pattern for the USA's dealings with the Spanish-speaking half of the American continent. It was the occasion for Thoreau's withholding his taxes in protest and getting slung in jail for his trouble. His incarceration was mercifully brief – his aunt bailed him out.

[332] GAHNITE – see THÉNARD'S BLUE

[333] GAIA HYPOTHESIS
In 1979, scientist and environmentalist **Dr. JAMES EPHRAIM LOVELOCK** (b. 1919) published a book entitled *Gaia: a new look at life on Earth*. In it he put forward the theory that our planet and all living things on it are parts of a single, self-organising and self-regulating entity. He gave it the name GAIA, a classical Greek word (γαία) meaning "earth", "soil", "land", or "homeland", and by extension "Mother Earth". In Greek mythology, Gaia was the mother of the 12 TITANS by her son URANUS, the sky god. (They did things differently then.) By his choice of name, therefore, Lovelock was consciously personifying the planet. The idea that animate and inanimate nature are not separate entities but parts of a single whole is not altogether new and not difficult to get one's head round. Blake would have been perfectly happy with the notion, and so would Wordsworth. In religious terms it already has a respectable history under the name Pantheism – the belief that the Godhead is immanent in all created things, living or otherwise. And still earlier, it may said to have been encapsulated in the Neoplatonists' concept of the World Soul. But as a scientific theory it has revolutionary implications. For a start, it implies that a single whole cannot be both living and dead. It must be all one or all the other. So Science, if it is to embrace this view, must abandon the arbitrary distinction between life science and physical science. That involves a fundamental change of outlook. And if the planet is, in effect, a living entity, it is reasonable to suppose that it possesses the quality common to all living things – the instinct of self-preservation. This in turn has a sobering, even sinister implication: that the planet we so cheerfully abuse and maltreat, can and will act to protect itself from us and our reckless assaults on it. So if Lovelock is right, the human race may in the not-distant future find itself on notice to quit. We have been warned.

[334] GAINES BASS WHEEL
The bass player's life is hard, lonely and toilsome. Not only must he face the daily

purgatory of lugging his instrument along crowded streets, struggling to get it in and out of taxis, or fighting his way with it onto rush-hour tube trains, but, on top of all this, he has to put up with every voter who fancies himself a bit of a wag calling out "Give us a tune then" or, even wittier, "That's a big fiddle. Ho, ho." There's nothing to be done about these sallies. The tendency to shout "That's a big fiddle" is deeply embedded in the human genome and the only effective riposte is a blast from a twin-barrelled shotgun – difficult when you've got both hands full of musical instrument. But while a degree of psychological damage* is, therefore, inevitable, someone has at last done something about the purely physical labour of getting one's bull fiddle from A to B. **DONALD FRANK GAINES** (b. 1936), Emeritus Professor of Chemistry at the University of Madison-Wisconsin and an avid bassist from his youth, has invented the wheel! The **GAINES BASS WHEEL**, is simplicity itself, so much so that one wonders why it hasn't come along sooner. It consists of a wheel eight inches in diameter with an inflatable tyre. The wheel and its axle are held in a yoke which terminates in a pin. The pin fits into the hole provided at the bottom of the instrument for the "spike" or end-pin,** which it temporarily replaces. Problem solved. Halved, anyway.

* Damage, that is, additional to the scars left by cruel and wounding jokes from fellow-musicians ("How many bass-players does it take to change a light bulb?" " None – the piano player can do it with his left hand.")

** The purpose of this spike is to permit jaunty flourishes such as spinning the bass around on its axis between notes – a practice frowned on by Herbert von Karajan and other conductors of the old school, but still the only way the poor bass player can get himself noticed.

[335] GALILEAN TELESCOPE

The refracting telescope (*i.e.* one with lens optics, rather than the mirrors of the reflecting telescope – see **NEWTON**) was probably a Dutch invention of 1608, usually attributed to a spectacle-maker, Hans Lippershey, using two convex lenses. This design inverts the image, but that doesn't matter much to astronomers, so it's called the astronomical telescope. A superior model for terrestrial purposes – the **GALILEAN TELESCOPE** – consists of a convex objective lens combined with a concave eyepiece lens, which delivers an erect image. It is now used typically for opera glasses. This optical refinement provides the excuse to include in this compilation one of the most celebrated names in the entire history of science – that of the Italian physicist, astronomer and mathematician, frequently accorded the honorific title "Father of Modern Science", **GALILEO GALILEI** (1564-1642), who otherwise does not have a lot named after him. Born in Pisa, Tuscany, he studied medicine, then mathematics at the University, was elevated to the chair of mathematics in 1589, but was prised out by the Aristotelian opposition, so moved to Padua in 1592. Among Galileo's major contributions to kinematics were the fall of weights with uniform acceleration under gravity; the parabolic trajectory of a thrown or fired object, laying the foundations of the science of ballistics; and the harmonic motion of the simple pendulum. In 1610, his telescope famously revealed four of the satellites of Jupiter, called the **GALILEAN MOONS**, which he somewhat sycophantically named Cosimo, Francesco, Carlo and Lorenzo after members of the ruling Florentine family Medici. The names did not stick, being displaced by the more classical Io, Europa, Ganymede and Callisto. Galileo also observed telescopically the phases of Venus, sunspots, starfields in the Milky Way, and the craters of the moon (one now eponymous). Many of his astronomical findings provided fresh evidence for the essential correctness of the **COPERNICAN SYSTEM,** whose publication and teaching were prohibited by the Church in 1616 (see also **PTOLEMAIC SYSTEM** and **KEPLER'S LAWS**). Galileo's close encounter with that pre-eminent force for unreason, the Holy Roman Inquisition, was therefore inevitable. In 1632 Galileo published his *Dialogue Concerning the Two Chief World Systems*, wherein his discussion of the Copernican system unwisely waxed immoderate in its caricature of the opposition. Some thought this satirised Pope Urban VIII, who had previously been well-disposed. Galileo's trial quickly followed in 1633, and found him "vehemently suspected of heresy". He was threatened with torture to ensure that he recanted his heliocentrism and remained silent thereafter on the subject of cosmology. Having acquiesced with abject humility, Galileo was detained, under comfortable house arrest, attended by **TORRICELLI**, until his death. The Catholic Church took 359 years before it apologised to the shade of Galileo for this injustice, when in 1992 Pope John Paul II finally lifted the Edict of Inquisition against him, although some Catholic historians still defensively maintain that Galileo was entirely responsible for bringing about his own persecution. Hmmn… Today, any Catholic prelates who lose their way in central Italy are free to give thanks to Galileo, for his name now aptly adorns the recently-launched European satellite navigation and global positioning system, and an unmanned space craft sent by NASA to study Jupiter. (MW)

[336] GALLIUM

A very low-melting metallic element, atomic number 31, symbol Ga, whose existence was predicted by **MENDELEEV** as "eka-aluminium". **GALLIUM** was first discovered spectroscopically, then isolated in 1875 by the Gallic physical chemist Paul Émile Lecoq de Boisbaudron (1838-1912), who was born in Cognac, Charente. Although nominally honouring his Latinised native land, *Gallia*, his chosen name for the new element was also taken as a sly (or dare one say "cocky"?) reference to his own third given name: Latin, *gallus* = "a rooster". This *canard* (ho! ho!) was, however, publicly denied in 1877 by de Boisbaudron himself, who went on to discover the rare earth elements **SAMARIUM** and dysprosium (see **GADOLINIUM**). Gallium is now extensively used in semiconductor technology for making transistors, solar cells, and all those pretty little light-emitting diodes. (MW)

[337] GALTONIA

The Galtonia or "Summer Lily" is an African bulb named after **Sir FRANCIS GALTON** (1822-1911), biologist and African traveller. Galton is now remembered chiefly as the founder of the (?)science of eugenics and for his work on fingerprints, while the importance of his championship of Darwin (his cousin) and his pioneering studies of human intelligence viewed as a biologically-determined faculty are sometimes undervalued.

[338] GALVANOMETER

An instrument (later called an ammeter – see **AMPÈRE**) for the detection and measurement of an electric current, which is allowed to flow through a coil suspended in a magnetic field, thus causing a deflection of the coil (see **FARADAY**), which is signalled by an attached pointer. The device was invented by Johann Salomo Christoph Schweigger (1779-1857) a scientist of Nuremberg, in 1819, but he generously named his invention in honour of the Italian physicist-physiologist **LUIGI GALVANI** (1737-1798). The latter was born in Bologna, where he became lecturer at the University in 1768 and professor in 1782. By touching frogs' leg-muscles with dissimilar metals – copper and zinc connected together – and seeing them twitch, Galvani claimed to have discovered "animal electricity", thinking that the "electric fluid" was generated in the organic tissue. Although there is an element of truth in Galvani's idea of bioelectricity, his rival, **VOLTA** recognised the correct explanation of the phenomenon: *viz.*, that the electricity was not animal in origin, but due to the contact of metals, which constituted a primitive electric battery, also generously named the **GALVANIC CELL** by **VOLTA,** who then went on to make his **PILE**. "**GALVANIZING**", on the other hand, is the process of dipping iron or steel objects into a bath of molten zinc, to provide them with a coating that inhibits corrosion – also an electrochemical process. (MW)

[339] GARDENIA

Genus comprising some 250 species of trees and shrubs named in honour of Scottish botanist and physician **ALEXANDER GARDEN** (1730-1791). The most widely-grown species is *G.* augusta or "Cape Jessamine" (jasmine), an evergreen with intensely-scented flowers. After a spell as a naval surgeon, Garden taught medicine and botany at Edinburgh University before re-locating to South Carolina in 1752, whence he sent back numerous and in many cases non-descript botanical and zoological specimens to European correspondents notably **LINNAEUS** and the English naturalist John Ellis (1710?-1776), who authored the name *Gardenia*. In 1782, thanks to his pro-British sentiments, Garden's American estates were confiscated and he was made to feel unwelcome in the Land of the Free. He settled in London where, despite failing health, he brought a distinguished career to a close as Vice-President of the Royal Society. His son, Alexander junior (1757-1829), born in America and educated in Britain, joined the American Revolutionary Army, rose to the rank of major, and left memoirs of his military experiences described by the *Dictionary of American Biography* as "valuable and entertainingly written".

[340] GARRYA

American evergreen shrub or small tree introduced by David Douglas (see **DOUGLAS FIR**) in 1828 and named by him in honour of **NICHOLAS GARRY** (1782-1856) an employee and eventually Deputy-Governor of the Hudson's Bay Company, who assisted Douglas in his North American botanising and plant-collecting expeditions. The species *Garrya elliptica* is the one normally found in English gardens.

[341] GATLING GUN

RICHARD JORDAN GATLING (1818-1903) was the son of a South Carolina planter and slave owner. He devoted most of the early part of his career to designing and manufacturing agricultural machinery, notably a seed drill for rice and other crops, and a steam plough. In 1850, having developed an interest in medicine, he qualified as a doctor at the Ohio Medical College. At the outbreak of the Civil War he turned his attention to fire-arms and to the invention of the weapon which bears his name. By 1862 he had perfected a multi-barrelled revolving rifle capable of firing 350 rounds a minute. The war, however, was almost over before the Federal authorities consented to its adoption. From then on, its virtues were widely and rapidly recognised so that, in the words of *Encyclopaedia Britannica* (11th ed.), "within ten years it had been adopted by almost every civilised nation."

[342] GAUSS

CGS unit, now obsolete, of magnetic induction.* It carries the name of **CARL FRIEDRICH GAUSS** (1777-1855), the range and importance of whose contributions to mathematics and physics have earned him a reputation and respect comparable to what in the world of music would accrue to a man who combined in one person the talents of a Bach, a Mozart and a Beethoven. The "Prince of Mathematicians" as he is sometimes known, showed early evidence of genius, pointing out at the age of three an error in his shopkeeper father's payroll calculations. Gauss published relatively little, so that many of his staggering achievements became known only after his death. Many of these achievements bear his name, as do subsequent discoveries based on Gauss's work. They include: in mathematics and statistics, **GAUSS'S CONVERGENCE TEST**, **GAUSS'S DIFFERENTIAL EQUATION**, **GAUSS'S THEOREM**, **GAUSSIAN QUADRATURE**, **GAUSSIAN ELIMINATION**, **GAUSSIAN CURVATURE** and **GAUSSIAN DISTRIBUTION**; and in physics, **GAUSS EYEPIECE** (optics), **GAUSSIAN NOISE** (a.k.a. "white noise"), **GAUSSIAN RESPONSE**, **GAUSSIAN UNITS**, **GAUSSIAN POINTS**, **GAUSSIAN WELL**, **GAUSS'S LAWS OF ELECTROSTATICS**, the **GAUSS METER**, the **GAUSSIAN BLUR** (a filter used to conceal the facial features of certain persons in TV newsreels – the electronic equivalent of standing between two policemen with a blanket over your head), and not forgetting the **DE-GAUSSING BRIDLE** developed in WWII to protect ships against German magnetic mines. De-gaussing is still a necessity in computer monitors which use cathode ray tubes, to counteract the parasitic magnetism which might otherwise cause image distortion. Though Gauss fathered seven children, mathematics definitely took precedence over his personal life. It is said that when he was told that his wife was dying, he sent back a message asking her to hold on until he had finished a problem he was on the verge of solving. (GB)

* Replaced by the **TESLA**.

[343] GAY-LUSSAC'S LAW

The volumes of gases combining chemically, and of their products, are in the ratios of small whole numbers. This generalization, first put forward on the basis of empirical evidence, can now be seen as a natural consequence of the molecular hypothesis and the behaviour of "ideal" gases. Announced in 1808 it provided the basis for **AVOGADRO'S HYPOTHESIS**. The study of *pneumatics*, the preparation, handling and measurement of pure gases, begun by **ROBERT BOYLE** and **ROBERT HOOKE** in the mid-17th century, thus provided the key to understanding chemistry quantitatively, because the chemical combining ratios of gas volumes are obvious and simple, unlike those of liquids or solids. **JOSEPH LOUIS GAY-LUSSAC** (1778-1850) was an outstanding French man of science born in Saint Léonard de Noblat and educated in Paris at the École Polytechnique, where he became professor in 1809. His contributions to chemistry and chemical thermodynamics included the rediscovery of **CHARLES'S LAW** in 1802 (Charles himself had omitted to publish his findings of 1787) and the exploration of the atmosphere with Jean-Baptiste Biot, appropriately by **CHARLIÈRE** balloon flights in 1804, rising to a record altitude of 7000 m., at which he almost expired. To discover the varying composition of the atmosphere, samples were taken and analysed in collaboration with **ALEXANDER VON HUMBOLDT**, whom he accompanied on scientific journeys to volcanoes in 1805. On several occasions Gay-Lussac crossed scientific swords with his exact contemporary in England, **HUMPHRY DAVY**, over the elemental identification of the new substances: potassium (1808), chlorine (1809), and iodine (1814). In collaboration with **LOUIS THÉNARD**, he prepared potassium from molten potash and red-hot iron, and used the reactive metal in 1808 to isolate the element boron. Together they also established new methods for the quantitative analysis of organic substances during 1810-11. With his preparation of pure hydrogen cyanide ("prussic acid") in 1811 and cyanogen gas in 1815, Gay-Lussac opened up a whole new area of chemistry, and was fortunate to survive his close encounters with these lethal poisons. His reputation stands high in the history of chemistry for the soundness, accuracy and extent of his work, both in the characterization of new substances, and the invention of new instruments. These included an "alcoholometer", thanks to which the units of the measure of alcohol by volume (ABV %) are known in some countries as **DEGREES GAY-LUSSAC** (see also **BRIX**). (MW)

[344] GEIGER COUNTER

The insidious audible clicking of this instrument for detecting radioactivity is familiar to all who have worked in the nuclear industry. Its principle is simple: ionizing radiation knocks electrons out of molecules, and thus promotes the passage of electricity through a gas; the resulting pulse of electric current is easily detected and amplified. **JOHANNES WILHELM GEIGER** (1882-1945) was a German physicist from Erlangen who joined **RUTHERFORD** in Manchester in 1907, there to make significant contributions to the knowledge of atomic structure. He invented the **GEIGER COUNTER** in 1908 for detecting alpha particles and, with his student Walther Müller in 1928, refined the sensing element – called a **GEIGER-MÜLLER TUBE** – so that it detected beta particles too. Geiger subsequently returned to Germany: to Kiel, Tübingen, and finally Berlin, where he only just survived WWII. (MW)

[345] GEISSLER TUBE

The prototype of the neon sign: a glass tube, often fancifully shaped, fitted with metal electrodes sealed into each end, and containing a gas at low pressure. A high voltage – originally from a **RUHMKORFF COIL** – applied across the electrodes causes a "luminous gas discharge" *i.e.* the tube lights up in a colour which depends on the gas, as its atoms are ionized and excited. **JOHANN HEINRICH WILHELM GEISSLER** (1814-1879) was a Thuringian glass-blower who founded a scientific instrument company in Bonn in 1852 (see **KIPP'S APPARATUS**) and discovered this constructive outlet for his talents in 1857, inventing the gas discharge tube and the mercury vacuum pump essential for its functioning. These were publicly demonstrated in 1864. By the end of his life, Geissler tubes were being mass produced for "scientific" entertainments. Both devices are essential precursors to some important experimental physics – see **CROOKES' TUBE**. (MW)

[346] GENERAL BELGRANO

The Argentine navy cruiser named after **General MANUEL JOSÉ JOAQUÍN CORAZÓN DE JESÚS BELGRANO** (1770-1820), hero of Argentina's 1816 War of Independence, the second Argentine vessel of that name, was sunk with a loss of a third of her crew by a British submarine *HMS Conqueror* during the Falklands War. Even in Britain, at that time in the grip of jingoistic fervour whipped up by the gutter press, the propriety/legality of the sinking was a matter of controversy, it being alleged that as the *Belgrano* was running for home when she was attacked, she ought to have been left alone. The same might have been said of the sinking of the *Bismarck* but wasn't. The sinking of the *Belgrano*, however tragic the loss of life, was nevertheless an outstanding instance of what military persons call "the principle of economy of force" in that a single salvo of three torpedoes* took the entire Argentine navy out of the war – and perhaps in the process spared many lives.

* Though *Conqueror* was a nuclear-powered submarine, the torpedoes used were conventional Mk8 torpedoes of a design dating back to the 1920s (see **WHITEHEAD TORPEDO**)

[347] GEORGE'S STAR – see URANUS

[348] GERRYMANDER

The practice of re-drawing electoral boundaries in order to influence the outcome of a vote has a long history as part of the democratic process. Indeed, as some cynics have observed, in the home of the brave and the land of the free, vote-rigging is as old as democracy itself and still, visibly, has plenty of life left in it.* The technique is irrevocably if not perhaps quite fairly associated with the name of **ELBRIDGE GERRY** (1744-1814), Governor of Massachusetts from 1800-1812 and, briefly thereafter, Vice-President of the USA under James Madison. In 1812, when Gerry's party, the Republicans, were redistricting the state of Massachusetts to ensure the return of a larger number of state senators than Republican voting strength would normally justify, someone noticed that the shape of one re-jigged boundary resembled a salamander (a lizard-like amphibian) and the hybrid coinage **GERRYMANDER** was created to describe it. The usage caught on. It was at first used to denote both the electoral district and the member returned by that district, though it was soon pressed into service as a verb, now its main use. It is normally pronounced with an initial "j" sound, while Gerry's name was pronounced with a hard "g".

* Pots and kettles, of course – witness the recent "banana republic" shenanigans in Birmingham over postal votes.

[349] GHIORSIUM

The reader who has encountered any of the entries for: **CURIUM, EINSTEINIUM,**

FERMIUM, MENDELEVIUM, NOBELIUM, LAWRENCIUM, RUTHERFORDIUM, SEABORGIUM, BOHRIUM, MEITNERIUM and RÖNTGENIUM, will have realised that it is a mark of the highest distinction in science to have a chemical element named after one. This honour is also richly deserved by Californian nuclear scientist ALBERT GHIORSO (b. 1915) who has been a co-discoverer of many of these new "synthetic" elements with atomic numbers from 95 to 106. In 1999 the synthesis of the heaviest element yet known, of atomic number 118, was first claimed by the team at Lawrence Berkeley National Laboratory led by Victor Ninov; the name GHIORSIUM was proposed for it. Unfortunately, this turned out to be "the element that never was". The experimental results proved unrepeatable, and accusations of data falsification stirred up a scientific scandal, resulting in the departure of the team leader. The element 118 was finally made in 2006 in Dubna by a joint US/Russian collaboration; chemically it should be a noble gas, but no-one has ever had enough to confirm this, since only three atoms of it are believed to have existed, briefly – *i.e.* for about one millisecond. According to the Byzantine rules of chemical nomenclature, element 118 is now provisionally labelled with the infelicitous title of Ununoctium, until an international committee reaches agreement on who or where it should celebrate. It shares this nominative limbo with all the new elements beyond atomic number 112. (MW)

[350] GIBBERISH

Unintelligible speech – otherwise babble, jabber, gabble, gobbledygook, twaddle and balderdash – the origins of this word may simply be onomatopoeic, but a favoured attribution is to GEBER the Latinised name adopted by a 14th-century alchemist of uncertain identity, possibly the Franciscan monk, Paul of Taranto. His pseudonym was protection from ecclesiastical disapproval, because the practice of alchemy was proscribed by Pope John XXII in 1317. Like all medieval alchemists, Geber was notorious for the obscurity of his writings (see HERMETIC TEACHINGS). What is certain is that Geber was trading on the good name of the most celebrated and influential of 8th-century Islamic alchemists, ABU MUSA JÂBIR IBN HAYYÂN (*ca.* 721-815), who was born in Tus, Persia, became court physician to Caliph Harun al-Rashid, and made significant contributions to proto-chemical knowledge, including nitric acid (*aqua fortis*) and ammonium chloride (*sal ammoniac*). He is also credited with the sulphur-mercury theory of metal formation. Numerous works in the alchemical canon under the authorship of "Geber" are now thought to be pseudepigraphical: a goldmine for scholars. (MW)

[351] GIBBS FREE ENERGY

American mathematician JOSIAH WILLARD GIBBS (1839-1903) was born in New Haven, Connecticut, of a distinguished academic dynasty. Having graduated and obtained his PhD at Yale, in 1866 he departed to Germany for three years, where he was influenced by **KIRCHHOFF** and **HELMHOLTZ,** but returned to his *alma mater* in 1869 to become professor of mathematical physics in 1871, for the rest of his productive life. He was an outstanding theoretician of the physical sciences, especially thermodynamics, of which he is regarded as a founding father (see **CARNOT** and **BOLTZMANN**). He also invented vector analysis. **GIBBS FREE ENERGY** is given the symbol G: it is the thermodynamic quantity that determines the position of chemical equilibria. The core equation is $\Delta G = \Delta H - T\Delta S$ where Δ signifies "the change in...", H is the enthalpy (heat content), S is the entropy (degree of disorder) of the system, and T the temperature in **KELVINS**. One of the many formulations of the Second Law of Thermodynamics states that, for a spontaneous reaction, ΔG must be negative. So chemical reactions are driven not only by giving out heat, but also by increasing entropy. More of Gibbs eponymous brain-children are the **GIBBS-DUHEM EQUATION,** the **GIBBS-HELMHOLTZ EQUATION** and **GIBBS PHASE RULE** – of great value and generality in the theory of heterogeneous equilibria. (MW)

[352] GIDEON BIBLE

"The Gideons" are members of an evangelical association founded in 1899 in Boscobel, Wisconsin. They take their name from the biblical hero Gideon, a judge of the Israelites, for whom they entertain a particular admiration. Their method of propagating the gospel is as simple as it is practical: they place copies of the Bible (usually the **KING JAMES VERSION**) in hotel rooms, prisons, and hospitals. Nearly one and a half billion copies of Holy Writ have been distributed in this way since the practice started in 1908. That's a lot of bread cast upon a lot of waters – though with what results, God alone knows. The organisation has as its symbol a torch and pitcher in reference to the part played by these homely items in Gideon's resounding defeat of the dreaded Midianites related in *Judges*, chapter 7. Following his liberation of Israel from Midianite oppression, Gideon was offered the kingship and refused.

[353] GILBERT

The **GILBERT** is the c.g.s. unit, symbol Gi, of magnetomotive force (see also **OERSTED, GAUSS** and **TESLA**) and is defined by $10/4\pi$ **AMPÈRE**-turns. English physician **WILLIAM GILBERT** (1544-1603), also known as **GYLBERDE,** was born in Colchester, Essex. He was educated at St. John's College, Cambridge, and elected fellow in 1561. He settled in London in 1573 to practise medicine, became President of the College of Physicians in 1600, and was appointed physician to Queen Elizabeth in 1601, in the last years of her reign, and subsequently to King James I. Gilbert is reputed to be "the father of magnetism and electricity". His *De*

Magnete, Magneticisque Corporibus, et de Magno Magnete Tellure of 1600 is often cited as a milestone marking the beginnings of modern science – "the first textbook of physics". Within its six volumes, Gilbert was the first to describe and explain terrestrial magnetism (he was an early **COPERNICAN**), modelling the Earth with a spherical lodestone,* which he called a *terella*, and demonstrating how a compass needle, called a *versorium*, not only pointed North but also exhibited the "angle of dip" which had been discovered in 1581 by mathematical instrument-maker Robert Norman.** Gilbert even tried to account for the deviation of the magnetic Pole. From his studies of the attractive force generated by rubbing amber (Greek: *elektron*) Gilbert coined the new Latin word *electricus* ("like amber") to describe the effect, which gave rise to the English word "electricity" in 1646. (MW)

* A naturally-magnetized piece of the mineral, magnetite, Fe_3O_4, magnetic iron ore – first noted in the 6th century BC by **THALES OF MILETUS**.

** *The Newe Attractive*, London 1581.

[354] GILLETT METHOD – see SCOVILLE TEST

[355] GINI COEFFICIENT

CORRADO GINI (1884-1965) was an Italian statistician and sociologist. In his 1912 paper "Variabilitá e mutabilitá" he proposed a measure of statistical dispersion that has since become known as the **GINI COEFFICIENT**. Its most common use is as a measure of inequality in the distribution of incomes. It is expressed as a decimal fraction from 0 (perfectly equal distribution – i.e. everyone has the same income) to 1 (perfectly unequal – i.e. one person has all the income and no one else has any). Countries with a small number of very rich people and a large number of very poor people – an increasingly common situation world-wide – would therefore have a high Gini number, and countries where the gap between rich and poor is less glaring would have a low one. The advantage of the Gini coefficient is, therefore, that it reveals the inequalities which another measure such as average per capita income or total GDP would conceal. In oil-rich Azerbaijan, for instance, where per capita GDP is rising steadily, the appearance of general prosperity is belied by the fact that the country's Gini coefficient rose from 0.275 in 1989 to 0.58 in 2002 and is almost certainly still rising.* Gini was a supporter of Fascism and had an interest in eugenics that would today be considered unhealthy.

* *Geographical Journal* 173.3 2007, pp. 210, 212.

[356] GLASITES – see SANDEMANIANS

[357] GLAUBER'S SALT

Called *sodium sulphate decahydrate* by chemists and *mirabilite* by geologists, when it occurs naturally. A colourless, soluble, crystalline salt, with a saline, bitter taste, it was used formerly as a laxative, but is today important for the manufacture of detergents, glass, and paper pulp. This rather dull substance belies the original name, *sal mirabile Glauberi*, so enthusiastically bestowed on it in 1658 by its German discoverer, the alchemist **JOHANN RUDOLF GLAUBER** (1604-68), who was born at Karlstadt but eventually settled in Amsterdam. The miraculous healing powers that he attributed to his salt turn out to have been overstated. (MW)

[358] GODOLPHIN ARABIAN

A stallion of Yemeni stock born around the year 1724, one of four horses sent by the Bey of Tunis to King Louis XV of France. Three of the four were turned loose in the forests of Brittany to "improve" the local breed. The fourth was bought by Edward Coke of Derbyshire and on his death in 1733 bequeathed by him to **LORD GODOLPHIN** (1678-1766), the 2nd Earl. The Arabian, also known as "The Barb" after his homeland in "High Barbaree", lived until 1753 and is counted one of the three founders of the English Thoroughbred race. (See also **BYERLEY TURK** and **DARLEY ARABIAN**). The French writer Eugène Sue (1804-1857) based a novel on the traditions, many of them spurious, surrounding this famous horse, A second (children's) novel was written around him by Marguerite Henry and entitled *King of the wind* (1991).

[359] GODWIN'S LAW

States that: "As an online discussion grows longer, the probability of a comparison involving Nazis or Hitler approaches 1." Its author, American lawyer **MICHAEL WAYNE GODWIN** (b. 1957) has certainly hit on an important truth here, and, judging by the frequency with which such comparisons are resorted to in ordinary discourse, one which applies more widely than to wrangles conducted on the internet. Note that Godwin's observation says nothing about the appropriateness or otherwise of any particular reference to Nazidom. Clearly, the appellation "little Hitler" applied in the heat of the moment to traffic wardens and the like is well over the top. On the other hand, there can surely be general agreement that Hitler and Hitler's Germany set a standard of nastiness by which other nastinesses can legitimately be measured.

[360] GOETHEANUM

This impressively idiosyncratic piece of architecture, located at Dornach, near Basel, was designed, and its construction supervised, by Austrian-born **RUDOLF STEINER** (1861-1925) founder of the Anthroposophical Society, and named in honour of German culture-hero **JOHANN WOLFGANG VON GOETHE** (1749-1832), whose papers on scientific subjects Steiner had helped to edit. The present structure, which is a protected national monument, is actually the second on the site. The first

GOETHEANUM, which was constructed entirely in wood, was erected between 1913 and 1920, and intended as a centre for the artistic and educational activities of the Anthroposophical movement. On New Year's Eve 1922-3 it was destroyed by arsonists, possibly Nazi-inspired. Its successor, in appearance something between the Agia Sophia and the Guggenheim Museum, and built this time entirely in poured concrete, was also designed by Steiner though he died before its completion. (For more on Steiner's work and ideas, see **STEINER SCHOOLS.**)

[361] GOETHITE

An iron-bearing mineral, universal in its occurrence, which may explain why it is named after a universal man: **JOHANN WOLFGANG VON GOETHE** (1749-1832). The mineral is familiarly called "brown iron oxide", but chemists would insist on iron(III) oxide hydroxide, $FeO(OH)$. It is a major component of rust and occurs in most soils. It is the commonest iron ore next to haematite. Iron is the second most abundant metal in the earth's crust, amounting to 6.2%. Known since prehistoric times, **GOETHITE** has always been used as an earth colour by artists: clays stained with varying amounts of it constitute the familiar ochre, sienna, and umber pigments, which were used 17000 years ago in the celebrated cave-drawings of Lascaux. For minerals which, by contrast, *are* named after their discoverers, see **SCHEELITE**. (MW)

[362] GOLDBACH'S CONJECTURE

This is one of the last great problems that still remains unsolved in the branch of mathematics called Number Theory (see also **MERSENNE NUMBERS**). **GOLDBACH'S CONJECTURE** is so deliciously simple that even mathematical dunces should have no difficulty getting their heads around it: *any even integer (i.e. even whole number) greater than 2 can be expressed as the sum of two prime numbers.** Thus:

4=2+2   6=3+3   8=3+5   10=3+7 or 5+5   12=5+7   14=3+11 or 7+7
16=3+13 or 5+11   18=5+13 or 7+11 ...etc.

these are known as **GOLDBACH PARTITIONS**. No one has ever found an exception to this rule, but no one knows if it is *always* true. No proof has been offered. It has been tested by computer and found true for all even numbers up to about 10^{18}; beyond that – who knows? Prussian mathematician **CHRISTIAN GOLDBACH** (1690-1764) was born in Königsberg (Kaliningrad) and became professor at the Imperial Academy of St. Petersburg. His conjecture was stated in 1742 in a letter to **EULER,** with whom he is also partnered in the **GOLDBACH-EULER THEOREM** – which is a tad too hard for mathematical dunces. (MW)

*A prime number is divisible only by 1 and itself. Mathematicians no longer consider 1 to be a prime number. (Why?)

[363] GOLDSCHMIDT'S REACTION

As its alternative name of "thermite" implies, this is a very energetic chemical reaction, between powdered aluminium and iron(III) oxide (sometimes other oxides – of chromium, manganese or copper – are used for specialist purposes). The reaction can only be initiated at very high temperature with a "fuse" – usually burning magnesium metal – whereupon the aluminium grabs the oxygen from the iron oxide, reducing it to molten iron; the heat evolved makes the process self-sustaining, generating temperatures approaching 2500° Celsius. The materials are highly portable, and provide a very useful "low-tech" way of welding railway or tram tracks together *in situ*; while the thermite lance, using the same reaction, is a handy tool for boring holes in tough substances such as reinforced concrete or the doors of bank vaults to which someone has lost the key. **JOHANNES WILHELM GOLDSCHMIDT** (1861-1923) was born in Berlin, and studied at the University there under **ROBERT BUNSEN**. He invented the thermite reaction in 1893, and patented it in 1895. The family firm of *Chemische Fabrik Theodore Goldschmidt*, founded by his father, was the corporate progenitor of the present-day chemical giant *Evonik-Degussa GmbH*, which bears the stigma of having manufactured *Zyklon-B* during WWII. (MW)

[364] GOODNIGHT-LOVING TRAIL

In the aftermath of the Civil War, Texas cattlemen braved long and dangerous journeys to get their cattle from Texas (where they had almost no value) to markets in Kansas, Missouri, and elsewhere. Some of these droving routes were named after the men who pioneered them, and among the most enterprising of these hardy types was ex-Texas Ranger **CHARLES GOODNIGHT** (1836-1929), who drove cattle north from the Texas panhandle in 1866 with an older partner **OLIVER LOVING** (b. 1812). Loving died on the journey of wounds suffered in a fight with Comanche Indians but Goodnight survived and in the years that followed vastly expanded the scope and range of his operations, taking herds as far north as Colorado and Montana. He is credited with the design of that indispensable aid to trail-driving, the "chuck wagon". In our own day, Goodnight and Loving ride again, so to speak, as Woodrow Call and Augustus McCrae in Larry McMurtry's wonderful western epic *Lonesome Dove*. Lonesome Dove's black cowby Deets also has his real-life counterpart in Goodnight's Bose Ikard, for whom his employer wrote the following epitaph:

> *Served with me for four years on the Goodnight-Loving trail, never shirked a duty or disobeyed an order, rode with me in many stampedes, participated in three engagements with the Comanche, splendid behavior.*

(See Larry McMurtry in *New York Review of Books*, May 29 2008.)

[365] GORDON RIOTS

LORD GEORGE GORDON (1751-1793), the youngest son of Cosmo George, Duke of Gordon, served in the Navy, resigned after a quarrel with LORD SANDWICH, and entered Parliament in 1774. (The pocket borough of Ludgershall was bought for him a by a political rival who wanted to stand unopposed in Inverness-shire where Gordon was a candidate.) In 1778, a Relief Act was passed which removed the civil disabilities hitherto imposed on Roman Catholics. In 1780 Gordon put himself at the head of an anti-Catholic protest movement demanding repeal of the Act and led a mob on a march to Westminster under the "No Popery" banner. Things got out of hand, the rabble turned nasty, and there followed several days of rioting, mayhem, civil disorder, destruction of property, and religious excitement the like of which has probably not been enjoyed by London's lower orders before or since. Prisons were broken open, Newgate set on fire, a number of Catholic chapels burnt to the ground, the Bank of England and other public buildings attacked, and the houses of prominent Catholics ransacked. This glorious spree was only ended at the cost of some 500 killed and wounded when the inevitable military crack-down followed. 21 of the rioters were hanged. Gordon himself was accused of High Treason but got off. However, given that his lordship was definitely several sandwiches short of a picnic, it was not to be expected that his erratic career as troublemaker would end there. And it did not. It ended in Newgate Prison where he was confined in 1788 following his conviction on charges of libelling Marie Antoinette, the English justice system, and the French ambassador. Meanwhile he had been (briefly) exiled to Holland, excommunicated by the Archbishop of Canterbury, and converted to Judaism. The Gordon Riots form the background for one of Dickens' least successful novels, *Barnaby Rudge*.

[366] GOSIO GAS

Probably the only eponymous gas, this is a metabolic by-product of certain micro-organisms feeding on arsenic-containing media. It enjoys a fascinating forensic history of insidious poisoning and death, caused by moulds growing on wallpaper decorated with arsenical pigments. *See* SCHEELE'S GREEN. The Italian physician, BARTOLOMEO GOSIO (1865-1944) was called upon to investigate an epidemic of sudden infant deaths, which he attributed to toxicity in the environment. In 1891, by growing common bread mould on mashed potatoes laced with arsenic oxide, he isolated the highly poisonous vapour, GOSIO GAS, which kills by paralysing the nervous system – as many lab rats discovered to their detriment. Gosio isolated several such active strains of "arsenic fungi", and from chemical analysis, he concluded that the gas was diethylarsine. It wasn't until 1931 that the English scientist Frederick Challenger, while investigating cases of arsenic poisoning in the Forest of Dean, correctly identified GOSIO GAS as trimethylarsine.

The presence of this poison is usually betrayed by its powerful garlic odour, although certain cuisines may mask its threatening smell. (MW)

[367] GOUGH MAP

The earliest known road map of Britain dating (on palaeographic and place-name evidence) from about 1360 and showing the principal towns, the roads connecting them, and the distances between them. The outline of mainland Britain, aligned so that east is at the top, is drawn with remarkable accuracy as regards the east and south of the country but becomes more speculative in the highland zones of the west and north. The map is drawn on vellum and measures roughly 46 by 21 inches. It takes the name by which it is commonly known from the English antiquary **RICHARD GOUGH** (1735-1809), who acquired it at auction for a price of two-and-sixpence in 1774. Nothing is known of its authorship or provenance. Gough was a considerable scholar, historian, linguist and bibliophile with a special interest in British topography, a Fellow, and later Director, of the Society of Antiquaries, and a Fellow of the Royal Society (1775). Among his principal works is the snappily-titled 3-volume *Sepulchral Monuments of Great Britain, applied to illustrate the history of families, manners, habits, and arts at the different periods from the Norman Conquest to the Seventeenth Century.* His first considerable work *Atlas renovatus or Geography modernised* was published in 1751 when Gough was only sixteen. On his death, he bequeathed his collection of books, prints and manuscripts to the **BODLEIAN LIBRARY** where the map may be inspected today.

[368] GOWLAND'S LOTION

In Jane Austen's *Persuasion,* the egregious Sir Walter Elliott advises Mrs Clay to use **GOWLAND'S LOTION** to "freshen" her complexion. The lotion, named after its inventor, the apothecary **JOHN GOWLAND** (d.1776), contained mercuric chloride (then known as "corrosive sublimate") and acted as what today would be called a "face peel". It remained popular throughout the 19th century as a means of removing facial blemishes. In 1872, for example, it was selling for 4 shillings and sixpence a pint to ladies who had incautiously exposed themselves to sunshine and fresh air with consequent damage (roughening, redness) to their delicate skins. What Sir Walter didn't mention to Mrs Clay was that Gowland's lotion was widely employed to hide or remove visible marks of venereal disease.

[369] GRADGRIND

The name of a leading character in Dickens' *Hard Times* (1854) has come to stand for a person whose approach to education is rigid, formal, fact-obsessed, and unimaginative. We may reasonably assume that the first element of **Mr THOMAS**

GRADGRIND'S surname is meant to echo the name of a school textbook, the *Gradus ad Parnassum,* known to every Victorian schoolboy simply as "*the gradus*", which aimed to teach the elements of Greek and Latin poetry by listing words and marking the "quantities" (long/short – see **SAPPHIC STANZA**) of each syllable. In other words, in the wrong hands it could be used to teach poetry as if the writing of it were a merely mechanical process whereby poems could be put together just by putting the right numbers in the right order. So the gradus came to stand for rote learning and the death of creative imagination and was properly hated by children as an instrument of dull and repressive authority. The first *Gradus* was compiled in 1702 by the Jesuit Paul Aler, but 19th-century schoolchildren are more likely to have been acquainted with those of C.D. Yonge (1850) or Ainger and Wintle (1890) – both for Latin poetry – or, for Greek poetry, those of Maltby (1815) or Brasse (1828).

* The second half of the surname, of course, describes what Mr Gradgrind, an industrialist, is doing to the faces of the poor.

[370] GRAFENBERG INTER-UTERINE RING – see G-SPOT

[371] GRAHAM'S CELESTIAL BED

Medical charlatan **JAMES GRAHAM** (1745-1794) has been described, somewhat anachronistically and perhaps too indulgently, as a "sex therapist" (a confusing term which doesn't make it clear whether sex is the object or agent of the therapy), though it is undeniable that his m.o. relied heavily on a simultaneous appeal to two universal human preoccupations – sex and health. Graham was born in Edinburgh and studied at the University there but without graduating. On a trip to America, he became interested in electricity and magnetism and, like **MESMER,** proclaimed a possibly quite genuine belief in the medical possibilities of these exciting novelties. Following various peregrinations, the climax of "Doctor" Graham's career came in 1779 when he opened his "Temple of Health" at the Adelphi in London. Here he offered paying customers an unusual blend of quasi-erotic spectacle, sensual delights, and medical lectures and demonstrations. In 1781 Graham launched a new enterprise, the "Temple of Hymen" in Pall Mall. Here, the centrepiece was the "**CELESTIAL BED**", which was not on public display but could be rented out by the better-heeled or more desperate for £50 a night, a stiffish sum but cheap at the price as it offered a guaranteed cure for impotence or infertility or both. The gorgeously canopied bed, was fitted with hundreds of concealed magnets* weighing a total of 15 cwt, and was equipped with mechanisms for giving its occupants an occasional stimulating belt of electricity, whiff of perfume, or blast of music. It was mounted on glass legs, and measured 12 feet by 9. The sheets were of silk, and the mattress was stuffed with high quality wheat straw or, on occasion, high quality horsehair ("produced at vast expense from the tails of English stallions" in the words of Graham's prospectus). Sadly, Graham's talent for showmanship wasn't matched by financial acumen and he was forced to sell up and return to Edinburgh with empty pockets. In 1786, however, he was back in London demonstrating his latest discovery – "earth therapy", which involved his burying himself in mud for days on end. By this time Graham's behaviour was becoming increasingly irrational and he had developed an obsessive interest in **ONANISM**, or "self-pollution" as he called it, which he saw as the root of all evil, medically speaking. Finally, he succumbed to religious mania and died in Edinburgh at the age of only 49.

* Hitler's deputy Rudolf Hess slept in a bed aligned according to feng-shui principles, over which were suspended powerful magnets designed to increase his sexual potency.

[372] GRAHAM'S LAW

of 1829 refers to the rate of diffusion (properly *effusion*) of a gas through a porous barrier or narrow orifice: *the rate is inversely proportional to the square root of the molecular weight of the gaseous substance*. The justification comes from the kinetic theory of "ideal" gases: essentially, the lighter the molecules, the faster they travel, on average. This scrap of basic physical chemistry may sound boring, but one of its historical applications was literally earth-shattering. To obtain fissile material for the first atomic bomb, it was necessary to enrich the proportion of the lighter isotope of uranium, U^{235}, the minor component (0.7%) in the naturally occurring element, which is 99.3% U^{238}. These two isotopes are chemically identical and cannot be separated by any reaction; their only distinction is this tiny (~1%) mass difference, which can be exploited by gaseous diffusion. The feasibility of doing this was first proposed by Franz Simon at Oxford in 1940 (see **MAUD COMMITTEE**). The enrichment was subsequently achieved during the WWII Manhattan Project, in the "K-25" plant on the secret "Site X" of the Oak Ridge, Tennessee, reservation. K-25 was then the largest building in the world and, when switched on, consumed one sixth of the total US electricity supply. The natural uranium metal was converted into the most volatile of its known compounds, uranium hexafluoride UF_6 (no mean feat chemically, because this stuff is ferociously corrosive). The gaseous "hex" was then passed through a "cascade" of thousands of diffusion vessels with porous barriers; whereupon the molecules containing the heavier isotope lagged slightly behind, as required by **GRAHAM'S LAW**, successively enriching the concentration of the fissile U^{235} to "weapons-grade" levels – as the unfortunate people of Hiroshima were to discover on 6th August 1945, when history took a new path. Scottish chemist **THOMAS GRAHAM** (1805-1869) was born in Glasgow, became professor there in 1830, and moved in 1837 to University College, London. In 1855 he was appointed Master of the Mint. In 1841 he founded the Chemical Society of London, which was granted its Royal Charter in 1980, becoming the Royal Society of Chemistry. Its administrative headquarters in Cambridge are named **THOMAS GRAHAM HOUSE**, but its dignified home since 1857 has always been **BURLINGTON HOUSE**. Graham also discovered the principles of dialysis – to the eternal benefit of renal patients everywhere. (MW)

[373] GRANGERISE

In 1769, **JAMES GRANGER** (1723-1776), vicar of Shiplake in Oxfordshire and a celebrated print-collector, published a *Biographical history of England* containing blank leaves onto which the purchaser might paste prints – perhaps cut from other books – depicting the characters mentioned in the text. More loosely, the verb "grangerise" came to mean to illustrate with pictures or photographs. Thus T.E. Lawrence writing to D.G. Hogarth* in 1927 speaks of "Graingerising" a copy of *The seven pillars of wisdom* the next time they meet.

* (1862-1929) Archaeologist, traveller and scholar. Director of the Arab Bureau in Cairo during WWI.

[374] GRANT'S GAZELLE

Gazella granti is one of three African creatures named after the soldier and explorer **JAMES AUGUSTUS GRANT** (1827-1892) who accompanied Speke (the discoverer of Lake Victoria and hence of the source of the Nile) on Speke's second East African expedition of 1861-3, which confirmed Speke's earlier discovery. See Grant's *A walk across Africa* (1864) and Speke's *Journal of the discovery of the Nile* (1863). The other two creatures bearing Grant's name are **GRANT'S DESERT GOLDEN MOLE** (*Eremytalpa granti*) and **GRANT'S ZEBRA**, a subspecies of the Common Zebra (*Equus burchelli*). The Golden Mole is the African version of the European mole with a total of 15 species. For another example, see **STUHLMANN'S GOLDEN MOLE**.

[375] GRAY

The SI unit, symbol Gy, of a dose of radiation. It measures the amount of energy delivered when the radiation is absorbed by matter. One **GRAY** is defined by the dose of radiation that liberates one **JOULE** of energy per kilogram of substance. It replaces the older unit of the rad, and is equal to 100 rads. **LOUIS HAROLD GRAY** (1905-1965) was a British nuclear physicist who studied under **RUTHERFORD** at the **CAVENDISH LABORATORY** but became interested in the biological effects of radiation, so founded and developed the subscience of radiobiology. He performed most of his work at Mount Vernon Hospital, London, founding there the **GRAY LABORATORY**. (MW)

[376] GREGG SHORTHAND – see PITMAN SHORTHAND

[377] GRESHAM'S LAW

Sir THOMAS GRESHAM (?1519-1579) acted as financial adviser to Edward VI, and to Queens Mary and Elizabeth, negotiating foreign and domestic loans for the government. He founded the Royal Exchange in 1565, Gresham's College in 1575. His observation that if two coinages were in circulation, one being more debased than the other, the "good" coins would tend to be hoarded so that only the "bad" remained in circulation. In 1857 this observation was formulated as "bad money drives out good" by economist and banking theorist H.D. MacLeod (1821-1902) and christened by him "GRESHAM'S LAW", though in fact the idea was not original to Gresham but had previously occurred to earlier writers including the French savant Nicolas Oresme (1320-1382).

[378]
GRIGNARD REACTION

The sub-science of organic chemistry (*i.e.* that of the compounds of carbon) is a veritable hothouse of rampant eponymy. Immortality in the annals of organic chemical fame is guaranteed by devising a new reaction. In consequence there are well over a thousand named organic reactions, most of them celebrating successful organic chemists. They are required reading for unfortunate students of the subject. A full listing here is impossible, since it would exceed the rest of this volume in length but, as a token offering, here are the names of some whose eponymous organic reactions have earned them a NOBEL PRIZE in chemistry: FISCHER (1902) GRIGNARD (1912) DIELS and ALDER (1950), and WITTIG (1979). The chief characteristic of all these reactions lies in their cunning ways of forming bonds between carbon atoms, thereby enabling the construction of ever more complicated molecules from simpler precursors. This is the whole art of organic synthesis, without which we should not be enjoying the benefits of today's pharmaceutical industry. The French chemist FRANÇOIS AUGUSTE VICTOR GRIGNARD (1871-1935) was born in Cherbourg, the son of a sailmaker, and became professor at the University of Nancy. His nationality is exceptional – most other organic laureates are German, suggesting that the disciplines of organic chemistry may hold a special appeal for the Teutonic mind. HERMAN EMIL FISCHER (1852-1919), who worked at the Universities of Munich, Erlangen, Würtzburg and Berlin, ranks as one of the greatest organic chemists: his name is attached to indole synthesis and, among much else, the FISCHER PROJECTION for delineating the precise shapes of sugar molecules. OTTO PAUL HERMAN DIELS (1876-1954) and his student KURT ALDER (1902-1958) of Kiel University, are celebrated in the DIELS-ALDER REACTION, while GEORG WITTIG (1897-1987) of Tübingen has both a reaction and a rearrangement named in his memory. There are many, many more. (MW)

[379] GROLIER BINDING

The term **GROLIER BINDING** is familiar to book-lovers, and more especially to those specialist bibliophiles who are more interested in a book's cover than in its contents. The gentleman in question **JEAN GROLIER, Vicomte D'AGUISY** (1479-1575) was not, as might carelessly be supposed (tsk tsk), a bookbinder but a book collector who held important offices of state under François I, King of France. He assembled a library of some 3000 volumes, magnificently bound by Italian, and later French, craftsmen operating under Grolier's direction. The Grolier style, in its developed form, features a tracery of coloured strap work, with intricately-tooled goldwork patterns filling the spaces. The books were stamped with the inscription *IO. GROLIERII ET AMICORUM* on the front cover, and on the back, *PORTIO MEA DOMINE SIT IN TERRA VIVENTIUM* ("Let my portion, O Lord, be in the land of the living"). Grolier's library was broken up in the seventeenth century but between three and four hundred of his books are known to have survived. Meanwhile the term "Grolier binding" has come to mean any binding in a style even vaguely resembling Grolier's originals.

[380] GROTTHUSS-DRAPER LAW

The First Law of Photochemistry, attributed originally to Grotthuss in 1817, is intuitively obvious: *for light to induce a chemical change in a substance it must be absorbed.* But the converse does not follow that all light absorbed by a substance necessarily induces chemical reaction in it – instead it may be re-emitted (as fluorescence or phosphorescence, see **BALDWIN'S PHOSPHORUS**) or converted into heat. At the time this idea lacked promulgation and was soon forgotten, but lay ripe for rediscovery when scientific interest in the effects of light had been sharply focussed by the invention of photography *ca.* 1839 (see **DAGUERREOTYPE** and **TALBOTYPE**). Photochemist, John Draper then re-invented this generalization *ca.* 1841 and thereby acquired a part-share in the credit. German chemist **Freiherr CHRISTIAN JOHANN DIETRICH THEODORE VON GROTTHUSS** (1785-1822) was born in Leipzig. He is also known for the **GROTTHUSS MECHANISM** of electrolytic conduction in aqueous media (1806). Scientist and philosopher **JOHN WILLIAM DRAPER** (1811-1882) was born in St. Helens, England and studied at University College, London. Following his father's death in 1831 the family emigrated to Virginia and Draper became a naturalised US citizen, graduated in medicine from Pennsylvania, and by 1838 was professor of chemistry at New York University. He has a number of photographic "firsts" to his credit: the first portrait, the first astrophotograph, and the first detailed picture of the moon. He was also the first President of the American Chemical Society. (MW)

[381] G-SPOT

While resident at Kiel, the gynaecologist **ERNST GRAFENBERG** (1881-1957), creator of the **GRAFENBERG INTRA-UTERINE RING** and thus the inventor of the IUD, described in a 1950 article in the *International Journal of Sexology* the existence of a bean-sized bundle of nerves in the female reproductive system which, when stimulated, produces intense sexual arousal leading in some women to significant ejaculation at orgasm. The evidence for this claim was purely anecdotal and it was not until 1982 that the significance of the **GRAFENBERG SPOT** or **G-SPOT** became a matter for wider debate. Whilst the existence and/or reproductive significance of the G-spot remains controversial, 1,850,000 references on the World Wide Web point to the continuing public and professional fascination with this area of female anatomy. (GJ)

[382] GUILLOTINE

This simple but effective device for separating people from their heads owed its conception and adoption partly to the vast number of people who needed to be executed in the name of Liberty and Fraternity in revolutionary France but partly also to the demands of Equality – what today would be called Political Correctness. Previously, the custom throughout Europe had been to execute common persons by hanging and toffs by beheading with sword or axe. It was Assemblyman **Dr. JOSEPH IGNACE GUILLOTIN** (1738-1814) who pointed out the injustice of this class-biased arrangement, and proposed (1st December, 1789) that in the new France every malefactor, regardless of social status, deserved a business-class send-off. The problem was that skilled beheaders were thin on the ground and the procedure tended to be expensive, drawn-out and fiddly. The answer, clearly, was mechanisation. The proposal was submitted to Dr Antoine Louis, secretary to the Academy of Surgeons, who recommended the adoption of a machine such as that suggested by Guillotin. The Assembly adopted Louis' report (which didn't mention Guillotin by name) and the construction of the machines – for which prototypes already existed in various parts of Europe – was entrusted to a German piano-maker by the name of Schmidt, who contracted to produce a machine for each French *département*. The first public demonstration took place in Paris on 25 April 1792 when it successfully decapitated a highwaymen called Pelletier. The machine was at first christened *Louison* or *Louisette* by the populace, but a juster appreciation of where credit was due led to the official adoption of the name *Guillotine* after its original proposer, who made desperate but unsuccessful efforts to refuse the honour. Guillotin, it should be noted, cannot be said to have *invented* the machine named after him, as similar devices – such as the famous Halifax gibbet – had already been in use for centuries.

[383] GUNNING FOG INDEX

In 1952 an American businessman named **ROBERT GUNNING** published a book entitled *The technique of clear writing*. In it he proposed a formula for assessing the "readability" of any piece of English prose. A sample of about 100 words consisting of complete sentences is selected. The number of sentences is divided by the number of words to give an average sentence length. To this figure is added the percentage of "complex" words (*i.e.* words of 3 or more syllables). Add the two figures and multiply by 0.4. The result is the number of years of formal education that the reader would need to understand the passage. This paragraph, up to the word "passage" has an index of 8, which should mean it is accessible to a pretty wide audience. But prose which is meant to be understood by virtually anybody would need an index of less than 8. This is a fact of some significance in the grimy world of the tabloid press, where the guiding principle is one of contempt for its readers, who are assumed to be stupid. Contempt for the people on whom one depends for a living is not a recipe for psychological health.

[384] GUNTER'S CHAIN

Suveying instrument consisting of a 22-yard-long chain composed of one hundred links, each 7.92 inches in length. The device bears the name of its inventor **EDMUND GUNTER** (1581-1626), clergyman and mathematician, who devoted much of his life to the study and improvement of intruments designed to make life easier for non mathematicians – navigators and surveyors, for example – whose work nevertheless involved mathematical calculation. It has been pointed out that Gunter's division of 22 yards into one hundred parts enabled traditional measures (mile, furlong, acre, and so forth) to be expressed in decimal notation. This still doesn't explain how the number 22 became the base unit of land measurement in this country. It gives us the mile of 1760 yards, the furlong of 220 yards, the acre of the strip-field system – 22 x 220 yards – and, of course, the length of the cricket pitch. All this suggests a set of traditional measurements based on multiples of 11 (a prime number and so not conveniently sub-divisible), but no 11-yard *unit* appears ever to have existed. If it had, it would have been two rods, poles or perches in length (twice five-and-a-half yards). And what might it have been called?

[385] GUPPY

Poecilia reticulata, a popular and attractive freshwater aquarium fish, native to tropical America and the Caribbean, was discovered in Trinidad in the 1860's by British-born naturalist **LECHMERE GUPPY** (1936-1916). The fish was originally christened *Girardinus guppii* (Günther 1866), but the name was later found to be in synonymy and is now in abeyance, though **GUPPY** survives as the common name. For more on the colourful career of the ichthyophilous Mr. Guppy, the reader is directed to *The Reverend Guppy's aquarium* (2009) by Philip Dodd, a miscellany of trawlings through the sometimes weird world of eponymy. Anyone who has enjoyed *What's Who?* will enjoy Mr Dodd's excellent little volume. Contrary to popular belief, Mr. Guppy was not, it seems, a clergyman.

[386] GURNEY

In American usage, a wheeled bed or stretcher ("trolley" in English) used in hospitals and by ambulance services. The name is that of **J. THEODORE GURNEY** who in 1883 patented a form of horse-drawn cab which the hospital gurney supposedly resembles.

[387] GUTENBERG BIBLE

JOHANNES GENSFLEISCH, who adopted the name **GUTENBERG** is generally credited with having produced the first European book printed from movable type – the 42-line* Bible of 1453.** It wasn't in fact, the first book he printed and he was not exactly the inventor of the process – it was, so to speak, in the air at that time. But he certainly invented major improvements in the associated technology, including an adjustable mould for casting type and an oil-based ink. For a man associated with so crucial an event in the history of European (indeed, world) culture, it is surprising that so little is known of his life. He was born in Mainz, probably about 1395, probably trained as a goldsmith, spent most of his working life there or in Strasbourg, and died in Mainz, probably in 1468. His place of burial is unknown and his name does not appear on anything printed by him. The few hard facts we have concerning his career come from the records of lawsuits brought against him by people who had lent him money to advance his business and saw no return. It is supposed that his constant need for fresh capital was due to Gutenberg's unwillingness to commercialise his process until it was perfected, while the constant dissatisfaction of his creditors arose from their being kept in the dark by Gutenberg's secretive habits where the details of his work were concerned.

* *I.e.* 42 lines in each of 2 columns per page. The British Library holds two copies, one on paper and one on vellum. The rarer 36-line Bible is also referred to as "the Gutenberg Bible".

** Aficionados of "turning points in history" will note that this is the date of the fall of Constantinople and the official end of the Hundred Years' War between England and France.

[388] GUYOT PRUNING

Of the various methods of pruning and training grape vines, the **GUYOT SYSTEM** is generally preferred in the more northerly vineyards such as those of Burgundy and Canada. During the autumn and winter following the grape harvest, all but two shoots are pruned away. The longer of these, bearing between 6 and 10 buds, will carry the next season's fruiting branches and is tied into a training wire. The shorter of the two is cut back to only two buds from which will grow the two shoots to be left after the next pruning. The system is named after the French physician and scientist **Dr. JULES GUYOT** (1807-1872). Guyot made a special study of the way viticulture was practiced in all the wine-producing departments of France. His years of research bore fruit in his magnum opus, the 3-volume *Étude des vignobles de France* published in 1868. Guyot is particularly revered in Burgundy and died at Savigny-lès-Beaune in the heart of the Côte d'Or. He is commemorated in the **INSTITUT JULES GUYOT** in Dijon, affiliated to the University of Burgundy and dedicated to teaching and research in viticulture and oenology. (RJ)

H

[389] HABER-BOSCH PROCESS

The **MALTHUSIAN** problem of sustaining the food supplies for the growing human population of this planet has been offered a solution by chemical industry: the "fixation" of nitrogen from the atmosphere.* Regrettably, this same solution also guarantees the provision of sufficient explosives to destroy the said population. Whether we demand ammonia for fertilizers, or nitrates for munitions, these cannot be supplied in sufficient quantity just by animal dung.** Without the industrial Haber-Bosch process for making ammonia out of nitrogen and hydrogen, WWI might well have ended soon after it began. The process was on hand, however, to furnish nitrate explosives for Germany, when it was cut off from supplies of Chilean saltpetre. The process had been invented and patented in 1908 by German chemist **FRITZ HABER** (1868-1934), who found the trick to persuade these unreactive gases into combination by the use of very high pressure, elevated temperature, and a catalyst of metallic oxides: a highly energy-consumptive business. It was commercialised by his brother-in-law, **CARL BOSCH** in 1910. Haber studied at Heidelberg under **BUNSEN**, became director of the Kaiser Wilhelm Institute in Berlin, and received the **NOBEL PRIZE** for Chemistry in 1918. He also enjoyed the unenviable reputation of being the "father of chemical warfare" for his work on chlorine in WWI, but owing to his Jewish connections, he was forced out of Germany by the Nazis in 1933. (MW)

* Nitrogen from the atmosphere is efficiently fixed – at ordinary temperature and pressure – by humble bacteria living within the root nodules of every bean plant. Synthetic chemistry still has a lot to learn from Dame Nature.

** In Elizabethan England, saltpetre (potassium nitrate) for gunpowder was extracted directly from deposits formed in dung-heaps and there existed special government-appointed operators who had the right to invade any and every dung-heap in the kingdom in search of this precious substance. (See Carlo M. Cipolla *Guns and sails in the 16th century* 1965.)

[390] HADRIAN'S WALL

The first phase of the Roman occupation of Britain (43-47 AD) took the invading forces to a stop-line which ran roughly speaking from Exeter to the Humber – the same line which we have since come to know as the "North-South divide". South of this line, marked by the road we know as the Fosse Way, was the best farmland and for the next three centuries this remained the region in which Roman civil settlements (as evidenced by surviving villas – *i.e.* farms) were concentrated. North of the line, occupation was essentially military in character, based on the three legionary fortresses at Caerleon, Chester and York, (all situated, it should be noticed, in places where good farmland was to be found north of the Divide: Gwent and the Vale of Glamorgan, the Cheshire plain, and the Vale of York). Further north again, lowland Scotland was occupied and then given up (we don't know why), and the northern frontier of Roman Britain was fixed along the Tyne-Solway line. It was along this line that in the reign of the **EMPEROR HADRIAN** (117-138) the wall which bears his name was built. Its builders were Roman legionaries but they didn't garrison the finished wall. This task was deputed to auxiliary units, non-citizen troops from formations raised in different parts of the Empire, and in some cases outside it. (On campaign, legionary and auxiliary forces in roughly equal numbers were brigaded together in much the same fashion as British and native troops were in India.) The precise tactical and strategic functions of the Wall are a matter of debate among historians. Though it was clearly constructed to resist assaults from the north, it should not be supposed that the Romans envisaged it as purely defensive. Roman forts and fortresses were built with strong defences but it was not the practice of the Romans to fight from behind walls. Fortresses, rather, were designed to serve as secure bases for offensive operations. It therefore makes sense to regard the Wall as, so to speak, a linear fortress and a jumping-off place for forward operations into bandit country, and not as an early example of the Maginot Line mentality.

[391] HAKLUYT SOCIETY

RICHARD HAKLUYT (1552?-1616) was an English clergyman who made it his business to collect and publish the first-hand accounts of travellers and navigators, both of his own and earlier times. His labours bore fruit in three principal publications: *Divers voyages touching the discovery of America...* (1582); *The principall navigations, voiages and discoveries of the English nation...* (1589); and a revised and much enlarged edition of the *Principall voiages* in 3 volumes (1598-1600). Coming at a time when the maritime nations of Europe, England among them, were discovering a wider world, Hakluyt's work was both timely and influential. In modern times that work has been carried on by the **HAKLUYT SOCIETY** founded in 1846. Between that year and the present the Society has published over 300 volumes of travel narratives, explorer's journals, and accounts of voyages of discovery in every age and in all parts of the world. Each volume is a work of impeccable erudition, expertly edited, fully annotated, translated where necessary, and beautifully produced. This has been a service of incalculable value both to specialist academics and to the general reader with an interest in the history of travel and exploration, since many – indeed most – of these works would otherwise be available, if at all, only with great difficulty and to a privileged few.

[392] HALLEY'S COMET

The famous comet named after **EDMUND HALLEY** (1656-1742) appears in our skies roughly every 76 years. Halley was an English astronomer and mathematician who was the first to calculate its orbit. In 1705 he published *A Synopsis of the Astronomy of Comets*, in which he described the parabolic orbits of 24 comets that had been observed from 1337 to 1698. He showed that the three historic comets of 1531, 1607, and 1682 were so similar in characteristics that they must have been successive returns of the same object and he accurately predicted its return in 1758. It appearance in 1066 was seen by William the Conqueror as a favourable omen but by the English as an augury of doom. The Normans adopted the slogan "*A new star, a new King*" while Harold, only months later, perished at Hastings with most of his army. An image of the comet appears in the Bayeux tapestry above the heads of a group of terrified Saxons and the caption reads "*They are in awe of the stars.*" The first recorded sighting of Halley's Comet has been dated to 239 BC, towards the end of the First Punic War and it was last sighted in 1985-6. Other notable appearances were in 1301, after which Giotto immortalised it by depicting it as The Star of Bethlehem in his painting *The Adoration of the Magi* in the Arena Chapel, Padua; and 1607 when it was sighted by American colonists, who were subsequently plagued by rampant diseases, hostile Indians and near-starvation. In 1456 it appeared to the opposing armies of Turks and Christians facing each other at the Battle of Belgrade. It was reported that it was shaped like an avenging sword, pointing towards the Turks. The Christians won. In general, however, the comet was regarded with superstitious dread and after the fall of Constantinople a prayer was added to the Ave Maria: "*Lord save us from the devil, the Turk, and the comet.*" Ecclesiastical authority saw Halley's comet as an agent of the devil, which led to the myth that the Pope had excommunicated it. The appearance of comets was popularly associated with major disturbances of the natural order – war, pestilence, the deaths of kings, and the fall of nations – a line of thinking embodied in the word "disaster" whose root meaning is " unnatural star" (*cf.* the phrase "ill-starred"). (RS)

[393] HAMILTONIAN MECHANICS

Irish mathematical genius **WILLIAM ROWAN HAMILTON** (1805-1865) was a precocious child who at the age of five could speak Latin, Greek and Hebrew. At age 15 he found an error in the *Méchanique Celeste* of Laplace – one of the great mathematicians of his era. Aged 20 Hamilton was appointed professor of astronomy at Trinity College Dublin. He fell in love with Catherine Disney, who was married off by her family to a parson fifteen years older than she. Heartbroken, he took to drink and poetry. He abandoned astronomy and subsequently made major contributions to mechanics, optics, geometry and algebra. In 1835 he re-cast Newton's laws of motion in a powerful, general way expressing the energy of mechanical systems as special variables. This formula is known as "the Hamiltonian" and was crucial to 20th century quantum mechanics. He later invented quaternions to describe rotations in three dimensions. He began drinking heavily after his marriage to Helen Bailey and died in 1865 following a severe attack of gout. Hamilton was extremely prolific but much of his work never saw the light of day thanks to his habit, while working at his desk, of putting down each filled page of calculations on top of dishes of uneaten or half-eaten food. (GB)

[394] HANSARD

The official printed record of parliamentary proceedings owes its name to LUKE HANSARD (1752-1828) and THOMAS CURSON HANSARD (1776-1833), father and son, both printers by trade. The elder began printing the *Journals* of the House of Commons in 1774, which continued until his death. His work was valued for its accuracy and promptitude. (The scholar Richard Porson reckoned him the most trustworthy printer of Greek texts.) From 1803, the younger Hansard set up his own press and, working independently of his father, started printing the *Parliamentary Debates*, founded by William Cobbett. In 1810 he was imprisoned for libel as Cobbett's printer, Cobbett having, to his credit, fallen foul of the Government by his denunciation of flogging in the army. Thomas Hansard invented an improved type of hand press and was the author of a history of printing entitled *Typographia* (1825). After the death of the elder Hansard, his business was carried on by Thomas's two younger brothers, and the printing of parliamentary records remained in the hands of the Hansard family until 1889. Today *Hansard* is published by an organism calling itself "The Department of the Official Report". Parliamentary speeches are reported almost *verbatim* – minor editing of repetitions, obvious mistakes, etc. is allowed under rules set out in ERSKINE-MAY, the ultimate authority in all matters of parliamentary procedure.

[395] HANSEN'S DISEASE

It is a core principle of Political Correctness, our miserably indequate substitute for good manners, that anything generally regarded as disagreeable or derogatory can be rendered less so – de-stigmatised, in effect – by changing its name. Euphemism rules! So it is not surprising that diseases have been a major target of the renaming programme, among whose victims is leprosy, henceforth to be known as Hansen's Disease. The attribution, however, is fair. It was the Norwegian physician GERHARD HENRIK ARMANER HANSEN (1841-1912) who first identified the causative agent *Mycobacterium leprae*. It would be interesting to know whether the leprosy museum named after Hansen in his home town of Bergen is a big tourist draw.

[396] HANSOM CAB

A two-wheeled, one-horse-drawn people carrier named after architect and inventor, JOSEPH ALOYSIUS HANSOM (1803-1882) who designed and patented it in 1834. It is readily recognisable by the situation of the driver who occupied an elevated seat at the *back* of the vehicle. It would accommodate two passengers. In most people's minds the hansom is first and foremost a device for whirling Sherlock Holmes through fog-bound streets of Darkest London. The word "cab" is a contraction of "cabriolet". Wearing his other hat, Hansom was the architect of Birmingham Town Hall.

[397] HARRISON'S CHRONOMETERS

The problem of determining position at sea was not solved until almost three centuries after the great pioneering voyages of Columbus, Da Gama and company. Latitude can be easily determined by taking the altitude (angular distance above the horizon) either of the Pole Star or that of the Sun at noon. (Noon itself can be fixed by observing the moment at which the Sun appears to hesitate in its upward course before starting to head back towards the horizon.) Longitude is another matter. As early as the sixteenth century it was realised that since a difference in longitude equates to a difference in time, a comparison between two clocks, one set to a known base meridian (Greenwich for example) and the other set to local noon, would tell the mariner what meridian he was currently sitting on. The problem was that the technology of clock-making simply wasn't equal to constructing a timepiece that would remain accurate to within seconds over periods of weeks or months at sea and despite the perturbing effects of the ship's motion, changes in temperature, and variations in barometric pressure. This was the challenge that was met and overcome by the Yorkshire carpenter turned clock-maker* JOHN HARRISON (1693-1776). Between 1735 and 1770 Harrison made five sea-going time-keepers, each more technically perfect than the last. Though they incorporated a number of subtle mechanisms of Harrison's own invention for counteracting the various obstacles to sustained accurate going, it is perhaps fair to say that their excellence was due less to any revolutionary technological advances than to their maker's infinite capacity for taking pains. Patience and persistence were also required of him in his long struggle for proper recognition. Harrison had to wait until shortly before his death at the age of 83 before he was paid in full for his heroic labours by a grateful Government. His clocks were transferred to Greenwich Observatory, where they were found after WWI in a state of disgraceful neglect by the historian and retired naval officer Rupert Gould, who spent years lovingly restoring them at his own expense. Harrison's grave may (and should) be visited in Hampstead church-yard. (For the best general history of marine navigation, see E.G.R Taylor *The haven-finding art* 1956: for Harrison's biography, Dava Sobel *Longitude* 1995; for a detailed technical account of the work of Harrison and other makers, R.T. Gould *The Marine chronometer* 1923 and reprints.)

* Harrison's clock-making career started with a timepiece made entirely of wood.

[398] HARTREE

This is a non-SI unit of energy, used for calculations on the atomic scale of things. Specifically, one **HARTREE** is twice the *binding energy of the hydrogen atom*.* It is defined rather neatly by setting the values of several fundamental constants of nature – such as the mass and charge of the electron, and **PLANCK'S CONSTANT** – equal to one, instead of their usual values in SI units. So the binding energy of the hydrogen atom conveniently becomes 0.5 **HARTREES**, to be compared with the awkward SI value of 2.179872×10^{-18} **JOULES**. Englishman **DOUGLAS RAYNER HARTREE** (1897-1958) was born in Cambridge. His studies at the University were interrupted by ballistics work during WWI, and he obtained his PhD in 1926. In 1929 he was appointed to the Beyer chair of applied mathematics at the University of Manchester, where he built (out of Meccano) a mechanical differential analyser for solving differential equations numerically. He was elected FRS in 1932, and returned to Cambridge in 1946 as Plummer professor of mathematical physics, where he was involved in early applications of digital computers. His chief contribution to theoretical chemistry was to introduce the self-consistent field (SCF) theory for the many-body atom in 1927 which, with some independent input from the Russian physicist **VLADIMIR ALEKSANDROVICH FOCK** (1898-1974) in 1930, provided the **HARTREE-FOCK METHOD** for *ab initio* quantum-mechanical computations, still widely used today. (MW)

* Also called the ionization energy. *i.e.* the amount of energy that must be supplied to separate the H atom into a free electron and a free proton, infinitely far apart and immobile.

[399] HEATH ROBINSON

The name of English artist cartoonist and illustrator **WILLIAM HEATH ROBINSON** (1872-1944) has come to be attached adjectivally to any device or system, usually an improvised and wildly over-complicated lash-up, for performing simple tasks in an unnecessarily roundabout way, or, more generally, to any unreliable-looking structure or machine. His many illustrated books include editions of *Don Quixote* and *The Arabian nights*, but it is for his humour and his love of the absurd and the fantastic that he will be remembered. In America, cartoonist **RUBE GOLDBERG** (1883-1970) demonstrated the same love of the complex and the ridiculous and so finds his name commonly followed by the word "contraption".

[400] HEAVISIDE LAYER

The uppermost reaches of the earth's atmosphere are affected by ionising radiation from the sun and from cosmic rays and thus earn the name *ionosphere*, originally proposed in 1926 by Robert Watson-Watt (1892-1973) of radar fame. The ionosphere in turn is divided into a number of layers on the basis of their atomic composition and electromagnetic properties and labelled (in ascending order of height above the Earth's surface) D. E. E$_S$ and F. In 1902, following initial experiments by NIKOLA TESLA, American physicist and electrical engineer ARTHUR EDWIN KENELLY (1861-1939), and British physicist and mathematician OLIVER HEAVISIDE (1850-1925) simultaneously and independently proposed the existence of a layer of ionised gas at a height of 90-150 km. Its existence was proved in 1924 by Yorkshireman EDWARD VICTOR APPLETON (1892-1965), who was awarded the Nobel prize for his work, while the layer in question was named after Kenelly and Heaviside, though the terms KENELLY-HEAVISIDE layer or more simply HEAVISIDE LAYER have now given way to the designation E layer. Appleton's name was given to what is now called the D layer situated above the Heaviside layer at heights of 150-1000 km. The discovery of the Heaviside layer was of crucial importance to the development of radio communication since it was found that medium-frequency radio signals would bounce off it and back to earth and thus make possible radio communication beyond the horizon.

[401] HECK HYPOTHESIS

The crop-circle phenomenon has been and continues to be the cause of much puzzled head scratching. Most of us, rather lazily, are content to assume that crop circles are made by Martians using a bit of rope and a couple of planks, and leave it at that. However, KENNETH M. HECK, a retired actuary from Carlisle, Iowa, has taken enlightenment a giant step further with his discovery that crop circles are actually warnings of future impacts from comets deliberately aimed at the earth by some Outside Intelligence.* It's unfortunate that the intelligence of the Outside Intelligence apparently doesn't extend to the use of language. Though of course there may well be situations when plain language isn't the best way of attracting attention. After all, the Bible tells us that God chose to open communication with Moses by setting fire to a bush (*Exodus* 3.2.). Even so, Mr Heck's discovery still leaves quite a lot of questions unanswered, including the question as to how the ropes-and-planks thing actually works.

* Kenneth M. Heck: *The Heck hypothesis* 2009.

[402] HED-METEORITES – see DIOGENES SYNDROME

[403] HEIMLICH MANOEUVRE

Technique invented in 1974 by American thoracic surgeon HENRY J. HEIMLICH (b. 1920) for clearing an obstruction from a patient's airway. It involves a sharp upward compression of the diaphragm, the operator standing behind the patient with his arms round the patient's waist. Recently, medical opinion has somehwat downgraded the Heimlich manouvre in favour of other techniques such as chest compression and back slaps. In 1964, Heimlich invented a simple VALVE, also named after him, for draining blood and air from the chest cavity of patients with gunshot wounds. This device is credited with having saved the lives of hundreds if not thousands of US soldiers in Vietnam.

[404] HEINLEIN'S RAZOR – see MURPHY'S LAW

[405] HEINZ BAKED BEANS
If "Beanz Meanz Heinz", the converse is also true: "Heinz Baked Beans" remains the flagship product in the UK for Pittsburgh-based processed-food manufacturer Heinz, despite being on the market for more than a century. Even today it is probably the case that 99% of the population of this country have never seen, let alone cooked or eaten, a bean that didn't come from a tin. The bean in question is the haricot, also commonly known as the "Navy" or "Boston" bean. Once processed the beans are sold in a sauce, most commonly tomato, sometimes accompanied by other ingredients such as bacon or sausage. Heinz Baked Beans and the company that produces them are named after HENRY JOHN HEINZ (1844-1919), a German immigrant to the United States, who in 1869, along with L. C. Noble, founded the Anchor Pickle and Vinegar Works in Sharpsburg, Pennsylvania. Following the company's bankruptcy in 1875, Heinz re-established the business, aided by his cousin and brother. The business was called F. & J. Heinz until 1888, when the company changed its name once more, settling on its current appellation. The company's slogan "57 varieties" has entered the language as as synonym for "gallimaufry", or, in the case of dogs "mongrel". (BS)

[406] HEISENBERG'S UNCERTAINTY PRINCIPLE
To measure something is to disturb it. For large objects, the disturbance is quite negligible, but for something as small as an electron the act of measuring one property, its position, say – which would involve bouncing a photon off it – affects the value of another property, its momentum. This uncertainty or indeterminacy makes it impossible to state precisely where the electron is and, simultaneously, how fast it's moving. The UNCERTAINTY PRINCIPLE was first recognised and quantified in 1925 by WERNER KARL HEISENBERG (1901-76) and lies at the heart of the wave-mechanical theory of matter, which replaces precise quantities by probabilities. Heisenberg was born in Würzburg, educated at Munich University, and occupied the chairs of physics at Leipzig and then Berlin, where he was one of the founders of quantum mechanics. During World War II he headed the German effort to harness nuclear power, but evidently suffered from divided loyalties, though his claim to have prevented Hitler's acquisition of the

atomic bomb by a deliberate over-estimate of the amount of fissile material required is still contentious. He was awarded the NOBEL PRIZE for physics in 1932. (MW)

[407] HEKTOR – see LEICA

[408] HELMHOLTZ COIL

A device consisting of twin electric coils for producing a region of uniform magnetic field. It is just one of the many inventions of the all-round Prussian savant HERMANN LUDWIG FERDINAND VON HELMHOLTZ (1821-1894). Born in Potsdam, the son af a *gymnasium* headmaster, he became professor of physiology at Königsberg (1849), Bonn (1855), and Heidelberg (1858), then professor of physics at Berlin (1871). Having studied both medicine and physics, he was well-equipped to make original contributions in an astonishingly wide range of fields: thermodynamics – the HELMHOLTZ FREE ENERGY and the Law of Conservation of Energy (*Uber die Erhaltung der Kraft* 1847); physiology – the YOUNG-HELMHOLTZ trichromatic theory of colour vision and the perception of motion; optics – invention of the ophthalmoscope (1851); acoustics – the HELMHOLTZ RESONATOR (1863); electromagnetism – the HELMHOLTZ COIL; mathematics – the HELMHOLTZ EQUATION; hydrodynamics – three HELMHOLTZ THEOREMS of non-viscous flow (1858) and the KELVIN-HELMHOLTZ INSTABILITY in the theory of turbulent vortices. This is to say nothing of his contributions to aesthetics, and philosophy. (MW)

[409] HENRY

A fluctuating magnetic field (see WEBER) induces an electric current (see AMPÈRE) in a wire conductor, and, reciprocally, a fluctuating electric current in a wire coil produces a magnetic field. These are the phenomena of electromagnetic induction (see FARADAY). The magnitude of the inductance is measured by an SI unit named after American physicist JOSEPH HENRY (1797-1878). Born in Albany NY, in humble circumstances to immigrant Scottish parents, he achieved fame as professor at Princeton (1832) and first secretary (1846) of the SMITHSONIAN INSTITUTION. His discovery of electrical induction rivals that of FARADAY (who published first) and he constructed the first electric "motor" in 1829, but the fact that this had a rocking, rather than a rotatory action may have limited its scope. His work on the electromagnetic relay formed the basis of the electric telegraph (see MORSE and WHEATSTONE). (MW)

[410] HENRY'S LAW

The Manchester-born son of an apothecary, WILLIAM HENRY (1774-1836) trained in medicine at Edinburgh, but became a chemist among the Mancunian scientific circle (see **JOULE**) and a founder of the Mechanics' Institute. **HENRY'S LAW** states that the amount of gas dissolved by a liquid is proportional to the partial pressure (see **DALTON**) of the gas. (MW)

[411] HERB BENNET

According to Geoffrey Grigson*, *Geum urbanum*, a flowering plant of meadows and hedge-bottoms for which the English common name is **HERB BENNET**, is not, as one might suppose on the analogy of **SAINT JOHN'S WORT,** named after Saint Benedict of Nursia (*fl.* 500), the founder of Western monasticism – and this despite its modern French name *Herbe de Saint-Benoît*. Instead it should be interpreted as *herbe bénite* ("blessed herb") by virtue of its property of expelling evil/diabolical influences from the house in which it is kept. Its merely physical properties include its medicinal uses (digestive complaints) and the fact that its roots, when bruised, exhale a fragrance of cloves. Whence its alternative common name "clove-root" ("Nelkenwurz", "racine de giroflée").

* *The Englishman's flora* (1958).

[412] HERB ROBERT

Geranium robertianum, a common wildflower of woods, walls and waysides, belonging to the cranesbill family. While all are agreed that its pink flowers are pleasing to the eye, there is equal agreement on the fact that its leaves, especially when crushed, are offensive to the nose, with a smell described as "loathsome" by Gerard, and "mousy" by Richard Mabey, while according to a French authority, they smell like the urine of people who have eaten asparagus.* It is presumably the nasty odour which allows people to suppose a connection between the name **ROBERT** and the gremlin-like spirit of domestic dirt and disorder placatingly named **ROBIN GOODFELLOW****, the English equivalent of the Irish *leprechaun* or the Greek *kallikantzaros* – beings who from mere malice invade houses at night, sour the housewife's milk, spoil her food, break her crockery, foul her floors and overturn her furniture.

* Gerard's Herbal (1597) qu. Geoffrey Grigson *The Englishman's flora* (1958); Mabey *Flora Britannica* (1996); Jean Palaiseul *Nos grand-mères savaient* (1972).

** An apotropaic euphemism – compare the Greek "Eumenides" ("kindly ones") for the Furies, bringers of divine vengeance.

[413] HERMETIC TEACHINGS

In the Middle Ages, scholars in western Europe became aware of the existence of a collection of religious/philosophical texts known as the **CORPUS**

HERMETICUM after their supposed author, the mysterious character **HERMES TRISMEGISTUS** (= Hermes Thrice-Greatest), who was seen as a repository of ancient Egyptian lore and identified with the Egyptian god Thoth, god of wisdom. Though known-of, the material was difficult of access until in 1460 a Greek manuscript version of the corpus reached Florence where Lorenzo de' Medici commissioned a Latin translation from the scholar Marsilio Ficino (1433-1499) a member of Florence's so-called Platonic Academy. Ficino, though chiefly remembered today for his excellent Latin translation of Plato (1482), had a keen interest in the Ancient Egyptians as well as in Pythagorean doctrines and the writings of Plotinus, the 3rd-century religious mystic. In 1471 Ficino published the results of his labours in a work he called *The Pimander*. The Hermetic texts were a hotch-potch of Hebrew, Egyptian, Greek and Roman myths and beliefs with a strong leaning towards the gnostic and the mystical, and proved highly influential upon Renaissance scholars such as Pico Della Mirandola (another member of the Platonic Academy), Giordano Bruno, and the Welsh Wizard Dr. John Dee, court astrologer to Elizabeth I. As a result, the mixture of philosophical, religious, magical and mystical material in the texts was rapidly absorbed into Renaissance Neoplatonism, alchemy, cabbalism, and similar esoteric traditions. It was, however, the Swiss-born classical scholar Isaac Casaubon* (1559-1614) who first demonstrated that the *Corpus Hermeticum* had post-Christian origins and dated from the second century AD, thus severing the link with the Ancient Egyptians. After this, interest among respectable scholars cooled. It seems, however, that the Hermetic texts are still taken seriously as sources of empowering knowledge by a few intellectually dysfunctional groups like the Rosicrucians.** Texts and commentaries on the Corpus are available in modern editions from the Amsterdam-based J.R. Ritman Library. (RS)

* This might well be where George Eliot found the name for the musty, deracinated character in *Middlemarch* (1871), whose vast and never-to-be-completed opus, *The key to all mythologies*, is presented as a sort of Millennium Dome of wasted intellectual effort. Nevertheless, Dr. Casaubon, despite his having blighted the life of the novel's heroine Dorothea, is a figure for whom all dictionary-makers (harmless drudges!) must feel at least sympathy and even a measure of respect.

** For a sober (and fascinating) account of modern anti-rational sects and societies, see James Webb *The flight from Reason* (1971) and *The occult establishment* (1976).

[414] HERSCHEL EFFECT

It is one of the injustices of history that the only reason for including the name of **SIR JOHN HERSCHEL** in this compilation should be this obscure photographic effect. An invisible latent image formed on a photographic plate or film can be "bleached out" – before it is developed – by further exposure to light of long wavelengths, red or infrared. The **HERSCHEL EFFECT** finds a use in "direct duplicating" films, i.e. those that make a positive from a positive and a negative from a negative, rather than the usual tonal inversion. **JOHN FREDERICK WILLIAM HERSCHEL** (1792-1871), was born in Slough, the son of the celebrated astronomer, Sir William Herschel. In 1813 he graduated from Cambridge (where with **BABBAGE** and others he was a founder of the Analytical Society) as Senior Wrangler in the Mathematics Tripos. He then dedicated himself to completing his father's work in astronomy, but in spare moments he also co-invented photography (and so named it) with **HENRY TALBOT**, and made many contributions to chemistry and mathematics. He was showered with honours and prizes, but a turn of duty from 1850 to 1855 as Master of the Mint broke his health. On his death he was likened to a previous Master, **NEWTON**, and although Herschel's name is not attached to any one major innovation, possibly as a consequence of his innate modesty, he was esteemed by many of his peers as the leading British scientist of his day. (MW)

[415] HERSCHEL SPACE OBSERVATORY

Placed in orbit in May 2009 by the European Space Agency using an Ariane-5* heavy launch vehicle (the term "rocket" hardly does justice to this mighty engine), this satellite now occupies a lissajous** orbit with a period of 1 year at a **LAGRANGIAN POINT**, 1,500,000 km out from planet Earth. It is dedicated to carrying a far infra-red and sub-milllimeter telescope (acronymned as FIRST) for observing the cooler bits of the universe at very long wavelengths. The observatory is named both for the astronomer **Sir FRIEDRICH WILHELM HERSCHEL** (1738-1822) and for his astronomer sister and co-observer **CAROLINE LUCRETIA HERSCHEL** (1750-1848), one of the most famous of early women scientists, (see **SOMERVILLE COLLEGE**) who discovered several comets. Appropriately, **Sir WILLIAM HERSCHEL** (as his name is generally de-germanified) was the original discoverer of infra-red radiation in 1800 – he found it by placing a thermometer beyond the visible red end of a solar spectrum dispersed by a prism. For a bibliographic note on this Hanoverian bandsman turned British astronomer-knight, see **URANUS**.*** The **WILLIAM HERSCHEL TELESCOPE**, on the other hand, is earthbound: one of the group of **ISAAC NEWTON** telescopes located at the Roque de los Muchachos Observatory, La Palma in the Canary Islands. Finally completed in 1987 following protracted budgetary difficulties, this 4.2 meter diameter cassegrain reflector represents the Northen Hemisphere's counterpart to the very successful, but anonymous, 3.9 m Anglo-Australian telescope of 1971 at Coonabarabran, in the Warrumbungles, New South Wales. (MW)

* The French spelling for the Ariadne of Greek myth.

** Lovely word! = (roughly) a figure composed of crossed loops at right angles to one another. After French physicist Jules Antoine Lissajous (1822-1880).

*** The Herschels' contributions to astronomy, and much else of historical note, are described in Richard Holmes's absorbing book *The Age of Wonder* (2008).

[416] HERTZ

This SI unit of frequency per second, s^{-1}, is represented by the symbol Hz. It describes the frequency of any periodic phenomenon in "cycles" per second, and is often numerically prefixed, as in kHz, MHz, or GHz. It is named after **HEINRICH RUDOLF HERTZ** (1857-94) a German physicist, born in Hamburg, who studied under **KIRCHHOFF** and **HELMHOLTZ** at Berlin, and became professor at the University of Karlsruhe in 1885. In 1887 he fulfilled the theoretical predictions of **JAMES CLERK-MAXWELL** by demonstrating the existence of electromagnetic radiation that could travel across free space. Using a spark-gap transmitter driven by a **RUHMKORFF** coil, he generated VHF radio waves, of meter wavelength, which were radiated by a half-wave dipole antenna (see **YAGI**). By totally discounting his own new findings – which ultimately transformed human life – Hertz exhibits an outstanding case of "Discoverer's Modesty Syndrome". His throwaway comment: "I do not think that the wireless waves I have discovered will have any practical application" is a clear winner. (MW)

[417] HERTZSPRUNG-RUSSELL DIAGRAM

Stars have two obvious characteristics which can be measured fairly readily: brightness and colour, or in more scientific terms, luminosity and spectral type; the latter is an indication of the surface temperature of the star. For thousands of observable stars, these two properties can be plotted, each star represented by a dot on a scatter-graph, where the vertical scale is increasing luminosity, and the horizontal scale is temperature decreasing from left to right. It can be seen that the two are related. This plot is the famous **HERTZSPRUNG-RUSSELL DIAGRAM**, which provides a classification for various types of star at different stages of their lifetimes. The majority, like our Sun, tend to congregate along a "lazy-S" shaped line on this graph called the "Main Sequence", running from top left (bright and hot blue-white stars) to bottom right (dim and cool red stars). Our sun, which is about half way through its life of roughly ten billion years, sits in the middle. There are also outlying regions of clustered dots for red giants and white dwarves, above and below the Main Sequence respectively. Danish astronomer **EJNAR HERTZSPRUNG** (1873-1967) was born in Frederiksberg, trained in chemical engineering at Copenhagen Polytechnic, and worked as a chemist for ten years before obtaining a post as astronomer at Potsdam Observatory (1909-1919), by which time he had discovered the relationship between brightness and colour; he was appointed Director of the Leiden University observatory in Holland from 1919 to 1946, and made the first measurements of distances outside our galaxy. American astronomer **HENRY NORRIS RUSSELL** (1877-1957) was born in Oyster Bay, New York, and studied at Princeton, where he became professor of astronomy and director of the observatory in 1911. He developed a theory of stellar evolution, from dwarf to giant stars, which has now been superseded. In the rather different field of atomic physics, with Frederick Saunders, he also developed the important system of **RUSSELL-SAUNDERS COUPLING** to describe the quantum states of many-electron atoms, which is fundamental to the theory of atomic spectra and magnetism. (MW)

[418] HEULANDITE – see SCHEELITE

[419 HIGGINS BOAT

ANDREW JACKSON HIGGINS (1886-1952) was a New Orleans timber-merchant turned boat-builder. In the 1920's Higgins designed and built a fast, shallow-draft, flat-bottomed vessel specifically adapted to working in the swamps and bayous of the Mississippi Delta. The flattened curve of the prow enabled the boats to be run up on shallow banks and backed off again and the propeller was protected from snags and shoals by being recessed into the hull. According to legend, Higgins did good business selling his boats to the rum-runners bringing in booze from Cuba during the Prohibition Era, enabling them to run rings round the Coast Guard. Then, with admirable even-handedness, he sold his boats to the Coast Guard who needed to close the mobility gap. With the war in the Pacific and the need for landing craft, Higgins' design swept the board in tests organised by the Navy and Marine Corps, requiring only the addition of a landing ramp to the prow (copied from the Japanese). By the war's end. Higgins' boat works and other yards building boats to his design under licence had produced some 20 thousand vessels. Eisenhower called Higgins "the man who won the war for us" – a generous tribute which neatly parallels Montgomery's homage to the designer of the **BAILEY BRIDGE**.

[420] HIGGS BOSON

A possible member of the group of sub-atomic particles which obey the laws of **BOSE-EINSTEIN STATISTICS** (see **EINSTEIN**). The **HIGGS BOSON** is named after British physicist **PETER WARE HIGGS** (b. 1929), emeritus professor of theoretical physics at the University of Edinburgh, who was born in Newcastle upon Tyne and studied at Kings College London. It is a hypothetical particle – *i.e.* it may or may not exist. Though Higgs put forward the idea as long ago as 1960, "his" boson still eludes detection, and is the last remaining elementary particle of the so-called "Standard Model" of particle physics to be confirmed (see **FEYNMAN DIAGRAM**). Its importance lies in the fact that if it could be shown to exist, it would explain how different elementary particles attain their mass, and why different classes of particle have different masses. This in turn would have radical implications for our understanding of the entire cosmos since the answer to these questions would, it is believed, be a giant step towards the physicist's ultimate goal, the Grand Unified Theory which will finally bring together all known physical forces under the same explanatory umbrella. Hopes for a successful outcome to the search for the elusive Higgs particle are currently pinned on the Large Hadron Collider at CERN in Geneva.

[421] HILLOTYPE

The American pastor, REV. LEVI L. HILL (1816-1866) of West Kill, New York, announced in 1850 that he had discovered a method of making DAGUERREOTYPES in natural colour – without hand-painting. This sensational claim (true colour photography was not achieved for another half-century) caused professional daguerreotypists to fear for their livelihoods. Hill received conspiratorial threats from the Committee of the New York State Daguerrean Association. He was denounced as a mountebank, but defended by the likes of SAMUEL MORSE. Hill's 1856 *Treatise on Heliochromy*, which criticized the "infernal Committee", was seized under a libel writ and pulped; it detailed a photochemical procedure of Byzantine complexity, and horrific toxicity. Evidently such dangers were unconsidered by a man who habitually inhaled bromine vapour to relieve his bronchitis! Throughout most of the orthodox history of photography, Hill's photographs in natural colour – which he modestly called *heliochromes* but are now known as HILLOTYPES – have been dismissed as bogus. However, recent examination of a re-discovered archive of 62 hillotypes in the SMITHSONIAN INSTITUTION does show some vestiges of dull colour in the images, and likewise in a modern recreation of Hill's process, which was carried out in 1986 by an intrepid experimentalist, Joseph Boudreau. (MW)

[422] HIPPOCRATIC OATH

The original physicians' oath attributed to HIPPOCRATES OF COS, "The Father of Medicine", (*ca.*460-*ca.*377 BC).* Hippocrates was honoured in his lifetime for his work as a careful physician, his approach being characterised by wide-ranging and painstaking observation. He adhered to the four-humour theory of disease causation, which prevailed in Europe until the seventeenth century.** The HIPPOCRATIC OATH, originally sworn to the gods of medicine – Apollo, Asklepios (Aesculapius), Hygeia and Pancaea – together with later variations on the text, historically forms the basis of the ethical code governing the medical profession, even when not formally administered as such. A fundamental idea in all versions is "to do no harm", even when these words do not appear in exactly that form. The welfare of the patient is the doctor's first concern and the oath, either in a form of words or simply in their spirit, is the basis of the trust which has to subsist between doctor and patient. When this trust is violated – as, for example in the case of a doctor hastening the deaths of elderly patients in order to benefit from their wills, or, as sometimes happens, in cases of unqualified persons posing as doctors – the effect is shocking and trust can only be restored by retributive justice. And when, as has recently been found to be the case, physicians and psychologists in the pay of the Pentagon and the CIA have been engaged in devising and supervising torture regimes for terrorist suspects, and apparently enjoy total immunity for their crimes, they dishonour themselves and their profession irremediably. (To be fair, we should add that the lawyers who lent themselves to the "legitimation" of torture at the President's bidding, behaved no less despicably but then, as any lawyer worth his salt will tell you, their remit doesn't include ethics.)

* Not to be confused with his contemporary Hippocrates of Chios, called by George Sarton (*A history of science...through the Golden Age of Greece* 1952) "the greatest mathematician of the [5th] century".

** The collection of seventy or so medical texts known as the HIPPOCRATIC CORPUS involves numerous problems of attribution. Among the important texts of which Hippocrates is assumed to be the author are: *Aphorisms*, *Prognostics*, and *Concerning airs, waters, places* (various eds.).

[423] HIRSCH FUNNEL – see BÜCHNER FUNNEL

[424] HOBSON'S CHOICE
The equivalent of Henry Ford's "Any colour you like as long as it's black", HOBSON'S CHOICE means in effect "no choice at all". The reference is to a 16th-century Cambridge carrier and livery stable owner who allowed his customers to choose any horse they fancied as long as it was the one nearest the stable door. The earliest literary mention of Hobson's business methods comes from the *Pilgrimage to Parnassus*, an anonymous drama performed in Cambridge in 1600 by the students of St. John's College: "*Would it not greeue a man of a good spirit to see Hobson finde more money in the tayles of 12 Jades, than a scholler in 200 bookes?*" (See: *The Oxford dictionary of English proverbs* 1935, 1948.)

[425] HODGE
Much as "Tommy Atkins" is, or used to be, a generic term for a private soldier and "Jack Tar" for a sailor, so the name HODGE, was once a generic name, dating back to the later Middle Ages, for the farm-worker or rural labourer. Hence the title, *Hodge and his masters*, of Richard Jefferies' classic study of life in a West Country farming community, first published in 1880 and still in print. Hodge was also the name of DR. JOHNSON's cat, on which he doted. When informed that a madman was going about London shooting cats with a pistol, Johnson reassured his feline companion, who was sitting on his chest at the time, with the words "Hodge shan't be shot."

[426] HODGKIN'S LYMPHOMA – see BRIGHT'S DISEASE

[427] HOLLERITH TABULATOR

HERMANN HOLLERITH (1860-1929) graduated Columbia School of Mines 1879, PhD Columbia University 1890. Whilst on the staff of MIT, he developed a method of storing data on punched cards said to have been inspired by the system used by railroad inspectors who recorded a passenger's appearance for anti-ticket-theft purposes by edge-punching selected data on the ticket (first instance of biometric data recording?). Hollerith developed a 24 x 11 hole format on $3\frac{1}{4}$" x $6\frac{5}{8}$" manila card as the storage device for his data tabulation system. Transcription of data from ordinary manuscript forms onto these cards was performed by clerks who rapidly became adept in using the keyboard and punch devices designed by Hollerith and who achieved quite astonishing throughput rates at this laborious task at which women excelled. (History records no difficulty with hanging chads!) Once data was transcribed to punched cards, Hollerith's tabulation system could be used to accumulate statistical data by "scanning" each card in a simple reader with a set of electrical plungers connected to counters via the holes in the scanned cards or blocked where no hole existed; and/or to sort cards into categories by electrically opening the appropriate storage box into which the operator dropped the processed card. The connections between the scanner (which Hollerith called the press) and the counters and sorting boxes could be simply varied by cross-connections on an electrical patch panel, this being a key feature of the tabulation system enabling its application to a wide variety of data processing tasks by mapping the possible 264 holes (binary digits – bits) to the 40 counters – the foundation of "batch processing". Use of Hollerith's rented equipment by the US Census Office to process the 1890 census was hugely successful. Data transcription from the 15 million schedules (census forms) to the 64 million cards was at least twice as fast, and data tabulation ten times faster, than any other system then available. In modern jargon, Hollerith provided a turnkey system where every aspect of census work was supported and improved by the several parts of his total system solution. In 1896 Hollerith founded the Tabulating Machine Co., the egg from which IBM was hatched. Whilst the use of punched cards was not new, their use in the **JACQUARD LOOM** was entirely mechanical, while the cards used by Hollerith were designed for electrical reading from the outset. The punched card (in its eventual 80 column format) as a binary data store carried the flag for most forms of calculation, tabulation and computing until the late 20th century saw electronic computers sweep away all forms of mechanical and electro-mechanical data storage. (GJ)

[428] HOOKE'S LAW

Refers to the behaviour of an elastic object such as a helical spring or rubber band when stretched: the extension produced is proportional to the stretching force applied. In the compact Latin favoured by Hooke: *ut tensio, sic vis* ("as the extension, so the force"). Hooke announced this in 1676 only in the scrabbled form "*ceiiinosssttu*" – a standard technique of the day to establish one's priority to a new discovery, should it be disputed, without actually giving the game away. HOOKE'S LAW is the principle behind the familiar spring balance and HOOKE'S CONSTANT of proportionality is the precursor to the more general YOUNG'S MODULUS of elasticity. ROBERT HOOKE (1635-1703) was born in Freshwater, Isle of Wight, the son of a curate. He was educated at Westminster School and Christ Church, Oxford, where he formed an enduring friendship with Christopher Wren. Both were members of the circle centred on ROBERT BOYLE, which founded the Royal Society in 1660, whereafter Hooke was appointed its Curator of Experiments (1662-1677). He was a polymath, and effectively the first professional experimental scientist, known then as a "natural philosopher". He was close to the origins of several major scientific and mechanical innovations, some of which he claimed as his own but was robbed of the credit. Historiography now remembers his name only by his Law. Hooke's cantankerous manner provoked malign responses from some of his peers. His claim to have acquainted NEWTON with the inverse square law of gravitation and elliptical orbits of planetary motion alienated the great man, to Hooke's enduring detriment. Newton's opinion of him as "a man of strange unsociable temper" held sway with biographers ever since. Indeed, the lack of any surviving portrait of Hooke is attributed to Newton's having them destroyed. Nonetheless there is ample evidence for Hooke's contributions: to pneumatics – constructing air pumps for Boyle; to optics and astronomy – constructing gregorian telescopes to observe the moon and planets; to meteorology – for which he designed barometers and other new measuring instruments; to microscopy – where he was a skilled observer and talented draughtsman, as attested by his great work *Micrographia* (1665) in which he identified and first named the living "cell". He also held the post of Surveyor of the City of London, and as assistant to Wren produced numerous architectural designs for the rebuilding of churches after the Great Fire of 1666. In 2006 there came to light a 520-page folio of lost Royal Society minutes, rough notes written by Hooke as Secretary during 1677-1683 (which he should have written up and filed but didn't – one reason he was sacked from the post). This document is being eagerly studied by Hooke scholars, and has already resolved one priority dispute, with Christiaan HUYGENS, that Hooke did indeed invent the anchor escapement for clock mechanisms *ca*.1658. (MW)

[429] HOOKER'S GREEN

An artists' pigment originally obtained by mixing Prussian blue (see TURNBULL'S BLUE) with gamboge. It was the creation of WILLIAM HOOKER (1779-1832), an English pomological illustrator, *i.e.* a painter of edible fruit,* who devised the pigment especially to render accurately the hue of leaves. He was appointed official draughtsman to the Horticultural Society of London, later to become the Royal Horticultural Society, and published his magnum opus, *Pomona Londinensis* in 1818, exquisitely illustrated with aquatint engravings. He was esteemed as "the finest of all fruit illustrators", but bore no known relation to his more illustrious namesake, botanist Sir William Jackson Hooker (1785-1865), professor of botany at Glasgow, who became Director of Kew, or to the even more illustrious son of the foregoing, Sir Joseph Dalton Hooker (1817-1911), botanist, explorer and friend of Darwin. (MW)

*Pomology, the study of fruit culture from the consumer's point of view, distinguishes itself from carpology, the botanical study of the fruit of all flowering plants, edible or not.

[430] HOOLIGAN

The name of an Irish family living in south-east London in the 19th century. By 1898, their anti-social behaviour was sufficiently notorious for the name to be used – as an adjective and still with the initial capital – as a synonym for "ruffianly" (OED). It is surprising that the word has not yet been proscribed under the iron laws of Political Correctness as potentially offensive to Irish persons and, of course, to hooligans.

[431] HOOVER

The trade name, patented in 1927, of a firm of vacuum-cleaner manufacturers, which in Britain, to the company's displeasure has come to be used as a noun and verb for both the machine and its use, even when applied to machines of the same type made by other companies. It was **WILLIAM H. HOOVER** (1849-1932), a saddler of North Canton, Ohio, who saw the potential of an "electric suction cleaner" invented in 1907 by James Spangler, a department store guard, who constructed the first such machine using a soap box, an electric motor, a broom handle, and a pillow-case. Spangler, an asthma sufferer, suspected the carpet-sweeper he was using at work of causing his attacks. He gave one of the machines to his friend Susan Hoover, who was impressed by the machine and told her husband about it. Hoover bought the patent from Spangler in 1908 and set up a company to manufacture and market the device, retaining Spangler as a partner. It is thus almost by accident that we are not calling our vacuum-cleaners "Spanglers", which has a more poetic ring to it. ("*Just spanglering the carpet, dear...*"). Hoover continued to develop the machine, sales of which expanded globally. The Hoover Company in the US was absorbed by the Whirlpool Corporation before being sold in 2006 to the China-based Techtronic for $100 million. The UK Hoover company split from its parent in 1993 and is now owned by the Italian Candy Corporation.

[432] HOPE DIAMOND

A famous blue diamond, named after the American HENRY PHILIP HOPE (d. 1839), heir to a banking fortune, who became one of its very many owners in 1824. Its history is known in detail, starting with its acquisition in India (supposedly by theft from an idol, one of whose eyes it formed) by the French traveller Jean-Baptiste Tavernier (1605-1689). The alleged curse on any possessor of the stone is the purest nonsense and need not detain us. The HOPE now forms part of the gem collection in the SMITHSONIAN MUSEUM, Washington.

[433] HÖRBIGER'S COSMIC ICE THEORY

HANNS HÖRBIGER (1860-1931) was an Austrian engineer with an interest in astronomy. The appearance of a comet in 1892 led him to wonder whether comets might not be made of ice. Not so crazy – but then ice became an obsession with him. He convinced himself that the Moon was made of ice and worked hard to persuade other astronomers of this fact. From there it was but a short step to the conviction that ice was the building material of entire star systems, which were formed by explosive collisions between masses of hot gases (oxygen and hydrogen) with lumps of "cosmic ice". From here Hörbiger proceeded, by a route whose details are far from clear, to the discovery that the earth had been bombarded at various times in the past by entire moons of the stuff and that these cataclysmic impacts are commemorated in surviving myths and legends. This process was not over, since our present moon must at some time in the future make the same journey down to earth with spectacular results. Hörbiger's notions were published in 1912 in a work entitled *Glazialkosmogonie* which Hörbiger co-wrote with a convert to his theories, the amateur astronomer Philipp Fauth. His ideas were taken up enthusiastically by the German occult underground. Believers are said to have included Hitler (who compared Hörbiger to Copernicus), and certainly included Himmler, who made Cosmic Ice a special part of the curriculum of the *Ahnenerbe*, the pseudo-academic research division of Himmler's SS. Part of the attraction was that Hörbiger's theories fitted in well with speculations about Atlantis, already popular in occult circles, and with the Nazis' interest in the myths and folklore of the frosty Scandinavian north. Yet, inevitably, the question arises as to how otherwise seemingly intelligent people could be brought to take such garbage seriously.* A short answer might be that anyone who, like Himmler, could persuade himself that a lethal clown like Hitler was a fit person to guide the destinies of a great nation, could believe absolutely anything. A more considered answer would have to take account of the fact that successful revolutions (America, France, Russia) engender the need for a thoroughgoing break with the past. This would explain, for example, something as trivial as the Americans' reform of English spelling, the French adoption of the Revolutionary Calendar, or Stalin's embracing LYSENKOISM. In the case of the

Nazi revolutionaries, the perceived need was for a new ideology, a new culture, a new cosmology, and a new science that were wholly and perfectly Germanic and untainted by Judaeo-Christian traditions. To this one would have to add that cranky theories and cranky religious sects find the bulk of their following among people who are intelligent enough to ask questions, to want to understand the world they live in, but insufficiently educated to know when the answers they are being given are rubbish. (See also **BOOK OF MORMON.**)

* A question that applies not just to Hörbiger. His was just one among many such flowers in the weird garden of Nazi irrationality. For fuller accounts see Webb *The occult establishment* 1976, and Goodrick-Clarke *The occult roots of Nazism* 1985. It should be added, perhaps, that Hörbiger was not the only deluded amateur cosmologist to be fixated on ice. The Scot John Finlayson (1770-1854) believed that the stars were lumps of ice hung in the firmament by a thoughtful Deity to make the night sky look more interesting, while the Englishman Charles Palmer published in 1789 a lengthy defence of his contention that the sun was made of ice illuminated by "God's radiance". (See Philip Ward *A dictionary of common fallacies*, 2nd ed. 1980,Vol 2.)

[434] HOUSTON'S WHITEBEAM

In 2009 *Watsonia*, the journal of the Botanical Society of the British Isles (BSBI) announced the discovery of 5 new taxa* of Sorbus (rowans and whitebeams) in the Avon Gorge. Rowans and whitebeams readily hybridise and it takes an expert eye to recognise the often minute differences between the many and various guises in which the genus presents itself. Such an expert eye belongs to **LIBBY HOUSTON** (b. 1939), poet, botanist and alpinist. One of the five newcomers, *sorbus x houstoniae* is, in the words of the authors of the *Watsonia* article, "named after Ms Libby Houston, the 'guardian angel' of the Avon Gorge, who not only first discovered it, but whose natural habitat seems to be the same – clinging to impossible cliffs in remote parts of the gorge." (*Watsonia* 27 [2009])

* *Taxa* (singular *taxon*): a useful portmanteau term used by biologists to signify any or all of the categories (sub-species, species, genus, family, etc) of scientific nomenclature.

[435] HOWARD LEAGUE

An organisation dedicated to the search for a better prison regime and/or a better alternative, and named after **JOHN HOWARD** (1726-1790). Inherited wealth, strong religious principles (he was a Dissenter), and a natural bent towards paternalism led Howard to build model homes for the tenants of his Cardington estate and to pay for the education of their children. His concern for penal reform dates from his appointment (1773) as High Sheriff of Bedfordshire. An inspection of his own county jail (which once housed John Bunyan) revealed shocking abuses, among which was the practice of detaining prisoners solely on the grounds of their inability to pay the gaoler's fee – money paid to the owner or keeper of the prison for upkeep. He took this issue to parliament, and in 1774 Howard was called to give evidence on prison conditions, including sanitary conditions, to a House of Commons select committee. He was particularly concerned by the incidence of gaol fever and smallpox, which were endemic in many institutions. So began his extensive tours of inspection of prisons, bridewells, houses of correction, and hospitals, not only in Britain but throughout Europe, Russia and Turkey. These travels and labours, in which he showed himself both fearless and tireless, occupied most of the last seventeen years of his life. He died of "camp fever" (?cholera) in the Chersonese. He was the first civilian to be honoured with a statue in St. Paul's Cathedral. In 1866 the Howard Association was formed in London, for the "promotion of the most efficient means of penal treatment and crime prevention" and "a reformatory and radically preventive treatment of offenders". In 1921 it merged with the Penal Reform League (founded 1907) to create the **HOWARD LEAGUE FOR PENAL REFORM.** Howard's published works include: *The State of the Prisons in England and Wales* (1777), an *Appendix* to the same (1780), and *An account of the principal lazarettos in Europe* (1789) which included a narrative of a period of voluntarily-undergone quarantine in Venice. (RS)

[436] HUBBLE'S LAW

It is fair to say that the biggest single step forward in our understanding of the cosmos during the 20th century was the discovery by American astronomer and amateur boxer **EDWIN POWELL HUBBLE** (1889-1953) that the universe is expanding. This discovery, based on the so-called "red-shift" – the displacement of light coming from other galaxies towards the red end of the spectrum – is explicable only by the fact that they must be moving away from us (see **DOPPLER EFFECT**) and, since the same effect is observed no matter in which direction we look, from each other – *i.e.* it is *space* that is expanding. When Hubble turned to estimating the speed at which the galaxies were receding, he found that speed increased with distance: the further away, the faster they were moving. This *aperçu* is now known as **HUBBLE'S LAW**. The *rate* at which the galaxies are moving away from each other is represented by a factor symbolised as H_0 and known as the **HUBBLE CONSTANT**. Astronomers have now determined its value with reasonable confidence to be 70 kilometers per second per megaparsec (km/s/Mpc)* – give or take. The reciprocal of the Hubble Constant, $1/H_0$, known as the **HUBBLE TIME**, is an indication of the age of the universe, dating from the Big Bang. A few moments spent with a calculator reveal this to be 14 billion years – give or take.** However, the appellation "Constant" might turn out to be a bit of a misnomer for Hubble since H_0 is suspected of changing with time, but measurements at present leave us uncertain which way. The resolution of this question is crucial to the future of the universe: if accelerating, then our galaxy is going to be very lonely in the distant future. If diminishing, which seems less probable, then we can look forward to the "Big Crunch" eventually. As a tribute to Hubble's importance as an astronomer, the **SPACE TELESCOPE** which was put into 95-minute earth orbit in 1990 by the space shuttle *Discovery* was named after him. Its mission was to scan the universe unobstructed by the Earth's atmosphere and report its findings. First results were disappointingly fuzzy thanks to a fault in the main mirror which should have been spotted before the telescope left the ground. The problem was partially corrected by astronauts working *in vacuo* in 1993, and further repairs were carried out in 2009. The telescope, though still not perfect, has performed, and continues to perform, immensely valuable work.

* A megaparsec (Mpc) is the astronomers' preferred unit for specifying intergalactic distances. One Mpc is 31 million, million, million (31 x 10^{18}) kilometers. Our nearest neighbour, the Andromeda Galaxy, is a mere 0.77 Mpc away.

** All billions in this book are of the US variety: one thousand million, 1,000,000,000 = 10^9.

[437] HUMBOLDT CURRENT

A cold current, also known as the *Peru Current* flowing northward from Antarctica along the west coast of South America. It forms a major component of the counter-clockwise circulation of the South Pacific Ocean and is responsible for tempering the climate of tropical northern Chile. It is also associated with the *El Niño* phenomenon whereby, at intervals of about ten years, the warm eastward-flowing Equatorial current strengthens and, meeting the Humboldt current off the shores of Peru, overlies the nutrient-rich cold waters, depriving marine life of sustenance. The fish die. El Niño events in turn are associated with far-reaching climatic disturbances ranging from heavy rainfall in Peru and parts of Brazil, violent storms in the southern United States, and drought conditions in places as far apart as northern Australia and Madagascar.* The reputation of **ALEXANDER VON HUMBOLDT** (1769-1859), German traveller and naturalist, is largely based on a journey of scientific exploration he made with the French naturalist Aimé Bonpland (1773-1858) to South America, Mexico and (briefly) the United States between the years 1799-1804. Though it did not generate any world-changing theoretical insights, Humboldt's 5-year journey may justly be compared with Darwin's *Beagle* voyage, if only in respect of the sheer amount of work that he achieved. His principal interest was natural history, but his eye was everywhere, backed by indefatigable industry, accurate observation, and by a penetrating intelligence, resulting in valuable contributions to geology, astronomy, vulcanology, geomagnetism, orography, oceanography, climatology, and the use of guano as a fertiliser. His journey brought him fame, the friendship of princes, and the universal admiration of the scientific community of Europe and America. In his later years, and in the intervals between numerous other calls upon his time (including a thousand-mile journey through Russia and Siberia), Humboldt composed and published a massive work entitled *Kosmos*, intended to bring together everything he had learned about the world, our place in it, and its place in the universe. Four volumes were published, the first in 1845 when Humboldt was in his 76th year, and a fifth, unfinished, volume after his death. It is said by competent critics to be heavy going. More accessible, perhaps, are the 30 volumes of the *Voyage aux régions equinoxiales du Nouveau Continent fait en 1799-1804 par Alexandre de Humboldt et Aimé Bonpland* (Paris, 1807 et ff.) The Humboldt Current is best-known of his eponyms, but also named after him are: in addition to innumerable plant species, the genus **HUMBOLDTIA**; five species of fish; an Amazonian primate **HUMBOLDT'S WOOLLY MONKEY** (*Lagothrix humboldtii*); twelve towns – one in Canada, one in Argentina, and the remainder in the USA; a glacier in Greenland; a lake; a river; a salt marsh; a Californian bay; a mountain in New Zealand; another mountain in New Caledonia; and a mountain range in Nevada. Oddly, however, the **HUMBOLDT CRATER** on the moon, a respectable 189 km in diameter, is apparently named after Humboldt's beloved elder brother **KARL WILHELM HUMBOLDT** (1767-1835), diplomat and philologist, who made the first scientific study of the Basque language and founded the University of Berlin. Among his works is a seminal essay on the influence of language upon thought and the way different languages embody different ways of looking at the world (*cf.* **SAPIR-WHORF HYPOTHESIS**).

* "Associated with" in both the above instances is a fudge. "A is associated with B" means in practice that the interaction between A and B is so complex that it is difficult to be sure whether A causes or is caused by B, or whether the influence is mutual, or, indeed, whether the two phenomena are not causally related at all but merely coincidental.

[438] HUMITE – see SCHEELITE

[439] HUNTINGTON'S CHOREA

A rare, inherited and incurable disease of the central nervous system, characterised by involuntary, jerky movements and, in the later stages by personality changes and dementia. It is sometimes referred to as "chorea major" to distinguish it from "chorea minor" or **ST. VITUS' DANCE**. The name is that of American physician **GEORGE HUNTINGTON** (1850-1916) who first encountered the disorder when accompanying his father, Dr George Lee Huntington on his rounds in his rural practice in Massachusetts. After qualifying in medicine, he made a study of the disease and presented his conclusions to the medical profession in 1872 when he was only 22 years of age. A famous sufferer from Huntington's was the folk singer Woody Guthrie who died of the disease in New York in 1967 but lives on in the hearts of all who loved him and what he stood for.

[440] HUTTERITES

The Hutterites are communal-living Anabaptists*. They are mainly present in Canada and to a lesser extent in the United States (South Dakota and Montana), though colonies have also been established in Nigeria and Japan. Their numbers are estimated at between 40 and 50 thousand in North America, the descendants of 19th-century immigrants (today we should probably call them asylum-seekers) from Mitteleuropa and the Ukraine. They speak an antique German dialect, hold possessions in common, and subsist mainly by farming. They are pacifists, refuse to wear uniforms, bear arms, or hold public office. In the US they have won the right not to have their photos on their driving licences, thus avoiding a breach of the Commandment forbidding graven images. The sect takes its name from one **JAKOB HUTTER** (= Jacob the Hatmaker), a 16th-century native of the Austrian Tyrol who, after his conversion to Anabaptist beliefs, was active as an organiser, preacher and evangelist, spreading the good word and acquiring a considerable following. But as a proponent of beliefs that were both politically unacceptable and in religious terms damnable heresies, he could not have expected the authorities to regard his activities with equanimity. He was burned at the stake in Innsbruck in 1536. (RS)

* The name Anabaptist is generally applied to those Protestant sects (including the Mennonites and the Amish) which quite reasonably hold infant baptism to be invalid (for lack of informed consent) and that therefore true believers need to be re-baptised as adults

[441] HUYGENS EYEPIECE

The **HUYGENS EYEPIECE** of the 1660s was the first compound eyepiece to employ two planoconvex lens elements, to diminish chromatic aberration (see also **DOLLOND** and **ZEISS**), and it is still used for inexpensive refracting telescopes and microscopes. Dutch mathematical physicist and astronomer **CHRISTIAAN HUYGENS** (1629-1693) was born at The Hague and studied mathematics and law at the University of Leiden and the College of Orange in Breda. He made significant astronomical discoveries, including the rings of Saturn and its moon **TITAN** (1655). (Appropriately, the spacecraft that landed on Titan in the **CASSINI-HUYGENS MISSION** to Saturn in 2005 was named the **HUYGENS PROBE.**) In mechanics, he developed the theory of collisions of elastic bodies, formulae for circular motion and centripetal force, and a mathematical analysis of the pendulum; in optics he was a proponent of the wave theory of light, embodied in the **HUYGENS-FRESNEL PRINCIPLE**; and he noted the phenomenon of birefringence in Iceland Spar (see **NICOL PRISM**). His inventions included the micrometer (1655) and a major contribution to horology, the pendulum clock (1657); but over the spring balance-wheel clock he fell into a priority dispute with **HOOKE** concerning who had been the first with the escapement mechanism (**HOOKE** was vindicated only in 2006). Huygens visited London in 1660 and was elected FRS in 1663. He lived in Paris from 1666 to 1681, holding a position at the *Académie des Sciences* under the patronage of King Louis XIV, but as a Protestant in an increasingly intolerant Catholic country, he found it prudent to return to the Hague. (MW)

I

[442] IAPETUS

The planet Saturn, in addition to its rings, has 18 named moons plus a multitude of moonlets too insignificant to qualify for baptism. IAPETUS is one of the four moons discovered by the Italian-born French astronomer GIOVANNI DOMENICO CASSINI (see CASSINI'S DIVISION) between 1671 and 1684. Their names, taken from Greek mythology, are those of the offspring of URANUS and GAIA known collectively as the Titans. One of these, IAPETUS, was the father of Prometheus (see PROMETHIUM), who, for reasons unknown, formed the first human beings out of mud, bequeathed to them fire stolen from Mount Olympus, and was made to suffer for it. The largest and brightest of the satellites and the first to be discovered (HUYGENS 1655) is called simply TITAN. It is sometimes considered as potentially capable of producing organic life as it has its own nitrogen-rich atmosphere. It isn't exactly an ideal holiday destination, however, as it has a surface temperature of minus 178 °C and it rains methane, though in Kurt Vonnegut's *Sirens of Titan* (1959), an affectionate send-up of the science-fiction alien-invasion novel, the planet is actually habitable.

[443] IDESIA

Idesia polycarpa is a deciduous tree native to China and Japan, introduced to Britain around 1864. Named after the Dutch traveller and plant collector EVERT YSBRANT IDES, an account of whose 3-year overland journey from Moscow to China via the Gobi Desert* (1682-4) appeared in English translation in 1706.

* Actually a tautology (or a pleonasm?) as "gobi", apparently, means "desert" in Mongolian. Compare "River Avon", "Lake Windermere", etc.

[444] IMHOFF TANK

An improved form of septic tank in which the solids in raw sewage are rapidly separated from liquid by sedimentation and subjected to anaerobic fermentation, resulting in an inoffensive sludge. The device was invented by German sanitary engineer Dr. KARL IMHOFF and patented by him in 1906. Imhoff tanks were installed for municipal sewage treatment in Essen in 1908 and were introduced into America in 1911.

[445] IMMELMANN TURN

MAX IMMELMANN (1883-1916), Germany's first WWI fighter ace with 17 victories, is credited (on somewhat dubious authority) with the definition of one of the most basic and useful aerial combat manoeuvres, comprising a half-loop and half roll. The result of this sequence is that one ends up flying at 180 degrees to one's original course and at a height defined by the top of the half-loop, usually above and behind one's adversary – a very desirable position. The inverse manoeuvre, also beloved of fighter pilots as a break-off manoeuvre is the Split-S (a half-roll followed by an inside downward half-loop). The latter results in flying at a lower height with extra energy – but if one's initial height is inadequate, this can terminate in a sudden escape from these mortal coils. The Immelmann turn will be familiar to those of adventurous bent who frequent roller-coasters, where it is a popular feature. (GJ)

[446] INCARVILLEA

A genus of some 14 species of herbaceous perennials native to the mountains of western China and Tibet. Named after the French Jesuit missionary to China **Father PIERRE LE CHÉRON D'INCARVILLE** (1706-1757). *I. delavayi* and *I. grandiflora*, both bearing pink flowers, are commonly grown as garden plants.

[447] INTERNATIONAL FORTEAN ORGANIZATION – see FORTEANS

[448] IRVING JACKET

Sheepskin-lined leather flying jacket issued to RAF aircrew during WWII and made by the American **LESLIE L. IRVING's** Irving Air Chute Company, founded in 1919, to design and manufacture parachutes. The Irving (sometimes Irvin) jacket was favoured by bomber crews, but fighter pilots found it too bulky and took instead to wearing white polo-necked woollen sweaters under their uniform jackets, creating an iconic mode that has come to typify the spirit of the period and of the men who wore it.

[449] ISLETS OF LANGERHANS

No one who has ever participated in a pub quiz can now be unaware that the Islets of Langerhans are not to be found on any map of the world but are groups of endocrine cells cunningly hidden in the pancreas of most vertebrates. They commemorate the German physician and specialist in microscopical anatomy **PAUL LANGERHANS** (1847-1888). He discovered the existence of these structures but not their function, which is to produce, among other substances, insulin. Langerhans was a TB sufferer who settled in Madeira for his health, where he made a study of marine invertebrates and wrote a book praising the islands' health-giving climate. He died in Funchal aged only 41.

J

[450] JACK RUSSELL

Type of terrier originating from a line bred by the REV. JOHN RUSSELL (1795-1883), a "sporting" parson of Swimbridge near Barnstaple in Devon. These feisty, great-hearted little dogs are loved for their character and energy, and forgiven for their ungovernableness. The PARSON RUSSELL terrier is a longer-legged version, bred essentially for the show-bench (see CRUFT'S).

[451] JACOB SHEEP

The JACOB SHEEP is a primitive, goat-like, multi-horned, multi-coloured breed, probably originating in Scandinavia and not, as once used to be thought, in Spain. Like another primitive breed, the Soay, though not to so marked an extent, the Jacobs exhibit little flocking behaviour and so can be hard to manage for both shepherd and dog. They are hardy and require little attention and virtually no supplementary feeding. The wool, because of the natural variation in colour, is prized by hand-spinners and knitters. The name Jacob has replaced an earlier designation "Piebald" and derives from the account in *Genesis* Chapter 30 of how JACOB THE SON OF ISAAC, the brother of poor hairy Esau and a trickster-like figure for whom, apparently, dishonesty was always the best policy, paid himself out of his employer and father-in-law Laban's flocks and herds by *"removing from thence all the speckled and spotted cattle, and all the brown cattle among the sheep, and the spotted and speckled among the goats."* Following which, Jacob engaged in a surreptitious programme of controlled breeding which resulted in the deterioration of Laban's remaining stock to the benefit of Jacob's own.

[452] JACQUARD LOOM

The beginnings of the science of cybernetics (communication and control in machine processes) can be traced back to the year 1725 when holes punched in strip of paper were introduced by the Frenchman Basile Bouchon as a means of controlling the lifting and lowering of warp threads on a hand loom. His invention was improved by Falcon in 1728, VAUCANSON in 1745, and finally resulted in the perfected machine produced in or around the year 1801 by the French inventor JOSEPH MARIE JACQUARD (1752-1834). In the Jacquard loom, punch cards replaced the paper strip of Bouchon. Thus the mechanisation of hand-loom weaving was an important first step on the road to the modern computer, hole/no-hole standing for the 0 and 1 of the computer's binary arithmetic. (See also HOLLERITH TABULATOR.)

[453] JACUZZI

The originator was Italian-American **CANDIDO JACUZZI** (1903-1986), one of seven brothers who emigrated to the States in the early 1900's and set up an innovative aero-engineering company in Berkeley, California. Among their products was a new kind of hydraulic pump which, in or around 1948, one of the brothers, **CANDIDO JACUZZI** (1903-1986) fitted to a hot tub to provide hydrotherapy treatment in the home for his son Kenneth, a sufferer from rheumatoid arthritis. In common parlance, "a jacuzzi" has come to mean any bath that provides a soothing or stimulating massage effect by the use of underwater water-jets. Like the **HOOVER** company, the Jacuzzi company has been unable to prevent what it regards as a proprietary trade name becoming generalised in this way – an illustration of the fact that the everyday speech of ordinary people has a life of its own, not subject to direction by pedants or patent lawyers (see **JOHNSON'S DICTIONARY**).

[454] JAEGER SANITARY WOOLLENS

The firm of Jaeger, a well-known maker of fashionable woollen garments, traces its origins to the theories of **Dr. GUSTAV JAEGER** of Stuttgart (1832-1917), physician, physiologist and zoologist, who promoted the notion that for the sake of human health only garments made of animal fibre should be worn next to the skin.* (Bad news for cotton growers, and for anyone old enough to remember the scratchy miseries of woollen vests and underpants.) The patent rights to Jaeger's ideas and garments were acquired by British businessman Lewis Tomalin who started manufacturing them in 1884, soon adding outer- to under-garments. The firm's success owed something to clever public relations through the supply of Jaeger woollens to exploring expeditions including those of Scott and Shackleton, as well as to the endorsement of converts like George Bernard Shaw, the well-known health crank. Since then, the health-promoting aspect of Jaeger woollens has been down-played in favour of their fashionableness.

* See his *Die Normalkleidung als Gesundheitsschutz* 1880.

[455] JALBERT PARAFOIL

A soft kite, without rigid spars or struts, which self-inflates in the wind. Its chambers are made of ripstop nylon, with an aerofoil cross section, and several are stitched together to provide a self-forming rectangular aerodynamic wing, which is a most efficient lifting kite if tethered by a line or, if free, performs as an excellent steerable parachute or paraglider. French-Canadian **DOMINA CLEOPHAS JALBERT** (1904-1991) was born at St-Michel-des-Saintes, northern Québec, and had a hardy upbringing on Hudson Bay, which may have inspired his passion for all things wind-powered; he flew kites from the age of four. As the 17th of 21 children he received little formal education. In 1918 the family moved to Woonsocket, Rhode Island, where he obtained American citizenship, and worked in the woollen mills. He was an early aviator, gaining his PPL in 1927. On the outbreak of WWII he worked for the United States Rubber Company in Naugatuk, Connecticut, on the construction of barrage balloons, which ended up defending London. His hybrid kite-balloon the "kytoon" derives from this period, and provided the proverbial "skyhook" with innumerable applications for surveying, expeditions and aerial research. After the war he settled in Boca Raton, Florida, founding the Jalbert Aerology Laboratory in 1949 where he invented the ram-air inflated flexible wing in 1957, and patented it in 1963. This new generic kite design was a paradigm shift and several modern air-sports, and many fliers, owe their existence to the **JALBERT PARAFOIL**. (MW)

[456] JAMES'S "MORAL EQUIVALENT"

The phrase **"MORAL EQUIVALENT OF WAR"** is perhaps more bandied about than properly understood. In the essay of 1910 which bears this title, **WILLIAM JAMES** (1842-1910), American philosopher and psychologist, brother of the more famous Henry, made a simple but telling point: that if the aim of eliminating war from the conduct of human affairs was ever to have a chance of realisation, a substitute activity would have to be found. And this activity, whatever it might be, would have to promote what are universally – and ineradicably – regarded as the warrior virtues: courage, comradeship, discipline, self-sacrifice, honour, and a sense of duty. Such a substitute has yet to be found, but something of the sort must have been in President Kennedy's mind when in 1961 he signed the Executive Order which brought the "Peace Corps" into being.

[457] JANSKY

A physical unit for measuring the strength of a received radio signal, per unit of bandwidth. It's not strictly SI, but compatible, with a big built-in numerical factor: one **JANSKY**, symbol Jy, is a spectral flux density of 10^{-26} Watts per square meter per Hertz ($W/m^2/Hz$), so extremely feeble signals can be conveniently categorised as having intensities of a few Janskys. American radio engineer **KARL GUTHE JANSKY** (1905-1950) was born in Oklahoma and studied physics at the University of Wisconsin-Madison. In 1931, while an employee of the Bell Telephone Labs in New Jersey, he was assigned to the task of identifying the source of troublesome radio noise and "static" that was interfering with international communications. He built a ramshackle steerable radio antenna (see **YAGI**) tuned for 20 MHz, to find the direction of the source. Besides the crackle of lightning storms, he discovered significantly that the noise ("hiss") fluctuated with a period of one sidereal day rather than one solar day,* and so concluded that these radio emissions were coming from the Milky Way. Thus Jansky became the founder of the science of radioastronomy; but that evidently cut no ice with Ma Bell, who had no billing address for little green men (see **DRAKE EQUATION**), so he was reassigned to other duties. Radioastronomy remained at a standstill until the termination of WWII which had, meanwhile, promoted the improvement of radio receivers. Except for his eponymous unit, Jansky's name remains largely unsung today, but had he not died at the early age of 44, he would have been in the running for a Nobel prize. (MW)

* The sidereal day is the period of Earth's rotation with respect to the fixed stars: 23 hours 56 minutes – give or take.

[458] JCB

The highly versatile machine which combines the functions of digger and earth mover, known in this country as a **JCB** and to the Americans as a "backhoe", is an acronym for the engineering firm founded in 1945 by **JOSEPH CYRIL BAMFORD** (1916-2001). After wartime service in the RAF, Bamford hand-built his first machine, a tipping farm trailer, in a rented lock-up garage. The iconic yellow-painted digger first came on the market in 1953. Today the firm which bears Bamford's initials is a world-wide operation employing over 6000 people.

[459] JEHU – see JEZEBEL

[460] JERDON'S PALM CIVET

Paradoxurus jerdoni is a cat-sized arboreal carnivore belonging to the family Viverridae, cousins to the mongoose and the meerkat. There are some twenty species of civet, found mainly in South Asia and Indonesia. Though classed as carnivores, many civets live mainly on fruit and plant material, while some particularly relish the sap of palm trees. The home of Jerdon's Palm Civet is the jungle-covered Western Ghats of south India. **THOMAS CAVERHILL JERDON** (1811-1872) was an army medical officer posted to the Madras Presidency as assistant surgeon in the service of the East India Company in 1835. He remained in India until 1870, visiting every part of the sub-continent, until forced home by ill-health in 1870. As a naturalist, Jerdon's inclination was towards ornithology and he published a major survey of Indian birds in 1862-4, but he spread his net wide and his *Mammals of India* appeared in 1867. The civets have a certain economic importance thanks to the vile-smelling musk, also known as civet*, extracted from their anal glands, which finds a use in perfumery. In addition, the Common Palm Civet, *Paradoxurus hermaphroditus*, a species native to Indonesia and the Philippines, is highly valued among the kind of people who claim to enjoy (for instance) snail-egg caviare or raw monkey brains, as the source of *kopi luwak* – super-expensive coffee made from beans swallowed but not digested by the animal and extracted from its faeces. Two other civets are eponymous, those of **HOSE** and **OWSTON**.

* The derivation is from Arabic.

[461] JEROBOAM

A cloud of unknowing surrounds the fanciful names given to oversize wine bottles: **JEROBOAM, REHOBOAM, METHUSALEM** (or **METHUSELAH**), **SALMANAZAR, BALTHAZAR, NEBUCHADNEZZAR**, and the rest (the list is not exhaustive). When these names were allotted, by whom, and above all, how they were chosen, are questions that remain to be answered. It seems likely that the first of the family, **JEROBOAM**, was produced in the Bordeaux region in about 1725. Currently its content is set at 4 standard (0.75 litre) bottles (6 in Burgundy), as opposed to the better-known magnum, which holds only 2. The capacities of the remainder are: 6, 8, 12, 16 and 20 bottles respectively. Unfortunately it isn't even clear which historical Jeroboam is meant, as the Bible offers us two, both rather undistinguished kings of Israel (see *1 & 2 Kings, passim*). The remainder, with the exception of **BALTHAZAR** whose name is a mediaeval invention for one of the three "wise men" mentioned in the Gospel of Matthew,* are likewise figures from biblical history though none would appear to have any particular connection to wine or to magnitude. In France, there are regional differences in bottle names as between the three classic producing regions of Bordeaux, Burgundy and Champagne. In Burgundy, wine traded between growers and merchants is measured not in bottles but in *pièces* (barrels) but even here there are local variations. In the Côte d'Or a *pièce* measures 228 litres but in the Mâconnais and Beaujolais only 215, while in the Yonne (where Chablis comes from) they prefer the *demi-pièce* or *feuillette* of 132 litres.

* Matthew doesn't actually specify their number. That too is a mediaeval invention.

[462] JEZEBEL

Among the numerous examples of antonomasia* derived from the Bible, the name of **JEZEBEL**, wife of Ahab, King Of Israel, has come to mean any deceitful scheming female. Jezebel's moral turpitude covered a lot of territory but her main offence was to worship Baal, a traditional Semitic fertility God, in defiance of several important Commandments and to the great scandal of the prophet Elijah the Tishbite (*I Kings* 18). She was killed on the orders of **JEHU SON OF NIMSHI**, who acceded to the throne after despatching Ahab's son and successor Joram with an arrow in the back. The death of Jezebel, as related in *II Kings* 9, is memorable, even startling, for the matter-of-fact way in which it recounts an act of extreme violence – a stylistic trait which vividly recalls the characteristic tone of the Icelandic sagas. **JEHU**, whose trademark was his "furious" style of chariot management, has in turn lent his name to another type-figure, that of the fast driver. The term was popular in the horse-drawn 19th century when owning a hard-driving, don't-spare-the-horses coachman carried the same kind of kudos that today attaches to owning a fast car, or, for that matter, a fast chauffeur.

* See SCROOGE

[463] JOB – see RIZLA

[464] JOHN HANCOCK

JOHN HANCOCK (1736/7- 1793) was a Massachusetts merchant, politician, and forceful advocate of "liberty" as it was then known. The *Dictionary of American Biography* calls him "the richest if not the most intelligent New Englander on the patriot side". As the first signatory of the Declaration of Independence (1776) his name became in colloquial speech a synonym for "signature" so that instead of saying "Sign this" an American might say, "Put your John Hancock here." Hancock demanded to be made commander-in-chief of the revolutionary army but fortunately for the Americans it was Washington who got the job – fortunately because Hancock's performance in command of a Massachusetts detachment in an action in Rhode Island in 1778 was a humiliating disgrace. In spite of this he remained a popular figure and was twice elected Governor of Massachusetts (1780, 1788).

[465] JOHN RYLANDS LIBRARY

was established in his memory in 1899 by Enriqueta Augustina Rylands, the widow of JOHN RYLANDS (1801-1888) an English entrepreneur and philanthropist, born at Parr in Lancashire. From modest beginnings as a manufacturer of hand-looms, he became Manchester's first multi-millionaire, and his textile manufacturing concern was the largest in the UK. The Library building on Deansgate, Manchester, designed by architect Basil Champneys, is a fine example of Victorian Gothic. It was originally intended to house a collection of theological books, reflecting the ecumenical concerns of John Rylands, but is now part of the major repository of knowledge known collectively as the JOHN RYLANDS UNIVERSITY LIBRARY OF MANCHESTER which also inhabits a large building on the university campus. (See also SPENCER.) (MW)

[466] JOHNE'S DISEASE

A debilitating and ultimately fatal form of contagious enteritis affecting ruminants, both wild and domestic. The causative agent is *Mycobacterium avium subs. paratuberculosis*, first isolated by the German veterinarian and bacteriologist HEINRICH A. JOHNE (1835-1910) in 1905. The condition is found world-wide, though carriers are often asymptomatic. Once the symptoms appear, there is no cure, but spread of the disease can be restricted by strict hygiene. A related form of *Mycobacterium avium* is responsible for the lung infection known as **LADY WINDERMERE SYNDROME**, supposedly, but for reasons not clear, named after the fastidious heroine of Oscar Wilde's play.

[467] JOHNSON'S DICTIONARY

Risking a truism, we might say that a nation needs three things to make it a nation: its land, its history, and its language.* And both land and language have their own history and their own landmarks. In the history of the English language, one such landmark is the Dictionary published in 1755 by **Dr. SAMUEL JOHNSON** (1709-1784). A dictionary presents, as it were, a snapshot of a language at a particular moment in its history. But the compiler of the dictionary has a decision to make: is he to present the language as she is spoke, or as she ought to be spoke? Is the dictionary, in other words, to be *de*scriptive or *pre*scriptive? The 8th century Northumbrian scholar Alcuin wrote,"*Grammar is the science of letters and the guardian of right speech and writing; it depends on Nature, Reason, Authority, and Custom.*" The trick, of course, is to get the right balance between Authority and Custom. Johnson lived in an age which took as a given that the educated élite – a conveniently small group in his day – had both the right and the duty to establish and promote canons of good taste, good sense and good usage. And he had before him the example of the French Académie which for the past century had been engaged on a massive dictionary designed to *fix* the language according to the best models. Languages, however, do not stay fixed. They evolve faster than any lexicographer can work, and they evolve in ways that at times almost make it seem as though they had a life and will of their own independent of their speakers. As a result, excessive devotion to a model of classical correctness has the effect of opening a gap, which may become unbridgeable, between the formal literary language and the language in everyday use. On the other hand, any concerned observer cannot but be aware of the fact that a fair proportion of changes in vocabulary and usage arise from plain mistakes, which reference to a reliable dictionary would have prevented. (Recent instances would include the misuse of words and phrases such as *hopefully*, *epicentre*, and *beg the question*, mispronounced words like *primarily* and *harass*, hijacked words like *gay* and *gender*, or solecisms of the type He *gave it to my wife and I*. All of these, except one hopes the last, will in due course be accepted as normal usage.) Balancing these considerations leads almost inevitably to the conclusion that a middle course between description and prescription is the way to go. And this, on the whole, is the way English dictionary makers, Johnson among them, have gone. Johnson was saved from nit-picking fanaticism (what the 18th century would have called "enthusiasm") by his famous common sense. His method of illustrating different uses of a word by extracts from what he called "polite authors" (Milton,

Shakespeare and Dryden were favourites) implicitly recognised the evolving nature of the language while setting the standard for future dictionary-makers, including that other mighty monument to the English language, Murray's *Oxford English Dictionary*. Johnson contracted with a group of London booksellers to produce the dictionary for a fee of £1,500,** calculating that it would take him three years. In the event it took him nine years, working almost entirely alone, a Herculean labour which he, in a famous moment of ironic self-deprecation, referred to as the work of "a harmless drudge". The dictionary, though its high cost limited numbers sold, went through five editions in Johnson's own lifetime, remaining a pillar of English literary culture and, along with the Bible, a regular item of domestic furniture for the next hundred and fifty years. In *Vanity Fair* (1847), when Thackeray's rebellious anti-heroine Becky Sharpe tosses out of her carriage window the copy of Johnson's dictionary which she has been given on leaving school, we are being shown, through the wrong end of the binoculars, as it were, a measure of the respect in which the Dictionary was held by later generations.***

* Truism: a truth so obvious as to be not worth repeating. Yet one which the planners (if that is the right word) of our national education system have forgotten, or chosen to ignore. With the results that we see.

** The Earl of Chesterfield (Philip Stanhope, 4th Earl) chipped in ten quid, showed no interest while the work was in progress, and when it was finished puffed it in the hope that Johnson would dedicate the dictionary to him as his Patron. Johnson rightly perceived this nugatory assistance as the act of what Patrick O'Brian's Jack Aubrey would have called a "scrub", and responded by excoriating His Lordship in a famous letter, denouncing his would-be patron as "one who looks with unconcern on a Man struggling for Life in the water and when he has reached ground encumbers him with help."

*** On the other hand it is true that "I prefer Doctor Johnson to Mister Boz" from Miss Jenkyns in *Cranford* (1853) is certainly meant to show how far behind the times the lady was in her literary tastes.

[468] JONES

A unit of electronic detectivity proposed in a 1957 paper by **R. CLARK JONES** to measure the sensitivity of receiving devices to radiant energy. Jones, an American physicist working mainly in the fields of optics and acoustics, has also lent his name to the **JONES VECTOR**, a means of describing the polarisation of light.

[469] JONES REDUCTOR

A vertical glass tube *ca.* 2 cm in diameter filled with a 40-50 cm long column of granulated metallic zinc, lightly amalgamated (*i.e.* treated with mercury). This is a potent reducing agent towards any solution trickled through it – *i.e.* it adds electrons, reducing the common oxidation state of many metal cations to lower oxidation states that are hard to reach by other chemical means, *e.g.* those of titanium, vanadium, chromium and uranium. Its chief use is analytical and it was originally devised within the mining industry for the estimation of the iron content of ores: the metal may be reoxidised quantitatively by titration with permanganate or dichromate (see **MOHR'S BURETTE**). It was the work of American chemist **CLEMENS JONES** of Pennsylvania, an employee of the Thomas Iron Company, and published in the *Transactions of the American Institute of Mining Engineers* for 1888. (MW)

[470] JONES'S NUMBER – see DUNBAR'S NUMBER

[471] JONESTOWN
JAMES WARREN JONES (1931-1978) was the founder of a "church" in California which he called "The People's Temple". His announcement that he was the reincarnation of both Jesus *and* V.I. Lenin brought him a numerous and devoted band of disciples, obedient to his every whim – of which he had many, and of a predictable kind. These same whims led to disquieting rumours about Jones's personal behaviour and he must have seen the writing on the wall because next thing you know this latter-day Peter the Hermit, who naturally has taken the precaution of relieving his disciples of all their money, is in a position to carry them off to the jungles of Guyana to set up "The People's Temple Agricultural Project", more generally known as **JONESTOWN**. Here the Reverend Jim reckoned he would be safe from the coming nuclear holocaust (a particular concern of his, and not an unreasonable one at the time) as well as being free from outside interference, as Jonestown was reachable by no road and all communication was by river-boat. In this secluded environment, Jones's combination of paranoia and megalomania flourished like the green bay tree, with the result that his New Jerusalem rapidly came to resemble a cross between a Stalinist gulag and an Alabama prison farm. Escapees who made it back to the States reported horrific abuses but were ignored until a California Congressman, Representative Leo J. Ryan, decided to investigate. Jones made Ryan and his companions* welcome but then, as the visitors were boarding a plane to leave the country, had them shot by his guards. The jig was now well and truly up. Jones announced to his followers that the time had come for them to pass on to a better life. On command, the entire population, men, women and children killed themselves by drinking a mixture of cyanide and sleeping pills sweetened with orange juice. Objectors were shot or forced to drink at pistol point. Small children had the poison squirted into their mouths from hypodermic syringes without needles. Finally Jones shot himself. 909 bodies were later counted at the site. Despite the horrifying dénouement, one is left not quite sure how sorry one ought to feel for people who unwisely entrusted their own lives and fortunes, and those of their families, to a man who was visibly unhinged.**

* Ryan had with him a reporter, sound man, and photographer as well as whistle-blowing former Jonestown resident Patty Parks.

** It is sometimes said that the inability to spot a phony is a particularly American failing. But this is nonsense. The British electorate, after all, fell hook, line and sinker for Tony Blair's cardboard charm, cheesy grin, and con-man's patter, and there are still Russians who regard Stalin as a sort of saint.

[472] JOSEPH

In the not altogether pristine world of second-hand car dealing, a JOSEPH is a car that has been re-sprayed in different colours with suspicious frequency. The reference, of course, is to the Bible (*Genesis* Ch. 37) and the polychrome outfit worn by JOSEPH THE SON OF JACOB, which aroused such envy among his brothers that they took the rather extreme step of selling him into slavery, having first relieved him of his technicolour dream-coat.

[473] JOULE

This SI unit of energy, symbol J, is defined by the work done in applying a force of one NEWTON through a distance of one meter. In practical terms, an 80 kg person walking upstairs (4 meters high, say) lifting his own weight against the force of gravity, expends 3136 Joules (3.136 kJ). We are accustomed at breakfast to reading the symbol kJ, for kilojoules, on our cornflakes packets – which tells us the heat energy released if the contents are entirely combusted. The JOULE now replaces that time-honoured heat unit from pre-SI years, the calorie (which equals 4.18 Joules), but would-be slimmers show little enthusiasm, as yet, for counting the kilojoules. The unit is named after JAMES PRESCOTT JOULE (1818-1889) the most famous Mancunian student of JOHN DALTON. Joule's chief claim to fame was demonstrating the mechanical equivalent of heat (1843), which he found very difficult experimentally, and even more difficult to persuade other scientists that he was correct. He also formulated JOULE'S FIRST LAW which expresses the heat generated by an electric current flowing through a resistance, and JOULE'S SECOND LAW which states that the internal energy of an ideal gas (see BOYLE'S LAW) depends only on its temperature. His work led to the idea of the conservation of energy and the First Law of Thermodynamics, in which he collaborated with KELVIN. He was elected FRS in 1850 and received numerous honours during a productive scientific life. (MW)

[474] JOULE-THOMSON EFFECT

When a compressed gas is allowed to expand, without doing work and without transfer of heat, it usually cools, (although there is a critical temperature, called the inversion temperature, above which the gas will heat up on expansion instead). If the gas were "ideal" or "perfect" in its behaviour (see BOYLE and VAN DER WAALS) these manifestations of the JOULE-THOMSON EFFECT would not happen. On free expansion, to counter the attractive forces between molecules of the gas, energy is required, which must be supplied from its kinetic energy – the agitation of the molecules – and so is manifested as loss of heat. The effect is named from an experimental collaboration between **JAMES PRESCOTT JOULE** and **WILLIAM THOMSON**, later to become 1st Lord **KELVIN**. It is important in cryogenics for the liquefaction of gases (see **DEWAR**). (MW)

[475] JUSSIEUA

Genus of 3 species of aquatic plants found in bogs and named after **BERNARD JUSSIEU** (1699-1777), one of a celebrated family of French physicians and botanists. Its other notable members were **ANTOINE** (1686-1758), author of a *Traité des vertus des plantes* (1715); **JOSEPH** (1704-1779), who collected plants in South America; **ANTOINE LAURENT** (1748-1836) a systematising botanist and author of *Genera plantarum...* (1788); and **ADRIEN** (1797-1853) who wrote *Embryons moncotylédonés* (1831). Bernard Jussieu is also remembered for having brought to France from England, two Cedars of Lebanon, one of which is still to be seen at the Jardin des Plantes, Paris.

K

[476] KAEMPFERIA

Genus of tropical Asian plants named after the German physician-naturalist ENGELBERT KAEMPFER (1651-1716), traveller to Russia, Persia and the Far East. In the service of the Dutch East India Company he reached Japan in 1690, whence he brought back seeds of the tree *Gingko biloba*. An English translation of his *History of Japan* appeared in 1727 and includes his observations on that country under the Tokugawa Shogunate. Of the plants named after him, *K. angustifolia* is grown as an ornamental foliage plant and *K. galanga* is a culinary spice and reputed hallucinogen.

[477] KALASHNIKOV

In late 1941 a Russian soldier MIKHAIL KALASHNIKOV, recovering in a war hospital from wounds and shell shock, began thinking about an improved automatic infantry weapon for the Soviet armed forces. The eventual result was the frighteningly efficient AVTOMAT KALASHNIKOVA, MODEL 1947 – better known as the **AK-47**, a weapon capable of pumping out 650 rounds a minute. Its success has been such that as many as 100 million AK-47s are thought to be now in circulation world-wide. Like other Russian-designed, mass-produced weapons (*cf.* T-34, KATYUSHA) it owes its success to its robust construction, ease of manufacture, and reliability in use. Within two years it became the main personal infantry weapon of the Soviet Army and proved its worth in, for example, the suppression of the 1956 Hungarian uprising. In the same year, production outside the Soviet Union started with China. In Vietnam, the Americans, finding themselves on the wrong end of Kalashnikov's invention, were so impressed that they started producing their own AKs, manufactured by Bingham's of Georgia from 1976.* The huge, now semi-derelict Izhmash plant in Izhev was the AK's birthplace, but ironically it has been almost driven out of business by foreign competition. Mikhail Kalashnikov was born to a poor peasant family in Russia's southern Altai region in 1919 and in WWII was drafted into the army and served as a tank commander during the initial German invasion. He was a self-taught inventor whose first major design was a device that counted the number of shells fired by the tank's machine gun. Kalashnikov, now a retired general, refuses to accept blame for the misery his brainchild has caused and has been quoted as saying, "Whenever I look at TV and I see the weapon I invented to defend my motherland in the hands of these bin Ladens, I ask myself the same question: How did it get into their hands? I didn't put it in the hands of bandits and terrorists, and it's not my fault that it has mushroomed uncontrollably across the globe." In 2004 his company diversified into vodka-distilling. Again, no blame attaches to the manufacturer for possible adverse consequences of the misuse of his product. (RS)

* In a memoir of his combat experience in Vietnam, Col. David H. Hackforth recounts an occasion on which "one of the dozers uncovered a slightly moldy VC body, complete with AK-47. I jumped down in the hole and yanked the AK out of the mud... I pulled the bolt back and fired thirty rounds – the AK performed as though it had been cleaned that day rather than buried in a marsh for a year. This was the kind of weapon our soldiers neeeded and deserved, not the M-16 that had to be hospital clean or it would jam." (David H. Hackworth with Eilhys England: *Steel my soldiers' hearts* 2002.)

[478] KALMIA

The kalmia or calico bush, a genus of 8 species of hardy flowering N. American shrubs, is named after the Swedish botanist **PETER KALM** (1715-1779) a pupil of **LINNAEUS**. Kalm spent three years travelling in N. America. An account of his journeys (in Swedish) was published in Åbo (3 vols. 1753-61). An English version, *Travels into North America* (London 1770-1771, 3 vols.), was translated by Johann Reinhold Forster, the tetchy German-born savant who with his son Georg shipped as naturalists on Cook's third and fatal expedition (1778-1780). In addition to the one genus, there are 90 species of plants named after Kalm. There is (also and by the way) a town named Kalmia in Autauga County, Alabama. (See also *The America of 1750: Peter Kalm's travels in North America* ed. A.B. Benson, 2 vols. N.Y. 1927, repr. 1966.)

[479] KATYUSHA

Many experts consider the Russians to be the premier artillerists of WWII. Among their most effective and most feared weapons in this sphere was the BM-13 multiple rocket launcher with its variants the light BM-8 and the heavy BM-31. The troops named the weapon **KATYUSHA** ("Katie") in reference to a sentimental wartime ballad of the same name popular with the troops – the Russians' *Lilli Marlene*, so to speak. The weapon, usually truck-mounted to facilitate "shoot and scoot" tactics, was produced in vast numbers as it perfectly suited the Russian preference for relatively cheap and simple weapons, often reverse-engineered from pirated western designs, that lent themselves to standardisation and mass-production (a lesson the Germans never learned). Work started on the Katyusha in 1938 in response to Germany's development in 1936 of a similar weapon, the *Nebelwerfer*. It remained in service throughout the war, and its descendants are still in service today in various parts of the world. The Germans had their own name for the Russian rocket launcher. They called it the **STALIN ORGAN** (*Stalinorgel*), an instrument which **BRUCHMÜLLER**, no doubt, would have been delighted to include in his "orchestra".

[480] KAYSER

A unit of the c.g.s. system – not strictly S.I., but still employed – this is a reciprocal centimeter, written cm^{-1}, and sometimes given the symbol K (an unfortunate clash with Kelvin degrees). Often called "wavenumber" by the initiates, spectroscopists use it to quantify electromagnetic radiation instead of wavelength or frequency, which are less convenient units. The wavenumber is defined as the number of vibrations, or waves, per centimeter and is directly related to the energy of the radiation by **PLANCK'S LAW**. For example, green light with a wavelength of 500 nm (nanometers) has a wavenumber of 20,000 cm^{-1} or, in short, 20 kK (kilokaysers). **HEINRICH GUSTAV JOHANNES KAYSER** (1853-1940) was a German physicist born at Bingen am Rhein, who studied at the University of Strasburg under **KUNDT**. In 1895 he discovered helium in the earth's atmosphere. He succeeded **HERTZ** as Professor of Physics at the University of Bonn. His spectrometric researches rivalled those of **RYDBERG**, and he published his *Tabelle der Schwingungszahlen* in 1925. (MW)

[481] KAYYAM'S TRIANGLE – see **PASCAL'S TRIANGLE**

[482] KEKULÉ STRUCTURE

Benzene – a colourless, volatile, flammable liquid – was once a commonplace solvent and fuel, but is now rarely encountered since it was revealed as a human carcinogen. **MICHAEL FARADAY** first isolated this substance from oil in 1825, but his analysis yielded a formula, C_6H_6, which puzzled chemical theorists. How the six carbon atoms could be bonded was first explained by **FRIEDRICH AUGUST KEKULÉ** (1829-1896), an architect *manqué*, who was persuaded by **LIEBIG'S** chemistry lectures at the University of Giessen to change direction in his studies. Turning to the architecture of molecules, **KEKULE'S STRUCTURE** for benzene visualised a hexagonal ring of six carbon atoms linked together cyclically. The idea is said to have come to him in a dream in 1865, and has since become an icon, likened to that alchemical symbol, the Greek "ouroboros": a serpent devouring its own tail. The benzene ring is the foundation stone of one whole edifice of organic chemistry designated as "aromatic", which somewhat belies its name because many benzene derivatives do not have strong aromas, and many fragrant substances are not derived from benzene. Among examples of familiar benzene-derived chemicals, we have: aspirin, phenol (a.k.a. "carbolic acid"), TNT, polystyrene, nylon, and thalidomide. (MW)

[483] KELLNER EYEPIECE – see LEICA

[484] KELLOGG'S CORN FLAKES

The brothers JOHN HARVEY KELLOGG (1852-1943) and WILL KEITH KELLOGG (1860-1951) have a name that has become synonymous with "breakfast cereal". The elder, John, trained as a doctor, graduating in 1875. Subsequently, he and his brother joined forces at Battle Creek Sanitarium, Michigan (one to supply the medical and the other the commercial expertise) where they developed a process for rolling and toasting wheat and corn into crisp flakes that made a nourishing breakfast for their patients. John Harvey was the innovator who in 1877 created a cereal called "granola", but commercial success had to wait for his invention of "CORN FLAKES" in 1902. Precooked dry cereals had already been made since 1863 by James Jackson who broke up hardened loaves of unleavened whole-grain bread into small brittle chunks to be served for breakfast after an overnight soaking in milk.* But it was the Kellogg brothers who achieved mass success when, in or around 1897, they founded the Sanitas Food Company to sell their products. By 1906 W. K. had underhandedly gained exclusive control of a new company called *The Battle Creek toasted cornflake company*, which explains why today the company's products are sold as Kellogg's, not Kelloggs'. However, of the two brothers it was John Kellogg who had actually instituted a major revolution in human diet, though his interests went well beyond breakfast cereals, these being only a part of his frankly cranky obsessions concerning human health. Born into a Seventh Day Adventist family, he later become editor of an Adventist monthly publication *Health Reformer* (which he renamed *Good Health* in 1879), and the Battle Creek Sanitarium was run on strict Adventist principles. Here Kellogg gave free rein to his theories about "biologic living", or "the Battle Creek idea", which stressed the role of "natural medicine" and a vegetarian diet. He developed other health foods such as coffee substitutes and soybean-derived milk; he advocated low calorie diets, developed peanut butter, warned that smoking caused lung cancer decades before this link was studied (or admitted), and remained a practising surgeon all his life. Some of his beliefs were distinctly questionable such as his opposition to any form of sexual activity from masturbation** to marital intercourse (he allegedly never consummated his marriage). But his greatest obsession was with the bowel and elimination. By pumping yoghurt into the rectums of America's rich and famous he claimed that he had managed to cure "cancer of the stomach, ulcers, diabetes, schizophrenia, manic depressives, acne, asthenia, migraine and premature old age". In addition, he concerned himself with eugenics and racial purity or what he called "race betterment". He wrote over 50 books promoting his ideas and his cures. For a fuller account of the hygienic-industrial history of the Corn Flake, see Gerald Carson: *Cornflake Crusade*, 1957. (RS)

* Somewhat reminiscent of a Welsh miners' dish called *siencyn*: a bowlful of hot milky tea poured over broken pieces of stale bread and small lumps of cheese. Reckoned sovereign against stomach upsets.

** As a preventive, Kellogg recommended early circumcision (of males) without anaesthetic, calculating that the pain would drive the lesson home. It would certainly help to make the occasion memorable, if nothing else. Some anthropologists believe that the painful rites of passage undergone by the males of certain aboriginal Australasian tribes (involving such practices as slitting the penis with a sharpened fragment of shell) are similarly using extreme pain to underline the importance of the ceremony.

[485] KELVIN SCALE

The Scottish mathematician, physicist, engineer, and inventor, **WILLIAM THOMSON** (1824-1907), born in Belfast, became known as Lord Kelvin after he was created **1st Baron KELVIN OF LARGS** in 1892. As professor at Glasgow University from 1846-1899, he was a pivotal figure in 19th-century physics, in 1848 establishing the scale of absolute temperature which now bears his title. He argued for the existence of an absolute zero of temperature, below which it was impossible to go, at zero degrees **KELVIN**, abbreviated to 0 K. This is the same as –273.15 degrees **CELSIUS**. The Kelvin degree and the Celsius degree are equal in size, only the scales' starting points differ. Kelvin was a founder of the sub-science of thermodynamics, but his calculations on the rate of solar "combustion" caused him to oppose Darwin because the sun could not be old enough for the eon of time required by Darwinian evolution. Kelvin was, of course, unaware of one of Dame Nature's more deeply-concealed secrets: nuclear fusion. (See also **JOULE-THOMSON EFFECT**) (MW)

[486] KEPLER'S LAWS

JOHANNES KEPLER (1571-1630) was born in Württemberg, Germany, and studied at Tübingen, becoming not only a mathematician and astronomer, but also a Lutheran theologian and professional astrologer. Kepler's preoccupation with the mathematical harmonies discovered in classical antiquity drew him to polyhedra, and he produced some new solids to his credit: the **KEPLER-POINSOT* POLYHEDRA** are beautiful stellations of the dodecahedron and icosahedron (see **PLATONIC SOLIDS**). Kepler's *stella octangula* consists of two interpenetrating tetrahedra. In his publication *Mysterium Cosmographicum* (1596) he showed how a nested set of the five **PLATONIC SOLIDS** – in an appropriate order – provided a model for the solar system, because the relative radii of their inscribed and circumscribed spheres replicated the mean distances from the sun of the, then, six known planets (*cf.* **BODE'S LAW**). Although observed eccentricities in their orbits led Kepler to modify this platonic view, he never totally abandoned it. **KEPLER'S LAWS** describe, to a good approximation, the orbital motions of the planets in our solar system (and presumably in any other, having just one sun and relatively small planets):

•   The orbits of the planets are ellipses with the sun at one of their foci.

- A line joining planet and sun sweeps out equal areas in equal intervals of time.
- The squares of the orbital periods (i.e. planetary "years") are directly proportional to the cubes of their mean distances from the sun.

Kepler inferred these three laws from the accurate and painstaking** celestial measurements of the Danish astronomer, Tycho Brahe (1546-1601), for whom he went to work in Prague in 1600, and whom he succeeded in 1601 as court astronomer to Emperor Rudolf II. Kepler announced the first two laws in his *Astronomia Nova* (1609) and, after ten years' more labour, the third law in *De Harmonice Mundi* (1619). (Additionally, in his *Ad Vitellionem Paralipomena* (1604) Kepler had been the first to formulate the inverse square law of the sun's illumination: the intensity of light decreases in proportion to the square of the distance from the source.) Much later (1684) NEWTON was able to derive KEPLER'S LAWS theoretically, by applying his fundamental laws of motion and universal gravitation to the "two body" problem (see also LAGRANGIAN POINTS) – a great vindication of the essential correctness of NEWTONIAN MECHANICS. The heliocentric cosmology which Kepler shared with COPERNICUS and GALILEO, was thus vindicated over the convoluted geocentric PTOLEMAIC SYSTEM favoured by the Catholic Church. Nonetheless, Kepler's science was informed by a strong metaphysical undercurrent, seeking "the harmony of the spheres", reflecting his religious faith, and manifested in his high reputation for casting successful horoscopes, including those of the Emperor himself and the Imperial general Wallenstein. His study of the Bible led him to calculate the date of the Creation. He put it at 3992 BC, which would mean that archbishop James Ussher was out by 12 years. Finally, and as an illustration of the fact that the enquiring mind never lacks food for thought, it is worth recording that Kepler was the first person, as far as we know, to observe that while all snowflakes are six-pointed, no two are in other respects alike. He published a little book on the subject *De nive sexangula* (1611). (MW)

* LOUIS POINSOT (1777-1859), French mathematician and physicist, inventor of geometrical mechanics. A street in Paris and a crater on the Moon are named after him.

** A necessary precondition since the planetary orbits are only slightly elliptical and their deviation from strict circularity might have escaped a sloppy observer.

[487] KERRIA
Monospecific genus of deciduous spring-flowering shrubs, native to China and Japan, introduced to this country in 1834 by WILLIAM KERR a plant-collector for Kew Gardens. Not named after him is *Kerria laca* (synonym: *Lucifer laca*), an East Asian beetle which infests a wide variety of tree-species and produces two useful secretions, one being a red dye and the other the resin known as "shellac".

[488] KHAKI CAMPBELL

A breed of domestic duck valued for its ability to produce vast numbers of eggs – up to 340 a year in the best cases. It takes its name from a **MRS ADELE CAMPBELL** of Uley in Gloucestershire who, around 1898, inaugurated the breed when she obtained a particularly prolific fawn-and-white Indian Runner which had laid 182 eggs in 196 days. She crossed it with a Rouen (a French-domesticated strain of mallard) and the rest is history. In appearance, the Khaki Campbell (there is also a White version) somewhat resembles the mallard but has more upright posture derived from the Indian Runner, a breed readily recognisable by its resemblance to a clockwork hock bottle.

[489] KILNER JAR

Commonly used to house preserved fruits and vegetables, pickles and chutneys, the **KILNER JAR** depends for its effectiveness on a airtight seal produced by its three-part lid: a plate-shaped glass stopper, a rubber ring, and a screw-on metal collar to hold the lid down and in place. It takes its name from Yorkshireman **JOHN KILNER** (b. 1792) who set up a company to manufacture his patented jars in 1842. It continued in business until 1937 when its patents were bought out by the United Glass Bottle Company, a conglomerate which still produces a modernised version of the Kilner Jar. John Kilner has a second claim to fame as the great-great-great-grandfather of television broadcaster and fearless opponent of Political Correctness Jeremy Clarkson. The American equivalent of the Kilner Jar is the **MASON JAR**, invented by **JOHN L. MASON** in the 1850's.

[490] KIM'S GAME

When the eponymous boy hero of Kipling's *Kim* is being considered for recruitment as a secret intelligence agent, he is subjected to a test by the English officer Lurgan Sahib: he is shown a tray on which there are 15 jewels and ornaments, each one different. He is told to look at them carefully. Then the tray is covered and he has to describe its contents in detail. This exercise, which Kim calls "the jewel game", becomes an integral part of his training. (Interestingly, it is also an integral part of the system of mind-training known as **PELMANISM**.) The plot of *Kim* is not mere fantasy. At a time when the English in India were hag-ridden by fears of a Russian invasion from the north, the collection of topographical information of possible military use in the no-man's land between the two empires, was given a high priority. But this involved areas of Tibet and the North-West Frontier where a European dare not venture unless accompanied by a fair-sized army, and here Indian agents were used, posing as merchants or – as in Kim's case – pilgrims. These agents, known as "pundits" were very brave men, needing both luck and cunning to survive, as their non-European status would not have saved them had their activities been unmasked.

[491] KING JAMES BIBLE

It is impossible to overestimate the importance of the "Authorised" Bible of 1611 which bears the name and imprimatur of JAMES I (1566-1625) to the culture, language, literature (and of course the spiritual life) of this country.* Though King James was in some ways a contemptible little person and had in full measure the Stuarts' well-deserved reputation for untrustworthiness (as Sir Walter Raleigh, among others, discovered to his cost), for this one action, the publication of the first full translation of the Bible from original sources into English, we are forever in his debt. The finished work (which, incidentally, was the product of that much-derided creature, a committee), carried on and completed the earlier heroic labours of Wycliffe and Tyndale. The *Epistle dedicatory* which prefaces the Bible of 1611 is, it must be said, almost sickeningly fulsome in its flattering expressions of gratitude to the monarch for his patronage, but to the general tenor of its sentiments we can all say "Amen".

* Just as it is impossible to overestimate the damage done to our cultural heritage by its modern replacement, although, to be fair, the motive behind the substitution was exactly the same as that which animated the translators of the Authorised Version – namely, to make the Word of God accessible to ordinary people ("ordinary" meaning, according to Kingsley Amis, people who couldn't understand words like "ye" and "unto").

[492] KINSEY SCALE

American biologist ALFRED CHARLES KINSEY (1894-1956) was Professor of zoology and entomology at Indiana University from 1920. In 1947 he set up within the University the Institute for Sex Research known today as the KINSEY INSTITUTE. The research in question, which largely involved interviews with hundreds of human subjects to elicit intimate details of their sexual behaviour, resulted in two controversial but ground-breaking publications: *Sexual behaviour in the human male* (1948), commonly known as the KINSEY REPORT, and *Sexual behaviour in the human female* (1953). Investigations of homosexual behaviour led Kinsey to the conclusion that there is no clear boundary between homo- and heterosexual but rather a spectrum, and that homosexual inclination varies in intensity not only between individuals but in given individuals at different periods in their lives. In order to locate his subjects on the spectrum, Kinsey developed a numerical scale running from 0 (exclusively heterosexual) to 6 (exclusively homosexual). Kinsey's own rating on the scale is still a subject of speculation but it is now accepted that his interest in sex verged on the pathological and that his research embodied a considerable element of what can only be called voyeurism.

[493] KIPP'S APPARATUS

A triple-chambered apparatus, looking rather like a glass snowman, traditionally used in the chemistry laboratory for the controlled generation of certain gases, resulting from the reaction of a solid with a liquid, usually a mineral acid. The solid is placed in the closed centre chamber which is fitted with a stopcock; when this is opened, the acid flows up into it from the bottom vessel, being replenished from the open reservoir above via a central tube. Gas is evolved – usually either hydrogen (from zinc), hydrogen sulphide (from iron sulphide) or carbon dioxide (from marble chips). When the tap is closed, the build-up of gas pressure forces the acid back, out of contact with the solid, and up into the reservoir, so the reaction ceases. This ingenious apparatus was the brainchild of Dutchman **PETRUS JACOBUS KIPP** (1808-1864) who qualified as a pharmacist in Delft. At this time the pharmaceutical profession in Holland was oversubscribed, so Kipp turned to dealing in scientific apparatus for a living, and he had the first prototype of his gas generator made in 1844 by the glassblower **GEISSLER**. (MW)

[494] KIR

Alcoholic drink, normally served as an aperitif, and composed of white wine mixed with a measure of blackcurrant liqueur (*crème de cassis*). Strictly speaking, the wine should be Bourgogne Aligoté, the only white burgundy not made from the Chardonnay grape. It is named after **Canon FÉLIX KIR** (1876-1968), priest, Resistance hero, and mayor of Dijon in Burgundy from 1945 until his death. Kir cannot be said to have invented this drink, formerly known simply as "blanc-cassis", but his fondness for it and his insistence on serving at mayoral functions a refreshing drink whose ingredients are both local specialities justify the attribution. To maintain the regional identity, a **KIR ROYALE**, made with champagne, should ideally be made with Burgundy's own sparkler, *Crémant de Bourgogne*.

[495] KIRBIGRIP (KIRBY GRIP)

A sprung hair grip, originally manufactured by the firm of Kirby, Beard & Co. The firm was founded in 1743, but **KIRBIGRIP** was not registered as a trade name until the mid twenties of the last century when the fashion – revolutionary in its day – was for short "bobbed" hair styles in which the traditional hair-pin could get no purchase.

[496] KIRCHHOFF'S LAWS

German physicist **GUSTAV ROBERT KIRCHHOFF** (1824-87) was born in Königsberg, and became professor at Heidelberg (1854-75), then Berlin (1875-86). **KIRCHHOFF'S LAWS** are several and various, from different branches of physics. Two formulated in 1845 relate to electricity: the conservation of electric charge, and the conservation of energy, in any electric circuit; *i.e.* they effectively re-state the impossibility of perpetual motion in electrical systems. Kirchhoff's radiation law arose from his studies of heat. In 1859 he stated that, at thermal equilibrium, the emission and absorption of a body are equal. He coined the term "black body radiation" in 1862 to describe a perfect emitter and absorber of thermal radiation (see **PLANCK**). In a collaboration with **BUNSEN** on optics and spectrum analysis, Kirchhoff shared the discovery in 1859 of the new alkali metal elements, rubidium and caesium. His three "laws of spectroscopy" from *ca.* 1860 are not so much laws as empirical observations relating to the generation of continuous emission spectra from incandescent solids, versus line spectra (having only discrete wavelengths) from gaseous discharges. (MW)

[497] KIRLIAN PHOTOGRAPHY

A process discovered in 1939 by **SEMYON DAVIDOVICH KIRLIAN** (1898-1978) a Russian of Armenian descent. In the 1930's he worked as an electrician in Krasnodar on the eastern coast of the Black Sea. In 1939 he witnessed a demonstration of a high frequency electrotherapy device and spotted a spark of light between the machine's electrodes and the patient's skin and considered whether he could photograph it. In experimentation he replaced glass electrodes with metal ones and took his photographs. The resulting image was startling as it showed an apparent energy discharge around his hand. The next ten years were spent trying to perfect the apparatus, a high frequency oscillator that operated at 75,000 to 200,000 cycles per second. There was no camera as such, only an electric current and photographic film. He and his wife, Valentina, made photographs of the leaves of plants and claimed that they could detect incipient plant disease before it was otherwise detected. They also went on to claim that their Kirlian photographs could provide an indication of a person's physical health as well as showing the acupuncture points on the human body. The Kirlians first published a scientific paper in 1961 in the Russian Journal of Scientific and Applied Photography. In the West these unusual, mysterious images became well known in the 1960's at a time when there was a resurgence of interest in the mystical and paranormal. People then speculated that what we were seeing were halos or physical proof of a life force, though unfortunately for the theory inanimate objects such as coins produced similar results. Appearing at the crossroads between science and science fiction these images have captured the popular imagination and have inspired such luminaries as David Bowie in his cocaine-fuelled 1970's fascination with matters supernatural, as well as the makers of *The X-Files* TV series which features in its credits a Kirlian hand print. (RS)

[498] KIT-CAT CLUB

The origin of the name of this 18th-century Whig political and literary society has been the subject of much speculation. The usually accepted answer relates it to one Christopher ("Kit") Catling who owned a pie-shop near Temple Bar, which was the club's first meeting place. The membership, originally 39 in number but later raised to 48, consisted of "wits" and *bon viveurs* drawn from the politically active aristocracy (a raft of Dukes, a belted earl or two) as well as leading lights from London's literary scene. Congreve, Vanbrugh, Swift, Addison, and Steele, all belonged at one time or another, as did the painter Sir Godfrey Kneller who was charged with producing portraits of the leading members to a standard format dictated by the proportions of the room at Barn Elms where the club had its later meeting place.

[499] KJELDAHL FLASK

More chemists' kit: a round-bottomed glass flask with an unusually long neck intended to prevent any loss of liquid boiling within it. It is used specifically for the analytical determination of the nitrogen content of organic substances. Danish chemist **JOHAN GUSTAV CHRISTOFFER THORSAGER KJELDAHL** (1849-1900) was born in Jaegerspris, Copenhagen, and studied there at the Royal Polytechnic. He became Director of the Carlsberg Laboratory in Copenhagen (1876-1900) and invented his flask and method of nitrogen analysis in 1883 in order to find the protein content of the barley grains used for fermentation. Chemists, in general, owe a huge debt of gratitude to breweries. (MW)

[500] KLEIN BOTTLE

Three-dimensional version of the **MÖBIUS STRIP** named after the German mathematician **FELIX KLEIN** (1849-1925) who first described such an object – one where one can pass from inside to outside without ever crossing an edge – in 1882. Klein also made important contributions to the mathematical theory of knots and succeeded in proving, to everyone's surprise, that knots cannot exist in 4-dimensional space (*Mathematische Annalen* ix. 478). Anyone intending to construct a Klein bottle should be warned that it can only exist in non-Euclidian space since the neck of the bottle has to pass through the side of the bottle without touching it. This would seem to rule out most practical applications that one might otherwise imagine for Klein's invention.

[501] KNICKERS

In 1809 the American author Washington Irving published a *History of New York* ostensibly written by one **DIEDRICH KNICKERBOCKER**, the name being chosen as archetypical of the first Dutch settlers of New York (then New Amsterdam). The edition of the book illustrated by George Cruikshank showed these Dutchmen in knee-length breeches which rapidly came to be known as "knickerbockers", later shortened to "knickers". "Golf knickers" is still the accepted term in America for what we call "plus-fours", but the stages by which the same word "knickers" ("panties" in America, "slip" in France) came to be applied in England to women's most intimate undergarment is somewhat mysterious.* However, we should note than any item of vocabulary which concerns, even tangentially, the dreaded nether regions between knee and navel is subject to continuous semantic shift – think of "lavatory". Even so basic a word as "sex" has shifted in the space of a generation from describing a biological category (male/female) to describing a popular form of leisure activity (though it is curious that people are said to "have" rather than "do" sex). Meanwhile the word "gender" has necessarily changed its meaning *pari passu* and shifted from being a term used only by grammarians to filling the slot once filled by "sex".

* See also **BLOOMERS**

[502] KNOLLYS MITRE

The Hundred Years' War between France and England had this much in common with most other wars in that it was the non-combatants who bore the brunt of its destructive effects. Between 1337 and 1453 France was torn apart and laid waste by wandering armies of what were effectively mere bandits, some French, some English, and some of uncertain loyalties or none. The endless and indiscriminate orgy of looting, rape, and arson that marked this squalid episode is symbolised by what was known at the time as the "Knollys mitre", formed by the still-standing gable ends of a burned and ruined dwelling. The honour of having this sad symbol named after him goes to **Sir ROBERT KNOLLYS** (d. 1407), a leading English military commander, who died rich thanks to his energetic participation in England's continental maraudings. In a later century and another continent, the route of Sherman's march from Atlanta to the sea was waymarked by similar grim memorials in the brick and stone chimneys of the wooden houses his troops had burned in their passage. "War is cruelty," said Sherman, "and you cannot refine it."

[503] K-NUMBERS

The man who first set about the giant task of cataloguing Mozart's vast musical output was not himself a musician but a botanist and mineralogist **LUDWIG VON KÖCHEL** (1800-1877), a man with, we may suppose, a scientist's penchant for orderly classification. The numbers allotted to to each piece, preceded by a "K" or a "KV" (it doesn't matter which) reflect the chronological order of the works' composition as far as it could be established. Köchel's list has, not surprisingly, undergone a number of later revisions, notably that of Alfred Einstein in 1937. The catalogues of the works of Bach and Beethoven (in Bach's case a particularly severe task as he published little in his lifetime and on his death his manuscipts were scattered) do not reflect the names of the scholars who worked to establish them. For Bach we have the BWV (*Bachwerkeverzeichnis* or "list of Bach's works") catalogue established by Wolfgang Schmieder in 1950 but drawing on the work of numerous earlier scholars, and for Beethoven, Opus numbers.

[504] KOHLRAUSCH'S LAW

FRIEDRICH WILHELM GEORG KOHLRAUSCH (1840-1910) was born in Rinteln, Germany, into a family with strong scientific traditions. He studied at Erlangen and at Göttingen, where he became professor of physics in 1866, subsequently taking up chairs at the Universities of Zurich (1870), Darmstadt (1871), Würtzburg (1875), Strasbourg (1888), and Humboldt University, Berlin (1900). As President of the *Physikalisch-Technische Reichsanstalt* (1895-1905) he made notable contributions to the standards of instrumental measurement in magnetism and electricity. He was a pioneer of the theory that ionic electrolytes, when dissolved in water, split into positively charged cations and negatively charged anions which, under an applied electric field, are attracted and migrate to the cathode (negative electrode) and anode (positive electrode) respectively, of an electrochemical cell. KOHLRAUSCH'S LAW states that the electric current is conducted independently by both the anions and cations, which each have specific mobilities. (MW)

[505] KOURNAKOFF IRON

Also known as the "offset iron" – a form of stirrup invented by and named after a Russian cavalry officer. The slit in the arch of the stirrup through which the leather passes is placed off-centre with the effect (it is said) of helping the rider keep his/her foot at the right angle and making for closer contact with the saddle.

[506] KREBS CYCLE

The whole of Mother Nature's animal kingdom is kept going by this sequence of chemical reactions: the cells of every aerobic organism* – including us – use it to convert the products of splitting sugar molecules from food (*glycolysis*) into energy, in the form of bodily heat and muscular activity, with carbon dioxide as waste product which is exhaled (thereby increasing the burden of "greenhouse gas"). The overall catabolic reaction is:

$$glucose + oxygen \rightarrow carbon\ dioxide + water$$

The **KREBS CYCLE** is also called the *citric acid cycle*, thus identifying one of the key substances in the closed chain of nine biochemical reactions, each brought about by an enzyme (a complicated biochemical catalyst). The detailed structure of the cycle was established in 1937 by German-born, British citizen, **PROFESSOR SIR HANS ADOLF KREBS** (1900-1981) who was born in Hildesheim, studied medicine at the Universities of Göttingen and Freiburg, obtained his PhD at Hamburg and studied chemistry in Berlin, assisting Otto Warburg at the Kaiser Wilhelm Institute for Biology. In 1932 he discovered the *urea cycle*. At the time, Jewish ethnicity barred him from practising medicine in Germany so he emigrated to England in 1934 to become lecturer, then in 1945, professor of biochemistry at Sheffield University, then professor at Oxford from 1954-67. He was awarded the Nobel Prize in physiology for the **KREBS CYCLE** in 1953 and knighted in 1958. (MW)

* Anaerobic organisms – certain bacteria and archaea – derive their energy from sources other than oxygen. Plants, of course, perform the reverse reaction, courtesy of chlorophyll and sunlight.

[507] KUIPER BELT

Since the 1950's astronomers have speculated on the existence of a ring of objects, too small to qualify as planets, lying outside the orbit of **NEPTUNE** at a distance of 40-55 AU* from the sun. The area of space occupied by these objects has been christened the **KUIPER BELT** after the Dutch American astronomer **GERARD KUIPER** (1905-1973), who is remembered and respected in the annals of astronomy for his lifelong study of our solar system. The existence of the Kuiper Belt has now been established by observation and some 7,000 "sub-planetary" bits and pieces have been counted to date. This area of the outer Solar System differs from the much further distant **OORT CLOUD** in that the existence of the Oort Cloud remains hypothetical, though widely accepted as a likely source of "long-period" comets, while the Kuiper Belt is the likely origin of other "short period" comets.

* AU (Astronomical Unit): the mean distance of the Earth from the Sun, widely used for measuring distances within the Solar System – about 93 million miles in old money.

[508] KUNDT'S TUBE

In the physics lab of every boys' grammar school, this was once a cause of much suppressed sniggering among the smutty-minded. It is unlikely that this piece of acoustical apparatus remains on the GCE Physics curriculum today, but it visibly demonstrates the existence of standing longitudinal waves in the air column of a sounding organ-pipe. It consists of a transparent tube closed by an adjustable plunger, dusted on its interior with lycopodium, or similar fine powder. When the air column resonates with sound, the powder gathers into regularly-spaced little piles at the least disturbed regions of the tube (the nodes), the distance between them equal to half of the wavelength. Knowing the frequency of the vibration, a measurement of the wavelength in Kundt's tube yields a value for the speed of sound in a gas, as the product of the two: *speed = frequency × wavelength*. **AUGUST ADOLF EDUARD EBERHARD KUNDT** (1839–1894) was born at Schwerin in Mecklenburg, Germany, and pursued his scientific studies at the Universities of Leipzig and Berlin, being elevated to a chair of physics at Zürich Polytechnic in 1868, and called to the new University of Strasbourg in 1872. He returned to Berlin in 1888 as successor to the illustrious professor **HEINRICH VON HELMHOLTZ**. (MW)

[509] KWOK'S QUEASE

A fulminating asthmatic condition caused by intolerance of monosodium glutamate, and also known as "Chinese restaurant syndrome". Reportedly, its onset can be so sudden that diners in Chinese eateries may be perfectly normal one moment and face down in a bowl of noodles the next. The condition is named after **ROBERT HO MAN KWOK** of the US National Biomedical Research Foundation who, in a letter to the *New England Journal of Medicine*, described his own experiences in Chinese restaurants. His conclusions are contested. (See *New England J. Med.* 305.19, Nov. 1981, and *Singapore Med. Journal* 10.4 (supp 43), Dec. 1969. *Cf.* **MONTEZUMA'S REVENGE**.)

L

[510] LABANOTATION

System of choreographic notation devised by Hungarian dancer and ballet director **RUDOLF VON LABAN** (1879-1958). After a successful performance career in Austria and Germany and a period as ballet director for the Berlin State Opera, he moved to England in 1938 where he actively promoted his educational ideas and founded the Art of Movement Studio, now known as the Laban Centre and attached to Goldsmith's College, University of London. Laban's notation, though influential and widely used, is not the only proposed system for the difficult business of committing terpsichorean evolutions to paper. One influential rival is **BENESH MOVEMENT NOTATION** devised by mathematician **RUDOLF BENESH** (1916-1975), whose wife Joan was a dancer with Sadler's Wells. Benesh notation is written on a five-line musical stave with bar lines and so can be readily matched to a musical accompaniment, whereas Laban's system is more concerned with detailing spatial rather than rhythmic qualities.

[511] LADY AMHERST'S PHEASANT

WILLIAM PITT, 1st EARL OF AMHERST (1773-1857) was appointed Governor-General of India in 1823 following the failure of his diplomatic mission to China (see **ABELIA**), and during his term of office managed to get into a shooting war with the King of Burma, in which the British came out on top. Among the spoils accruing to the victor were Assam, and a pair of rare Burmese pheasants, *Chrysolophus amherstiae*, which were brought back to England and the species named in honour of his wife (*cf.* **BOUGAINVILLEA**). It is characterised by extreme shyness and a preference for running over flying, which is probably a life-saving strategy, given the queer British prejudice against shooting birds on the ground. (A sitting duck, surely, is a more reliable meal-ticket than an airborne one?)

[512] LADY WINDERMERE SYNDROME – see JOHNE'S DISEASE

[513] LAGRANGIAN POINTS

JOSEPH-LOUIS, COMTE DE LAGRANGE, (1736-1813) was born in Sardinia as **GIUSEPPE LODOVICO LAGRANGIA** and appears to have enjoyed both Italian and French nationality. He succeeded **EULER** at the Berlin Academy in 1766, but was invited by Louis XVI to return to France in 1787. Unlike some of his less fortunate peers, Lagrange survived the Revolution, to become a leading figure in the Parisian mathematical hothouse. His most notable contributions lay in the foundations of group theory, later to be developed by Augustin Louis Cauchy (1789-1857), and the ill-fated Évariste Galois (1811-1832), whom space will not allow us to celebrate here in full. In celestial mechanics, the **LAGRANGIAN POINTS** are locations in the plane of an orbit of one body about another (*e.g.* the Moon around the Earth) where the gravitational attractions balance the centrifugal force so as to permit a relatively small third body (*e.g.* a communications, or spy satellite) to remain in a stationary position relative to both larger ones. Lagrange showed in 1772 that there are five such points, thereby discovering a restricted solution to the notorious "three-body problem", which does not admit of explicit solution in the general case. In the process of tackling this problem, Lagrange reforged the tools of **NEWTONIAN MECHANICS** into a more powerful mathematical formalism, now known as **LAGRANGIAN MECHANICS.** (MW)

[514] LAKE VICTORIA – see VICTORIA

[515] LAMARCKISM

JEAN-BAPTISTE MONET, Chevalier DE LAMARCK (1744-1829), French botanist and zoologist, specialised in the study of invertebrates, and taught invertebrate biology at the Paris Natural History Museum from 1793, publishing heavy tomes on the subject (1801, 1815-22). The philosophical underpinning of his work (*Philosophie zoologique* 1809) was the belief that species evolved in response to two forces: the influence of their environment, and a spontaneous tendency inherent in all living things to strive for perfection.* He further concluded (a) that the changes brought about by these forces could be passed on by an organism to its offspring, and (b) that the general tendency of evolution was from the simple to the complex – a fact not as obvious in his day as it is now. Because his theories were eventually supplanted by those of Darwin** and the discoveries of modern genetics, Lamarck is seldom given the credit he deserves as the first European scientist to offer a coherent explanation for the variation of species over time. Science proceeeds by the method of successive approximations, advancing incrementally towards an unreachable final truth. Lamarck's theory was, so to speak, a first approximation. Darwin's the second. There may yet be a third.

* A mediaeval or even older concept and one which he shared with Aquinas who, however, couched the idea in theological terms – the striving of all things towards God, thus accounting for (among other things) gravity. A science fiction writer whose name I forget penned an excellent tale in the "alternative history" mode in which wireless telegraphy is invented by mediaeval monks who explain its operation as invisible angels forming a chain with their wings along which a message can pass.
** Except in Stalin's Russia (see **LYSENKOISM**).

[516] LAMBERT – see BEER-LAMBERT LAW

[517] LANGRIDGE SHOT – see SHRAPNEL

[518] LARSON TRAP

A device used by gamekeepers for catching crows, rooks and magpies, regarded as enemies by the hunting-shooting fraternity because they eat the eggs and nestlings of birds *not* regarded as enemies by the hunting-shooting fraternity. Of the latter class of birds, only three qualify as friendly: the partridge, the grouse, and the poor silly pheasant. The rest are vermin. The trap consists of two chambers, the lower of which contains a live decoy bird, and an upper chamber which is entered by a spring-loaded one-way trap-door. Birds caught in this way can be left to perish miserably or, more humanely, have their necks wrung at the keeper's convenience. The hatred of gamekeepers for wild creatures (which in Scotland extends to the deliberate poisoning of eagles) is notorious and easy to understand, though less easy to admire. Perhaps this may go some way to explain why the humble compiler of these pages has been unable to discover after which LARSON this odious device is named. Clearly, he's lying low, courting obscurity. There is a good old country tradition in Britain dating back at least to Norman times whereby the gamekeeper is commonly the most hated man in the village.

[519] LAVOISIER'S LAW

One of the most fundamental axioms of early science: LAVOISIER'S LAW requires that the total amount of matter, or mass, is conserved in any chemical reaction. Although it is now replaced by the conservation of mass-energy, thanks to EINSTEIN'S $E=mc^2$, that refinement can be ignored for chemical purposes. It only becomes significant when you're doing nuclear physics. Most famous of all French chemists, ANTOINE-LAURENT DE LAVOISIER (1743-1794) was the acknowledged "father of modern chemistry". He was born in Paris, into privilege, but made good use of it: his inherited wealth funded his research. He took a law degree at Collège Mazarin, but rather than practice law he preferred to study mathematics and sciences, and was elected to the *Académie Française* at 25. Lavoisier was the man who finally put the science of chemistry on the right track after a millennium of alchemical moonshine. It must be conceded that he had some unintentioned help from the British chemists, Joseph Black, Joseph Priestley and HENRY CAVENDISH, whose findings he adopted – sometimes without acknowledgement – and his wife Marie-Anne was a veritable treasure around the lab. By careful quantitative work with the chemical balance, Lavoisier established the correct theory of combustion, in which he identified the role of oxygen and so named it in 1777 (Gr. "oxu-gennao" = "sharp-making" *i.e* "acid-making"*). With LAPLACE he used calorimetry to demonstrate oxygen's involvement in animal respiration, and in rusting. Thus he did away with the erroneous *phlogiston* theory of 1667, due to Joachim Johann Becher which, with the support of Georg Ernst Stahl, had held back chemical understanding for a century.

Lavoisier's contribution to modern science lay in the power and generality of his theoretical perceptions rather than any discovery of new substances or invention of new apparatus, so nothing else bears his name. He began a listing of the 33 then-known chemical elements, which was to lead to **MENDELEEV'S PERIODIC TABLE**, and he described the formation of chemical compounds from them with a systematic notation. These principles he set down in the first textbook of modern chemistry, *Traité Élémentaire de Chimie* of 1789. Of a liberal disposition, he was also involved in social reform, economic and political matters, and the application of chemistry to agriculture. He was appointed Commissioner of the Royal Gunpowder and Saltpetre Administration, and was an advocate of the introduction of the Metric System. However, it was his role as a tax collector for the *Ferme Generale* that made him a target of the Revolutionaries, although his real undoing was probably to have previously offended Marat. During the 1794 Reign of Terror, Lavoisier was arraigned and condemned, his liberal sympathies notwithstanding. Alongside 27 fellow tax-farmer companions he was summarily **GUILLOTINED** at the Place de la Revolution the same day. It is said that a final appeal for his life was dismissed by the judge with: "*La Republique n'a pas besoin de savants*" – a disavowal from which French chemistry has never entirely recovered. At the execution, his colleague **LAGRANGE**, whom he had protected from persecution by the same gang, observed bitterly: "*Il ne leur a fallu qu'un moment pour faire tomber cette tête, et cent années peut-être, ne suffiront pas pour en reproduire une semblable.*" ("It took them only a moment to cause that head to fall, and a hundred years, perhaps, will not suffice to produce another like it.") (MW)

*His influential theory that all acids contain oxygen turned out to be his biggest mistake.

[520] LAWRENCIUM

Chemical element 103, symbol Lr, was synthesised, like some dozen other transuranic elements,* at the Lawrence Berkeley National Laboratory (LBNL) of the University of California. Both element and lab take their name from the latter's founder, the American physicist **ERNEST ORLANDO LAWRENCE** (1901-1958). Born and educated in South Dakota, with a Ph.D. from Yale, he was appointed Professor of Physics at the University of California in 1928, where he became an ardent advocate and practitioner of "Big Science", thus successfully establishing his Radiation Laboratory in the 1930s as the world hub for research in nuclear physics. In 1931 he invented the cyclotron, which, being realised in ever larger versions, would prove itself as a major instrument for element nucleosynthesis, and for which Lawrence was awarded the Nobel Prize for physics in 1939. Lawrencium, however, was made in the Heavy Ion Linear Accelerator (HILAC) in 1961 by bombarding californium with boron ions. The longest-lived isotope of 103 so far known has a half life of about three hours (see **SEABORGIUM**). (MW)

*The sequence of named elements following **URANIUM** reads, in short: Np Pu Am Cm Bk Cf Es Fm Md No Lr Rf Db Sg Bh Hs Mt Ds Rg Cn.

[521] LAYARD'S BEAKED WHALE

The "beaked" or "bottle-nosed" whales belonging to the family *Ziphidae* are smaller relatives of the sperm whale. 18 species are known, some very rare. LAYARD'S BEAKED WHALE (*Mesoplodon layardi*), otherwise known as the Strap-toothed Whale, is named after the naturalist and ornithologist EDGAR LEOPOLD LAYARD (1824-1900), brother of the excavator of Nineveh Sir Austen Henry Layard (1817-1894). While curator of the South African Natural History Museum, Layard wrote the first description of this creature, based on its skull, which features two long, arching, tusk-like teeth of flattened section in the lower jaw. Layard went on to collect birds in Brazil, and in Polynesia where he held the post of Honorary British Consul at Noumea (New Caledonia). From there, working with his son, he sent important collections back to Europe. LAYARD'S PARAKEET has the scientific name *Psittacula calthropae*, the second element of which honours his wife Barbara Anne Calthrop. Layard's *Birds of South Africa* was published in 1887.

[522] LE CHÂTELIER'S PRINCIPLE

"Things tend to follow the path of least resistance." This intuitive truth is restated by LE CHATELIER'S PRINCIPLE of 1885 in more dignified scientific language, thus: *If a system in chemical equilibrium suffers a constraint (e.g. a change in temperature, pressure or concentration of a component), then the equilibrium will shift so as to relieve that constraint.* An important example is the HABER-BOSCH PROCESS for reacting the gases nitrogen and hydrogen to make ammonia. Writing a balanced chemical equation for this:

$$N_2 + 3H_2 = 2NH_3$$

we can see that the reaction entails a halving of the total number of molecules, because it's 4 (=1+3) on the left, and only 2 (of ammonia) on the right. Remembering AVOGADRO'S HYPOTHESIS the intrinsic volume therefore decreases to about one half. So if the volume is fixed, the pressure must halve (BOYLE'S LAW). LE CHÂTELIER'S PRINCIPLE therefore tells us that increasing the pressure makes this reaction equilibrium go over to the right hand side – producing more ammonia. Hence the process gives the best yield at high pressure: squeeze the system and it seeks a way of contracting. A more everyday example is provided by water which expands when it freezes. So compressing ice causes it to melt, making possible our recreation with coherent snowballs and ice-skating. French/Italian chemist HENRY LOUIS LE CHÂTELIER (1850-1936) studied at the École Polytechnique, taught chemistry at the École des Mines, Paris, and later at the Sorbonne. He was promoted through the ranks of the *Légion d'Honneur* to the penultimate degree of *Grand Officier* in 1927. (MW)

[523] LEBLANC PROCESS

The chemical industry began in the 18th century with the large scale manufacture of alkalies, especially soda (sodium carbonate) – which is a necessary ingredient for manufacturing those essential commodities: glass, paper and soap, besides its uses for domestic cleaning, baking, and medicine. In the USA, soda can be dug out of the ground as the mineral *Trona* (from the Arabic *Natron*), but it does not occur naturally in Europe in useful amounts, so has to be prepared chemically from that widespread substance, common salt (sodium chloride). This is not as easy as it sounds. In the LEBLANC PROCESS, salt was first heated with sulphuric acid to convert it into sodium sulphate, called "salt cake" (see GLAUBER'S SALT; the other product, gaseous hydrochloric acid was absorbed, converted to chlorine by the Deacon process, and used in the cotton industry for bleaching). The "salt cake" was then heated with carbon (charcoal or coal) and calcium carbonate (chalk or crushed limestone) in a rotating furnace to form a crude alkaline mixture of sodium carbonate and calcium sulphide. This was then extracted with water in Shanks's Lixiviating Tanks to purify the soda. NICOLAS LEBLANC (1742-1806), was a French physician, born at Ivoy-le-Pré, and trained at the École de Chirurgie, becoming in 1780 surgeon to Louis Philippe Joseph, Duc d'Orléans, who interested him in chemistry and the problem of alkali manufacture. Improving on a method of 1777 due to the Benedictine chemist Abbé Malherbe, Leblanc devised his process in 1789 and was granted a secret patent in 1791 when, capitalised by the Duke, he set up a works at St. Denis, near Paris, for the manufacture of soda. During the Revolution, the Duke became known as Philippe Égalité, but was nonetheless guillotined in 1793 by the lovers of liberty and fraternity, whereupon his soda factory was confiscated and closed in 1794, and the Committee of Public Safety forced Leblanc to reveal his process, which was rapidly taken up by others. Finally, the dilapidated factory was returned to Leblanc in 1802, by which time, lacking legal redress for his losses and denial of income, Leblanc was too penurious to operate it. He died by his own hand in 1806 of a gunshot to the head. The LEBLANC PROCESS became the most important single industry in Britain during the period 1860-1880, producing *ca.* 500,000 tons of soda per annum, but it was highly polluting and displaced by the more economic SOLVAY PROCESS in the 1880s. (MW)

[524] LEE-ENFIELD

The LEE-ENFIELD RIFLE, .303 calibre, was the standard British infantryman's weapon for over half a century and through two world wars and is still in use today in corners of the world (including Afghanistan) where the boots, boots, boots of Thomas Atkins once trod. The second half of the name, of course, is that of the Royal Small Arms Factory, Enfield (*cf.* Bren gun, STEN GUN). The first is the name of gunsmith and weapons designer JAMES PARIS LEE (1831-1904) who arrived in the US via Scotland and Canada in 1858. Lee contributed two crucial elements to the design: the bolt, and the detachable 10-round box magazine. These innovations, after exhaustive trials, were adopted by the War Office and resulted in the **LEE-METFORD RIFLE**, which came into service in 1888. It bears the name of **WILLIAM ELLIS METFORD** (1824-1899), the British engineer who designed the weapon's 7-groove rifling. Metford's barrel design was later modified to accommodate smokeless powder and the result was the officially-titled **"RIFLE SMLE"** (Short/Magazine/Lee-Enfield), in general issue from 1907, and which, in its several variants, remained in service with the British and Commonwealth armed forces until supplanted by the Belgian FN self-loading rifle (SLR) from the late fifties onwards.

[525] LEE-METFORD RIFLE – see LEE-ENFIELD

[526] LEICA
LEICA is synonymous with the poshest of 35 mm cameras, a *sans pareil* of optical and mechanical engineering perfection.* The name derives from LEitz CAmera, after **ERNST LEITZ SR** (1843-1920), who in 1869 renamed after himself the business he had taken over from the Optical Institute, founded in 1849 by optician Carl Kellner (1826-1855)** in Wetzlar, Hesse, Germany. **ERNST LEITZ JR** (1871-1956) succeeded his father in 1920, running the company of **ERNST LEITZ GMBH** according to enlightened paternalistic traditions, and acting creditably towards Jewish employees during the Third Reich. His management was succeeded by three sons, but by 1986 the last family member had retired from the board, and the parent company changed its name to **LEICA** due to the strength of the brand. It is now divided into three, manufacturing different types of precision optical equipment: **LEICA CAMERA** (1996), **LEICA GEOSYSTEMS** (1997), and **LEICA MICROSYSTEMS** GmbH (1998). The prototypical **LEICA** was designed in 1913 by German optical engineer and precision mechanic, Oskar Barnack (1879-1936), the "father of 35 mm photography", but was not manufactured for the public until 1925. Over the years since, the *marque* has passed through many modifications, refinements and additions to produce a historical range of models so extensive that it can only be fully understood by obsessive, and very wealthy, collectors of photographic hardware. Devotees of canine eponymy (see **TALBOT, BEDDGELERT**) should know that an early wide-angle lens for the **LEICA** was named after Barnack's dog, **HEKTOR**. (MW)

* It had a worthy competitor in the Contax camera manufactured by the **ZEISS OPTICAL WORKS,** also in Wetzlar.

** Inventor of the **KELLNER EYEPIECE** in 1849, an achromatic eyepiece superior to those of **HUYGENS** or **RAMSDEN**.

[527] LEIDENFROST PHENOMENON
When a drop of water falls onto a hotplate below 220°C (the **LEIDENFROST TEMPERATURE** for water) it sticks, sizzles, and boils away in a few seconds as we

intuitively expect. But if the surface is above 220°C the drop becomes highly mobile and skates around for more than a minute before finally evaporating, because it is supported like a hovercraft on a very thin bed of water vapour, insulating it from the hotplate and lowering the friction. This homely test for the temperature of a skillet, griddle, frying pan, or smoothing-iron, is the **LEIDENFROST PHENOMENON** or **EFFECT**, first observed in 1732 by Dutch physician Hermann Boerhaave (1668-1738) but named in 1756 after **JOHANN GOTTLOB LEIDENFROST** (1715-1794) who was born in Stollberg, Germany, and studied medicine at the universities of Liepzig and Halle. After serving in the first Silesian War* he became a professor at Duisburg. The thermal insulating effect of a thin layer of water vapour, or other trapped gas, also permits some hazardous "party tricks" to be performed with impunity – on occasion, such as dipping wet fingers into molten lead, or taking liquid nitrogen into the mouth. But all such experiments should be accompanied by Batman's statutory health warning: *Don't try this at home, folks!* (MW)

* 1740-1742, between Austria and Prussia with Silesia as the prize. Outcome was inconclusive and two re-matches followed: 1744-45 and 1756-62. Prussia ended up with the lion's share of the disputed real-estate.

[528] LEISHMANIASIS

A serious, possibly fatal, protozoan infection carried by biting insects such as ticks and sand-flies, affecting mainly dogs, humans and certain rodents. The 2 main species of *Leishmania* are *L. donovani** and *L. chagasi***, found in the world's eastern and western hemispheres respectively. **LEISHMANIASIS** is the generic term allotted by Sir Ronald Ross (1857-1932), famous for his elucidation of malaria, to the diseases produced by these and related organisms. Treatment is with sodium stibogluconate ("Pentostam"®), which doesn't offer a hundred per cent certainty of cure and, like cancer chemotherapy, can entail unpleasant and even dangerous side-effects. **WILLIAM BOOG LEISHMAN** (1865-1926) was a Scottish-born army doctor who saw active service in India (Waziristan) in the 1890's. While in India, Leishman had opportunities for microbiological research which led to his discovery of the causative agent of the disease named after him, then known as "kala-azar" or "Dum-dum fever".*** Returned to England, Leishman was appointed professor of pathology at the Army Medical School and served as the War Office's expert on tropical diseases, on which he continued to work. He was knighted in 1909, elected FRS in 1910, and rose to the rank of Lt.-General and the post of Director-General of army medical services. He is buried in Highgate Cemetery.

* Lt.-Col. Charles Donovan (1863-1951) of the Indian Medical Service, Irish physician and naturalist.

** Carlos Chagas (1910-2000), Brazilian physician and epidemiologist (see **CHAGAS DISEASE**).

*** Dum-dum: army base and munitions factory outside Calcutta, birthplace of the notorious hollow-point expanding bullet.

[529] LEOTARD

A one-piece, skin-tight garment worn by athletes, acrobats and dancers and designed to allow unhampered body movement while showing off the more aesthetically attractive bits of the wearer's anatomy if he or she is fortunate enough to possess such. It is named after its inventor, the French aerialist JULES LÉOTARD (*ca.* 1840-1870). The original "daring man young on the flying trapeze" (1867), Léotard enjoyed a huge success in England as well as in his native France with stunts he was the first to perform such as aerial somersaults and swinging from one trapeze to another. He died in Spain, possibly of cholera.

[530] LEVI'S

The clothing manufacturer LEVI STRAUSS (1829-1902)*, was a German Jew born at Buttenheim in Bavaria. He emigrated to America in 1843 and was naturalised ten years later. His chosen profession of itinerant pedlar of cloth, clothes, buttons, scissors, threads and needles took him to California in 1853 at the height of the Gold Rush. In the mining camps where he hawked his wares there was, according to the official legend, a lively demand for strong nether garments from miners whose trousers were continually falling apart under the load of rocks and ore samples they insisted on carrying in their pockets. This demand he set about supplying with sturdy work clothes made from *serge de Nîmes* (whence "denim"). The unique feature of the classic blue jeans – the riveted seam – came later at the suggestion of a Latvian Jewish tailor named Davis based in New York. Strauss and Davis patented their copper riveting system in 1873, and so was born a true American classic which has gone on to conquer the world. Anyone old enough to remember the arrival on our shores of Levi's blue jeans in the late fifties, may also remember the quite complex process involved in getting them to fit. As they were not pre-shrunk, it was usual to buy a pair one or even two sizes too large. The wearer then sat in a bath of water to initiate the shrinking process while the water turned blue about him (or her – though levis designed for the female figure came only later). The jeans were then allowed to dry without being taken off and so moulded themselves to the wearer's body as a sort of creaky canvas carapace which it then required a longish period of wear to mollify. The appearance of a scattering of young people in our universities and art schools wearing these garments caused a shocked response among the general population, for whom the notion of trousers being made from anything but grey flannel (or at a pinch cavalry twill) was hard to swallow. Add beards and sandals to the mix and the Beatnik Horror, as one newspaper called it, is in full swing.

* Not to be confused with the French philosopher of nearly the same name.

[531] LEWIS & SHORT – see LIDDELL & SCOTT

[532] LEWIS FORMULA

Atoms are bound together into molecules by the "glue" of negatively-charged electrons, shared between them and mutually attracted to their positively-charged nuclei. For rather subtle reasons connected with **PAULI'S EXCLUSION PRINCIPLE**, these electrons prefer to hang out in pairs. Much of chemistry, therefore, is founded on G.N. Lewis's concept of 1916 of the *electron pair bond* or *covalent bond*, represented on paper by a line joining the atomic symbols for the elements involved. Such a diagram of a molecule is called a **LEWIS FORMULA** or, less appropriately, a **LEWIS STRUCTURE**. *E.g.* methane, CH_4, can be represented:

$$
\begin{array}{c}
H \\
| \\
H - C - H \\
| \\
H
\end{array}
$$

explicitly showing the four electron pair bonds between carbon and hydrogen, but the Lewis formula does not imply anything about the actual shape of the molecule in 3-dimensions (which is not flat and square, but tetrahedral, in this case). The value of the **LEWIS FORMULA** lies in the ease of counting electrons, which often obey **ABEGG'S RULE OF EIGHT**: four pairs of electrons in the outer shell of the central atom. If an electron pair is not connected to another atom it's called a *lone pair* and indicated in the Lewis formula by a double dot: thus a water molecule, H_2O, is written as:

$$
\begin{array}{c}
\cdot\cdot \\
: O - H \\
| \\
H
\end{array}
$$

with two lone pairs on the oxygen atom, which greatly affect the properties of the substance (see **DEBYE**). Some atoms can form double bonds (two pairs of electrons) as in carbon dioxide, CO_2, written O=C=O, or ethene (*aka* ethylene) C_2H_4 represented thus:

Triple bonds, involving three electron pairs, as in nitrogen N_2 , and ethyne (acetylene) C_2H_2 , are also possible. **GILBERT NEWTON LEWIS** (1875-1946) was an

American physical chemist who studied at Harvard and made his career at the University of California, Berkeley. Besides being the progenitor of the covalent bond, he is also responsible for the concept of acid-base behaviour in which an electron pair acceptor is called a **LEWIS ACID** and an electron pair donor, a **LEWIS BASE** – providing an alternative to Brönsted's protonic (hydrogen ion) theory of acidity. Lewis was nominated 35 times for a Nobel prize – but never awarded it. There are suspicions that this disappointment may have had some connection with his sudden death from presumed heart failure, while working in his laboratory with hydrogen cyanide. (MW)

[533] LEWISITE

This chemical weapon belongs to the class of vesicants – blister agents. Chemically, it is 2-chloroethenyldichloroarsine, $ClC_2H_2AsCl_2$. An oily liquid with a smell resembling geraniums, **LEWISITE** penetrates clothing and attacks skin viciously; if inhaled it can prove rapidly fatal. It is not terribly effective on the battlefield because it is easily decomposed by water. The substance was originally synthesised in 1904 from acetylene and arsenic trichloride, at the Catholic University of America, by chemist/priest, Father Julius Arthur Nieuwland, who was, in good faith, trying to make synthetic rubber at the time. After a brief spell in hospital, he wisely declined to publish his findings, beyond recording the preparation in his PhD thesis. Regrettably, the facts were there uncovered in 1918 by American chemist/soldier **Capt. WINFORD LEE LEWIS** (1879-1943), while seconded from his chair at Northwestern University to act as director of the Offensive Branch of the newly formed Chemical Warfare Service unit at the Catholic University. On the lookout for potential chemical weapons, his attention was directed to Nieuwland's thesis by the Reverend John Griffin, who had been his research supervisor. Lewis described the organo-arsenical enthusiastically as "the stuff beside which mustard gas becomes a sissy's scent!" It was christened "The Dew of Death" by General Amos Fries, commander of the American Expeditionary Forces' Gas Service and later director of the Chemical Warfare Service, who so named it because of plans to spray lewisite over Berlin from the air. Although the USA rushed it into production, it came too late for use in WWI. The only good thing to emerge from this episode was the development at the University of Oxford of an effective antidote, aptly named "British Anti-Lewisite", or BAL. This substance, a sulphurised glycerine molecule, is 2,3-dimercaptopropanol or "Dimercaprol" and proves effective not only against Lewisite, but also as a very useful drug for the treatment of **WILSON'S DISEASE** and cases of poisoning by heavy metals. (MW)

[534] LEYLANDII

In the year 1888, the first **LEYLAND CYPRESS** (*Cupressus x leylandii*) arose as an accidental hybrid of two American tree species, the Monterey Cypress and the Nootka Cypress, on the Powys estate belonging to descendants of Liverpool banker **CHRISTOPHER LEYLAND**. The result of this miscegenation is today as widely popular as it is cordially hated – popular because it offers a temptingly cheap and easy way of quickly producing a thick evergreen hedge; hated because if you as the proud owner of such a hedge omit to cut it back savagely every few minutes, it will transform itself overnight into a sixty-foot-high solid green wall which totally blocks the blessed daylight from your neighbour's garden and has him reaching for his solicitor, his chainsaw, or his shotgun. You have been warned.

[535] LIBAVIUS' FUMING LIQUOR

ANDREAS LIBAVIUS (1555-1616) was a German proto-chemist born in Halle, who became professor of history and poetry at Jena in 1588, and in 1607 director of the *gymnasium* at Coburg. In contrast to his alchemical peers, he wrote the first fairly sensible chemistry text-book, *Alchymia*, published in 1597. Although it displays its share of obfuscating mystical symbolism, this work also describes in plain language the chemical laboratory apparatus and reactions, and the discovery of some new substances. Libavius was noted for rebuking the Paracelsian iatro-chemists and spagyrists for their toxic medical remedies. In 1605, he discovered his **"FUMING LIQUOR"**, *spiritus fumans Libavii*, by distilling metallic tin with "corrosive sublimate" (mercuric chloride). Also called "Spirit of Tin", it proves to be stannic chloride, aka tin(IV) tetrachloride, $SnCl_4$. It is a colourless volatile liquid, and its fumes are due to hydrolysis by moisture in the air, forming tin(IV) oxide and hydrogen chloride. It is used as a mordant in calico printing and dyeing. Mixed with water it forms a hydrate, appetizingly named "Butter of Tin", but not recommended for the morning toast. (MW)

[536] LICHTENBERG FIGURES

When a very high voltage is discharged through an insulating object the branching passage of the electric current may trace out beautiful fractal patterns resembling trees or ferns. Such **LICHTENBERG FIGURES** in blocks of Perspex are sold as novelties. More damagingly, the patterns can also be imparted to the skin when lightning strikes animals or humans. Their appearance has been a source of conjecture: "In 1812 Mr Shaw communicated to the Meteorological Society a most peculiar case. Six sheep lying in an open pasture surrounded by woods were killed by lightning; the surrounding landscape was pictured so clearly on the inner surface of each skin that the view was immediately recognisable by those who were acquainted with the district. These skins were actually exhibited publicly at Bath for some time." (*British Journal of Photography*, 10 February 1888, p89.) "Jonesville, Michigan, 1887: farmer Amos J. Briggs is shooing cats away from his woodpile when it is struck by lightning. The cats die instantly. Briggs' watch explodes and his clothes are shredded. Returning inside, his wife is horrified to find the silhouette of a startled cat imprinted on his bald pate. The image fades after two days." (Mark Pilkington, *The Guardian*, 3 June 2004). This supposed generation of "photographic" images by lightning strikes has been termed *keraunography* (from Gr. *keraunos* = thunderbolt). **GEORG CHRISTOPH LICHTENBERG** (1742-1799) was born in Darmstadt, Germany, the youngest of 17 children sired by a polyphiloprogenitive pastor.* He acquired a considerable reputation as an aphorist and critical thinker, and was acquainted with Kant, Goethe, Volta, and Gauss, becoming extraordinary professor of physics at Göttingen in 1769. A notable Anglophile, he was elected FRS in 1793. His writings are little-known outside Germany, but deserve wider recognition. **LICHTENBERG FIGURES** is also the name given to patterns of powdered sulphur or red lead adhering by electrostatic attraction onto regions of an insulating plaque of resin bearing an electric charge. This principle is used in xerography, so Lichtenberg also deserves to be hailed as "the father of the Xerox machine". (MW)

* A **QUIVERFULL CHRISTIAN** *avant la lettre?*

[537] LIDDELL & SCOTT

In the days when the curriculum of English public schools consisted almost entirely of Latin, Greek, and cold baths, the Greek-English lexicon of **HENRY GEORGE LIDDELL** (1811-1898) and **ROBERT SCOTT** (1811-1887) was so omnipresent as to be known simply by the names of its two authors, or even by the abbreviation "L&S". The dictionary, first published in 1843, was based on earlier work by the German philologist and lexicographer Johann Gottlob Schneider and his successor Franz Passow. Of the two English compilers, Liddell is the better known – as Dean of Christchurch, Oxford, and father of Lewis Carroll's Alice.* Scott took his degree at Christchurch before going on to become a fellow, and later Master, of Balliol. The Latin equivalent of "Liddell and Scott" is, or rather was, "Lewis and Short" – the *Latin Dictionary* compiled by **CHARLTON T. LEWIS** and **CHARLES SHORT**. The main difference between the two dictionaries is that while Liddell & Scott has been continually revised, enlarged, re-edited and re-published up to the present day and still retains enormous prestige, that of Lewis and Short, though still in print, has not been updated or revised since its first edition of 1879 and has now been effectively superseded by the *Oxford Latin Dictionary* (ed. Glare). It is possible, though, that supersession is just around the corner for Liddell & Scott also, as work proceeds on the monumental *Diccionario Griego-Español* being published by the Consejo Superior de Investigaciones Cientificas, Madrid.

* Dean Liddell's descendants to this day continue to give the name Alice to one female member of each generation.

[538] LIEBER CODE

The German-born historian and political philosopher **FRANCIS LIEBER** (1798-1872), fought in the Prussian army at Waterloo, emigrated to America in 1827, edited the first edition of the *Encyclopaedia Americana* (1829-33), published three books on political philosophy, and taught at Columbia University from 1856 until his death. During the Civil War he drew up for the Union's War Department *General Order No. 100 (Instructions for the Government of Armies of the United States in the Field)* subsequently known as the "Lieber Code". It is generally agreed that Lieber's text is the single most important contribution to the establishment of an internationally recognised set of principles governing the behaviour of armies in wartime (*ius in bello*), and his adopted country should be as proud of him as it should be ashamed of the present Washington administration's insistence that America and America's armed forces are above the law.

[539] LIEBIG CONDENSER

This piece of chemical glassware probably owes its antecedents to the distillers of illicit liquor. A sloping delivery tube from a still is jacketed with a wider tube through which cooling water is continuously circulated to condense the hot vapours boiling off and convert them back to liquid. More efficient elaborations are associated with the names of Allihn, Vigreux, Graham, Dimroth, Davies, and Friedrich, who all have entries in the catalogues of laboratory glassware. **BARON JUSTUS VON LIEBIG** (1803-1873) was one of the most illustrious German chemists of the nineteenth century. He occupied the chairs at Giessen (see **KEKULÉ**) and Bonn, and was created Baron (*Freiherr*) in 1845. The Liebig condenser was not his invention, but dates back to 1771 and the *Gegenstromkühler* of chemist and botanist, **CHRISTIAN EHRENFRIED WEIGEL** (1748-1831). Non-chemists may be more familiar with a substance known as **LIEBIG'S EXTRACT**, a concentrated extract of beef (or, in Australia, mutton) protein, prepared according to a process devised by Liebig in 1840 in association with Max von Pettenkofer. 25 lbs of lean meat would yield on average 1 lb of the partially dehydrated extract. Liebig was a prolific chemist who devoted most of his energies to studying the chemistry of life-processes, both animal and vegetable. He vastly increased, for example, our understanding of plant nutrition and the nitrogen cycle. Thanks to its portability, Liebig's Extract became a favourite form of food concentrate for both 19th- and 20th-century travellers and explorers – Stanley for one. The Bovril company, formed in 1889, made their own, branded, form of beef extract (originally known as "fluid beef") as well as producing pemmican for British Polar expeditions in the 1930s and iron rations for the army. Liebig's Extract is still obtainable under the trade name "Oxo".

[540] LINNAEAN BINOMIALS

The work of Swedish naturalist **CARL VON LINNÉ,** Latinised as **CAROLUS LINNAEUS,** (1707-1778) is one of the rocks on which the edifice of modern biology is built. Every time we read or write the scientific name of an animal or plant, we are paying him his due. A protégé of **ANDERS CELSIUS,** he brought order to the naming of living things where before there had only been a chaos of competing systems or no system at all. Linnaeus' practice – which has since become general – was to confine each descriptive title to two elements – hence the term "binomial". Each species was allotted to a named genus and then given a specific qualifier to distinguish it from other members of the group. The language used was, of course, Latin, then still the *lingua franca* of the learned world (from which we have, alas, since lapsed back into Babel). Thus all clovers, for example, belong to the genus *Trifolium* which embraces a number of species named *Trifolium pratense, T. arvense, T. squamosum,* etc. In addition, in the technical literature the custom has grown up for the Latin binomial to be followed by an author's name, usually abbreviated. So, for example, "L", in this context, indicates a description authored by Linnaeus himself while "L.f." refers to Linnaeus' son Carolus Linnaeus junior. His passion for classification still unassuaged, Linnaeus later proceeded to group his genera into classes and classes into orders. Later still, the French scientist **GEORGES CUVIER** (1769-1832) took the further step of grouping orders into phyla. Linnaeus also attempted a classification of diseases. Of his 180-odd published works, probably the best known are his *Systema Naturae* (1735) and *Species plantarum* (1753). His preferred criterion for classifying plants was what he called the "sexual method", which depended on variations in the number, form and arrangement of the stamens.* (The idea that plants engaged in sexual reproduction caused an outburst of prurient scandalisation in some circles.) This approach, like the earlier systems of Cesalapino and Lobel (see **LOBELIA**) or that of **TOURNEFORT,** didn't in the end carry the day. So the history of botany continued – and continues – to be one of competing taxonomies, with today the new complication of a school of thought which aims to classify plants by their DNA. The importance and reputation of Linnaeus, accordingly, rests on his success in imposing the binomial method of identification on the rest of the scientific world, and on his influence as a teacher. At Uppsala, he attracted pupils from all over Europe and during his tenure of the chair of botany the number of students at the University trebled from five to fifteen hundred. Many of them went on to become travelling naturalists in the far corners of the earth. A recent and remarkable publishing venture consisting of 11 volumes under the general title *The Linnaeus Apostles* (The IK Foundation Company, 2008) has now made these travels and discoveries fully available for the first time.

* Linnaeus was the first to use ♂ and ♀, the astronomical symbols for Mars and Venus respectively, to stand for "male" and "female".

[541] LIPPMANN PHOTOGRAPHY

This is the only photographic invention for which a **NOBEL PRIZE** has ever been awarded – in 1908 to the French physicist **GABRIEL LIPPMANN** (1845-1921), who was appointed professor at the Sorbonne in 1886. He invented the process in 1891 – it was the first method of recording colour information in a single exposure. It is a subtle and elegant, but difficult, process of colour photography, using only a very fine grain silver-gelatin emulsion on a glass plate, exposed and viewed from the *verso*. The image colour information is generated by interference of the light waves as they traverse the thickness of the emulsion layer, caused by reflecting them back with a mirror of mercury in contact with the emulsion surface. Thus a standing wave interference pattern is set up, and on development, parallel laminae of silver particles are periodically laid down throughout the thickness of the emulsion, having spacings dependent upon the wavelengths of the light. (See **NEWTON'S RINGS**. Similar interference effects are observed in an opal, or thin layers of oil on water.) Later it was found that the mercury mirror could be dispensed with, because sufficient reflection occurred at the emulsion/air interface. Illumination by white light to view the image in transmission is geometrically critical to recreate the natural interference colours, which have an exquisite purity – unlike pigmented images. The technical difficulties and slow exposures of **LIPPMANN PHOTOGRAPHY** preclude its use for everyday colour snaps, so the process fell into abeyance in the 1920s: only a dozen or so skilled experimentalists have ever successfully practised this form of photography. Since the invention of the laser in 1960 there has been a revival of interest in Lippmann photography because of its relationship to holography. (MW)

[542] LISTERIA

Genus of six species of bacteria named after **JOSEPH LISTER** (1827-1912), the pioneer of antiseptic surgery. (Another example of the back-handed compliment of having something nasty named in your honour – *cf.* **YERSINIA, E. COLI**.) When ingested, *L. monocytogenes* causes listeriosis in humans – a comparatively rare but serious form of food-poisoning which can be lethal to unborn infants and the elderly. The listeria are hardy creatures, able to flourish within a wide temperature range, and need to be well-boiled or roasted before they are safe to eat. *L. invanovii* causes listeriosis in ruminants and is classed as a zoonosis, transmissible from animal to human, *e.g.* on the hands of a shepherd who has just lambed an infected ewe or handled an aborted foetus.

[543] LOBELIA

Genus of some 200 species of annuals, herbaceous perennials and sub-shrubs belonging to the family *campanulaceae* (bell-flowers) and including the ubiquitous denizen of virtually every summer hanging-basket in Britain. Another species, *L. syphilitica*, is named after the disease it was once used to treat. The genus takes its name from the Flemish physician and naturalist **MATTHIAS DE LOBEL** or **L'OBEL** (1538-1616), Latinised as **LOBELIUS**. In 1569 he left Flanders and settled in England where he was employed as superintendent of the botanical garden owned by Lord Zouche, then the best of its kind in England. Later he acted as personal physician and botanist to King James I. (At one stage, he undertook to copy-edit Gerard's *Herbal*, but when he had found upwards of a thousand errors, Gerard snatched the manuscript back from him.) Lobelius has an important place in the history of botany in that he was one of the first researchers to attempt a classification of plants by anything other than their magical or medicinal uses. His near-contemporary the Italian plantsman Andrea Cesalpino (1519-1603) had preceded him with a classification based on a typology of seeds and fruits, but Lobelius believed that leaf-form should be the organising principle. Neither system prevailed in the long term and a succession of competing systems followed them, each proposing a different criterion for plant classification. The grouping of plants into genera, families, etc. is a thorny issue that has still not been settled to everyone's satisfaction, even today, and the debate continues (see **LINNAEAN BINOMIALS**). Lobelius' principal published works are the *Stirpium adversaria nova* (1570) which he co-wrote with his friend Pierre Pena, and his *Plantarum seu stirpium historia* (1576).

[544] LOGANBERRY

Rubus x loganobaccus – a variety of soft fruit resembling an elongated red blackberry, obtained by the accidental(?) crossing of an American variety of raspberry with a variety of blackberry, *Rubus ursinus*, and named after its inventor/discoverer, American horticulturalist **JAMES HARVEY LOGAN** (1841-1928). The **BOYSENBERRY**, which bears the name of another American horticulturalist, **RUDOLPH BOYSEN** (1895-1950), is a bigger (?and better) loganberry obtained by crossing various strains of raspberry, blackberry and loganberry. Human interference with the sex life of the blackberry hasn't stopped with Messrs. Logan and Boysen. Subsequent additions to the pomological repertoire now include the Tayberry, the Veitchberry, the Tummelberry, the Youngberry, the Olallieberry, and the Marionberry.

[545] LOISELEURIA

L. procumbens is a small, prostrate, evergreen shrub of the family ericaceae (heathers) found in high alpine and sub-arctic regions. Common names: Alpine or Mountain Azalea. It is named after the French botanist **JEAN LOUIS AUGUST LOISELEUR DESLONGCHAMPS** (1774-1849). Since the name Loiseleur means "birdcatcher" (in English it would be "Fowler"), and the family arms feature a bird of indeterminate species, he seems to have chosen the wrong profession: according to the rules of Nominative Determinism (see **CRAPPER**) he should have been an ornithologist.

[546] LOSCHMIDT'S NUMBER

Like **AVOGADRO'S NUMBER** this is a scaling factor that connects the chemists' conceptual world of atoms and molecules with the everyday world of physico-chemical properties we can perceive. **LOSCHMIDT'S NUMBER** is now defined as the number of particles (*i.e.* atoms or molecules) in one cubic meter of a perfect, or "ideal" gas (see **BOYLE'S LAW**), at standard temperature (273.15 K – see **KELVIN**) and standard atmospheric pressure (101.325 kPa = 960 torr – see **PASCAL** and **TORRICELLI**). Its value is 2.687 x 10^{25} m^{-3}, and it is related to **AVOGADRO'S NUMBER** by multiplying the latter by the number of moles in one cubic meter of an ideal gas. **JOHANN JOSEF LOSCHMIDT** (1821-1895), was an Austrian physical chemist, born of humble Bohemian stock, who trained at Prague's Charles University, and occupied a chair at the University of Vienna from 1868-1891. He first calculated a value for his number in 1865, later using it to find a value for **AVOGADRO'S NUMBER**, which Avogadro himself had failed to do. (MW)

[547] LOTHARIO

The original **LOTHARIO**, a conscienceless libertine and seducer of the otherwise virtuous Calista, is a character in *The fair penitent,* a tragedy of 1703 by ex-barrister, playwright and Poet Laureate Nicholas Rowe (1674-1718). The name came to be applied to any heartless despoiler, or even would-be despoiler, of young virgins. Nowadays, when young virgins are mostly despoiled by people they are at school with, Lothario as a type-figure seems to have had his day, while seduction has become something of a lost art.

[548] LOU GEHRIG'S DISEASE

Amyotrophic lateral sclerosis (motor neurone disease) is commonly known in America as **LOU GEHRIG'S DISEASE** in memory of the much-loved baseball star **LOU GEHRIG** (1903-1941), who died of it at the shockingly early age of 36. The disease attacks the nerve cells which connect the brain to the muscles. It is progressive and incurable. Death normally takes place within three to five years of onset. A striking exception is the English theoretical physicist Stephen Hawking who has been a sufferer for over 40 years. In France the condition is known as *maladie de Charcot,* after the physician who first described it in 1869 (see **TOURETTE'S SYNDROME**).

[549] LUCIFER – see VESTA

[550] LUDDITE

In present usage a **LUDDITE** is any person who wilfully obstructs progress (however defined) and more especially technological progress. It was originally applied to the "machine-breakers" who, in the early 19th century registered by this method a violent protest against the factory system. Arguably, though stocking-frames and the like were the immediate target, these were merely symbolic of a system that was destroying traditional economically-based family and community structures. The riots began in Nottinghamshire and Leicestershire in 1811, spreading to Derbyshire, Lancashire and Yorkshire the following year. In April 1812, Yorkshire Luddism reached its height with six workshops attacked and two factories raided, including one mill whose story became famous as part of Charlotte Brontë's 1849 novel, *Shirley*. At the Lancashire Assizes in May, 10 Luddites were hanged, 38 transported and 18 imprisoned. In June, 38 men were arrested in Lancashire, and 20 more in Yorkshire in October and November. A factory was torched in Lancaster in September. There followed a lull during which the heart seemed to have gone out of the cause, but meanwhile protest had led to actual murder and in Huddersfield denunciation by an informer led to 14 men being hanged and 6 transported at the December Assizes. There was a serious resurgence in 1815 and 1816 following harvest failure, but severe repression and, perhaps, improved economic conditions, brought Luddism to an end as an activity, though not as an idea. The origin of the name "Luddite" is generally explained as a reference to a mentally-retarded apprentice named **NED LUDD** who in 1779 smashed two stocking-frames in a village in Leicestershire during a temper tantrum.* The etymology is shaky and other explanations have been advanced including a connection to the legendary King Lud or Ludd, a sort of Lord of Misrule, mentioned by Milton and Byron.

* See: Pellew's *Life of Lord Sidmouth* (1847); *Nottingham Review*, Dec. 1811.

[551] LUTTRELL PSALTER

This deservedly famous illuminated mediaeval manuscript (BM Add. Ms. 42130) takes its name from the person for whom it was created, the Lincolnshire landowner **SIR GEOFFREY LUTTRELL** (1276-1345) and is his only claim to fame. It dates from around 1330. The wonderful illustrations, of exceptionally high quality and of exceptional value as an iconographical resource, have been endlessly mined for their detailed depictions of daily life in the High Middle Ages. The psalter was acquired by the British Museum thanks to a loan from American financier and art-lover John Pierpont Morgan (see **PIERPONT MORGAN LIBRARY**) and is now held in the British Library.

[552] LYMANN SERIES – see BALMER SERIES

[553] LYNCH LAW

A number of alternative theories exist to account for the name commonly applied to the punishment, by hanging or otherwise, of suspected persons without the formality of a trial. The main candidates are: (1) the possibly apocryphal hanging in 1493 of his own son for murder by **JAMES FITZSTEPHEN LYNCH**, Mayor of Galway; (2) the extra-legal trials conducted by **CHARLES LYNCH** (1736-1796), a Virginia magistrate who during the American Rebellion dealt out summary punishments (short of hanging) to suspected pro-British elements; (3) a decision, at the same period, of the Virginia State Assembly which authorised the proposer of the measure **WILLIAM LYNCH** to arrest and punish evildoers in Pittsylvania County on the grounds that no properly constituted courts existed in that district.

[554] LYSENKOISM

In revolutionary Russia it was naturally and necessarily an article of faith that the Soviet economic system was inherently more efficient and more productive than that of the decadent capitalist countries. Maintaining this fiction was an absolute priority, so it is understandable (just) that a charlatan who claimed that he had discovered a way of doubling Russia's grain output should be fêted as a hero and should continue to be regarded as such even when his methods visibly didn't work. The hero in question was **TROFIM DENISOVICH LYSENKO** (1898-1976). From 1927 onwards, when Lysenko was employed at an agricultural research institute in Azerbaijan, a series of extravagant claims was made by him – or on his behalf by the Party's propaganda machine – of near-miraculous breakthroughs in techniques of agricultural production. The fact that none of these claims could be substantiated hardly seemed to matter. What mattered was convincing the Russian people and the world that Soviet science was working as advertised, bringing in a new age of universal plenty – a PR job which required no small measure of barefaced impudence during the Great Famine of 1932-3, for example, when millions of Russians were actually starving. As the son of peasants, Lysenko qualified for the iconic role of Heroic Socialist Worker (*cf.* **STAKHANOVITE**) and his ideas and methods were adopted, with Stalin's blessing, as official doctrine. Doubters were dismissed from their posts and lucky if they didn't end up in prison. Lysenko was made Director of the Moscow Academy of Agricultural Sciences and held this post until 1964, by which time it had become obvious even to the most hardened party-liners that Lysenko was not a genius but a manipulative, conniving little chancer.* Perhaps to give his work a colour of respectability, Lysenko had claimed to be carrying on the work of plant biologist Ivan Vladimirovich Michurin (1855-1935). It is true that Michurin, like Lysenko rejected Mendelian genetics. Both men were **LAMARCKIANS**, holding that heritable genetic changes were produced by environmental influences rather than, as most people now think, by random mutation. (In the early twentieth century, when the science of genetics was in its infancy, this was a perfectly reasonable hypothesis and has perhaps not yet had its last hurrah.) The difference between the two men is that Michurin, holding these beliefs, was able to do good work in science. He made valuable contributions to plant science and to Russian agriculture, successfully breeding (by selection and hybridisation) many useful new crop varieties, particularly of fruits. Lysenko, on the other hand, produced nothing. His contribution was strictly negative: the elevation of LYSENKOISM to the status of officially sanctioned orthodoxy is generally reckoned to have set back the progress of biology in Russia by a generation.

* In today's Britain he might have become Prime Minister.

M

[555] MACADAMIA NUT

A genus of 8 species (7 Australian and 1 Indonesian) of evergreen flowering trees named after **Dr. JOHN MACADAM** (1827-1865), Scottish-born Australian physician and chemist. They belong, like the **BANKSIA,** to the family Proteaceae. Two species are economically important: *M. integrifolia* and *M. tetraphylla,* yielding edible nuts and macadamia oil, used in cosmetics. The remaining species also bear nuts but these contain a form of cyanide and are not generally regarded as edible. However, they can and do form part of the diet of aboriginal hunter-gatherers, who have discovered how to remove the poisons by leaching in water (compare manioc/cassava) and have taught Ray Mears how to do it. All species are toxic to dogs. The nuts are extremely hard to crack, requiring the kind of pressure exerted by a bench vice, or a smart blow from a hammer, though certain parrots can open them without difficulty. Though Dr. Macadam has his so-to-speak nuciform memorial, the man who named the genus in his honour, his colleague the German-Australian botanist and explorer **FERDINAND VON MUELLER** (1825-1896), has an even more durable monument in bits of Antipodean geography named after him. These include notably the **MUELLER RANGES** and **MOUNT MUELLER** in Western Australia, **MUELLER'S RIVER** in Queensland, and the **MUELLER GLACIER** in New Zealand. Mueller published numerous tomes on Australian flora (hundreds of species have the authorial name "F. Muell." appended to them) and enjoyed the dubious distinction of acting as Hon. Sec. to the Exploration Committee which was responsible for the famous and ill-fated **BURKE AND WILLS EXPEDITION** of 1860-1861.

[556] MacGUFFIN

A term that is most frequently associated with English film director Alfred Hitchcock (1899–1980), though actually coined by his friend the screen writer Angus MacPhail (1903–1962) in 1935 for something that acts as a trigger for a book's or film's plot. In other words it can be viewed as an excuse or a diversion, it can be anything that serves as the impetus for the plot. Hitchcock, helpfully, compared the **MacGUFFIN** to a mythical "apparatus for trapping lions in the Scottish Highlands". Some notable examples of this key device from Hitch's *oeuvre* include "government secrets" (neatly opaque and undecipherable and never disclosed) used in *North by Northwest;* uranium ore hidden in wine bottles employed in *Notorious;* an anti-missile missile project known as Gamma Five in *Torn Curtain,* and, in *The Trouble With Harry*, Harry's dead body. The earliest appearance of the MacGuffin in a Hitchcock movie was in *Number Seventeen* (1932), where it is a necklace. Also from the 1930's is his famous adaptation of *The 39 Steps* where the hidden mainspring of the action takes the form of top secret plans for a new aircraft engine. Whatever it might be, it is more than a plot mechanism but also exerts an influence at the symbolic and psychological level. (RS)

[557] MACH NUMBERS
ERNST MACH (1838-1916) was born in what is now the Czech Republic and studied mathematics, physics and philosophy at the University of Vienna. Among physicists he is remembered for his work in optics and acoustics, among psychologists for his adherence to the theory that all knowledge comes from sense-perception, among philosophers for his influence on the Vienna School of logical positivists, and to the world at large for his system of speed measurement. **MACH NUMBERS** (we might equally well speak of a "Mach scale") relate the speed of a body moving through the air to the speed of sound. When the body is travelling at the speed of sound, its Mach number is 1, at twice the speed of sound, 2, and so on. It was Mach who established experimentally the changes in airflow that occur when a moving body approaches the speed of sound and the related phenomenon now known as the "sound barrier", as well as the "sonic boom" when the barrier is breached.

[558] MAE WEST
Inflatable life-jacket issued to troops in WWII. In use, it endowed the wearer with two large bulges in the chest area – hence the imagined resemblance to the similarly-endowed American film actress **MAE WEST** (1892-1980). The following piece of dialogue (from memory) between Miss West and Mr. W.C. Fields in the 1940 film *My little chickadee* may be apposite:

> WCF (*knocking on locked bedroom door*) Oh... honey?
> MW (*in bed*) Whadda ya want?
> WCF I have a couple of pear-shaped ideas.
> MW Shove 'em under the door
> WCF (*to himself*) Hm... There's an Ethiopian in the fuel supply

[559] MAECENAS
GAIUS CILNIUS MAECENAS (d. 8 BC) was a rich and powerful Roman who, as an ally of Octavian/Augustus played a significant part in the orgy of back-stabbing and power-grabbing that surrounded the end of the Roman Republic and the

establishment of the Principate (*cf.* **PORTLAND VASE**). That the name Maecenas has come to be synonymous with "wealthy patron of the arts" is largely due to his patronage of the poet Horace (Quintus Horatius Flaccus, 65-8 BC). Horace addressed to his benefactor a famous poem beginning -

Maecenas ativis edite regibus...

(Ode I)

which roughly means: "O Maecenas, offspring of royal forebears..." The words may seem to us a touch smarmy, but this is to overlook the fact that the patron-client relationship was an integral feature of Roman society (as it still is of some Mediterranean and Latin-American societies). Besides which, the line has an undoubtedly catchy rhythm.

[560] MAGNOLIA

Genus of between 100 and over 200 species* of flowering deciduous and evergreen trees found in the Americas and in East and Southeast Asia. The first-described magnolia was named after French botanist and physician **PIERRE MAGNOL** (1638-1715) by Charles Plumier (see **FRANGIPANI**), and **LINNAEUS** in his *Species plantarum* followed suit. Magnol was a French physician and botanist. He was born in Montpellier, where he held various posts including that of Professor of Medicine at the University (his students included **TOURNEFORT** and **JUSSIEU**). In the history of botany, and more especially of botanical taxonomy, Magnol is remembered as the inventor of the concept of plant families.

* The number depends on what taxonomic convention is being followed. In view of the intensely technical nature of the debate, non-specialists just pays their money and takes their choice.

[561] MAGNUS' GREEN SALT

In chemistry, the list of inorganic eponyms provides only the merest footnote to the thousand-strong roll of honour celebrating the achievements of organic chemists (see **GRIGNARD REACTION**). Nonetheless there are a few inorganic substances given "familiar" names that commemorate their makers: **MAGNUS' GREEN SALT**, *a.k.a.* tetrammineplatinum tetrachloroplatinate, is surprising because its two constituents are colourless and red, respectively; it was the discovery in 1828 of **HEINRICH GUSTAV MAGNUS** (1802-1870), a German chemist and physicist who also has **MAGNUS' EFFECT** to his credit. **FRÉMY'S SALT** is exceptional in being a long-lived free radical (but not in the political sense) synthesised in 1845, appropriately, by a French chemist, **EDMOND FRÉMY** (1814-1894). **ZEISE'S SALT** was the first organometallic compound, and prepared by Danish chemist, **WILLIAM CHRISTOPHER ZEISE** (1789-1847). It features in MW's DPhil thesis of yesteryear.

CARO'S ACID, peroxysulphuric acid, has a formula that looks like a schoolboy mistake: H_2SO_5. It is due to German **HEINRICH CARO** (1834-1910). Also down to a German chemist is the **RASCHIG REACTION**, a method for preparing hydrazine (it comes in handy for rocket fuel) by **FRIEDRICH AUGUST RASCHIG** (1863-1928), who invented the useful distillation aid, **RASCHIG RINGS**. It's uncertain if this relative paucity of entries should be attributed to the innate modesty of inorganic chemists compared with their organic brethren, or simply to a lack of productivity in their research. See also **TURNBULL'S BLUE**. (MW)

[562] MAILLARD REACTION

Chemistry can seldom be described as mouthwatering but this is a rare instance: a user-friendly chemical reaction that is responsible for most of those scrumptious toasty flavours and aromas acquired by cooking food, including toast itself, roasted coffee, caramelised onions, roast meat, and malted barley – the precursor to certain celebrated beverages. As eager readers of the **KELLOG'S** breakfast packet will know, the major useful constituents of all foods are carbohydrates and proteins. These two classes of substance (containing reducing sugars and amino acids, respectively) react together on heating by a complex organic condensation reaction to give a range of odoriferous molecules, many of which turn out to be highly agreeable to the taste buds. The **MAILLARD REACTION** is named for French chemist and physician, **LOUIS CAMILLE MAILLARD** (1878-1936) who studied it around 1912. He was born in Lorraine and studied science at the University of Nancy and joined the Faculty of Medicine at the University of Paris, moving to the Faculty of Medicine in Algiers after WWI.

[563] MALAPROPISM

The name of the character **Mrs. MALAPROP** in Sheridan's comedy *The rivals* (1775) is formed on the French phrase *mal à propos*, meaning "inappropriate" or "ill-chosen". Whenever Mrs Malaprop reaches for a fancy word, she finds the wrong one. For her, allegories sun themselves on the banks of the Nile, and caparisons are odious. We may laugh at her bumbling efforts to impress by her vocabulary, but we should not sneer. Which of us can raise a hand and solemnly testament that we have never used a word wrongly?

[564] MALTHUSIANISM

In his book *An essay on the principle of population* (1798) the English political economist the **REV. THOMAS ROBERT MALTHUS** (1766-1834) propounded the theory that population, increasing geometrically, must eventually outstrip food supply, which increases only arithmetically, and that therefore measures should be taken to restrict population growth. The particular measure Malthus had in mind was sexual self-denial, but the solution that has more generally been preferred is to increase agricultural production by technical means (see **HABER-BOSCH PROCESS**). There are, however, grounds for believing that this approach cannot be relied on indefinitely, that the resources of world agriculture are, in fact, finite. Meanwhile we would do well to remember that Malthus *has not yet been proved wrong*. We should know the answer shortly.

[565] MANBY APPARATUS

The life-saving apparatus with which is connected the name of **CAPT. GEORGE WILLIAM MANBY** (1765-1854) consisted of a line-throwing mortar by which a hawser could be passed to a foundering vessel up to 400 yards off shore and the passengers and crew hauled to safety one by one in a sling. Manby was inspired partly by his own experience of shipwreck while *en route* for Ireland in 1802, and partly by the wrecks in Yarmouth Roads in 1807 which cost nearly 150 lives. By the end of the latter year Manby had developed and tested his apparatus and it was first successfully used in February 1808. Manby was a Norfolk character, patron of artists, eccentric, and according to the author of *A perlustration of Great Yarmouth* (vol. iii 1886), "a man of excessive vanity and egoism". He had been a schoolfellow of Nelson, but held his commission in the Cambridge militia, not the navy. He first came to public notice via a self-published pamphlet (1803) in which he offered to settle England's current difficulties with France by personally assassinating Napoleon. In 1821 he accompanied Scoresby on a whaling expedition to Greenland to try out a harpoon gun of his own devising. He later campaigned actively for a knighthood in recognition of his public services, but without result. He was, however, elected a Fellow of the Royal Society in 1831. (On Manby's artistic interests, see: Andrew Moore, *The Norwich School of Artists*, Norfolk Museums Service/HMSO 1985.)

[566] MANDELBROT SET

An iconic symbol of the relatively new mathematical fields of fractal geometry and chaos theory. These fields are of fundamental importance in changing the metaphors available for understanding and modelling the universe around us and the terms have entered the language. They are used in creating artificial ("virtual") scenery for computer games and films, for modelling complex systems such as meteorological, organic and economic systems and have inspired much graphic art. When rendered graphically (see **ARGAND DIAGRAM**) the set is surprisingly beautiful (in a nerdy sort of way) and exhibits infinitely complicated structure even though it arises from a simple iterative formula. It is named after Warsaw-born polymath **BENOÎT MANDELBROT** (b. 1924). After studying mathematics in France, Mandelbrot qualified in aeronautics at CalTech before taking a doctorate in mathematical sciences from Paris. During a long, distinguished and eclectic career, Mandelbrot worked at the French CNRS, the IBM Thomas J Watson research centre, the Institute for Advanced Study at Princeton, at M.I.T. and at Harvard and Yale Universities, making contributions not just to mathematical theory but also to applications in economics, geographical mapping, cosmology and in modelling physiological structures. His influential book *The Fractal Geometry of Nature* (1982) brought these ideas to a wide audience, the writing style making difficult concepts accessible to many. Mandelbrot's many awards include the Wolf Prize for Physics (1993), the Lewis Fry Richardson Medal of the European Geophysical Society* (2000), the Japan Prize (2003), and the Einstein Lectureship of the American Mathematical Society (2006). The asteroid *27500 Mandelbrot* was named in his honour and he is an *Officier* of the French *Légion d'honneur*. (RC)

*Since 2002, the awarding body of this and other medals in related fields is the European Geosciences Union (EGU), formed in 2002 jointly by the European Geophysical Society (EGS) and the European Union of Geosciences (EUG). See **RICHARDSON MEDAL**.

[567] MANICHAEISM

Every believing Christian has to resolve, as best they may, the Problem of Evil. Simply stated, it is as follows: If God is, as we believe, all-powerful and all-good, and if, despite this, He allows Evil to persist in His creation, it must be either because He cannot or because He will not do away with it. If He cannot, then He is not omnipotent. If he will not, then his goodness – at least to human understanding – is flawed. Early in the history of Christianity an answer to the conundrum was proposed by the Persian religious leader **MANI** (*ca.* 215-276 AD). Taking his cue from the **ZOROASTRIANS** (who, however, considered him an enemy and eventually crucified him) he proposed a division of the universe between two equipotent and perpetually-warring deities, God and Satan, representing the opposing forces of Light and Darkness. Mani's teachings were condemned by the Church and his followers vigorously persecuted, but the idea that this world is Satan's particular province, in which he may (indeed, must) be opposed by the Good but never finally overcome, has proved hard to eradicate, and Manichaean doctrines are apt to reappear from time to time in various guises – for example in the Mediaeval sects of the Bogomils and the Cathars, who believed that the world as we know it is actually Satan's creation. And the Church still regularly exhorts us to abjure "the world, the flesh and the Devil" – a significant collocation of ideas. There is undoubtedly an attractive logic to Mani's approach to the problem posed by the seemingly ineradicable nature of evil. The English philosopher, Professor Joad (1891-1953) wrote: "Of all the views of the universe with which I am acquainted, Manichaeism has always seemed to me to account most satisfactorily for the apparent facts."* There is even a strong whiff of Manichaean dualism in Tolkien's otherwise impeccably Christian tract *The Lord of the Rings*.

* C.E.M. Joad *Guide to modern wickedness* 1939. On the historical side, see E. Le Roy Ladurie *Montaillou* 1978, and S. Runciman *The mediaeval Manichee* 1947.

[568] MANN ACT

Statute passed by the Congress of the United States in 1910 with the intention of criminalising the so-called White Slave Traffic. It takes its name from Republican Congressman **JAMES ROBERT MANN** (1856-1922). By making it a federal offence to "transport" females across a state border for immoral purposes, the Act asserted the right of Congress to regulate interstate commerce. But it was open to abuse since virtually any man crossing a state line in the company of a woman to whom he was not married could be prosecuted under its terms. One of the Act's first victims was the boxer Jack Johnson who rescued a woman (whom he later married) from a brothel, and took her with him to another state. He was sentenced to a year in prison. Other well-known persons charged under the Act include Charlie Chaplin, Chuck Berry, and Frank Lloyd Wright.

[569] MANSARD

A type of roof construction named after the influential* French architect **FRANÇOIS MANSART** (1598-1666), who worked on numerous prestigious buildings and who is associated with the Italian-inspired late-renaissance style of French architecture. The **MANSARD ROOF,** is a double-pitched roof supported by queen-post trusses, the lower half being steeply pitched and the upper half more shallowly. If the lower half is pierced, as is usual, with dormer windows, the result is not only a more convenient living-space under the roof, but an improvement in the overall proportions of the building as seen from the ground. The roof, which might otherwise present to the eye a blank expanse of tiles or slates, is (depending on viewpoint) only visible in its lower half where the windows break the monotony and, because the spacing of the dormers usually repeats that of the lower-storey windows, it ties the roof into the design of the facade. Mansart was the populariser but not the originator of the roofing technique named after him,** which had already been employed by a predecessor Pierre Lescot (*ca.* 1510-1578).

* An influence which reached as far as England: Mansart's design for a projected cupola on the Chapelle des Bourbons at Saint-Denis is said to have shaped Wren's design for St. Paul's.

** See **STIGLER'S LAW**.

[570] MARCO POLO'S ARGALI

The **ARGALI** (*Ovis ammon*), related to the European Mouflon, is the largest living feral sheep, and inhabits semi-desert regions of Siberia and Central Asia. The sub-species *O. ammon polii*, named after **MARCO POLO** (1254-1324), the Venetian traveller to China, has its home range on the Pamir Plateau and is recognisable by its huge, outward-spiralling horns which can reach a length of up to 75 inches.

[571] MARSH'S TEST

Arsenical poisoning, whether by accident or design, was commonplace in the Victorian era. This toxic element was freely available then as arsenic trioxide (also known as "the powder of succession"), and widely used as an insecticide and herbicide and for repelling rodent infestations. It even found some cosmetic application (see **MITHRIDATIZE**). As a homicide its symptoms are rather non-specific, resembling those of cholera which was also rife in that day, so arsenic poisoning could be misdiagnosed, and the chemical tests of the time were unreliable and unconvincing to juries. **MARSH'S TEST** of 1836 put this to rights (and ensured the conviction of one John Bodle for the murder of his grandfather) by providing a specific and highly sensitive forensic test for the presence of the element in bodily residues, foodstuffs, drinks etc. Reduction of the suspect sample in an apparatus generating hydrogen from zinc and sulphuric acid produces the gaseous hydride of arsenic, arsine AsH_3 (see **GOSIO GAS**), which can be thermally decomposed to give a tell-tale grey mirror-like deposit of elemental arsenic on the walls of a heated glass tube. **JAMES MARSH** (1794-1846) was a British chemist who worked at the Royal Arsenal, Woolwich on munitions, and assisted **FARADAY** at the Royal Military Academy from 1829 to 1846. Marsh's test for arsenic won him the Gold Medal of the Society of Arts, and he twice won the Society's silver medal: in 1823 for his work on electromagnetism with **PETER BARLOW** and in 1837 for his invention of a percussion cap for naval guns. (MW)

[572] MARSHALL PLAN

The **MARSHALL PLAN**, or to give it its official title, the European Recovery Programme, was the brain-child of American general **GEORGE CATLETT MARSHALL** (1880-1959). Despite never having seen front-line combat, Marshall has to rate as one of the finest soldiers America has produced and one to whom we in Britain owe a great deal. He graduated from the Virginia Military Academy in 1901 and in 1917 was on Pershing's staff in France. Here he rapidly revealed his talents as an operational planner and as an organiser of training. In the inter-war years he continued to oversee army training and in 1939 was promoted full general and appointed Army Chief of Staff on the day Hitler invaded Poland. In this position, which he retained throughout the war, he was responsible for the expansion of the Army and Air Force from a peace-time level of 200,000 to eight and a half million, properly armed and properly trained. At the same time he functioned as the President's leading military adviser and as overall co-ordinator of strategy in both the European and Pacific theatres. With good reason, Churchill called him "the organiser of victory." In 1945 Marshall resigned his post and was sent by Truman to China in a diplomatic role, charged with negotiating a compromise peace between Chiang and the Communists. In this he failed, and as a result was honoured with a vicious assault from the repellent Senator McCarthy, who accused him of deliberately "losing" China. From 1947 to 1949 Marshall served as Truman's Secretary of State and it was in this role that he proposed, and saw through to fruition, what was to be known as the Marshall Plan for rebuilding Europe's ruined economies with the aid of American technical and financial assistance amounting to some 13 billion dollars. Russia forbade her satellites to take part and the subsequent gaping economic divide between East and West Europe is a measure of the Plan's success, particularly as regards Germany which, remarkably, had furthest to go and yet recovered fastest. (RS)

[573] MARTINDALE

In the world of the prescribing medical practitioner and the dispensing chemist, the simple name "MARTINDALE" signifies the Bible of their profession: *The extra pharmacopoeia* by British pharmacist WILLIAM MARTINDALE (1840-1902) first published in 1883 and now in its 35th edition. Martindale achieved a remarkable prominence in medical circles by his energy, profound knowledge of his subject, his teaching, and his own researches which led to numerous important innovations in the calculation of dosages and means of delivery. *The extra pharmacopoeia* grew out of his regular contributions to the *Pharmaceutical Journal,* and its regular updating and publication was carried on by his eldest son William Harrison Martindale (1874-1933). Martindale owned a house in Winchelsea where the novelist Ford Madox Ford also had a home, and it was Ford who married Martindale's daughter Elizabeth, against her family's wishes. In his later years Martindale suffered from depression aggravated by ill health and finally committed suicide, choosing prussic acid as the means. A biography of Martindale by Juanita Burnby was published in 2004.

[574] MARTINET

A slightly derogatory term for a strict disciplinarian, from JEAN MARTINET (d. 1676), a French soldier made Inspector-General of Infantry by Louis XIV. His rigorous enforcement of a uniform system of drill and discipline contributed not a little to making the French army, in its day, the most efficient in Europe. Martinet unluckily fell victim to friendly fire from his own artillery while leading an assault at the siege of Duisburg. The same fusillade felled a fellow officer of Martinet's, a Swiss with the rather inappropriate name (for a soldier) of Soury, making him "Captain Mouse". In French the word "*martinet*" has a number of meanings: as well as being a diminutive of the proper name Martin, it can denote a trip-hammer, a member of the swift family (*cf.* our *house-martin*), a kind of pear, and, by a fortuitous convergence of ideas, a short-handled, multiple-thonged whip or scourge used for correcting the behaviour of unruly children – a practice now unfortunately in abeyance. (See also **POCOCK'S CHARVOLANT**.)

[575] MASOCHISM

Term coined by 19th-century psychiatrist Krafft-Ebing in 1890 after **LEOPOLD VON SACHER-MASOCH** (1836-1895). It describes the sexual pleasure derived from the experience of physical pain and humiliation as depicted in Sacher-Masoch's romantic novel *Venus in Furs (Die Damen im Pelz)** published in 1870, a work which gives free rein to Sacher-Masoch's fantasies and fetishes, especially in the matter of dominant women dressed in fur. The plot concerns the erotic relationship between dreamer and dilettante Severin von Kusiemski, and Wanda von Dunajew, a beautiful, free-spirited widow, to whom he becomes enslaved. The novel is based on thinly-veiled actual events in the writer's life. (He did his best to live out his fantasies with his mistresses and wives.) After Krafft-Ebing had coined the term 'masochism' Sacher-Masoch's reputation was ruined though his career had been both interesting and productive. He was born in Lemberg (Lvov) in what was then part of the Austro-Hungarian empire, the son of an Austrian police chief. He became a writer and journalist and was a utopian thinker who embraced the socialist and humanist ideals which inform all his work. He led a peripatetic life moving from lover to lover and city to city – to Graz, Salzburg, Vienna, Lindheim, and finally Mannheim where he died. His writings comprise some 80 novels, approximately 100 novellas and essays, and eight dramas. In addition, he wrote numerous articles for newspapers and magazines and was the editor and/or publisher of several magazines and reviews in Graz, Budapest, and Leipzig between 1866 and 1885. It seems a shame that so large and varied an output should be so entirely neglected and that what was clearly an intelligent and interesting person should be judged by a single work and remembered only for a single weakness. (RS)

* Available in English in the Penguin Classics series.

[576] MASON JAR – see **KILNER JAR**

[577] MASON-DIXON LINE

Originally drawn on paper in the mid-18th century by a Colonial court (but not surveyed on the ground), what came to be called the Mason-Dixon line was established to settle a border dispute between the Calvert and Penn families who held the charters to the colonies of Maryland and Pennsylvania respectively. In

1763, two English surveyors, **CHARLES MASON** (1728-1786) and **JEREMIAH DIXON** (1733-1779), contracted with the proprietors of Pennsylvania and Maryland to survey the boundary on the ground. They completed their work in 1766. The line ran along the southern border between Pennsylvania and what are now the states of Virginia and Maryland, then along the eastern border between Maryland and Delaware. The Missouri Compromise of 1820 created the political conditions which made the Mason-Dixon Line important to the history of slavery and it was during the Congressional debates leading to the compromise that the term "Mason-Dixon line" was first used to designate the dividing line between free states and slave states (Pennsylvania abolished slavery while Maryland, Delaware, Kentucky and Missouri did not). If an escaping slave could cross that line (into Pennsylvania or Delaware) he would be relatively safe, especially among the Amish and Quaker communities of Southern Pennsylvania. People such as Harriet Tubman and other "conductors" on what was referred to as the "Underground Railroad" would take groups of slaves to freedom across this line, from where they would then move on to points north. This situation persisted until the end of the Civil War in 1865. Thereafter the Mason-Dixon line has maintained both a cultural and symbolic significance to this day. It is possible but not certain that Dixon's name was the origin of the terms **"DIXIE/DIXIELAND"** to refer to the Southern States.* Mason's early career was as an astronomer at the Royal Greenwich Observatory where Dixon served as his assistant. In 1761 the two were selected by the Royal Observatory to observe the Transit of Venus at the Cape of Good Hope. After completing their American boundary survey they returned to their astronomical pursuits and went on to measure a degree of the meridian on the Delmarva Peninsula in Maryland. A fictionalised account of Mason and Dixon's careers entitled *Mason & Dixon* was published by Thomas Pynchon in 1997**. It is clearly meant as yet another contender for the title Great American Novel (every American novelist worth his salt has had a shot at producing a worthy successor to *Moby Dick* and/or *Huckleberry Finn*) but Pynchon's entry is difficult to judge as the prose is impenetrable by any means short of dynamite. (RS)

* The word **DIXIE** used in the British armed forces to mean a mess tin, is derived from a Hindi word meaning a small pot, and, like other terms originating in India in a military context (*dekko, dhobi, dum-dum...*), is falling into disuse with the severing of the British-Indian connection. *Khaki*, however, is a survivor.

** Among the historical figures who appear in Pynchon's mega-yarn are **JACQUES VAUCANSON** and his famous defecating duck.

[578] MATTHEW WALKER

The name refers to a sailor's knot, specifically, a way of forming a knob-shaped stopper at a rope's end. Its special claim to fame is that it is – or rather used to be – the only knot named after a person. The distinction, however, loses some of its lustre due to the fact that no one now has the remotest idea of Walker's identity (most likely a rigger in one of HM's dockyards). His unique claim to fame is further clouded by the fact that in recent years a number of mountaineers, anglers and suchlike (**PRUSIK**, Turle, Bachman, Kleinheist, Penberthy, Heddon, Albright...) have allowed their names to be attached (!) to a variety of newfangled – though no doubt ingenious – knots and hitches. (See Budworth: *Knots and ropework* London 1999, 2004; C.W. Ashley *The book of knots* N.Y. 1944, London 1947 and reprints.)

[579] MAUD COMMITTEE

A codename for the British secret committee of WWII set up by Sir Henry Thomas Tizard in 1940 to review the possibility of making an atomic bomb. Nominally **MAUD** has been taken as an acronym for **MILITARY APPLICATION OF URANIUM DETONATION**, but its origin as a "semantically empty" codename (see **BARBAROSSA**) appears to be more eccentric. When Denmark was overrun by the Nazis, atomic physicist **NIELS BOHR,** then professor at the University of Copenhagen, sent a telegram to his friend and fellow physicist Otto Frisch working at Birmingham University in England, including the words: "...tell... *Maud Ray Kent*" Eager cryptographers read this as a (near) anagram for *Radium taken*, but it turned out that one, Maud Ray, who had been the governess of the Bohr children in happier times, was indeed then living in Kent, and her name was appropriated. Based on the **FRISCH-PEIERLS MEMORANDUM,** the **MAUD COMMITTEE** made its final recommendations for atomic bomb construction in 1941 and disbanded, handing on the torch to the "Tube Alloys" project – the codename for Britain's secret atomic weapons programme, which was later subsumed into the American-based Manhattan Project. Bohr eventually escaped from occupied Denmark in 1943 via Sweden, to play an important role in the Manhattan Project at Los Alamos. See also **GRAHAM'S LAW.** (MW)

[580] MAUNSELL FORTS

GUY ANSON MAUNSELL (1884-1961) was a British civil engineer specialising in the use of reinforced concrete, of which he was an early advocate, and in structures with a marine connection (docks, bridges, lighthouses, ...) In WWI he worked for the Admiralty on a number of projects including concrete ships – a response to steel shortages. In WWII, he again put his talents at the disposal of the war effort and was involved in the design and construction of the floating harbours, codename "Mulberry", which played a vital role in the Normandy invasion. Unlike Mulberry, the so-called **MAUNSELL SEA FORTS,** weird-looking structures erected in 1942-3 in the Thames and Mersey estuaries for the Army and Navy to serve as AA platforms and as offshore bases for anti-submarine and anti-minelaying measures, are still standing. They provided a haven for pirate radio stations in the 60's, and one of the forts, christened "Sealand" declared itself an independent sovereign state owned and ruled by a royal family named Bates. Some of Maunsell's projects call to mind the fertile imagination and technical versatility of Geoffrey Pyke (see **PYKRETE**). For example, Maunsell's 1920's proposal for a floating aerodrome in the mid-Atlantic has a definite family resemblance in the boldness of its conception to Pyke's plan for building aircraft-carriers out of ice. (For Maunsell, see Nigel Watson and Frank Turner *Maunsell – the firm and its founder* 2005; for detailed information on the forts, numerous publications by Frank Turner.)

[581] MAUPERTUIS' PRINCIPLE

In biology, Dame Nature's procreative indulgences seem profligate (necessarily so – see **DARWIN**), but when She gets down to fundamental physics and chemistry we sense the hand of a strictly economic, even parsimonious mistress. A much-quoted instance is the fact that the skeletal structure of all mammals consists essentially of variations on a single basic model. Physical science, too, has been able to discern certain principles of minimal behaviour, the first of which was **FERMAT'S PRINCIPLE OF LEAST TIME** in optics (1660). **MAUPERTUIS' PRINCIPLE OF LEAST ACTION** (1744) is a generalised development of this idea in the field of mechanics. Maupertuis believed that these economic manifestations of "intelligent design" gave irrefutable proof of the existence of a Supreme Being whose perfection could be compatible only with the minimum expenditure of action. Nowadays we acknowledge that this is just how things have to work, otherwise we would not be here to appreciate them. French mathematician and philosopher **PIERRE-LOUIS MOREAU DE MAUPERTUIS** (1698-1759) was born at Saint-Malo and privately educated. He was admitted to the Académie Française in 1723 and became its Director in 1742. He took part in the French Geodesic Expedition to Lapland, successfully proving his prediction that the earth's shape is an oblate spheroid. His principle of least action was not very clearly expressed at the time, but it progressed in the hands of **EULER**, **LAGRANGE** and **HAMILTON** to provide one of the most fundamental theorems underpinning mechanics and the equations of motion. Maupertuis also speculated on biological evolution in his work *Vénus physique* (1745) which describes some early ideas of heredity. (MW)

[582] MAVERICK

Originally applied to semi-wild, unbranded cattle on the Texas ranges, the word has come to mean any independent-minded person, with an overtone of *dangerously unapproachable*. The name derives from Texas politician and landowner **SAMUEL AUGUSTUS MAVERICK** (1803-1870), who got his start in the ranching business with just such a herd of unbranded cattle. Born in South Carolina, Maverick moved with his wife and a few slaves to Texas in 1835, in time to become involved in the Texan rebellion. He was at the Alamo from where he was despatched on a political mission in time to miss the fate which overcame the rest of the fort's defenders. From a modest start, he built up a landholding amounting to some 300,000 acres of rangeland. He served in the Texas state legislature from 1851-1863 and later as Mayor of San Antonio. Though opposed to secession, he supported the Confederacy in the Civil War. He left ten children.

[583] MAXIM GUN

Emerson is widely quoted as saying, "Build a better mouse-trap and the world will beat a path to your door."* American-born inventor HIRAM STEVENS MAXIM (1840-1916) did just that – he designed a better mouse-trap. Along with a number of other useful inventions such as a menthol inhaler for bronchitis sufferers, an improved incandescent light-bulb, and a steam-powered aeroplane which actually got off the ground (just). But it wasn't until, like his near-contemporary GATLING, he turned from the arts of peace to the gadgetry of war that the path-beating really began for Maxim. He emigrated to England in 1881 and by 1883 had perfected his recoil-operated machine-gun, the first weapon of its kind. This was the means by which Maxim's fame and name were permanently secured, and in 1901 he was knighted by Queen Victoria. In 1896 patents for the gun were bought by the engineering firm of Vickers, and the water-cooled Vickers-Maxim gun (in later versions simply "Vickers") remained a standard piece of British army equipment up to and throughout the Second World War. Hence another oft-repeated quotation: Hilaire Belloc, regarding the question whether it was superior education, civilisation and culture that enabled the European powers so easily to dominate the rest of the world (the "Scramble for Africa" was then in full swing), thought there was a simpler answer. He wrote:

Whatever happens we have got
The Maxim Gun and they have not.
("The Modern Traveller" 1898)

Maxim's mouse-trap, incidentally, was supposed to re-set automatically – an ambitious undertaking whose mechanism he never perfected.

* This is probably a paraphrase by an acquaintance of Emerson's of something half-remembered. In his journal for February 1855, Emerson wrote, "*If a man...can make better knives, or crucibles, or church organs, than anybody else, you will find a broad hard-beaten road to his house, though it be in the woods.*" (Bartlett's *Familiar quotations*, 15th ed. 1980.) Bad news for the advertising industry, if true.

[584] MAXWELL-BOLTZMANN DISTRIBUTION – see BOLTZMANN CONSTANT

[585] MAXWELL'S DEMON

Scottish physicist **JAMES CLERK MAXWELL** (1831-1879) propounded a so-called thought experiment intended to raise doubts about the Second Law of Thermodynamics. He imagined a being with the ability to keep tabs on individual molecules and having control over a little trap door. If the demon spots a fast molecule approaching the trap door it/he/she lets the molecule pass, but if it's a slow molecule it/he/she does not. If the trapdoor is between two chambers initially containing gas at a uniform temperature, and all isolated from the rest of the universe, the actions of the demon would lead to hotter gas in one chamber, cooler in the other, thereby decreasing the total entropy of the system, which the Second Law says can't happen, or in the words of Flanders and Swann, "Heat can't go from a colder to a hotter". The experiment is debunked by the application to this case of one of the most universal of all laws, viz. "there are no free lunches". In this case basically the demon has to pay for doing the work required to keep tabs on the molecules and fiddle with the trap door, the cost being an increase of entropy somewhere. (PP)

[586] MAZDA LAMPS

Before **MAZDA** was the name of a car, it was the trade name throughout the first half of the 20th century of a popular make of light bulb produced by the General Electric company. It refers to the God **AHURAMAZDA** (or **ORMUZD**) the God of Light in the **ZOROASTRIAN** religion.

[587] McCLELLAN SADDLE

GEORGE BRINTON McCLELLAN (1826-1885) was a career US Army officer and West Point graduate, serving first in the engineers and later in the cavalry. In 1855 he joined a commission sent to Europe to study developments in military tactics and equipment, as a result of which he was present in the Crimea at the siege of Sebastopol. On his return, he proposed (1859) a design for a military saddle, which was adopted and remained, with some later modifications, the standard US military pattern saddle until WWII. It is still used on ceremonial occasions. McClellan claimed "his" saddle was based on a Prussian adaptation of a Hungarian original but in fact it most closely resembles a type of Spanish saddle in widespread use in Mexico as well as north of the Border. In the Civil War McClellan served for a time as General-in-Chief of the Union armies. After the Union defeat at Bull Run, the first major engagement of the Civil War, it was he who pulled the remnants together, rebuilt morale, and turned a uniformed rabble into a properly trained army. This done, however, McClellan had no very clear idea what to do with the tool he had forged and he proved ineffective as a field commander, largely through indecision and overcaution. After a series of reverses Lincoln replaced him with Burnside (see **SIDEBURNS**).

[588] McINDOE'S GUINEA PIGS

In WWII, burns were a frequent cause of terrible injury to both civilians and combatants. In many cases these involved disfigurement and resulting psychological as well as physical damage. One man who had both the technical skills and the human understanding to meet the needs of these patients was ARCHIBALD HECTOR McINDOE (1900-1960), consultant in plastic surgery to the RAF. He organised a special unit at the Queen Victoria Hospital, East Grinstead where he used skin-grafts to treat the burns. His second special gift, however, was in the psychological rehabilitation of his patients. Under his regime, the patients formed themselves into a kind of informal club, "THE GUINEA PIGS", whose collective ethos centred on mutual support, loyalty to McIndoe, and a fierce determination – carefully fostered by him – not to be excluded by disability or disfigurement from normal everyday life. McIndoe was knighted in 1947.

[589] McNAGHTEN RULES

A set of rules drawn up by senior judges in the House of Lords in 1843 to help determine whether and under what circumstances insanity might serve as a defence in a criminal prosecution. In essence they stated that an accused person could be absolved of criminal responsibility if his/her mental state was such that at the time he/she was unaware that what he/she was doing was wrong. The guidelines were drawn up following the 1843 trial of a Scottish carpenter DANIEL MCNAGHTEN (or McNAUGHTON) who had attempted to assassinate the Prime Minister Sir Robert Peel in the belief that the Government was conspiring against him.* In the event, McNaghten killed not the PM but the PM's secretary Edward Drummond. He was acquitted on the grounds of insanity and confined to Broadmoor. His case has similarities with those of Richard Dadd (1817-1886) and W.C. Minor (1834-1920). Dadd was an artist whose wonderful but weird painting *The fairy feller's masterstroke* is in the Tate. He killed his own father. Minor was an American army surgeon living in London who killed a workman named George Merrett passing by his house, in the belief that Merrett was a burglar. Both Dadd and Minor ended up in Broadmoor where Dadd continued to paint (wonderfully) and Minor became a valued contributor to what was to become the *Oxford English Dictionary* then being compiled by Sir James Murray. In both cases it was thought that insanity had been brought on, or at least aggravated, by traumatic experiences: Minor's in having to deal with the horrible wounds inflicted on the casualties of the American Civil war, plus his being obliged to brand with a letter D soldiers found guilty of desertion. In Dadd's case the triggering event was supposed to have been his having to witness, while on a painting tour in the Near East, a living camel being cut to pieces with knives after it had fallen, blocking a narrow street. The cases of Dadd and Minor do not, of course, complete the list of crazy but still creative people. One thinks of De

Sade, for instance, or poor Artaud, banged up in Rodez (and see articles on
CRUDEN and SAPPHIC STANZA).

* And how crazy is that? a cynic might ask. If Shaw was right and all professions are conspiracies
against the laity, why should the profession of politics be excepted?

[590] MEITNERIUM

Chemical element number 109, symbol Mt, was created in 1997 at the weightily-
titled *Gesellschaft für Schwerionenforschung*, (Institute for Heavy Ion Research) at
Darmstadt in Germany. Its name celebrates the woman whom EINSTEIN
(presumably wearing his Austrian Jewish hat) called "Our own Marie Curie" (for
her eponymous element, see CURIUM). Austrian-born LISE MEITNER (1878-1968)
was the second woman to receive a doctorate in physics from the University of
Vienna. In 1907 at the University of Berlin, she began a 30-year scientific
collaboration with chemistry professor, Otto Hahn (1879-1968). In 1917, at the
newly-founded Kaiser Wilhelm Institute for Chemistry, they discovered the
radioactive element protactinium (see URANIUM). Following the *Anschluss* of March
1938, Meitner's post at the Institute was terminated because she had a Jewish
grandparent. She fled from Nazi Germany in July 1938, to work at the Nobel
Institute of Physics in Stockholm, Sweden, where she became a citizen in 1949.
The Aryan Hahn remained working in Germany, however, and the pair continued
their research collaboration clandestinely, with Hahn performing the radiochemical
experiments, and Meitner interpreting the phenomena theoretically in terms of her
extraordinary new idea of nuclear fission,* which was destined to change the
course of history. Fortunately, Hitler expressed little interest in physics and
chemistry and failed to grasp the significance of uranium fission. Furthermore, it
was politically unthinkable in 1939 for an exiled "Jewish" scientist to be included, as
an author and co-discoverer, in Hahn's German publication. Hahn's reward for
remaining in Germany throughout WWII was the Nobel Prize for Chemistry in
1944, for "his" discovery of nuclear fission. The omission of Meitner's name from
this Nobel citation is now regarded by many historians of science as egregious.
Recently, some restitution for this injustice has been made in a nominal matter:
element 105 (first claimed by the Russians at Dubna in 1968) was honorifically
named HAHNIUM in 1994, but an element re-shuffle by the IUPAC naming
committee (see SEABORGIUM) withdrew this name in 1997, re-branding element
105 as Dubnium, while ratifying the given name of element 109. So it is Lise
Meitner, not Otto Hahn, who adorns the Periodic Table (see MENDELEEV).
Despite her discovery of nuclear fission, which made the atomic bomb possible,
she steadfastly refused to work on the development of weapons. (MW)

*In which the nucleus of the uranium atom, under neutron bombardment, splits into two – usually
unequal – fragments (lighter elements called fission products), with the release of much energy
($E=mc^2$) and more neutrons, which can therefore induce a self-sustaining chain reaction (see FERMI).

[591] MELBA TOAST

Australian *prima donna* **DAME NELLIE MELBA,** *née* **HELEN PORTER MITCHELL** (1861-1931) was born, educated and trained in Melbourne (whence by toponymy she derived her professional stage name). She studied in Paris, and made her debut at the Royal Opera House, Covent Garden in 1888, when her superbly fresh coloratura soprano voice won her worldwide acclaim, a DBE in 1918, and an august GBE in 1927. The *Diva* is thrice-celebrated in *Haute Cuisine* by gastronomic inventions of the legendary gourmet-chef **GEORGES-AUGUSTE ESCOFFIER** (1846-1935) at the London Savoy (see **TOURNEDOS ROSSINI**). His Melboid creations would suffice for a three-course nosh-up: for the *hors d'oeuvres*, **MELBA TOAST** (1897), extraordinarily thin and crisp, is considered *de rigueur* as a substrate for *pâté*; with the *entrée*, **MELBA GARNITURE** consists of chicken, truffles and mushrooms stuffed into tomatoes with velouté sauce; for the dessert, **PÊCHE MELBA** (1893) offers peaches with vanilla ice-cream and a **MELBA SAUCE** made from puréed raspberries and redcurrants thickened with icing sugar. **"DOING A MELBA"** is Australian slang for a return from retirement or a multiplicity of farewell appearances. (MW)

[592] MENDELEEV'S PERIODIC TABLE

The periodic table is the foundation stone of chemistry, underpinning the composition of all matter. If the chemical elements are listed in order of increasing atomic weight (see **AVOGADRO**), certain recurrent similarities become apparent – a periodicity in their properties, both physical and chemical (see **NEWLANDS** and **DÖBEREINER**.) These observations were best rationalised by Russian chemist **DMITRI IVANOVICH MENDELEEV** (1834-1907) who occupied the chair of chemistry at St Petersburg from 1863-90, (after which he worked for the Russian Bureau of Weights and Measures on setting standards for the strength of vodka). Mendeleev classified similar elements into groups – vertical columns of his table. He recognised that some elements must still be missing, presumed them to be undiscovered, and predicted their properties by interpolation. The subsequent isolation of germanium, **GALLIUM**, and scandium confirmed his predictions – the strongest proof of good science. The classification by atomic weight is complicated by the existence of isotopes, causing anomalies in the order, so a refinement was the idea of atomic number – see **MOSELEY'S LAW**. The completed **PERIODIC TABLE** of the elements has a curious pattern of rows, having lengths 2 8 8 18 18 32 32, each terminating in an inert gas. This is now fully explained by atomic theory in terms of the shell structure of the electrons "orbiting" around the nucleus (see **BOHR** and **SCHRÖDINGER**). Element number 101, synthesised by Seaborg at Berkeley in 1955 (see **GHIORSIUM**), was named honorifically as **MENDELEVIUM.** It has no uses, but its properties are – thanks to Mendeleev's principles – entirely predictable. (MW)

[593] MERCALLI SCALE

Unlike the **RICHTER SCALE** which uses instruments to measure the *intensity* of earthquakes, the **MERCALLI SCALE** measures their *effects* without the use of instruments but simply by observation. In this it bears a family resemblance to the **BEAUFORT SCALE**. Mercalli's scale runs from one to twelve, expressed as Roman numerals and in ascending order of severity (I = virtually imperceptible, XII = total devastation). A second point of difference is that Richter allots a single value to the magnitude (*i.e.* the amount of energy released) of any given seismic event, whereas in Mercalli's system the severity of the effects observed and the numerical value assigned to them may vary from place to place during a single event according as geological conditions affect susceptibility to damage. **GIUSEPPE MERCALLI** (1850-1914), born in Milan, was ordained as a priest and became a teacher of natural sciences with a special interest in vulcanology. He held various posts before being appointed to Naples University and to the directorship of the Vesuvius Observatory. He died in mysterious circumstances, apparently as a result of a fire in his rooms, but it is possible that the fire was started deliberately to cover up the fact of his having been robbed and then murdered. (Normal for Naples?)

[594] MERCATOR'S PROJECTION

It has become fashionable in some circles to decry the map projection devised in 1569 by the Dutchman **GERHARD KREMER*** (ca. 1620-1687) as a tool of imperialist propaganda on account of its distortion of continental land areas – exaggerating the dimensions of Canada relative to Africa, for example.** This is a view that could only be held by a person who has no understanding of what a map projection is or does. All projections involve distortion since all are attempts to depict on a 2-dimensional surface (a map) a three-dimensional object (the terrestrial sphere). And no critic of Mercator's political correctness has yet managed to explain the connection between European imperialism and the excessive magnification of Greenland. The principal virtue of Mercator's map is as an aid to marine navigation, and this for two reasons: (1) On the Mercator projection, the greatest distortion is at the Poles, where ships don't go, and least in the mid-latitudes, where most shipping is most of the time. (2) Since any two points on the surface of a sphere lie on the circumference of a Great Circle, the shortest line that connects them (a ship's course, for example) is a segment of that circle and therefore, by definition, curved. Mercator's projection allows such a curve to be represented on paper as a straight line, thus enabling mariners to plot courses with the aid of a ruler, which would otherwise be impossible.

*   Latinised as **GERARDUS MERCATOR** (German: *kremer* = *merchant*)

** Denigration of Mercator reached its apogee in the **PETERS WORLD MAP**, a cartographic embodiment of the political prejudices of German film-maker Arno Peters (1916-2002).

[595] MERCERISATION

Treatment of cotton fabrics with strong caustic alkali in order to pre-shrink and strengthen the fibres. The process was invented in 1850 by JOHN MERCER (1791-1866), a Mancunian calico-dyer and printer. As a self-taught colour chemist who started life as a handloom weaver and finished as a Fellow of the Royal Society, he was drawn to scientific experimentation, but unlike the amateur scientists of the Victorian leisured classes, his researches were inhibited by the exigency of having to run a business to earn his living. He might be numbered among the innovators of photography, having observed in 1828 the blueprint effect, a process invented by sir JOHN HERSCHEL in 1842. Mercer's only publication described his methods for making coloured photographs on fabrics to the 1858 meeting of the British Association for the Advancement of Science. There is an 1886 biography of this otherwise unsung hero by his nephew, Edward Parnell, *The Life and Labours of John Mercer.* (See also: Musson & Robinson *Science and Technology in the Industrial Revolution* 1969.) (MW)

[596] MERCURY – see TITANIUM

[597] MERENSKY REEF

The greatest known deposits of platinum ore on the globe were discovered in 1924 in Central Transvaal, South Africa, by the geologist DR HANS MERENSKY (1871-1952) the son of a German medical missionary, who had studied at Breslau and the University of Berlin. Following the discovery of alluvial platinum in the region, he prospected for the mother lode, and his geological insight led him to the MERENSKY REEF, extending nearly 100 km, about a metre in thickness and varying in depth from outcrops at the surface down to about 1000 metres. Since platinum supplies from Russia had dried up following the October Revolution of 1917, South Africa became the West's major source of the precious metal. Merensky's discovery initiated a large and profitable industry which saw the founding of Rustenberg Platinum Mines and their sole refiners, the Johnson Matthey Company of Hatton Garden, England. Platinum was "the eighth metal", following iron, tin, lead, mercury, copper, silver, and gold, which had all been known from classical times. In 1748 platinum was introduced into Europe by Spanish naval officer and colonial adminstrator Don Antonio de Ulloa, who had been seconded in 1735 to accompany a French scientific expedition to Quito, Ecuador.* His publication mentioned reports of a curious infusible metal called "platina" (Spanish = "little silver"), then regarded as an undesirable impurity in the gold extracts from the mines of Chocó. Science seized upon this metal from the Americas, because its inertness made it ideal for various physico-chemical apparatus. Later it came to be valued also for jewellery. OSTWALD'S discovery in 1902 of the catalytic power of finely-divided "platinum black" to promote chemical reactions was in good time for the extensive manufacture of the nitrate explosives needed for WWI, conferring upon platinum the status of a "strategic material" during the excitements of 1916, when the British government forbade its use for jewellery and photographic printing by William Willis's platinotype process. (MW)

* An account of the expedition is included in Pinkerton's *General collection of voyages* (17 vols. London 1808-1814). Antonio de Ulloa is not be confused with Francisco de Ulloa who, sent by Cortés, explored the coast of California as far north as Cape Mendocino in 1539-1540 (account in HAKLUYT).

[598] MERRYWEATHER'S TEMPEST PROGNOSTICATOR

Like the ALDINI BATTERY, this ingenious device depends on mating biological with physical processes. One might object that there is nothing strange or special about such hybrid devices – what else, after all, is a horse-drawn plough? But not all such combinations of animal and machine are as surprising as that outlined by DR. GEORGE MERRYWEATHER (*fl.* 1830-1861) of the Whitby Literary and Philosophical Society at a meeting of that august body on 27 February 1851. Having read somewhere that leeches become agitated in stormy weather and climb to the top of any container they happen to be confined in, Merryweather conceived the idea of a leech-powered barometer. It consisted of twelve glass bottles arranged in a circle*, each containing an inch of rainwater and one leech. At the top of each bottle was a narrow tube housing a piece of whalebone to which was attached a fine wire, attached in turn to a striker acting on a brass bell. The idea was that when a change in atmospheric pressure tipped the leeches to the fact that a storm was on the way, they would head for the tops of their respective bottles, dislodging the whalebone trip and causing the bell to ring. The more leeches that responded and the more the bell rang, the worse the expected storm. A sumptuous model of the Prognosticator, its style inspired by Mogul architecture, was constructed for the Great Exhibition of 1851. A replica was made for the 1951 Festival of Britain and is now in the Whitby Museum. There is a second working model in the Barometer Museum in Okehampton (Devon). Merryweather expected his invention to be taken up by the government and installed at suitable (but numerous) locations round the coasts of Britain. In this he was disappointed.

* The point of the circular arrangement was to allow the leeches to see each other and so avoid, in Merrryweather's words, "the affliction of solitary confinement". The famous animal-lover and eccentric Squire Waterton (1782-1865) had the same idea when he had stables constructed with little windows in each partition so that the horses in their separate stalls could the better converse with their neighbours. See also BENTHAM'S PANOPTICON.

[599] MERSENNE NUMBERS

Numbers equal to one less than a power of two, (*i.e.* formed by means of the expression 2^p-1 where p is a positive integer) were called **MERSENNE NUMBERS** by William Walter Rouse Ball (1850-1925) of Trinity College, Cambridge in his *Mathematical Recreations and Essays* of 1892. The most interesting of these arise when p is a prime number (*i.e.* one having no factors – divisible only by 1 and itself),* in which case the resulting Mersenne number *can* also be prime, when it is then called a **MERSENNE PRIME**. The snag is there is no guarantee that it *will* be prime, and for three centuries mathematicians have expended much thought-energy on trying, unsuccessfully, to predict when. Here are the **MERSENNE NUMBERS** M_p resulting from the first few primes, p:

p =	2	3	5	7	11	13	17	19	23	29	31
M_p =	3	7	31	127	2047	8191	131071	524287	8388607	536870911	2147483647

Of these, three are composite (*i.e.* not prime):

$2047 = 23 \times 89;$ $8388607 = 47 \times 178481;$ $536870911 = 233 \times 1103 \times 2089$

MERSENNE'S CONJECTURE of 1644 concerned which values of p, for the first 55 primes up to a value p = 257, generate **MERSENNE PRIMES**. He stated – without proof – that only eleven of them did:

2 3 5 7 13 17 19 31 67 127 257

and all the rest (44 of them) give composites. It turns out that he got it nearly right: his 67 should be 61; he missed the primes 89 and 107 which also yield Mersenne primes; and 257 actually gives a composite, so is struck off. The correct list is:

2 3 5 7 13 17 19 31 61 89 107 127

But the real mystery is this: what was the basis for Mersenne's assertion of 1644? Even today there is still no general theoretical principle to predict which primes will "work" to produce a Mersenne prime, and there is no general method for testing whether any number is prime, apart from "brute force" methods of trying every possible divisor. As p goes up, we see how $M_p = 2^p-1$ increases enormously;** so for very large numbers this testing became an impossibly lengthy procedure until the first application of a computer to the problem, three hundred years later. The largest Mersenne prime found to date (2009) is for p = 43112609. It is a number with nearly 13 million digits, which would fill a dozen volumes, so we shall refrain from attempting to calculate it here. French scholar and natural philosopher **MARIN MERSENNE** (1558-1648) was born at Oizé, Maine, and educated at the Jesuit College of La Flèche. In 1611 he became a friar of the

Order of Minimi, taught theology at Nevers, then in 1620 settled at a convent in Paris. He studied acoustics and the theory of music and corresponded widely, especially with mathematicians such as **FERMAT** – whence the problem probably originated in the first place. (MW)

* For academic reasons, mathematicians do not regard 1 as a prime number.

** So this is a good way of generating very large numbers which *may* be prime – such things are useful in public-key cryptography, which relies on our inability to find two very large prime factors of an even larger composite number.

[600] MESMERISM

The Austrian thaumaturge **FRANZ** (*a.k.a.* **FRIEDRICH**) **ANTON MESMER** (1733-1815) was a qualified doctor with an interest in astrology. He neatly combined the two when he discovered that the universe was filled with a force or substance he called "animal magnetism" which affected human bodies and which he, Mesmer, had the power to control and direct in order to cure disease. In 1778 he found his way to Paris where he soon made numerous well-heeled (healed?) converts who attended carefully stage-managed group séances in his apartments. Originally Mesmer had effected his cures by stroking the patient with magnets, but later found that he could produce the same results by simple manipulation or even just pointing his finger. All this might seem perfectly reasonable to a modern adept of Chinese physiological theory, but the French medical authorities viewed Mesmer's antics with the cold eye of suspicion, and a commission of the Académie des Sciences* was appointed to look into the matter. The Commission reported that whatever it was that was affecting Mesmer's patients (and there *were* observable effects, probably hysterical in nature), it wasn't animal magnetism. Mesmer fell from favour and some cynical souls even went so far as to call him a charlatan. He left Paris for Switzerland, where he died. It may be symptomatic of something or other that on the very eve of the Revolution, *le tout Paris* (*i.e.* the idle rich) could find nothing better to do with its time than flock to Mesmer's séances. Among his converts was the Polish Princess Lubomirska (1733-1816), mother-in-law of the traveller and historian Count Jan Potocki. One of her entourage records in his memoirs that "*la ville était tout occupé du magnétisme de Mesmer. La vive imagination de notre princesse saisit aussitôt de cette nouveauté. Sur des tables de chevet autour de son lit étaient disposés des vases avec des branches magnétisées. Des fils étaient attachés par un bout à ces branches et par l'autre aux cheveux de la princesse; elle assurait que, grâce à ce traitement, ses cheveux qui se faisaient rares avaient abondamment repoussé.*" On a Channel crossing, destination London, the Princess was accompanied by, among others, "*un certain M. Lamotte**, l'un des premiers disciples de Mesmer... Lamotte voulait magnétiser la mer et le bateau; mais le capitaine Cornu qui était superstitieux fut près de le jeter par-dessus bord. Combien de fois, assis dans la voiture, nous avons dû, la princesse, M. Potocki, l'abbé Piatoli, Lamotte, le jeune prince Henri Lubomirski et moi, aux ordres de Lamotte, nous tenir par la* *main pour former une chaîne magnétique; tout le monde disait éprouver diverses sensations, sauf moi qui fus reconnu* rebelle au magnétisme."***

* One of the Commission's members was **BENJAMIN FRANKLIN** and another the unfortunate **Dr. GUILLOTIN**.

** Clearly a soul brother as well as a namesake of the Brigadier Lamotte who made a killing with his patent medicine at the court of Louis XIV (see **BESTUSCHEFF'S NERVINE TINCTURE**).

*** Quoted and translated from Polish by François Rosset and Dominique Triare, *Jean Potocki*, 2004, p.124. See also R. Darnton *La fin des Lumières: le mesmérisme et la R évolution* Paris 1984

[601] MESSERSCHMITT

In 1927 aircraft designer **WILLY MESSERSCHMITT** (1898-1978) joined BFW, a fledgling firm of Bavarian aircraft manufacturers which in 1938 became Messerschmitt AG. His single-wing fighters, the Bf 109 and Bf 110 (subsequently designated Me 109 and 110) made up the bulk of Germany's fighter force in the first part of WWII and may therefore be considered the German counterparts of the Hurricane and Spitfire. In the latter part of the war, instead of sticking to large-scale production of tried and tested models, Messerschmitt's firm engaged, as did other sections of Germany's armaments industry, in a wild search for war-winning superweapons such as rocket- and jet-propelled fighters* and a bomber capable of reaching New York (*cf.* **HEINKEL**). When peace broke out in 1945, Messerschmitt's firm turned, perforce, to strictly pacific projects including a "bubble car", a form of transport which enjoyed a brief vogue in the Fifties. Wheels aside, the Messerschmitt car bore so close a resemblance to the cockpit of a fighter plane as to give rise to the popular belief that it was built from redundant aircraft parts. This was not the case, though the car was the creation of an aircraft designer, Fritz Fend.

* The jet-powered Me 262, and rocket-powered Me 163 – both world firsts.

[602] MESSIER CATALOGUE

In 1771 a Frenchman named **CHARLES MESSIER** (1730-1817) compiled a list of 108 galaxies, nebulae and star-clusters, which subsequently became known among astronomers as the **MESSIER CATALOGUE**. The listed objects were designated by number – M1 M2, M3 and so on – and many of these numbers are still in common use despite the numerous star catalogues that have been devised since Messier's time and with the aid of better telescopes. Probably the best-known is M31, the "Great Nebula" in Andromeda, which can be seen with the naked eye. What is slightly odd about Messier's initiative is that he wasn't interested in galaxies, nebulae and star-clusters. He was interested in comets, and compiled his catalogue only to assist him in determining which celestial objects were *not* comets. This interest, amounting almost to an obsession, dated from Messier's being the first to detect the predicted return of **HALLEY'S COMET** in 1758.

[603] METHUSELAH

The Bible tells us that **METHUSELAH**, the grandfather of Noah, lived for 969 years (*Genesis* 5.27), setting a hard-to-beat record for human longevity.* For this reason, the name Methuselah is commonly given to any exceptionally long-lived person or creature. An example is the **METHUSELAH TREE**, a Bristlecone Pine growing at a secret location in the White Mountains of California. When last tested (in 1957), its age was put at 4,789 years, which makes it the oldest known living organism. Research into ageing, longevity, and rejuvenation is promoted by the **METHUSELAH FOUNDATION** which awards the **METHUSELAH MOUSE PRIZE** to anyone who can dramatically extend, by whatever means, the lifespan of laboratory mice. The Foundation's prize fund currently stands at over $4.5 million. (See also **JEROBOAM**.)

* Noah ran him a close second with 950 (*Genesis* 9). It is clear from the Bible that life-spans which we would consider unusually long were less unusual in antediluvian times since Adam lived 930 years, Methuselah's father Enoch notched up 365 and Methuselah's son Lamech would have needed 595 candles on his last birthday cake. (*Genesis* 5, *passim.*)

[604] MICHELS' LAW OF OLIGARCHY

In any society, all questions relating to political and social organisation can be reduced to one: Who rules? In the search for a method of ensuring that only fit people get to govern us, we are no further advanced now than were the Babylonians. But such solutions as have been tried so far have tended to follow one of two broad tendencies: to concentrate power in the hands of a single individual (tyranny), or to distribute authority as widely as possible among the members of society (democracy). Athens was the first society we know of to try both solutions, but both, unsurprisingly, turned out to have a down- as well as an up-side, and that has been the common experience ever since. One possible, if Utopian, solution to this dilemma is to try and so organise society that *no-one* has any power over anybody else, and this is the solution preferred by the Anarchist wing of political thought. The German sociologist and political scientist **ROBERT MICHELS** (1876-1936) made a close study of these matters and came up with a depressing conclusion which he called the "Iron Law of Oligarchy"*. The Iron Law states that *all societies, and all organisations within societies, however democratic in structure and intention, will tend to become oligarchies, to concentrate power and authority in the hands of a few.* For Michels the conclusion must have been especially depressing since he was a philosophical anarchist by conviction. The fact that he later moved to Italy and became a supporter of Mussolini perhaps illustrates the point that the political spectrum is not linear but circular, and that extreme Left and extreme Right meet around the back.

* See his book *Political parties*, published first in German (1911). English translations appeared in 1915 and 1962.

[605] MICHELSON-MORLEY EXPERIMENT

Early thinking about light as a wave motion required something to propagate it – in the same way that air carries sound, or water the ocean waves. This "something" – evidently exceedingly tenuous and unobservable, with near-magical properties – was dignified with the title of "the luminiferous aether" (also spelt "ether") by 19th-century physics, and the word persists in our vocabulary even today. It was realised that the Earth, moving through space relative to the "fixed" stars, should encounter an aether "headwind", and that the speed of light should therefore vary in different directions, depending on this "aether drift". Now, Michelson's strong suit was measuring the speed of light very accurately with a sensitive instrument called a **MICHELSON INTERFEROMETER**, so in 1887 he and **MORLEY** set out to measure the speed of light in two mutually perpendicular directions simultaneously, to see if they could detect any difference. To a high precision, they observed none. This is the most significant negative result in the whole of physics, and was subsequently confirmed by many other experimentalists. It knocked the "luminiferous ether" hypothesis firmly on the head, while paving the way for **EINSTEIN'S** special theory of relativity. **ALBERT ABRAHAM MICHELSON** (1852-1931) was born of Jewish parentage in Strelno, Poland (then in the Kingdom of Prussia). The family emigrated to the USA in 1855, and thereafter Michelson received a scientific education at the US Naval Academy, followed by a distinguished career as an academic physicist; in 1907 he became the first American to win the Nobel Prize. American **EDWARD WILLIAMS MORLEY** (1838-1923) was born in Newark, NJ, and became Professor of Chemistry at Western Reserve College (later Case Western Reserve University) after failing to become a Congregational minister. The Nobel Prize eluded him, but Michelson and Morley were jointly honoured in the specially commissioned musical composition by Philip Glass entitled *The Light*, first performed in 1997 by the Cleveland Symphony Orchestra under their conductor Christoph von Dohnányi. (MW)

[606] MILLER-UREY EXPERIMENT – see UREY-MILLER EXPERIMENT

[607] MILLS BOMB

Sunderland-born engineer, inventor and entrepreneur **WILLIAM MILLS** (1856-1932) trained as a marine engineer and served for seven years in that capacity in the merchant navy. In 1885, having swallowed the anchor, he established an aluminium foundry, the first in Britain, at Monkwearmouth. The outbreak of WWI saw Mills happily engaged in the design and manufacture of aluminium golf clubs. By 1915 he had designed, patented and was manufacturing an entirely new type of hand-grenade, the **MILLS BOMB**, at the Mills Munitions Factory he had set up in Birmingham. Mills' design with its cast body, segmented pineapple shape and spring-loaded, pin-locked cocking lever was immediately adopted by the

Army. The need for such a weapon, invaluable in trench warfare, had been inadequately met up to then by a poorly designed stick grenade, as dangerous to the user as to the usee, and by improvised grenades made from army-ration jam tins. Mills' hand-grenade swept the board and, with minor modifications, was standard equipment for Britain's armed forces through both world wars, remaining in service until 1972. In 1922, Mills' contribution to the war effort was rewarded with a knighthood. Mills pattern golf clubs are now eagerly sought by collectors (of golf clubs).

[608] MINIÉ BALL

In the development of military firearms, the muzzle-loading rifle, which made its appearance around the turn of the 19th century, represented an intermediate or transitional stage between the smooth-bore, muzzle-loading musket and the breech-loading rifle. It had an inbuilt problem: the bullet had to be a loose enough fit to enable it to be forced down the barrel with a ramrod, but tight enough to fill the grooves in the rifling and form a gas-proof seal. A solution was found in the form of a cylindrical bullet, pointed at the top, and with a conical depression at the bottom which would expand to mate with the rifling when the propellant exploded behind it. This invention, dating to the 1840's, is historically associated with the name of **CLAUDE ÉTIENNE MINIÉ** (1804-1879), a French infantry officer in the Chasseurs d'Orléans. Minié's bullet and the rifle he designed to fire it were rapidly adopted by the British, French and American armies and were first used by the French in North Africa (1846). As so often in the history of technological or scientific advances, Minié's claim to priority is open to challenge. In 1835 the British government successfully tested, but did not adopt, a bullet of almost identical design from the Birmingham gunsmith William Greener (1806-1859). Then in 1852 the government paid Minié £20,000 for the use of his design. Belatedly (1857), Greener was awarded a stingy £1000 for "the first public expression of the principle of expansion".

[609] MIRANDA WARNING

The American equivalent of the British police caution, administered to a suspect at the moment of arrest in order to advise him of his rights. It gets its name from a 1966 Supreme Court decision in the case of *Miranda v. Arizona* regarding a suspect's constitutional right to avoid self-incrimination. The person in question was a certain **ERNESTO MIRANDA** who, without having been properly advised of his right to silence, confessed to charges of rape and kidnapping. His name has weirdly given birth to a transitive verb "to mirandise" (as in "I mirandised the suspect"), which sounds to an outside ear as though it should refer to a more glamorous and exciting procedure than the mere uttering of a verbal formula.

[610] MITHRIDATIZE

To acquire partial immunity to a poison by taking increasing doses. It is essential to suspend this regimen periodically, to ensure survival. The "Arsenic Eaters of Styria" are a case in point: 19th-century Austrian peasants who are reputed to have consumed otherwise lethal amounts of arsenic as a pick-me-up. It was said to produce "a blooming complexion, a brilliant eye, and an appearance of embonpoint". The reference is to **MITHRIDATES VI EUPATOR** (*ca.* 131-63 BC) King of Pontus, sometimes called Mithridates the Great, who conquered most of Asia Minor and Greece and was a formidable opponent of the Roman Empire. Having many enemies, he hardened his constitution against poisoning by daily sub-lethal doses, which built a tolerance. When finally defeated by Pompey and about to be captured, Mithridates unwisely chose poison as his means of suicide. Unsurprisingly – since he was fully mithridatized – his attempt failed, so he bade a follower kill him by the sword. He also devised a universal antidote, described by Celsus under the name **ANTIDOTUM MITHRIDATICUM** also called theriac*. This was a complicated mixture of botanical ingredients used for centuries to cure poisoning, especially during the Renaissance. A.E. Housman alludes to Mithridates' antidote in *A Shropshire Lad*, and the legend features in Dumas' novel *The Count of Monte Cristo* (MW).

* The word *theriac* is derived from a Greek phrase meaning "a remedy against wild beasts" and is the source of our word *treacle*.

[611] MÖBIUS STRIP

In contrast to the **KLEIN BOTTLE,** the properties of a **MÖBIUS STRIP** may be readily investigated by joining together two ends of a strip of paper after first giving one end a 180° turn, and then running a pencil along it. Wherever the pencil starts it will return to the same place without ever having crossed an edge, thus proving the counter-intuitive proposition that the strip, which started out with two sides, now has only one (and likewise only one edge). The name is that of German mathematician **AUGUST FERDINAND MÖBIUS** (1790-1868), a founding father of topology, a branch of mathematics that also has a lot to say about doughnuts.

[612] MOHOROVIČIĆ DISCONTINUITY

His study of earthquake propagation led the Croatian geologist **ANDRIJA MOHOROVIČIĆ** (1857-1936) to the conclusion that the earth's crust consisted of at least two layers and that the relatively plastic outer crust rested on a more rigid substrate from which it was sharply divided. The division between the two is now known as the **MOHOROVIČIĆ DISCONTINUITY**. The discontinuity lies at depths between ten and forty miles below sea level but is nearest the surface in the deepest parts of the ocean. In the 60s, it was planned to explore the discontinuity by drilling down to it at a spot in the South Atlantic where it lay only two miles below the sea-bed. The project, which originated with the oddly-named American Miscellaneous Society, was christened **"MOHOLE"**. In 1961, test drillings were made in the Gulf of Mexico which proved the possibility of drilling from an untethered platform but the project was abandoned in 1966 thanks to cost overruns and management difficulties, and the baton has now passed to the Japanese.

[613] MOHR'S CLIP

A simple spring clip which constricts the rubber tubing outlet of a **MOHR BURETTE**, a re-design from the original burette of **GAY-LUSSAC**: a glass tube accurately calibrated by volume.* **MOHR'S CLIP** can be opened in a controlled fashion by gentle pressure of forefinger and thumb to permit the dropwise flow of liquid needed for a precise analytical titration. It came to be hated by generations of chemistry students, until it was replaced by a glass stopcock or tap. Prusssian chemist **KARL FRIEDRICH MOHR** (1806-1879) was born in Koblenz, studied at Heidelberg and joined his father's pharmacy. He made several useful contributions to quantitative volumetric analysis by titrimetry: besides his modified burette and clip he is known for **MOHR'S SALT** − iron(II) ammonium sulphate, a primary standard reagent. His seminal *Lehrbuch der chemisch-analytischen Titrirmethode* appeared in 1855 and ran to eleven editions. (MW)

Burette is the French word for a cruet, or oil can. The expression *"casser les burettes"* is a vigorous French condemnation of something tedious or annoying, which only becomes comprehensible to the non-Francophone when one appreciates that in slang usage *"burettes"* means "testicles".

[614] MOHS' SCALE

Measures the hardness of minerals by comparing them with a range of familiar substances. The scale starts at zero with talc and goes up 10 (diamond). It was devised in 1812 by the German mineralogist and mining geologist **FRIEDRICH MOHS** (1773-1839), who was interested in classifying minerals by their physical as opposed to their chemical properties. It is still used by field-workers.

[615] MONKEY WRENCH

The tool which the English, rather sedately, call an "adjustable spanner" the Americans, more colourfully, call a "monkey wrench" − though usually without knowing why. It is named after **CHARLES MONCKY**, a Baltimore mechanic, who may or may not have invented it but certainly held an 1854 patent on it, which he later sold for $2,000 in order to buy a house in Williamsburg, New York. The term "monkey-wrenching" for sabotage directed against environmentally-damaging commercial activities (*a.k.a.* "eco-terrorism"), derives from the book *The Monkey Wrench Gang* (1975) by the American anarchist and environmentalist Edward Abbey (1927-1989). Abbey also wrote *The Brave Cowboy* (1956), filmed as *Lonely are the brave* and starring Kirk Douglas – probably his best film. (*Cf.* STILLSON WRENCH)

[616] MONROE DOCTRINE

The declaration of principle known as the **MONROE DOCTRINE** may be seen as a founding instrument of American exceptionalism, in the same way as the Magna Carta is seen as a founding document of British democracy. It dates from 1823, during the second term as President of **JAMES MONROE** (1758-1831), when the American Republic was still not half a century old and at a crucial moment in the history of the American continent when the Spanish colonies of South America had begun in their turn to revolt against their colonial overlords. On paper, Monroe's declaration was ostensibly (and no doubt in intention) a statement of support for the rebellious Spanish colonies. It simply re-asserted what had first been propounded by John Q. Adams (1767-1848): that no interference from any European power would in future be tolerated in the affairs of America, north or south. But it contained a hidden rider: if Europe was forbidden to meddle, the USA, at least by implication, was not. And in our own day, we see what the imagined special right of America to meddle in other countries' affairs has led to.

[617] MONTAGU'S HARRIER

MONTAGU'S HARRIER (*Circus pygargus*), one of the smaller Old World raptors, breeds in the temperate regions of western Eurasia, and winters south of the Sahara. It preys mostly on small rodents, small birds, and large insects. Though its numbers have been reduced by modern farming methods, the IUCN Red List of threatened species classifies it as of "least concern". Its common name honours **GEORGE MONTAGU** (1753-1815) a Wiltshire country gentleman and sometime army officer (he served against the American rebels in 1775-77) who followed the not-uncommon route from a passion for field sports to a passion for natural history. The precision of his observations and his orderly descriptions have led to his being called the Father of British ornithology.* His *Ornithological Dictionary, or, Alphabetical Synopsis of British Birds* was published in 2 volumes in 1802. His interests, however, spread wider to take in pioneering studies of British molluscs and crustaceans, and his name is attached to a number of diverse species including several marine creatures such as **MONTAGU'S BLENNY** (*Coryphoblennius galerita*) and a snailfish, **MONTAGU'S SUCKER** (*Liparis montagui*). He fathered six children by his wife and four more by his mistress and assistant Elizabeth Dorville, and died of tetanus after stepping on a rusty nail.

* A title sometimes accorded to George Edwards (1694-1773) who achieved international fame largely by the beauty and accuracy of his ornithological illustrations. These were published as hand-coloured etchings with descriptive text in four volumes as *A natural history of uncommon birds* (1743-1751). He was awarded the Royal Society's **COPLEY MEDAL** in 1750.

[618] MONTESSORI METHOD

The Italian educator and physician **MARIA MONTESSORI** (1870-1952) gave her name to a method of educating children which stresses development of a child's own initiative and natural abilities, especially through practical play. Her system is based on belief in children's creative potential, their drive to learn, and their right to be treated as individuals. It relies on the use of "didactic apparatuses" to cultivate hand-eye coordination, self-directedness, and sensitivity to pre-mathematical and pre-literary instruction. Followers of the Montessori method believe that a child will learn naturally if put in an environment containing the proper materials. These materials, consisting of "learning games" suited to a child's abilities and interests, are set up by a teacher-observer who intervenes only when individual help is needed. In this way, Montessori educators try to reverse the traditional system of an active teacher instructing a passive class. The typical classroom in a Montessori school consists of readily available games and toys, household utensils, plants and animals that are cared for by the children, and child-sized furniture, (the last an innovation generally attributed to Montessori). In order to advance motor abilities in young children there is also a great emphasis on physical education, kinetic movement and spatial refinement. Dr. Montessori's method was basically at odds with behaviourism, Freudianism, and other major 20th-century trends. Thus it was used originally by only relatively few private schools. Since the 1950's, though, there has been growing interest in the method. Maria Montessori was herself a remarkable woman. In 1894 she became the first woman physician in Italy. The obstacles she encountered in the course of her medical education reinforced her already well-developed feminist ideas. In 1904 she became a full professor at the University of Rome and from 1904 to 1908 held the chair of anthropology there. She was also a government inspector of schools, a lecturer, and a practicing physician. She started a school for deprived children in a housing project in Rome which opened in 1907 and which she called "Casa dei Bambini" or Children's House. The success of this school led to the opening of many others and to worldwide interest in Montessori's educational methods. The Montessori philosophy is built upon the idea that children develop and think differently than adults – that they are not merely "adults in small bodies" but, if properly guided and in a suitable environment, can by their own initiative develop into adults. She was an advocate of children's rights and believed that her work was a contribution towards eventual world peace. (For another form of "alternative" education, see **STEINER SCHOOLS.**) (RS)

[619] MONTEZUMA'S REVENGE

An affliction of modern travellers, caused by drinking unsterilised water or eating spicy food that visitors aren't accustomed to. It takes the form of diarrhoea and/or dysentery, with perhaps some associated vomiting. The usual cause is the enterotoxic **E. COLI** bacterium. This Mexican version refers to **MONTEZUMA II** (1466-1520), Aztec ruler at the time of the Spanish Conquest, who attempted to appease the invaders and was captured by them, deposed and eventually slain during an uprising which temporarily drove Cortes out of the capital city, Tenochtitlán. He had held power for 18 years and is often referred to as the last Aztec emperor, though in fact he had a short-lived successor, Cuatémoc, who was briskly despatched by Cortes as soon as the uprising was put down. Other Mexican-derived terms for Montezuma's Revenge include: Mexican fox-trot, Gringo Gallop and the Aztec Hop. The revenge element might allude to the way in which countries that were previously colonized by stronger countries are now, in this small way, getting their own back on their colonisers' descendents. However it must be said that the revenge is not restricted to ex-colonies. In the USA, for example, travellers, not all of them British, have been stricken with the Bronxville Bomb in New York and the LA Belly in California. Other synonyms abound and have an international flavour: Delhi Belly, Saigon Quickstep, Tokyo Trots, Gyppy Tummy, etc. (See also **KWOK'S QUEASE.**) (RS)

[620] MONTGOLFIÈRE

In 1783, two of the brothers **MONTGOLFIER, JOSEPH MICHEL** (1740-1810) and **JACQUES ETIENNE** (1745-1799), were running the family paper mill at Annonay near Lyons, France.* They conceived the notion of a gigantic hollow sphere made of textile and lined with paper, like an inverted flask, with a flaming brazier at the bottom of an open neck. Thanks to **ARCHIMEDES' PRINCIPLE,** the hot air so generated within, being less dense than the surrounding air (see **CHARLES'S LAW**), provides lift. The Montgolfier brothers did not understand this, but attributed the phenomenon to the generation of "Montgolfier Gas" which had the property of "levity". And so lighter-than-air flight or "*aerostation*" was born by means of the hot-air balloon. On 19th September 1783, before Louis XVI and Marie Antoinette, a 1000 m³ **MONTGOLFIÈRE**, as the balloons were called, ascended to 500 m from Versailles and made a 4 km, 8 minute flight, bearing the world's first aeronauts – a sheep, a rooster and a duck, which were all returned to earth unharmed. Next the Montgolfiers built a man-carrier, 1600 m³ in volume. On 21st November 1783, it ascended from the Bois de Boulogne, carrying the adventurous young teacher

JEAN-FRANÇOIS PILÂTRE DE ROZIER, accompanied by the Marquis d'Arlandes, for a 25 minute excursion over Paris. Buoyancy was maintained by burning bales of straw: "*Eh bien, cher ami, du feu!*", but frequent dowsing of the flaming paper envelope was necessary. Further developments in France were inhibited by the outbreak of the French Revolution, but ballooning became all the rage in England. Joseph was eventually created *Chevalier* by Napoleon. (MW)

* Fine-art and other special high-quality papers are today still being manufactured at Annonay by Montgolfier's successors, the firm of Canson.

[621] MOOG SYNTHESISER

The Moog Synthesiser was the first widely used electronic musical instrument. Inventor and entrepreneur ROBERT ARTHUR MOOG* (1934-2005) working at the Columbia-Princeton Electronic Music Center, created the first subtractive synthesiser to utilize a keyboard as a controller and demonstrated it in 1964. In 1966 he patented his unique low-pass filter and through his company he began to manufacture and market synthesisers. His early customers were influential, experimental figures such as choreographer Alwin Nikolais, who employed it in his T.V. ballet "The Relay," and composer John Cage. In 1971 Moog Music began production of the Minimoog Model D which was the first easily available, portable, and relatively affordable instrument. Moog's inventions changed the complexion of the pop and classical music worlds particularly after the release in 1968 of the best selling album "Switched-On Bach" by Wendy Carlos. In the rock music domain the instrument reached a high point in the hands of "progressive" bands such as Yes and Emerson, Lake & Palmer, which it has not subsequently regained. As a teenager in New York City where he grew up, Moog learned basic electronics from his radio-operator father and became fascinated with the THEREMIN, custom building and selling the weird-sounding electronic instrument as a hobby. At Queen's College, New York he earned a degree in Physics and another in electrical engineering from Columbia before gaining a Ph.D in engineering physics from Cornell University. During his working life he founded two companies, became a consultant and vice-president for a product research company, and in the early 1990's held the chair of music research at the University of North Carolina. (RS)

* Pronounced to rhyme with "vogue"

[622] MOORE'S LAW

The observation that the storage capacity of computer chips per unit of area doubles every 18 months to two years is attributed to GORDON E. MOORE (b. 1929) pioneer of integrated circuit technology and co-founder of Intel with Robert Noyce. It derives from an article that Moore wrote for *Electronics Magazine* in 1965, though Moore has since stated that he didn't intend a "law", carved in stone, or on silicon chips for that matter. Whatever the case, the rate of growth in capacity and its concomitant, reduction in size, has certainly been astonishing. To the point where the question now is where the limit of miniaturisation lies. At the molecular level, perhaps. Or even...?

[623] MORAN'S COLLAR

In the *Lebor Gabála Érenn* or "Book of the taking of Ireland", an 11th-century collection of myths and legends in poetry and prose concerning early Irish history, Feradach is one of the High Kings of Ireland, who married a daughter of Queen Boadicea. He was deposed following a rebellion led by a chief named Cairbre, who then assumed the crown. Feradach fled to England where he sought the help of the Roman governor Agricola. Cairbre, meanwhile, died of the plague and his son **MORAN**, who might then have declared himself king, instead used his influence to bring about Feradach's restoration to the throne. Feradach, in gratitude, appointed Moran his chief judge and law-giver. Moran, we are told, wore a collar which, if the wearer gave – or was about to give – a false judgement, would tighten of its own accord and strangle him. Moran, being a just judge, never suffered this fate. The story of Moran's collar prompts the thought that modern magistrates might perhaps be fitted with something along the lines of a dog-training collar which would administer a hefty belt of electricity every time they were tempted to turn loose some habitual criminal to continue making a public nuisance of himself.

[624] MORGANITE – see SCHEELITE

[625] MORGAN'S LOOKOUT – see DRYDEN'S ROCK

[626] MORIARTY'S POLICE LAW

Between 1929 when it was first published and 1974, the Peeler's *vade mecum* ran through 22 editions. Its author, **CECIL CHARLES HUDSON MORIARTY** was a graduate of Trinity College Dublin, joined the Royal Irish Constabulary in 1902, and rose through the ranks to become Chief Constable of Birmingham in 1935.* He died in 1958. More recently *Moriarty* has morphed into *Butterworth's Police Law* (named after the publisher) and then into simple *Police Law* and authored by Messrs. Jack English and Richard Card. This is currently in its 11th edition. Meanwhile there is another coppers' compendium on offer in the form of the four volumes of **BLACKSTONE'S POLICE MANUALS** (*General Police Duties, Evidence and Procedure, Crime, Road traffic.*)** Keeping these and similar publications up to date must be a considerable, not to say a Sisyphaean, task: since the "Labour" government came to power in 1997 it has so far (2009) managed to add some 3000 indictable offences to the statute book.

* It seems that just prior to Moriarty's appointment, the capacities of his predecessor were causing enough concern for questions to be asked in the House. *Hansard* recorded the following exchange which took place on 21 Feb. 1935:

> **Mr. Maxton**: asked the Home Secretary the name and age of the chief constable of Birmingham: and at what age and date he is due to retire?
>
> **Sir J Gilmour**: Sir Charles Rafter is the chief constable of Birmingham. He was appointed in 1899, and therefore, as provided in Section 29 (1) (b) (ii) of the Police Pensions Act, 1921, the provisions of that Act as to age of compulsory retirement do not apply to him. I am not in a position to state his age.
>
> **Mr Maxton**: Does that mean he can go on for ever?

** Disappointingly. there seems to be no connection (other than the name) between the legal publishing firm of Blackstone and the famous jurist Sir William Blackstone (1723-1780), author of the magisterial *Commentaries on the Laws of England.*

[627] MORNAY SAUCE – see BÉCHAMEL SAUCE

[628] MORPHINE

The chief alkaloid of opium. From it are derived in turn codeine and diamorphine (heroin). Morphine remains the most powerful agent we possess for the relief of extreme pain. But though no drug has yet been discovered to equal its analgesic qualities, it has, of course, the unfortunate side effect of producing addiction. Its name derives from **MORPHEUS**, a minor deity apparently invented by the Roman poet Ovid in his *Metamorphoses.* Morpheus is presented as one of the three sons of Somnus, god of sleep (Hypnos in Greek) and has the power to call up human shapes (μορφαί) in the dreamer's mind. (See also **Dr. COLLIS BROWNE'S CHLORODYNE.**)

[629] MORRIS MINOR

An icon of British style and engineering, in its time it served as the people's car for the British volk. **WILLIAM RICHARD MORRIS** (1877-1963) gave us a serviceable vehicle at a price within reach of the toiling masses and in the process became the richest man in England, morphing into the 1st Viscount Nuffield. Morris started out making bicycles, moved on to motor cycles, and in 1910 launched the Morris Motor Co., manufacturing cars at a disused military training college in Cowley, just outside Oxford. (The site later expanded to the point where it became the waggish fashion to refer to the University as the Latin Quarter of Cowley.) Among the company's early productions was the famous Bull-Nosed Morris which later became the Morris Oxford. Morris adopted Ford's techniques of mass production and applied them so successfully that his business overtook Ford's in the UK. In 1927, he acquired the bankrupt Wolseley Motor Co. and with it the prototype of an 8-hp car which was launched in 1928 as the first **MORRIS MINOR**. Post-war, the re-styled Morris Minor, whose appearance owed something to the VW Beetle, was immensely popular as both a personal and, in its van version, light commercial vehicle until displaced by the hugely successful Mini in the late fifties. Like most self-made men, Morris had no time for socialism. A Thatcherite *avant la lettre*, he delayed the introduction of trade unions in Cowley until 1956. But like many very rich self-made men he was a big-gun philanthropist. In 1943 he set up the Nuffield Foundation for the advancement of medicine and education, and donated land in Oxford which became the site of Nuffield College. (Morris had hoped for a college of engineering but to his chagrin the University authorities opted for the social sciences.) In 1947 he was instrumental in establishing a network of provident societies that we now recognise as BUPA (British United Provident Association). He died childless and the whole of his fortune went to the carrying-on of good works. (RS)

[630] MORRISON SHELTER – see ANDERSON SHELTER

[631] MORSE CODE
In the **MORSE ALPHABET** as it was originally known, each letter, numeral, and punctuation mark can be assigned a unique sequence of appropriately spaced short and long symbols – "dots" and "dashes". It is not strictly a binary code, but can be described as digital. Its value, as every boy-scout knows, is for sending messages via simple means, sometimes resulting in a string of audible tones that can be "read" by an adept. The pulses of the **MORSE CODE** can be formed by interrupting the flow of an electric current, as in the electric telegraph, or a beam of light, as with an **ALDIS LAMP** or heliograph, or even by waving a flag. It requires only the simplest type of radio transmission, called CW (for Carrier Wave, *i.e.* a signal unmodulated by speech), and was once vital for announcing emergencies at sea. Until recently, proficiency in morse was a condition of the "ham" (amateur) radio operators' licence, whether they liked it or not. Undoubtedly the most iconic letter in the Morse alphabet is Churchill's "V for Victory" – dit-dit-dit-*dah* – adopted by the Allies in WWII, probably in full awareness that it is also the opening phrase of Beethoven's Fifth Symphony. The code is the brainchild of American artist and inventor **SAMUEL FINLEY BREESE MORSE** (1791-1872) who was born at Charlestown, Massachusetts, graduated from Yale, and studied painting at the Royal Academy, London. He was appointed Professor of Painting and Design at New York University in 1832, in which year he conceived the idea of the electric telegraph, but had to wait until 1843 for Congress to fund the construction, by Ezra Cornell, of a telegraph line from Baltimore to Washington. It had the advantage over **WHEATSTONE'S** more complicated needle telegraph of requiring only a single conductor wire. On 24 May 1844 Morse sent the immortal message in his code which initiated the entire telecommunications industry:

"What hath God wrought?" – a question that remains unanswered. Thoreau, for one, was unimpressed by the possibilities of instant communication. "Our inventions... are but improved means to unimproved ends," he commented grumpily (*Walden*). Thanks to his invention, Morse died a rich man, but at the cost of prolonged litigation and the ending of his friendship with the physicist JOSEPH HENRY (1797-1878), first Director of the SMITHSONIAN INSTITUTION, who had helped reduce Morse's ideas to a workable system. (MW)

[632] MOSELEY'S LAW

This provided the final step in rationalising MENDELEEV'S PERIODIC TABLE of the chemical elements and in confirming the theory of the nuclear atom: the identification and measurement of the concept of atomic number as its true basis, rather than atomic weight. Oxford physics graduate HENRY GWYN JEFFREYS ("HARRY") MOSELEY (1887-1915) worked under RUTHERFORD at Manchester from 1910 to 1914. He found that the wavelengths of characteristic X-rays emitted by the elements under electron bombardment, bore a simple mathematical relationship to the atomic number: "*We have here a proof that there is in the atom a fundamental quantity, which increases by regular steps as we pass from one element to the next. This quantity can only be the charge on the central positive nucleus ...*" For the first time it became possible to state with certainty just how many chemical elements there were, and to close the remaining "gaps" in the Periodic Table. Moseley predicted the existence of the elements hafnium, atomic number 72, and rhenium, atomic number 75 – a prediction eventually confirmed long after his death in action at Gallipoli at the age of 27, one of Oxford's "lost generation". He was never nominated for a richly-deserved NOBEL PRIZE because this can be conferred only on the living. (MW)

[633] MÖSSBAUER EFFECT

Certain radioactive nuclei emit gamma rays, with very sharply defined energies. These can be re-absorbed by other nuclei of the same element. This phenomenon, reasonably called "recoilless emission and resonant re-absorption of gamma rays", was discovered by MÖSSBAUER in 1957. But if the absorbing nucleus finds itself in a chemical environment different from that of the emitter (*i.e.* in a different substance), the resonance is "de-tuned" by a minute change in its energy called the Chemical Shift. This measures the density of the electron cloud in which the nucleus sits, at the centre of the atom. The DOPPLER EFFECT can be used to impart a tiny energy difference to the gamma rays emitted, in order to bring the system back into resonance. This was originally achieved experimentally by mounting the source on a toy train. If that sounds altogether too recherché for this humble volume, then one example of the usefulness of Mössbauer's discovery might convince. Take a deep breath: **MÖSSBAUER SPECTROSCOPY** tells us how the iron atoms at the centre of the haemoglobin molecules in your red blood cells manage to bind the oxygen molecules in your lungs that keep you alive. **RUDOLPH LUDWIG MÖSSBAUER** (b. 1929) was born in Munich, and became professor of physics at the Technische Hochschule and, since 1961, visiting professor at the Californian Institute of Technology. He shared the 1961 **NOBEL PRIZE** for physics with Robert Hofstadter. (MW)

[634] MUDD

It used to be thought that phrases such as "his name is mud", "your name will be mud", etc. referred to the unfortunate **DOCTOR SAMUEL MUDD** (1833-1883) who treated John Wilkes Booth's injured leg when Booth went on the lam after assassinating President Lincoln in Ford's Theatre, Washington. Mudd was arrested and tried along with Booth's accomplices and sentenced to life imprisonment following a highly irregular trial by a kangaroo court. Unfortunately for the theory, instances of the phrase "his name is mud" have been found which predate Mudd. Another good story slain by an awkward fact. Meanwhile, Mudd's descendants are still engaged in attempts to clear their forebear's name (the defence hinges on Mudd's claim not to have known who Booth was or what he had done). If the campaign is successful, we can expect to hear expressions on the lines of "his name is as clear as mud" being bandied about. In fact, Mudd was partly rehabilitated in his own lifetime thanks to his sterling conduct in helping to deal with a yellow fever epidemic on the prison island in the Dry Tortugas to which he had been confined.

[635] MUELLER RANGES – see MACADAMIA NUT

[636] MUGGLETONIANS

The cruel religious wars and persecutions of the sixteenth and early seventeenth centuries centred essentially on the issue of Authority and were fuelled by the dissenters' insistence on the presumed right of the individual Christian to follow his own conscience in matters of belief however wildly it diverged from the dictates of the established Church. The result, inevitably, was an extreme tendency towards fissiparousness on the part of what might be called the Christian Left (paralleled by the same tendency in more recent times of the political Left) and a heady proliferation of mostly small and often mutually hostile sects, each with its own self-declared prophet claiming special personal Enlightenment. Typical of such groups were the **MUGGLETONIANS**. The sect came into being following revelations vouchsafed to a journeyman tailor named John Reeve (1608-1658) in 1652. He heard the voice of God telling him that he had been chosen to head the third and last heavenly dispensation (the first being that led by Moses, and the second by Jesus). The voice also mentioned that witnessing* to the new dispensation was to be the joint task of Reeve and his cousin and fellow tailor **LODOWICKE MUGGLETON** (1609-1698). The beliefs of the Muggletonians, as set out in a work entitled *The Divine Looking-glass* (1656) included, among other radical notions, a denial of the Trinity and the belief that God himself came down to earth in the person of Jesus, leaving Elijah to manage affairs in Heaven during his absence. Reeve and Muggleton, with Muggleton playing, as it were, Brigham Young to Reeve's Joseph Smith (see **BOOK OF MORMON**), were successful in attracting a small but dedicated band of adherents, even though as a group they consciously refrained from evangelism. It is the more surprising therefore that the sect survived well into the 20th century. The last Muggletonian, as far as is known, was a Kentish apple-grower named Noakes who in 1974 was found to have in his attic the entire archive of the Witnesses, saved during the War from the bomb-damaged Muggletonian reading room in Bishopsgate, London, and now lodged with the British Library.

* The Muggletonians called themselves "witnesses" on the authority of *Revelation* 11.3.

[637] MULESING

Name given to a procedure which involves cutting away a strip of wool-bearing skin from the tail and hind-quarters of lambs. The practice is widespread in Australia, where it has been legal since 1930 though it continues to generate controversy between animal welfare groups, who claim the procedure is barbaric and unnecessary, and the wool industry. The purpose of mulesing is to prevent myiasis (fly-strike), which potentially affects all breeds of sheep including Australian merinos. The causative agent is the larvae of the fly *Lucilia cuprina* which grow from eggs laid in the matted and faeces-stained wool around the anus and root of the tail, and feed by burrowing into the flesh of the host animal, literally eating it alive. Mulesing takes its name from **J.W.H. MULES,** a sheep farmer who is said to have discovered it by accident when his blade slipped while he was shearing a ewe, and who noticed that subsequently the animal he had injured appeared immune to fly-strike. Currently, mulesing is regulated by a code of practice which limits the age at which it may be carried out (max. 12 months) and which stipulates the use of antiseptics, though it does not require that anaesthetics or painkillers be used either during or after the operation. The objection to mulesing is partly fuelled by the fact that at bottom (no pun intended) its primary concern is not the welfare of the sheep but the farmers' profit margin, since not only does fly-strike adversely affect the sheep's market value, but the alternative, "crutching" (shearing the wool around the hindquarters), which has to be carried out at regular intervals, seriously increases the producer's labour costs. In 2004, representatives of the Australian wool producers agreed to phase out mulesing by 2010. In order to meet this deadline the wool industry is currently funding various research initiatives aimed at developing non-surgical alternatives. Mulesing is illegal in Britain. (BS)

[638] MÜNCHAUSEN'S SYNDROME

A serious and chronic factitious disorder whose sufferers routinely exaggerate, feign or self-inflict illness, mental or physical, in order to secure attention, treatment or sympathy. MÜNCHAUSEN'S SYNDROME (also referred to as hospital addiction syndrome) is distinguished from hypochondria by the fact that hypochondriacs genuinely believe themselves ill, whereas Münchausen's sufferers act duplicitously insofar as they are aware, in some sense at least, that their purported afflictions are not real. The disorder is considered extreme owing to the extraordinary lengths to which many sufferers are prepared to go in order to maintain the fiction, which may involve their undergoing tests and treatments even including surgery. The syndrome takes its name from **Baron VON MÜNCHAUSEN**, who in Rudolf Raspe's *The Surprising Adventures of Baron Münchausen* (1849) displays a penchant for recounting his wildly fictional adventures. The term was coined in a 1951 *Lancet* article by Sir Richard Asher of the Central Middlesex Hospital, who, after reflecting on the fabrications of certain of his patients, was put in mind of the tales told by Münchausen. The so-called MÜNCHAUSEN'S SYNDROME BY PROXY, manifests itself slightly differently. In these cases the sufferers exaggerate, feign or actually induce illness in another person in order to secure attention, sympathy and so on for themselves. Often the sufferer is a care-giver – parent, guardian or spouse. (BS)

[639] MUNROS

SIR HUGH THOMAS MUNRO (1856-1919) of Lindertis, Angus was a keen mountain-climber and hill-walker and a founder member of the Scottish Mountaineering Society. In 1891 he published in the Society's journal a list of peaks in Scotland over 3000 feet (914 metres) in height. These eminences are known today simply as THE MUNROS. The list currently comprises 284 names though the number of accredited Munros has fluctuated from time to time, either because changes in surveying methods have led to a re-calculation of their heights, or because of the uncertainty in many cases as to whether a given peak is a secondary summit of a main peak or an independent entity. Besides which, estimating the height of mountains is, even today, not as exact a science as the confidently precise numbers marked on maps might lead us to believe.* "Munro bagging" has become a popular pastime, the aim being to climb all 284. Monro himself was just two short of the total when he died of pneumonia in France, where he had been running a canteen for French soldiers during the War. The first known person to climb all the Munros was the Rev. Archibald Eneas Robertson (1870-1958) who completed the task in 1901 having started in 1889, even before Munro published his first list. It is unfortunate that 3000 feet – a nice round figure – doesn't translate into a nice round number of metres but into the untidy number 914. One may be reasonably sure that if Munro had been working in metres from the start he would have gone for 1000, in which case the list would stop at 137. Another factor which would threaten the eligibility of some Munros would be a substantial rise in sea-level.

* *Cf.* PIKE'S PEAK and see, for example, "The heights of mountains" in John Kirtland Wright *Human nature in Geography* 1966.

[640] MUPHRY'S LAW – see MURPHY'S LAW

[641] MURPHY'S LAW

MURPHY'S LAW (also known as SOD'S LAW) tells us, "*Anything that can go wrong, will go wrong.*" The man credited with this sombre adage and the butter-side-down world-view it embodies is (somewhat doubtfully) identified as an American engineer named EDWARD A. MURPHY (1918-1990), for whom no device ever worked properly. But it is equally possible that there never was a single "Murphy" to whom the saying can safely be ascribed, any more than it could be ascribed to an actual person named Sod. MURPHY'S LAW, however, is the likely progenitor of a now quite large family of similarly disenchanted formulations of which two may be mentioned, both ascribed to science-fiction writers (many of whom tend, perhaps surprisingly, to embrace, like their precursor Jonathan Swift, a frankly pessimistic view of humanity and its future). ROBERT HEINLEIN (1907-1988) is credited with HEINLEIN'S RAZOR, which takes the form: "*Never ascribe to malice what can be explained by stupidity.*" And THEODORE STURGEON* (1918-1985) gave us STURGEON'S LAW, which states, flatly: "*Ninety per cent of everything is garbage.*" The luminous simplicity of this penetrating insight conceals a diffculty which might engage a mathematician or logician, since logically ninety per cent of the ten per cent that is not garbage must be garbage, and ninety per cent of that ten per cent … and so on, in a ZENO-style inifinite regression. However, if we ignore this paradox, Sturgeon's Law seems in practice to work pretty well as a measure of most everyday experiences and a prophylactic against the disappointment that is the inevitable outcome of undue optimism.** Meanwhile, as a prophylactic against literary hubris, we have the more specialised MUPHRY'S LAW, which states that *anyone writing to an editor or publisher to complain about mistakes of fact, spelling or grammar will inadvertently but inevitably include at least one such mistake in his or her letter.*

* Sturgeon's name is sometimes assumed to be a *nom de plume.* It is, however, his real name, though not the one he was born with. For his pseudonymous persona we must look to Kurt Vonnegut's fictional character Kilgore Trout. Sturgeon promulgated a SECOND LAW which states, "*Nothing really important is ever either complicated or easy.*"

** Archbishop Tutu was asked in a BBC radio interview, "Are you optimistic?" He replied, memorably, "No. But I am always hopeful, hopeful."

N

[642] NAPIER'S BONES

The Scottish mathematician **JOHN NAPIER, LAIRD OF MERCHISTON** (1550-1617) is famous as the inventor (or discoverer?) of logarithms, an account of which he published in 1614 under the title *Mirifici logarithmorum canonis descriptio*. Mathematics was not Napier's only interest. As a landowner, he experimented with the use of manures and designed a form of **ARCHIMEDEAN SCREW** for removing water from mines. In 1615 he published another mathematical invention that he called "rhabdology" (Gk. ῥάβδος = rod). This employed a device that could be seen as a hybrid between an abacus and a set of multiplication tables. It consisted of a frame holding a series of interchangeable rods (the "bones") marked with numbers. Once the rods were set up for a particular operation, the result could be simply read off the relevant numbered boxes on the rods. The machine could handle numbers of up to ten digits. It principal use was for multiplication and division and, though Napier's Bones are not logarithms, they have this in common with logarithms that the operations of multiplication and division are reduced to a process of addition and subtraction.

[643] NARCISSISM

In common parlance, as opposed to Freudian psychospeak, **NARCISSISM** denotes an excessive fascination with one's own appearance and body image – a form of vanity which carries within it the seeds of a morbid obsession. The **NARCISSUS** of Greek mythology was a handsome young Thespian who, impervious to the advances of would-be lovers of both sexes, ended by falling in love with his own reflection as seen in a forest pool and, unable for obvious reasons to consummate the union, stabbed himself and died. From his blood a white flower grew, named after him by the ancient Greeks who represented this plant as a kind of lily. *Narcissus pseudonarcissus*, on the other hand, our wild daffodil and its horticultural variants, derives its English name from the plant known to the Greeks as *asphodel*, a flower which grows in the meadows of the underworld and is sacred to Persephone. Though modern plant names preserve in Latinised form a number of classical Greek plant names, the decisions of mediaeval herbalists as to which plants the old names referred to were largely guesswork.

[644] NATTERER'S BAT

The genus *Myotis* comprises 71 species of which the native British* **NATTERER'S BAT** (*Myotis nattereri*) is one. It bears the name of Austrian naturalist and explorer **JOHANN NATTERER** (1787-1843) who spent 18 in years in S. America and made important collections. The name, like that of **DAUBENTON'S BAT,** was allotted by German zoologist Heinrich Kuhl in 1817. Kuhl was assistant to **TEMMINCK** at Leiden. Also named after Natterer is **NATTERER'S SLATY ANTSHRIKE** (*Thamnophilus stictocephalus*) a bird of Brazil and Bolivia.

* Hurrah! But not *exclusively* British. Its range extends through Europe and into Asia as far as Japan.

[645] NEBUCHADNEZZAR – see JEROBOAM

[646] NECKER CUBE
A line-drawing consisting of two identical squares, displaced diagonally, with corresponding corners joined:-

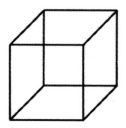

The brain seeks to interpret this image in 3-dimensions as an open cube, consisting only of its twelve edges, seen from an oblique viewpoint. The perspective is deliberately imperfect, however, with parallel edges lacking a vanishing point and with no depth clues, the brain cannot tell which face is near and which far. Confronted with this ambiguity, the mind's interpretation flips between the two viewpoints – from above and below, the former more commonly. This reversing optical illusion was published in 1832 by a Swiss geologist and crystallographer, as a consequence of his gazing at representations of cubic crystals. Although such perceptual ambiguity was not new – it can be seen in Roman floor mosaics and Renaissance tilings, and **BREWSTER** had published on "the conversion of cameos into intaglios" in 1826 – Necker's novel presentation of the reversing optical illusion attracted the attention of **WHEATSTONE** (1838) and many investigators since: **NECKER'S CUBE** is still used in cognitive psychological research. **LOUIS ALBERT NECKER DE SAUSSURE** (1786-1861) was born into an academically distinguished family in Geneva. His maternal grandfather was Horace Bénédict de Saussure (1740-1799) – see **SAUSSUREA.** His mother, Albertine Necker de Saussure was a niece by marriage of the financier Jacques Necker and so cousin (by marriage) of Necker's daughter Mme. de Staël. After studying geology in Geneva Louis Albert went to Edinburgh in 1806 to study chemistry and became a lover of Scotland and things Scottish, making the acquaintance of many intellectuals of the

Scottish Enlightenment. He toured extensively and produced the first geological map of Scotland. Returning to Geneva in 1810, he occupied a chair of natural philosophy there for three decades, but finally relocated to the Isle of Skye in 1841 for the remainder of his reclusive life. He is buried in Portree churchyard. (MW)

[647] NEPTUNIUM – see THORIUM

[648] NEWCOMEN'S ENGINE
The "atmospheric engine" (originally entitled "fire engine") built in 1705 by Devon-born engineer THOMAS NEWCOMEN (1663-1729) was the first practical application of steam as a medium for converting heat to work via a piston and cylinder. By about 1711 it was at work pumping water from mines and the Age of Steam was up and running. In the evolving history of heat engines (see CARNOT), Newcomen's engine is generally considered to be an improved version of the device pioneered by the French engineer and inventor DENIS PAPIN.

[649] NEWLANDS' LAW
One of the forerunners (see also DÖBEREINER'S TRIADS) of that great underlying structure to all inorganic chemistry, MENDELEEV'S PERIODIC TABLE OF THE ELEMENTS of 1869, NEWLANDS' LAW OF OCTAVES of 1865 observes that when the chemical elements are listed in ascending order of atomic weight, then similar properties recur with some regularity. Pre-dating Mendeleev, Newlands deserves credit for being the first to posit a Periodic Law: "The numbers of analogous elements generally differ either by 7 or by some multiple of seven," (the inert gases were then unknown, so this is closely related to ABEGG'S RULE OF EIGHT) "in other words, members of the same group stand to each other in the same relation as the extremities of one or more octaves in music." This musical analogy was unfortunate: when Newlands' letters to the editor of the *Chemical News* were published in 1864-66, his ideas were derided and refused publication in the Chemical Society's *Journal*. His attempt to draw up a table of the elements was too unsystematic compared with Mendeleev's version; but Newlands continued for a further 20 years to struggle unsuccessfully for recognition. JOHN ALEXANDER REINA NEWLANDS (1837-1898) was born in London, studied at the Royal College of Chemistry, became an analytical chemist, and worked in the sugar industry. Owing to Italian ancestry on his mother's side, he served as a volunteer with GARIBALDI in the *Risorgimento*. (MW)

[650] NEWTON
The NEWTON is the SI unit of force, symbol N, and has units of kilogram meter per second squared (kg m/s^2). This definition embodies NEWTON'S SECOND LAW of motion: force equals mass times acceleration. The other two NEWTON'S LAWS are intuitively more obvious: the first is that a body remains at rest, or in a state of

constant linear motion, unless acted on by a force; and the third states that action and reaction are equal and opposite. The name here commemorated, of course, is that of SIR ISAAC NEWTON (1642-1727), generally acknowledged as the greatest English mathematician and natural philosopher. Born at Woolsthorpe, Lincolnshire, he was admitted to Trinity College, Cambridge in 1661, where he was elected Fellow in 1667, and appointed Lucasian Professor of Mathematics in 1669, until 1701. During 1665-7 he retreated to his country seat to avoid an outbreak of the Great Plague, and there formulated a generalised binomial theorem, and developed his "method of fluxions", an early form of infinitesimal calculus, which brought him into a protracted priority dispute with German mathematician and philosopher, Gottfried Wilhelm Leibniz. This was regrettable because, although Newton had priority, both men were independently correct, and neither a plagiarist. In his most celebrated publication *Philosophiae Naturalis Principia Mathematica* (1687), Newton formulated the mathematical basis for what is today called NEWTONIAN or "CLASSICAL" MECHANICS, and his theory still holds good for most purposes, unless you happen to be travelling close to the speed of light (see EINSTEIN), or dealing with the sub-atomically small (see PLANCK). Included in this great work was his theory of universal gravitation (1684) which, when applied to planetary motion, explained KEPLER'S LAWS. Newton's other major publication, *Opticks* (1704) describes, *inter alia*, how the optical spectrum is obtained by refraction of sunlight through a prism. That different colours therefore have different refrangibility, accounts for the chromatic aberration at the focus of refracting telescopes (see GALILEAN TELESCOPE), so in 1669 he constructed the first reflecting, or NEWTONIAN TELESCOPE, which was used to such good effect by the astronomers Sir William and Caroline HERSCHEL, the Earl of Rosse, and most astronomers thereafter. Although Newton favoured a corpuscular theory of the nature of light, his observation of NEWTON'S RINGS – an interference effect between light waves reflected by two closely-spaced surfaces – demanded some acknowledgement of its wave nature also. Newton was elected FRS in 1672, but his first publication in the *Philosophical Transactions* was criticised by the Society's Curator of Experiments, and Newton's arch-enemy, Robert HOOKE, which led to furious polemics. In 1675, Newton was granted a special dispensation not to take Holy Orders (an obligation of every academic MA of the time); his dissent on the theological nature of the Trinity suggests he was a closet Unitarian. Later he settled in London, as Warden (1696) then Master (1699) of the Royal Mint; in which post he was vigorous in campaigning against corruption. He was elected MP for Cambridge University in 1689 and in 1701. He accepted the Presidency of the Royal Society in 1703, and was constantly re-elected to the post until his death. He received his Knighthood in 1705. Newton was unable to absorb the – far from obvious – truths of chemistry within his mechanistic framework: he penned a million words on alchemy, leaving manuscripts for scholars to grapple with for years yet to come. (MW)

[651] NICKEL

This familiar metallic element, atomic number 28 symbol Ni, is close to iron and copper in the first transition series of the Periodic Table, and is useful in many alloys, including stainless steel, in coinage, and for protective electroplating. It owes its name to the incompetence of the miners of Upper Saxony in the 17th century, who mistook its ore for that of copper,* which they were seeking. To justify the failure of their attempts to extract copper from this ore, they christened it "Devil's Copper" which, since the Devil is also known as "Old Nick",** emerged in German as *Kupfernickel*. When a shiny new metal was successfully extracted from this ore in 1751 by the Swedish chemist, Baron Axel Fredrik Cronstedt (1722-1765), it was naturally called **NICKEL**. Several metals enjoy their associations with deities (see **VANADIUM, CERIUM, THORIUM** and **TITANIUM**), but only **NICKEL** has a satanic distinction. Its neighbour, cobalt, atomic number 27, symbol Co, earned the miners' name for a Germanic goblin, *Kobald*. Their resentment was doubtless exacerbated by the presence of arsenic in these nickel and cobalt ores, which poisoned those trying to extract the metals. A Chapter in *The Periodic Table* (1975), the late, great Primo Levi's autobiographical memoir of his experiences as an industrial chemist, is devoted to nickel. (MW)

* Nickel arsenide, NiAs, called *niccolite,* superficially resembles *cuprite* (cuprous oxide Cu_2O).

** The etymology of this usage of "Nick" is obscure: it may come from the Dutch *Nikken*, the Devil, which has its origins in Nordic mythology, where one of the names for the evil spirit or destroying principle is *Nikke*. It is an egregious slur on Nicholases everywhere.

[652] NICOL PRISM

This was, in 1828, the first optical invention to produce *plane polarized light,* in which the light waves vibrate in one direction only. The prism is made of Iceland Spar, a very pure form of the naturally-occurring mineral calcite (a crystalline variety of chalk – calcium carbonate) which is *anisotropic: i.e.* its optical properties are not the same in all directions, due to alignment of the molecules within the crystal lattice. Light passing through the crystal produces two images slightly displaced from each other: the phenomenon of double refraction or *birefringence.* It has been hypothesized that this was known to the Vikings: Iceland Spar does indeed occur in Iceland, as "sunstone" and could have been used for navigation when the sun was not visible, by the polarization of light from the sky – for a recent scholarly examination of this question see:
http://rspa.royalsocietypublishing.org/content/463/2080/1081.full.

Scottish natural philosopher **WILLIAM NICOL** (1770-1851) was born in Humbie, East Lothian, and settled in Edinburgh where he taught at the University. To complement his prism, he also developed a technique for making thin transparent sections of rocks for microscopical examination, between two **NICOL PRISMS** – the polarizer and the analyzer – the first application of polarized light in petrology. (MW)

[653] NICOTINE

Toxic alkaloid found in the tobacco plant (*Nicotiana*) and mainly used as a horticultural insecticide. It takes its name from the French diplomat JEAN NICOT, SIEUR DE VILLEMAIN (1530-1600), who introduced tobacco to the courts of Portugal (where he was ambassador) and France. Nicot has a second claim to fame as the author of the first monoglot French dictionary, published in 1606. It is fortunate for us that Nicot's was the name attached to the tobacco plant, otherwise we might be having to try and get our tongues (and our lungs) round a substance called raleigh-ine.

[654] NIÉPCEOTYPE

Bitumen of Judaea – a kind of up-market tar – may seem an unpromising material for making images, but it is the substance of the "first photograph", a NIÉPCEOTYPE which may still be viewed in the Gernsheim Collection at the University of Texas in Austin. Bitumen has the property of hardening on exposure to light, which renders it insoluble in solvents such as clove oil and turpentine. In 1821, the French chemist and inventor, JOSEPH NICÉPHORE NIÉPCE* (1765-1833) used this property to make photocopies of engravings by contact-printing them in sunlight, modestly naming the process *héliographie*. In 1827 he put a bitumen-coated pewter plate at the focus of a *camera obscura* and, for a whole day at least, pointed it out of his window at Chalon-sur-Saône. The resulting image of the courtyard at Gras is now the iconic "first photograph", in which the sunlight illuminates opposite walls, due to the lengthy exposure. Niépce was the business partner of DAGUERRE, but died before he could receive full recognition for his invention. Photography was not Niépce's only interest. He designed a hydraulic pump, a bicycle, experimented with substitutes for indigo dye (unavailable on account of the continental blockade imposed by England), and in 1807 obtained from the Emperor Napoleon a patent for an internal combustion engine (*moteur à explosion*) – certainly the world's first, which he christened the *Pyréolophore*. Fuelled by *lycopodium* powder, it was intended as a means of propulsion for boats, and Niépce produced a working model capable of moving upstream on the river Saône. Niépce's nephew, inventor and army officer ABEL NIÉPCE DE SAINT-VICTOR (1805-1870), also interested himself in photography, using an albumen emulsion on glass plates, and invented a form of heliogravure on metal. (MW)

* There seems to be some doubt, even among the French, as to whether the first "e" in Niépce's name gets an accent, and if so which way it is to lean. The tide of opinion seems to be running in favour of an acute accent (é) but one is probably still free to regard it as optional. If omitted, his name would have to be pronounced "neeps" as in "neeps and tatties". (See *Le Robert encyclopédique des noms propres* 2007 and compare with earlier editions.)

[655] NIEREMBERGIA

Also known as "cupflower," a genus of 25+ species of flowering herbaceous perennials native to S. America. The name memorialises the Spanish Jesuit mystic JUAN EUSEBIO NIEREMBERG (1595-1658). Son of German parents, Nieremberg lived and taught most of his life in Madrid. But after being admitted to the Society of Jesus in 1614, he was posted for a time to Alcarria in New Castile (Peru) before being recalled to Madrid. This may explain why, in the extensive catalogue of his devotional writings is included a *Historia naturae*, an encyclopedic survey of New World flora and fauna published in Antwerp in 1635 and one of the first in its field. The great Cuvier found Nieremberg's work "interesting", but marred by the intrusion of "mediaeval" metaphysical speculation.

[656] NIMROD

The Biblical NIMROD, son of Cush, is described in *Genesis* (Ch. 10) as "a mighty hunter before the Lord". That is all we know about him, but by the magic of antonomasia (see SCROOGE) his name has come to be applied to any person particularly prone to slaughtering wild animals. It was, for example, used as a pseudonym by C.J. Apperley (1778-1843), a passionate fox-hunter, who wrote on this and allied subjects for the *Sporting Magazine*. However, the grand and moving "Nimrod" of Elgar's *Enigma Variations* (Op. 36) refers to no enemy of the fox and the pheasant but to August J. Jaeger (1860-1909), a harmless music critic and editor for music publishers Novello & Co., whose name happens to mean "hunter" in German.

[657] NIOBIUM – see VANADIUM

[658] NISSEN HUT

Temporary building designed for military use, semi-circular in section, and formed from curved panels of corrugated sheet steel, the ends being closed with brick or cement-block walls or with more corrugated sheet cut to shape. The original design was patented in 1916 by the British engineer officer Col. PETER NORMAN NISSEN (1871-1930). Ease of erection and all-round utility meant that Nissen huts were erected in enormous numbers during WWII. The American equivalent is the pre-fabricated QUONSET HUT, based on Nissen's design and named not after a person but after Quonset Point, Rhode Island, where they were first constructed.

[659] NOBEL PRIZE

ALFRED BERNHARD NOBEL (1833-1896), scientist, industrialist, inventor, entrepreneur, author and pacifist, was the son of engineer and arms manufacturer Immanuel Nobel. He trained as a chemical engineer and, after a meeting with

Ascanio Sobrero the inventor of nitroglycerine, began experimenting in his father's factory with ways of stabilising this dangerously sensitive liquid explosive. Eventually he found that a mixture of nitroglycerine with *kieselguhr* (diatomite)* yielded an explosive that could safely be handled and transported even under rugged conditions.** He patented his discovery under the name "dynamite" in 1867 (Gk. δυναμις = power, force). At the same time he devised the blasting-cap-and-fuse arrangement needed to get the dynamite to go bang. By the age of 40, Nobel had built up a world-wide industrial empire and a fortune to match. In his will he endowed a $9 million fund, the interest on which was to be used for annual prize awards to people whose work most benefited humanity. The first award ceremony took place in 1901 on the fifth anniversary of Nobel's death. The Nobel prizes are awarded in five categories: Physics, Chemistry, Medicine, Literature and Peace (a sixth for Economics, which is financed by the Swedish National Bank, was first awarded in 1969). The current money value of the Prize is 10 million Swedish kroner to each recipient, but the prestige that comes with it is beyond price. Nobel was a complex and enigmatic individual who said of himself, "I am a misanthrope and yet utterly benevolent, have more than one screw loose yet am a super-idealist who digests philosophy more efficiently than food." The chemical element **NOBELIUM** (atomic number 102, symbol No) is named after him. (RS)

* A naturally-occurring mineral found as a fine whitish powder and composed essentially of the siliceous skeletons of the tiny water-borne creatures known as diatoms. Being both heat-resistant and chemically inert, diatomite is also used in the manufacture of insulation materials and fireproof cement, and as a filtration agent.

** The plot of the 1953 French film *The wages of fear* (*Le salaire de la peur*, dir. Henri-Georges Clouzot) hinges on the dangers of transporting un-stabilised nitroglycerine.

[660] NOETHER'S THEOREM

Scientific thinking often looks for symmetry in its subjects: repeating patterns of structure or behaviour such that things appear the same after a symmetry operation as before. The value of discovering symmetry in any enquiry is apparent from **NOETHER'S THEOREM** which assures us that where there is continuous symmetry there is also a *conservation law* that will enable us to balance equations, make calculations simpler, and generally do good, accurate scientific book-keeping for quantities like energy, momentum, *etc.* Three cases will serve as illustration of this profound insight into Dame Nature's workings. (1) The physical laws that describe the forces acting on matter can be displaced to a different region of space and there remain identically valid. This "translational" symmetry implies the *conservation of linear momentum*. (2) The laws are also independent of a system's orientation in space, a "rotational" symmetry that implies the *conservation of angular momentum*. (3) The laws which applied in the past will continue to apply at any time in the future in exactly the same way: this is a "temporal" symmetry that implies the *conservation of energy*. NOETHER'S THEOREM of 1915 is a sophisticated algebraic derivation from the earlier MAUPERTUIS' PRINCIPLE OF LEAST ACTION. AMALIE EMMY NOETHER (1882-1935) was born in Erlangen, Germany of Jewish family. Her father was the mathematician Max Noether, (who has a few theorems to his own account). She was educated at the Universities of Erlangen and Göttingen, although discrimination against women in German universities in the early 20th century impeded her career, and as an "extraordinary" faculty member she remained unpaid for seven years. The objections of the male CHAUVINISTS to a female academic were overruled by mathematician David Hilbert: "We are a university, not a bath-house." EINSTEIN and several other notables considered EMMY NOETHER the greatest woman mathematician of all time, and her first theorem (she has others to her credit) was said to be the most important since PYTHAGORAS. Following antifeminism, she then had to endure antisemitism; when Hitler became *Reichskanzler* in 1933 she was dismissed from her post. Like many other Jewish intellectuals she sought refuge in the USA, and was welcomed at Bryn Mawr College, although at Princeton she found that antifeminism persisted. (MW)

[661] NONIUS – see VERNIER SCALE

[662] NORIE'S TABLES
In the days before satellite navigation (*i.e.* until very recently) mariners out of sight of land fixed their position by means of astronomical observation. For this, four things were required: an accurate chronometer (or, better, two); a sextant for measuring angles; a Nautical Almanac giving the Declination and Greenwich Hour Angle (roughly speaking the celestial latitude and longitude) of the Sun, Moon and "navigators' stars"* hour by hour for each day of the current year; and finally a copy of NORIE'S NAUTICAL TABLES containing mainly trigonometrical tables necessary for reducing the observations to a calculated position. "Norie's" first appeared in 1803, the work of JOHN WILLIAM NORIE (1772-1843) publisher of charts and works on navigation. (See also HARRISON'S CHRONOMETERS.)

* *I.e.* the stars visible during the period known as "nautical twilight", when it is dark enough for the brightest stars to appear but light enough for the horizon (the sextant's reference point) to be still visible.

O

[663] OCCAM'S RAZOR

The famous dictum "*Entia* non sunt multiplicanda praeter necessitatem*" translates as, "Entities are not to be multiplied beyond necessity", a positively Sibylline utterance. But if we translate the meaning rather than the words, we get something on the lines of, "*The simplest explanation is likely to be the right one.*"** Example: in the later Middle Ages it became increasingly difficult to maintain the geocentric theory of the universe. To explain such apparent anomalies as the retrograde motion of the planets, it became necessary to bolt on to the basic theory more and more refinements (the famous "epicycles") leading to increasing complication and less clarity. The situation was only resolved by the adoption of a simpler theory: that the Earth goes round the Sun.*** The "Law of Parsimony" as it is known, which plays a useful part in the step-by-step advance of science towards an unattainable Final Truth, is associated with the name of **WILLIAM OF OCCAM** (d. *ca.* 1349), a Franciscan monk who hailed from the village of Ockham in Surrey. It is not found in exactly the form quoted in any of his works (though it is so found in Aristotle), but it is fittingly associated with him as its spirit epitomises his approach to philosophical and theological questions. Occam spent much of his working life on the Continent and sided with the German Emperor in his quarrel with the Papacy after himself boldly accusing the Pope of heresy. He probably died in Munich, but his place of burial is not known.

* *Essentia* ("essences") in some formulations.

** An alternative, and perhaps more transparent, version has it that, "*Frustra fit per plura quod potest fieri per pauciora*" ("It is futile to do with more what can be done with fewer.")

*** See **COPERNICAN SYSTEM**, **PTOLEMAIC SYSTEM**, and **GALILEO**

[664] OEDIPUS COMPLEX

OEDIPUS*, the mythical hero of two plays by the 5th-century BC Greek tragedian Sophocles, was a walking disaster area who through sheer bad luck accidentally killed his own father and followed this up by accidentally marrying his own mother. Sigmund Freud (1856-1939), the founding father of psychiatry, seized on this cautionary tale to exemplify his theory that all men unconsciously** desire, virtually from birth, to murder their fathers in order to be free to roger their mummies. A neutral observer might wonder how Siggy the Soul-Doctor came to this conclusion since most of his patients were not men racked by festering incestuous longings but middle-class Viennese ladies who were harbouring neurotic symptoms because they had nothing better to do with their time.

* The name means "swell-foot", which suggests that Oedipus shared a physical impediment with Lord Byron, the French statesman Talleyrand, and the Emperor Claudius. The last of these, incidentally, gives his name to a French verb "*claudiquer*" meaning "to limp", while Talleyrand has left a material reminder of his disability in the extra handrail that had to be fitted for his benefit to the main staircase of the Travellers' Club, London.

** The Unconscious, as every schoolboy knows, is crucial to the whole enterpise of psychiatry since if a patient knew, unaided, what was going on in the remote depths of his psyche, he wouldn't need to have it pointed out to him and a lot of psychiatrists would have to re-train as plumbers.

[665] OERSTED

A physical unit of the obsolete, but reputable, centimeter-gram-second (cgs) system of measurement, before the communist-sounding Système International (SI) took over,* and replaced it with the TESLA. It measures the strength of a magnetic field (or the magnetic flux density). Introduced in 1932 this unit is closely related to the GAUSS, the unit of magnetic induction, and is identical with it in a vacuum. Danish physicist HANS CHRISTIAN ØRSTED (1777-1851) was born at Rudkobing and educated at the University of Copenhagen where he became professor in 1806, and in 1820 discovered electromagnetism – the magnetic effect produced by an electric current (for the consequences of this momentous discovery see FARADAY). Ørsted was also the first to extract metallic aluminium in an impure form in 1825, although the isolation of that element is usually credited to Wohler in 1827. Ørsted was a friend of his namesake, Hans Christian Andersen, and other notables of the Danish Golden Age. (MW)

*Is that why the USA still largely rejects it?

[666] OFFA'S DYKE

OFFA SON OF THINGFERTH ruled the Anglo-Saxon kingdom of Mercia from 757 until his death in 796,* and was responsible for the construction of a linear earthwork running north-south along his western border and stretching from the mouth of the Wye to the mouth of the Dee. This remarkable feat of engineering is first recorded by King Alfred's biographer Bishop Asser (d. 909?), who left us a chronicle of English history from 849 to 897 in which we read that "a certain vigorous king called Offa... had a great dyke built between Wales and Mercia from sea to sea." Though robbed- or ploughed-out in many places, the route of the Dyke is still traceable over some 80 miles of its length. It originally consisted of a ditch and bank, with the ditch on the Welsh side, and measured some 8m from the bottom of the ditch to the top of the bank. In the absence of the trained manpower and sophisticated logistical organisation available to the Romans on

Hadrian's Wall, it is difficult to imagine how the Dyke might have served as a defended military field-work, or what part it might have played in Offa's savage wars with the Welsh, though it must have served as a formal boundary. In *Wild Wales*, George Borrow notes that once "it was customary for the English to cut off the ears of every Welshman who was found to the east of the Dyke, and for the Welsh to hang every Englishman whom they found to the west of it." Perhaps its main function was psychological – to impress the Wild Welsh with the power and resources of its builder and induce an appropriate degree of timidity, causing would-be invaders to think twice before crossing the line. Offa was, in effect, King of England: by a combination of war, diplomacy and dynastic marriage, he extended his kingdom from the Thames to the Mersey and from the Welsh border to the fens of East Anglia, forged alliances with the two remaining most powerful kingdoms, those of Northumbria and Wessex, and had diplomatic contacts with the Frankish king Charlemagne, and with Rome. We have Offa to thank for fixing the penny coin as the basic unit of English currency and standardising its silver content with the coins in circulation across the Channel, with consequent benefits to both home and foreign trade. His name survives in a number of toponyms including Uffington (Berks.), Ovingham (Northumberland), Ovingdean (Sussex), and Ovington (Essex, Hants.), though we cannot be sure to which Offa the names refer. (RS)

* 794 in the *Anglo-Saxon Chronicle*, which records various of Offa's doings but without mentioning the Dyke.

[667] OHM

This SI unit of resistance or impedance to the passage of an electric current (see AMPÈRE) is given the symbol Greek omega, Ω. OHM'S LAW, published in 1827, states that the current flowing in a conductor is proportional to the voltage across it; by definition, a device has a resistance of one ohm, if one volt applied across it causes a current of one ampère to flow. The name is that of the German physicist, GEORG SIMON OHM (1789-1854), born in Erlangen, Bavaria. He was largely taught by his father, before attending the University of Erlangen. He began his researches while a high school teacher, using VOLTA's battery. Eventually he occupied chairs at Nuremberg and Munich. (MW)

[668] OKUN'S LAW

In a 1970 work entitled *The political economy of prosperity*, the American economist ARTHUR OKUN (1926-1980) advanced the theory that there was a regular mathematical relationship between a rise in unemployment and a decrease in GNP measured as the difference between actual and potential maximum GNP. This *aperçu*, based on a study of US economic statistics over the two decades preceding publication, became known as **OKUN'S LAW.** However, more recent figures have considerably lessened confidence in the idea that Okun had hit on a general truth. This would seem to support the view sometimes advanced that it is at best rash to dignify the conjectures of any economist as a "law". Economics has only a paper-thin claim to be considered as a science, if only because, even when approached in a spirit of rational enquiry, it yields no predictable regularities. There isn't even any clear agreement as to what is being studied. When we speak about "the economy" of a country like Britain, for example, what we are actually referring to is sixty million more or less irrational, more or less error-prone human beings fumbling about trying to make a living under conditions which no one fully understands and no one can properly control. The idea that useful generalisations could emerge from a chaos of mixed motives, conflicting theories, uncertain values, and misdirected effort has a strong whiff of wishful thinking about it.

[669] OLBERS' PARADOX

"Why is the sky dark at night?" This was the question posed in 1826 by the German ophthalmologist and amateur astronomer **WILHELM HEINRICH MATTHÄUS OLBERS** (1758-1840). If, Olbers pointed out, there is an infinite number of stars, evenly distributed, their light should cover the entire night sky, which, visibly, they do not. He suggested an answer to his own question – that the starlight was being partly obscured by interstellar dust. An alternative answer was proposed in the 20th century by Sir Hermann Bondi: that the expanding universe and the consequent red-shift of the stars and galaxies receding from us, diminished their luminosity. Something similar had been suggested by **HUBBLE**, who maintained that in an expanding universe, the velocity at which galaxies receded from the viewpoint of any given observer would increase with distance till it attained the speed of light, so that no light from these sources could ever reach us. It now appears however, that the real answer to Olbers' question is rather simpler: there just aren't enough stars to cover the sky. Their number is not infinite. According to the calculations of the astronomer Edward Harrison*, there would need to be far more stars than actually exist – ten trillion times more, in fact – to achieve that all-over twinkle.

* Edward R. Harrison *Darkness at night*, 1987.

[670] OLD MOORE'S ALMANACK

FRANCIS MOORE (1657-ca.1715) was a self-educated physician, astrologer and schoolteacher who published the first version of what became *Old Moore's Almanack* under the title *Vox Stellarum* ("Voice of the stars") in 1697. The staple of Moore's almanacs, as of other works of the same kind, was a calendar for the coming year with predictions of political, meteorological, celestial and other events of note, with tips on favourable days for various activities such as taking medicines, going on journeys, planting and harvesting, engaging in business transactions, and so forth. (Moore, in common with other almanac compilers advised farmers and gardeners to time their operations by the phases of the moon – sound biodynamic principles.) Moore's almanac sold, and continued to sell for the next two centuries, in tens of thousands of copies and is still being published today. How and why Moore became "Old" Moore, is something of a mystery. The etymology of the word almanac is similarly mysterious. The common supposition that it comes from an Arabic original via Spanish is now discredited. C.T. Onions in his *Oxford Dictionary of Etymology*, suggests a possible connection to a late classical Greek word which is found in only one locus (Eusebius, 4th cent. AD). (See also **WHITAKER'S ALMANACK, POOR RICHARD'S ALMANACK**.)

[671] ONANISM

In Chapter xxxviii of the book of Genesis we find a complicated genealogical anecdote concerning a certain Judah who married a Canaanite (usually a mistake in the Old Testament) by whom he had three sons. The eldest was named Er and the next in line, **ONAN**. Unfortunately, however, *"Er, Judah's firstborn, was wicked in the sight of the Lord; and the Lord slew him. And Judah said unto Onan, 'Go in unto thy brother's wife, and raise up seed to thy brother.' And Onan knew that the seed should not be his; and it came to pass, when he went in unto his brother's wife, that he spilled it on the ground, lest that he should give seed to his brother. And the thing which he did displeased the Lord: wherefore he slew him also."* After this second manifestation of divine disapproval, the story gets even steamier, as it goes on to relate a complex sequel in which Judah mistakes his daughter-in-law for an harlot, gets her pregnant, and demands that she should be burned for harlotry. There is, however, a happy ending. On the basis of the Bible account, there can be little doubt regarding the dire fate that awaits seed-spillers. It is less clear how and why a story clearly intended as a denunciation of *coitus interruptus*, came to be interpreted as a prohibition of masturbation, or what the Victorians more delicately referred to as "self-abuse" and more colourfully as "beastliness". Anyone wanting to take this enquiry further must consult *Onanism displayed*, a work of 1718 by the famously dodgy bookseller and hack-work publisher Edmund Curll (1675?-1745), who is credited with the coinage. Curll's more lubricious publications (for which he stood trial) posed as expressions of moral indignation, a technique that has put food on the tables of the gutter press ever since.

[672] ONDINE'S CURSE

(Congenital central hypoventilation syndrome.) A very rare but very dangerous disorder in which the sufferer is born without autonomic (*i.e.* unconscious) control of breathing. As every breath has to be consciously initiated, the usual outcome is fatal apnoea during sleep unless the patient is diagnosed in time and provided with some mechanical aid to breathing. The reference is to a German legend concerning the water-nymph **ONDINE**. She married a mortal who swore to be faithful to her as long as there was breath in his body. When she found him asleep in the arms of another woman, she pointed a finger at him whereupon he promptly expired.

[673] OORT CLOUD

In 1950, the Dutch astronomer **JAN HENDRIK OORT** (1900-1992) published his theory of the origins of comets. He posited a spherical volume of space surrounding the Solar System and inhabited by vast numbers (a "cloud" in fact) of asteroids, some of which are periodically hurled inwards towards the sun by gravitational disturbances and appear to us as comets (an idea that would have greatly interested poor **HÖRBIGER**). As Director of the Leiden Observatory, Oort played an important role in the development of 20th-century radio astronomy but is chiefly remembered for his discovery that the Galaxy is revolving about its centre. As with planetary orbits, the stars nearer the centre move faster than those further out. (Our own sun makes the circuit once every 200,000,000 years, give or take.) On this principle, Oort was able to explain the phenomenon of "star-streams" which divides the stars in our galaxy into two groups: those nearer the galactic centre which appear to be overtaking us and those further away which appear to be falling behind. However, Oort's conclusions on this topic were later thrown into doubt by the work of Vera Rubin (1977) who maintained that the whole visible Galaxy was revolving at the same speed though it might be revolving at a different speed from the far larger, and invisible, Dark Matter component which is presumed to surround it. The interested layman can only await further elucidation.

[674] ORFFYREUS' WHEEL

Among humanity's persistent delusions, the possibility of a perpetual motion machine must rank a close second to the possibility of world peace. Attempts to construct or describe such a machine – roughly speaking, a machine that can do work without any power input – can be traced back to the Middle Ages and the famous sketchbook of the 13th-century architect and draughtsman Villard de Honnecourt, and are still proceeding merrily today. The majority of proposals for achieving this visionary project have centred on the idea of an *overbalancing wheel*, that is, a wheel so constructed that one side of the rim is perpetually heavier than the other and so will turn under its own weight. All such schemes have one thing in common: they don't work. In the long history of attempts to obtain free energy in defiance of the laws of thermodynamics one name stands out, that of a native of Saxony **JOHANN ERNST ELIAS BESSLER** (1690-1745), who adopted the name **ORFFYREUS.*** Bessler's wheels (he constructed more than one) have a special, indeed a unique, status in the history of the search for perpetual motion by virtue of the fact that they *appeared* to work as advertised. Details of four of his machines are known. Each consisted of a drum enclosing the mechanism, mounted on an axle, and with a covering of oiled cloth attached to the rims and so concealing its inner workings. They varied in size from the first (about three feet in diameter by four inches thick) to the fourth and largest with a diameter of some 12 feet and a width of 14 inches. The dimensions, at least of the smaller wheels, precluded the possibility that they were being worked by a person hidden inside. And they were visibly not attached to any external source of power. A rope wound round the axle was used to lift weights, demonstrating the wheel's ability to perform work. Even so, the first three wheels he exhibited failed to convince, and Orffyreus moved from town to town followed by the boos and hisses of a hostile public. In or about 1716 he pitched up in Hesse-Cassel where the Landgrave took him under his wing, made him a Town Councillor, and found him rooms in which to live and work in his castle at Wassenstein. (The Landgrave was the only person ever allowed to see inside one of the wheels and he either would not or could not – at any rate did not – reveal the secret, merely stating that it was "simple".) Here Orffyreus constructed his largest wheel, which was subjected to external inspection by a number of notables including a Professor s'Gravesende of Leyden who left a description of the wheel in a letter to Sir Isaac Newton. In 1717, by way of an official test, the wheel was set going in a room which was then sealed, and found to be still going when the seals were broken and the room opened 54 days later. Orffyreus hoped to sell the secret of his machines for a hefty sum, but in this he was disappointed and he smashed the Wassenstein machine in a fit of pique, after which he lapsed into obscurity. It is hard to know how to characterise Bessler/ Orffyreus. He was no showman. Choleric and prickly, he totally lacked the ability to get the public on his side and instead manufactured hostile critics on a production-line basis. Nor can we, in all fairness, call him a confidence trickster, since no fraud was ever proved on him, and the means by which he produced the semblance of a self-moving machine remain a mystery to this day. (For a detailed account, see Rupert T. Gould *Oddities*, 1928, 1944. See also under "Perpetual Motion", *Encyclopaedia Britannica*, 11th ed.)

* Bessler's *nom de guerre* was arrived at by writing the letters of the alphabet in a circle and substituting the letter immdiately opposite for each letter of the name "Bessler" to yield the name "Orffyre". It then only remained to add a touch of academic distinction with the Latin termination "-us".

[675] ORNISH DIET

It might well be the case that the most popular and (in commercial terms) most successful of the multifarious diet plans on offer to the fat and unfit would appear to be those which promise their adepts the freedom to eat as much as they like – but only of certain things. The diet proposed by the American doctor **DEAN ORNISH** appears to be of this type. It makes two claims: it will enable you to lose weight while eating more, and it can reverse cardiovascular conditions otherwise thought to be incurable. The main planks of the program are an almost total exclusion of fats and oils from the diet and a concentration on high starch, high-fibre foods such as pulses, grains and potatoes. Meat is allowed in very limited quantities. The obvious problem with Dr. O's recommendations is that the foods he wants us to eat a lot of are simply not palatable – or even edible – without some fat or oil in their preparation. A baked potato with no butter is an unappealing object. And a dish of lentils cooked without oil would be very hard to swallow. So for anyone who has the remotest inclination to actually enjoy their food, the choice between the Ornish diet and heart disease may not be an easy one. One fascinating aspect of the Ornish regimen is its close resemblance to the diet enjoyed by the inhabitants of Mexico at the time of the Spanish invasions, a diet whose main features were an almost total absence of meat protein* and of any source of fats or oils except the avocado (which, interestingly, Ornish severely prohibits).

* Unless one subscribes to the theory proposed by (among others) anthropologist Marvin Harris (*Cannibals and kings* 1977) that the inhabitants of Tenochtitlán were *eating* the corpses of the hundreds of human victims being sacrificed each day to prevent the sun from going out. If they weren't, how were the bodies disposed of? Coprolithic evidence supports the hypothesis that anthropophagy was practised in Central America at this period.

[676] ORRERY

A clockwork model of the solar system which demonstrates the orbits of the moon and planets at their correct relative velocities. The first such machine was built around 1704 to the design of its inventor George Graham (1673-1751) and a copy of the original presented to Graham's patron **CHARLES BOYLE, 4TH EARL OF ORRERY** (1676-1731), Jacobite soldier, scholar, diplomat and author, in whose honour the machine was named.* Graham was an expert horologist and instrument maker, who invented the dead-beat escapement and the mercury pendulum, and built astronomical instruments for **HALLEY** and for the French Academy. He is buried in Westminster Abbey alongside another hero of British horology, Thomas Tompion (1639-1713).

* Probably the best-remembered scion of the Boyle family is the chemist Robert Boyle (1627-1691). See **BOYLE'S LAW**.

[677] OSTWALD RIPENING

A "precipitate" in chemistry is (quite literally) "thrown down" when two solutions are mixed and react to form an insoluble solid. The size of the particles of the solid depends inversely on the rate of its formation; thus, a rapidly formed precipitate has very small particles and may even be gelatinous; one slowly deposited will grow as large well-formed crystals. The speed of deposition depends on the degree of supersaturation, according to the **VON WEIMARN COEFFICIENT**, after **PETER PETROVICH VON WEIMARN** (1879-1935). It is also a fact that small particles are more soluble than large ones, so if a precipitate is simply left in suspension, the larger particles will tend to grow at the expense of the smaller ones and the average particle size will increase with time. This is the phenomenon of **OSTWALD RIPENING**, which is particularly important in controlling the manufacture of photographic silver halide emulsions where particle size determines speed and contrast of the photographic film or paper. **FRIEDRICH WILHELM OSTWALD** (1853-1932) was born in Riga in Baltic Germany (now capital of Latvia); he attended the Universities of Dorpat and Leipzig and, alongside **VAN'T HOFF** and **ARRHENIUS,** is esteemed as one of the founding fathers of physical chemistry, for which he was awarded the Nobel prize in 1909. He discovered catalysis by platinum metal (see **MERENSKY REEF**) used in the **OSTWALD PROCESS** for manufacturing nitric acid by the oxidation of ammonia (itself prepared by the **HABER-BOSCH** process). He is also remembered for the **OSTWALD VISCOMETER** and **OSTWALD'S DILUTION LAW**. (MW)

[678] OTTO CYCLE

This is the name commonly accorded to the four-stroke cycle (induction/compression/ignition/exhaust) of petrol and diesel engines. Though he was not the first to describe it, the German engineer and industrialist **NIKOLAUS OTTO** (1832-1892) earns the right to name it as he is generally credited with the invention of the first internal combustion engine to employ the four-stroke cycle. Though Otto made and sold only stationary engines, it is perhaps permissible to wonder why cars powered by them are not called ottomobiles. (See also: **CARNOT'S THEOREM, DIESEL ENGINE, STIRLING ENGINE, WANKEL ENGINE, NIÉPCEOTYPE.**) For a survey of possible modern rivals to Otto's spark-ignition engine, see Wilson: "Alternative automobile engines" (*Scientific American* 239.1, 1978.) Note that **OTTO FUEL,** a monopropellant (chemical reaction fuel) used in torpedoes, is named after **Dr. OTTO REITLINGER** (d. 1971).

[679] OTTOMAN

An article of furniture: an upholstered stool or bench without arms or back, domestically popular in Victorian times (*cf.* **CHESTERFIELD**). Adoption of this name in the West was probably intended to reflect the legendary luxury of the historic **OTTOMAN EMPIRE** (1293-1923) that was once enjoyed by what remains today as the modern Republic of Turkey (see **SYKES-PICOT AGREEMENT**). The Ottoman title derives in turn from the name of its founder and first ruler, Sultan

OSMAN I (1258-1324), more fully OTHMAN I EL-GAZI, whose name is said to mean "bone-breaker". How appropriately one can only guess. Under the Ottoman dynasty, the Empire expanded ultimately to include all of Asia Minor, Egypt, the Levant, and much of SE Europe. (MW)

[680] OWEN GUN

Blowback-operated 9mm submachine gun designed and hand-built in the 1930's by Australian inventor EVELYN "EVO" OWEN (1915-1949), a native of Wollongong, New South Wales. Owen had difficulties at first in getting the Australian army interested in his weapon but eventually, when it had proved its superior reliability to both the British STEN and American THOMPSON guns, it went into production and was issued to Australian troops engaged in jungle warfare against the Japanese. The gun, readily recognisable by its top-mounted stick magazine, saw further service in the Malayan Emergency and in the Korean and Vietnam wars and was only superseded in the mid-1960's. In all, some 50,000 were manufactured. After the war Owen used the money he had received from patent royalties to set himself up in a sawmill near Wollongong, dying at the age of only 33 from the effects of alcohol abuse.

[681] OWENS COLLEGE

Using a house in Quay Street, Manchester, this educational establishment was founded in 1851 under the terms of the will left by the successful textile merchant, JOHN OWENS (1790-1846), who died unmarried and without issue, bequeathing £96,000 for the purpose. The most laudable condition of his bequest was that there should be no religious test to qualify either as student or teacher. OWENS COLLEGE moved in 1873 to its present main building in Oxford Road, Manchester, one of the splendid erections by Victorian architect, Alfred Waterhouse. Upon being granted a Royal Charter in 1880, Owens College became, appropriately enough, the Victoria University of Manchester, but until very recently locals still referred to it as "Owens", to distinguish it from the University of Manchester Institute of Science and Technology (UMIST – see WHITWORTH). The first and largest of the so-called "civic" universities of Britain (the term "redbrick" seems both politically and architecturally incorrect) engendered by the prosperity of the Industrial Revolution, it cannot compete with ancient Oxbridge in attracting toffs, but can boast an honourable record of notable scientific and humanistic achievement, including 23 Nobel prizewinners. It nurtured the first programmable computer (see TURING), the structure of the atom (see RUTHERFORD), and the foundation of radio astronomy (Sir Bernard Lovell). In 2004, "Owens" merged with UMIST to become the University of Manchester – and still the largest in UK. (MW)

P

[682] PALLADIUM – see TITANIUM

[683] PALLAS'S SEA EAGLE

German-born physician-naturalist PETER SIMON PALLAS (1741-1811) was invited to Russia by the Empress Catherine the Great. He travelled widely in what might be called Outer Russia as far as the borders of China, observing and recording the geology, plants, birds, animals and peoples he encountered. He wrote and published voluminously (the French translation of his *Reisen durch verschiedene Provinzen des rüssichen Reichs* runs to 8 volumes of text and nine of plates). In addition to the SEA EAGLE (*Haliaeetus leucoryphus*), native to the Caspian and Black Seas, creatures named after him include: PALLAS'S CAT (*Otocolobus manul*), PALLAS'S SANDGROUSE (*Syrrhaptes paradoxus*) PALLAS'S REED BUNTING (*Emberiza pallasi*), PALLAS'S WARBLER (*Phylloscopus proregulus*), and PALLAS'S GRASSHOPPER WARBLER (*Locustella certhiola*). His name also survives in PALLAS IRON, a metal found in certain meteorites known as PALLASITES. Pallas also made an important contribution to the study of the languages of the Russian Empire.

[684] PANDER – see TROILISM

[685] PANTALOONS

Close-fitting breeches down to the ankle, a transitional form of nether garment betwen knee-breeches and trousers. The name is derived from a stock character in the Italian *commedia dell' arte*, PANTALONE, most often portrayed as a foolish old man in tight trousers and slippers. He is a miserly and often libidinous personage who is portrayed as a Venetian, sometimes as a father, husband or guardian. If he is rich, he is a slave to his money. If he is married, his wife is usually young – and flighty with it. He loves to give advice. He is always duped by someone and often he is the recipient of blows from his servant. He traditionally wears a large codpiece to show off his virility (this is a joke) plus a mask with a long hooked nose, a tight red vest, red breeches and stockings, a black cassock, slippers and a brimless hat. Shakespeare was familiar with the type, hence his "lean and slippered pantaloon" (*As you like it*). As with the names of many of the characters in the *commedia dell' arte*, the origins of Pantalone's name are puzzling. The derivation most commonly cited traces it to the phrase *pianta leone* or *plant the lion*. This is a reference to the lion emblem of Venice and Venice's conquests around the globe where Venetians have literally "planted the lion" (*sc.* flag). Another possible source may be *San Pantalone*, or **ST. PANTALEON** (d. 303 AD), a Roman physician and martyr. He was the son of a rich pagan, Eustorgius of Nicomedia, and had been instructed in Christianity by his Christian mother, Saint Eubula. In the mid-14th century in Western Europe he became the patron saint of physicians and midwives. (See also **BLOOMERS, KNICKERS.**) (RS)

[686] PAPIN'S DIGESTER

French engineer, inventor and physicist **DENIS PAPIN** (1647-1714) was among the Huguenots who sought asylum in this country (to our enormous benefit) following the revocation of the Edict of Nantes (1685). In Paris he had worked with **HUYGENS** on the air-pump, and in London worked with **ROBERT BOYLE**, who found him temporary employment with the Royal Society. He later moved to Germany where he taught at Marburg and Cassel and corresponded with Leibnitz. In 1707 he returned to London penniless and applied to the Royal Society for support. This was not granted, and Papin died in poverty and obscurity. While in Germany he had designed and built a man-powered four-wheeled paddle boat, but it was steam that held a particular fascination for him, and he came up with a number of contrivances for converting its power to useful work. These included the first working model of a piston-operated steam engine (see **NEWCOMEN'S ENGINE**), and the **PAPIN DIGESTER**, forerunner of the modern pressure cooker, which incorporated maybe the most useful of all Papin's wizard wheezes, the steam safety valve.

[687] PARKINSON'S LAWS

The literary output (some thirty titles) of **CYRIL NORTHCOTE PARKINSON** (1909-1993) testifies to the wide range of his interests and employments as naval historian, military instructor, political scientist, civil servant, academic, economist, historical novelist, and humorist. He is best and most widely remembered, however, for *Parkinson's Law* published in 1957 in which he takes a satirical swipe at the structure of bureaucracies and hierarchical institutions in general, and which contains his famous **FIRST LAW**, which states that "work expands to fill the time available for its completion". In *The law and the profits* (1960) Parkinson turned his attention to taxation and allied matters. He enunciated a **SECOND LAW**, "Expenditure rises to meet income", and showed how this applies not only to the household budgets of ordinary mortals but to the Government's infinitely-expanding appetite for other people's money.

[688] PARMENTIER

On the restaurant menu, the word Parmentier attached to the name of a dish signals the presence of potatoes.* "*Qui dit Parmentier dit patate*," as the Frogs have it. **ANTOINE AUGUSTIN PARMENTIER** (1737-1813), trained as a pharmacist and in this capacity joined the sanitary services of the French army in the Seven Years' War. While a POW in Germany, he was subjected to a potato-based diet and became convinced of the potato's nutritional value, despite the common French opinion at the time that it was at best a low-grade animal feed and at worst frankly toxic. On repatriation he set out to combat these notions and encouraged the planting of potatoes by example and demonstration. In particular he promoted them as an emergency food source in time of scarcity (*i.e.* following poor grain harvests) and showed how the versatile tuber could be employed to produce anything from bread to brandy. Parmentier's energies and talents brought him to official notice and he served in various public roles under Monarchy, Republic and Empire. His interests were by no means confined to potato-growing, and his large output of published books and papers covers a variety of topics from chestnuts to mineral water, mushrooms to military hospitals, and baking to viticulture. In the last of these, he collaborated with **CHAPTAL** and **JUSSIEU** in the 2-volume *Traité... sur la culture de la vigne* (1801). His grave and monument are in Père Lachaise cemetery in Paris. The famous account of how Parmentier inveigled the French army into eating potatoes by locking up a load of spuds in a warehouse under armed guard, thereby virtually inviting the troops to steal them, may well be apocryphal. But it recalls Captain Cook's dodge for getting his matelots with their notoriously conservative ideas about diet to eat the experimental anti-scorbutic foods he carried on his first exploring voyage: he simply let it be known that they were for officers only.

* For example, *Hachis Parmentier*, shepherd's pie with a French accent (and a touch of nutmeg).

[689] PARROTIA

Parrotia persica, the ironwood tree, belongs to the family *Hamamelidaceae* (witch-hazels) and is native to the mountains of northern Persia. It was introduced to this country in the 1840's where it is grown in several cultivars as an ornamental small tree or large shrub. It bears the name of German physician, botanist and traveller **F.W. PARROT** (1792-1841), who made the first recorded ascent of Mount Ararat – not counting Noah, who got there by boat. The plant-name was authored by Carl Anton Andreevich Meyer (1795-1855), Russian botanist and explorer, Director of the St. Petersburg botanical gardens from 1850 till his death.

[690] PARRY'S CANNON

WILLIAM EDWARD PARRY (1790-1855), English naval officer and Arctic explorer, commanded a ship on Sir John Ross's 1818 expedition and later led three expeditions of his own in search of the North-West Passage, as well as an attempt to reach the North Pole. He was an expert navigator with a strong scientific bent and served a term as acting hydrographer to the Navy. On his second (1821-2) voyage he overwintered, fast in the ice, at 66°N 83°W, and used the time to make scientific observations. These included an experiment to determine whether the speed of sound varied with air temperature. It involved firing a cannon whose muzzle flash would be noted by Parry and one other observer (the astronomer, the Rev. George Fisher) at a carefully measured distance. They would then, with the aid of pocket chronometers, time the interval between the flash and the arrival of the sound. The observations were made in darkness so the muzzle flash was clearly visible. The experiment was repeated 15 times and on several occasions during the series the observers reported hearing the command "Fire!" given by the officer in charge of the gun a split second *after* they heard the bang. The phenomenon remains unexplained. (For a fuller account, see: Rupert T. Gould *Enigmas* 1929 and later eds., and for the original report, *Appendix to Captain Parry's journal of a second voyage.* 1825.)

[691] PASCAL

The **PASCAL** is the SI unit of pressure, defined by one **NEWTON** per square meter, N/m^2, and is given the symbol Pa. It is a small unit; the standard pressure of the atmosphere (see **TORR**) is 101,325 Pa. It is named after the French philosopher and mathematician, **BLAISE PASCAL** (see under **PASCAL'S WAGER**). **PASCAL'S TRIANGLE** is obtained by writing rows of whole numbers symmetrically, beginning with 1, and having an extra entry on each successive row, where each number is the sum of those diagonally above it in the previous row:

$$
\begin{array}{ccccccccccc}
 & & & & & 1 & & & & & \\
 & & & & 1 & & 1 & & & & \\
 & & & 1 & & 2 & & 1 & & & \\
 & & 1 & & 3 & & 3 & & 1 & & \\
 & 1 & & 4 & & 6 & & 4 & & 1 & \\
1 & & 5 & & 10 & & 10 & & 5 & & 1 \\
\end{array}
$$

etc...

Each row gives the coefficients of the terms in the binomial expansion of $(x + y)^n$. The triangle has many curious and interesting mathematical properties. For instance, the table provides the numbers of *combinations: viz.* the number of ways of selecting k things out of a total of n things is given by the kth entry in the nth row (where the first row, and the first entry in each row, are numbered 0). For instance, the number of distinct ways of choosing a group of 3 people out of a total of 5 is immediately found to be 10. The triangle did not originate with Pascal but was known in the 10th century to Indian mathematics and in Persia, where it was called **KAYYAM'S TRIANGLE,** after **OMAR KAYYAM** (1048-1131), poet, astronomer and mathematician; in China it is known as **YANG HUI'S** (1238-1298) **TRIANGLE,** and in Italy as **TARTAGLIA'S TRIANGLE** after algebraist **NICCOLÒ FONTANA TARTAGLIA** (1500-1577). (MW)

[692] PASCAL'S WAGER

An argument that it is a better bet to believe that God exists than that he doesn't. It was advanced by the French mathematician, physicist, philosopher and theologian **BLAISE PASCAL** (1623-1662). Pascal made significant contributions in the fields of mathematics and physical sciences, but towards the end of his life he abandoned science for philosophy and theology and wrote the *Lettres Provinciales* and the *Pensées*. The latter contains his argument in favour of the belief in the existence of God – thereafter named "Pascal's Wager". In essence it goes as follows:

- If you choose to believe in the existence of God (and conduct yourself accordingly), and if after death you find that you were right, your reward is eternal bliss, while if you were wrong, you lose nothing.
- If, on the other hand, you choose to reject the existence of God and it turns out that you were right, you lose nothing, but if you find that you were wrong, you are condemned to roast eternally in Hell.
- It follows logically that to believe in the existence of God is the safer bet since, win or lose, you avoid the penalty for guessing wrong.

Pascal was an original thinker of his time. He died before completing the *Penseés*, and it is likely that he didn't mean to put his "wager" forward seriously – unless his mind was muddled by a mystical experience after a brush with death. Be that as it may, both believers and non-believers have kept his wager alive for three centuries. (JP)

[693] PASTEURISATION

A method of neutralising harmful bacteria in substances designed for human consumption by heating. The most familiar example is the pasteurisation of milk to destroy the tubercle bacillus. The French chemist **LOUIS PASTEUR** (1822-1895) is regarded as the father of modern bacteriology. His work on micro-organisms which grew out of his pioneering studies in crystallography had important economic applications in the wine, brewing and silk industries and elsewhere but he is now chiefly remembered for his pioneering work on inoculation with attenuated bacteria and their prophylactic use against diseases such as diphtheria, cholera, tuberculosis, plague (see **YERSINIA**) and rabies. It was for the treatment by inoculation of the last of these that the first **INSTITUT PASTEUR** was founded in 1888 with himself as director. The mother-house in

Paris has now become a family, with 27 other members in France and around the world.

[694] PAULI'S EXCLUSION PRINCIPLE

This is the most important principle in the whole of theoretical chemistry – and the most inscrutable. It is unlikely that the reader will enjoy knowing that the electronic wavefunction is antisymmetric with respect to pairwise interchange. Rather, let it be said that each electron in an atom has to be uniquely identifiable by its quantum state, so the exclusion principle requires that no two electrons can have exactly the same "label" – *i.e.* set of four quantum numbers. This principle, taken together with the solution of SCHRÖDINGER'S WAVE EQUATION for the hydrogen atom, elegantly explains the curious structure of the Periodic Table of the Elements (see MENDELEEV), which represents one of the most profound syntheses of scientific thought in the 20th century. WOLFGANG ERNST PAULI (1900-1958) was born an Austrian, in Vienna; while at the University of Hamburg during 1923-28 he developed the idea of electron "spin" (see DIRAC'S CONSTANT) and put forward his exclusion principle in 1925. In 1928 he moved to Zurich, and there in 1930 predicted the existence of the fundamental particle, the neutrino – its existence was not finally confirmed until 1959. In 1940 Pauli moved to the USA, becoming a naturalised US citizen in 1946, before returning to Zurich. He was awarded the NOBEL PRIZE for physics in 1945. (MW)

[695] PAVLOV'S DOGS

In 1903, Russian physiologist IVAN PAVLOV (1849-1936), whilst conducting research into the physiology of digestion, observed that a dog used as a test subject salivated not only when actually eating but, when accustomed to a feeding routine, at meal times even before food was provided. One famous experiment involved ringing a bell when the food was presented; after a sufficient number of repetitions, the bell alone elicited salivation even in the absence of food. Pavlov found that the nature of the stimulus was irrelevant – it worked equally well with whistles, or tuning forks. From these observations came the concept of the *conditioned reflex* (a reflex response that only occurs conditionally upon specific previous experiences), which became a key concept in the field of behavioural psychology (see also SKINNER BOX). Pavlov, was the son of a village priest and himself destined for the Church. He entered a theological college, but in 1870 left it to study chemistry and physiology at the University of St Petersburg. His work on the physiology of digestion was rewarded with a NOBEL PRIZE in 1904. In popular parlance "Pavlovian" has come to describe any unthinking reaction determined by previous experience. (RS)

[696] PÊCHE MELBA – see MELBA TOAST

[697] PEELER
The Metropolitan Police Force was set up in 1828 during the Home Secretaryship of SIR ROBERT PEEL (1788-1850), his name giving rise to both the colloquial terms for a police officer, BOBBY and PEELER. Though the second of these is now obsolete, "bobby" is still with us, usually preceded by the word "village", even though these persons, if they actually still exist, are presumably shy and nocturnal in their habits as reported sightings are few and far between. Incidentally, the generic term "filth" meaning "police", which we are led to believe has enjoyed a more recent vogue among the criminal classes, embodies an inversion of values that must surely qualify as pathological.

[698] PELAGIAN HERESY
In the centuries following the death of Christ, the paucity of anything that might be called dogma in the Master's teaching left His followers at liberty to adopt pretty much any theology they fancied. The resulting free-for-all came at least locally and temporarily to an end with the Council of Nicaea in 325 (see ARIAN HERESY), which managed to impose a degree of order in the form of a defined mainstream orthodoxy embodied in the Nicene Creed we know and still use today. This reduced a number of popular variants of Christianity to the status of heresies and put their adherents firmly on the wrong side of the sheep/goats divide. The same fate befell the British monk PELAGIUS (ca.360 – ca.420) who, nearly a century later, rejected the doctrines of predestination and original sin and was denounced as a heretic at the Synod of Carthage in 416. The idea that children are born innocent is not without its attractions but it has the unfortunate corollary that it sharply reduces humans' need for God. This theme was explored by James Blish in his brilliant science fiction story *A case of conscience* (1958), perhaps the only work in that genre where the plot hinges on a point (actually two points) of Christian theology. The orthodox counter to Pelagius (an innate propensity for evil) was memorably expounded by William Golding in his novels *The Lord of the Flies* (1954) and *The Inheritors* (1955). Pelagius, incidentally, as the only major heresiarch native to these islands (his name is a Greco-Latinisation of a Celtic proper name meaning "sea-born"), arguably deserves a place in the pantheon of Great British Inventors.

[699] PELLET PROCESS
A photographic blueprint process of 1877 which made a positive from a positive; it was a later development of the original cyanotype process invented by SIR JOHN HERSCHEL in 1842 which made a positive from a negative and *vice versa*. The PELLET PROCESS was patented in the UK, the USA, and in France (1881), where

it became known as *Papier Gommoferrique*. It found some reprographic use for duplicating maps of the Survey of India Photographic Office in 1887-8, but the process was complicated in its chemistry and uncertain in its outcome, so rapidly fell into desuetude. French chemist HENRI PELLET was employed in the sugar industry as attested by his many publications on the analysis and refinement of sugarbeet, where he is described as "*Chimiste de la compagnie de Fives-Lille*".* He was also the inventor of the PELLET BURETTE. (MW)

* Fives-Lille is today an engineering concern specialising in the manufacture of industrial furnaces and associated hardware.

[700] PELMANISM

The Pelman Insitute was founded in London in 1898 by CHRISTOPHER LOUIS PELMAN to promote a system of memory-training he had devised. Throughout the first half of the 20th century PELMANISM, as it was called, was sold through advertising in popular magazines and newspapers to people discontented with their lives, who were told that Pelman's system would improve not only their memory but their standing in the world and lead to SUCCESS in business and in life. The target audience was essentially the same as that aimed at by the body-builder Charles Atlas, who promised weedy, unregarded men a way of developing formidable musculature with which to overawe potential bullies and attract admiring glances from the fair sex. "Pelmanism" is also applied to the card game (a close relative of KIM'S GAME) which figured largely in Pelman's memory-training system. It may be played with ordinary playing-cards or with specially devised packs which are commercially available.

[701] PELTON WHEEL

The Pelton wheel is properly described as a form of water turbine but perhaps more usefully regarded as an improved water wheel since it was the water wheel that it displaced in many industrial uses. It was the invention, in 1870, of the American LESTER ALLAN PELTON (1829-1908), who became interested in water-power while prospecting for gold during the California Gold Rush. It consists of a revolving disc to the circumference of which are fitted a number of equally-spaced metal cups. These are played on by a jet of water emerging from a nozzle under pressure. The cups are so shaped that the jet is split into two and the water entering them is reversed in direction so that as it leaves the cup it has given up virtually all its energy. A governor is normally fitted to cope with variations in water-pressure. The main use of the Pelton wheel is as a generator of electricity, in which role it can achieve high levels of efficiency. Pelton wheels may vary in size from domestic appliances only inches in diameter to monster installations in power stations generating up to 200 megawatts.

[702] PENROSE TILING

Tiles can be square, hexagonal or even triangular, but they cannot usefully be regular pentagons, because any attempt to tile your bathroom with these would leave gaps. This is a practical demonstration that in 2-dimensions repetitive 5-fold rotational symmetry is geometrically forbidden, and what's more **EUCLID** can prove it. However, if the requirement for strictly periodic ("translational") repetition is removed, then local 5-fold symmetry becomes possible in filling the 2-D plane, but not with complete regularity. **PENROSE TILES** are derived as fragments of the regular pentagon and consist of two interlocking shapes. One such pair consists of quadrilateral "darts" with internal angles of 36° and 72° and "kites" with 72° and 144°. Another pair are "golden diamonds" – fat rhombi with angles 72° and 108°, and thin rhombi with 36° and 144°. Either pair can make an infinite variety of fascinating tessellations in which the golden ratio **PHI** (*q.v.*) is deeply embedded. See also **SCHECHTMANITE**. Mathematical physicist **SIR ROGER PENROSE** (b. 1931) was born in Colchester and educated at University College, London, and Cambridge, and is now emeritus Rouse Ball professor of mathematics at Oxford. He has received numerous awards and honours for his distinguished contributions to general relativity theory and cosmology, in which he acts as a foil to his opposite number, Stephen Hawking, the Lucasian professor of mathematics at Cambridge. His forays into recreational mathematics, besides the pentagonal **PENROSE TILING**, have also produced the **PENROSE TRIANGLE** as the simplest of many "impossible objects". (MW)

[703] PÈRE DAVID'S DEER

FATHER ARMAND DAVID (1826-1900), Lazarist* missionary to China from 1862, made himself known in scientific circles by the zoological and botanical collections he sent back to the Paris Natural History Museum. He was subsequently entrusted by the French government with missions to Mongolia (1866), to Tibet (1868-70), and to inner China (1872-4). On his return to France he published accounts of his travels. In March 1866, just before leaving for Mongolia, he discovered in the Emperor's hunting park south of Peking the species of deer now named after him, *Elaphurus davidianus*, which had been thought extinct and certainly no longer existed in the wild. The deer's original home is not known. He described them as "gentle and rather silly-looking". Also named after Père David is an ornamental tree *Davidia involucrata*, a native of W. China whose pendant flowers are surrounded by large white bracts which earn it the common name "pocket-handkerchief tree".

* Charitable order founded by St. Vincent de Paul in 1633. Its HQ was the priory of Saint Lazare in Paris, a former leper hospital, used as a prison during the Terror.

[704] PERKIN'S MAUVE

SIR WILLIAM HENRY PERKIN (1838-1907) was born in London, studied at the

Royal College of Chemistry under **AUGUST WILHELM VON HOFMANN**, and earned his place in the history of industrial chemistry through a stroke of serendipity which befell him at the tender age of 18. In 1856 he set out worthily to synthesise quinine, a proven anti-malarial medicine, but also a scarce and therefore expensive natural product from the bark of the cinchona tree which, until introduced into the East Indies from the late 1860's onward, grew only in Bolivia and Peru. From what was known of the chemical formula of quinine, Perkin reasoned naively that it ought to be possible to make it from common coal-tar derivatives, such as aniline and toluidine, by oxidation with potassium dichromate.* It comes as no surprise to us today that he failed: his product was a blackish gunge (a common outcome of failed organic reactions) which he managed to spill and, when mopping it up, noticed that his cloth was dyed purple. This inspired him to extract the coloured ingredient, and thus the synthetic dyestuffs industry was born. Perkin patented his "aniline purple" and opened a dyeworks in Harrow to produce it. **PERKIN'S MAUVE**, as it came to be called (Fr. *mauve* = mallow, *malvaceae*), met with the approval of Queen Victoria in 1862 and rapidly became the fashionable colour, which made Perkin's fortune. It was also used for a 1d postage stamp. Perkin's eldest son, also **WILLIAM HENRY PERKIN** (1860-1929), likewise became an organic chemist (as did his two siblings – a certain familial lack of imagination begins to be apparent here) and is known for an ingenious piece of laboratory glassware for vacuum distillation, called the **PERKIN TRIANGLE** – which was actually invented by Perkin junior's fellow-student, British chemist Leonard Temple Thorne (1855-1941). (MW)

* No theory of structural chemistry existed at that time. Perkin did not appreciate that it is not sufficient just to have the right numbers of atoms in the molecule – they must also be connected in the right way. The molecular structure of quinine was determined in 1908 and the substance first synthesised in 1944. The structure of mauveine (the chemists' name for Perkin's mauve) was not fully elucidated until 1994. It bears no resemblance to that of quinine.

[705] PERSEID SHOWER

Meteor showers are produced when the earth passes through a stream of debris left in the trail of a comet. The **PERSEID SHOWER** is observed each year between late July and early August* and is associated with the comet **SWIFT-TUTTLE**. Meteor showers are named after the constellation occupying their apparent point of origin, in this case the constellation which is itself named after the Greek mythical hero **PERSEUS,** slayer of Medusa and rescuer of Andromeda. The parent comet bears the names of **LEWIS SWIFT** and **HORACE TUTTLE** who discovered it independently in 1862. Its earlier passages through the solar system have since been traced back as far as 69 BC. There is a faint likelihood (once considered a certainty) that the comet will at some time in the future hit either the Earth or the Moon. Its last appearance was in 1992 and its next is predicted for 2126.

* Hence the common name "Tears of St. Lawrence" after the martyred Saint whose feast falls on August 10th.

[706] PETERS' DUIKER

PETERS' DUIKER (*Cephalophus callipygus**), a small Central African antelope, and **PETERS' MANGABEY** (*Cercocebus galeritus*) a rare East African primate, are named after the German explorer and colonialist **Dr. CARL PETERS** (1856-1918), who played a major part in securing a large tract of Africa now known as Tanzania for Germany and was thus a major player in the "scramble" for territory in East Africa between Germany and Britain. Peters' method for adding this not inconsiderable acreage to the Kaiser's empire consisted of making "treaties" with the headmen of villages he happened to pass through. This was the normal practice on both sides at the time (Stanley's method was identical). With the so-called German East African Protectorate legally established by the Heligoland Treaty of 1890, Peters was appointed Imperial Commissioner for the new colony and posted to Kilimanjaro.** Here his violent mistreatment of the Africans in his care became an open scandal and he was recalled to Germany to face a judicial enquiry which found him guilty *in absentia*, Peters having scarpered to London. He was later pardoned and pensioned in response to the demands of the German public, to whom he was a hero. Hitler greatly admired Peters, calling him "a model colonial administrator, strict but fair". (Note: botanical names carrying the authorial name "Peters" refer to the German naturalist Wilhelm Peters (1815-1883), who travelled and collected in Mozambique in the 1840's.)

* "Callipygus" – a Greek-derived term meaning "having a lovely bottom".

** On a whim of Queen Victoria's (her grandson the Kaiser had expressed a desire to own a mountain in Africa), the boundary between British and German "spheres" was obliged to make a little detour to leave Kilimanjaro on the German side of the line.

[707] PETRARCHAN SONNET

The Italian poet and scholar **FRANCESCO PETRARCA** (originally it was **PETRACCO**, but he changed it for reasons of euphony) lived from 1304 to 1374. His verse output consists largely of odes and sonnets, the latter being a verse-form invented in Italy in the 13th century, it is not certain by whom. As practised by Petrarch, it consists of an eight-line stanza (octet) rhyming ABBA ABBA, followed by a six-line stanza (sestet) rhyming either CD CD CD or CDE CDE. All sonnets are 14 lines in length, but within this basic format variations are possible. Shakespeare's sonnets, for example, take the form of three quatrains followed by a couplet, the rhyme-scheme being ABAB CDCD EFEF GG. Milton, on the other hand, follows the Petrarchan model in, for example, the sonnet on his blindness (*When I consider how my light is spent...*), as does Wordsworth in his sonnet on Westminster Bridge (*Earth has not anything to show more fair...*). The sestet in Hopkins' *Felix Randal* rhymes CCD CCD. (The last line, incidentally, in this poem is one of the finest in the whole corpus of English poetry.) Camoens, Portugal's national poet (1524-1580), left some three hundred sonnets which follow the Petrarchan format. The majority of Petrarch's large output was addressed to his muse and mistress Laura, who may or may not have been a real person.

[708] PETRI DISH

A piece of laboratory glassware in the form of a shallow, cylindrical, lidded dish mainly used by microbiologists for growing cell-cultures. It owes its form and its name to German military doctor **JULIUS RICHARD PETRI** (1852-1921) who was born in Barmen and trained at the Kaiser Wilhelm Academy. He invented it in 1877 while working as an assistant to the pioneer bacteriologist Robert Koch (1843-1910). It was Koch who first isolated and studied the bacilli responsible for anthrax, tuberculosis and cholera. In modern laboratories, single-use plastic petri dishes may be preferred to glass.

[709] PETZVAL LENS

A revolutionary design of camera lens from 1840, an invention stimulated by the birth of photography. This embryonic art-science benefited from the larger aperture of the **PETZVAL LENS** (f/3.7) than hitherto (f/16 typically), thus shortening photographic exposure times from minutes to seconds – a boon for **DAGUERREOTYPE** portraiture, which was an uncomfortable experience at best. The **PETZVAL LENS** design was the first to be computed mathematically: two achromatic doublets of crown and flint glass (see **DOLLOND LENS**) were separated by an aperture stop; some residual spherical aberration was mathematically resolved by the inventor in the **PETZVAL SUM,** an equation still used by lens designers for evaluating flatness of field. This optical configuration remains the basis even today for some long-focus and projection lenses. The Hungarian mathematician **JOSEF MAXIMILIAN PETZVAL** (1807-1891) was born of German origins in Spisská Belá in the Austro-Hungarian Empire (today Slovakia), and studied physics and mathematics at the Institutum Geometricum in Budapest. In 1838 he was appointed professor of mathematics at the University of Vienna and occupied the chair until 1877. In 1840, for a single payment, he licensed the manufacturing rights of his lens design to the camera manufacturer Peter Wilhelm von Voigtländer (1812-1878), and subsequently rued the day that he did so. After his retirement, **PETZVAL** lived a reclusive life, and died almost penniless, in the Vienna suburb of Kahlenberg. (MW)

[710] PHI

The Greek letter **PHI,** written Φ, is the initial letter of the name of **PHIDIAS** (*ca.*

490-430 BC), born in Athens to become the most celebrated of all classical Greek sculptors. He was commissioned by Pericles in 447 BC to execute some of the principal statuary of the city of Athens, namely, the marble *Athena Parthenos* in the Parthenon itself, and the massive bronze *Athena Propagos* in the Propylaea, the entrance to the Acropolis. He is also famed for his statue of Zeus in the temple of Olympia and a bronze group of heroes and gods at Delphi. All his originals have been destroyed, but Roman copies, and his reputation, survive. **PHI** (ϕ) is also the mathematical symbol chosen in Phidias' honour to represent the omnipresent *Golden Ratio* or *Golden Section* of classical art, which is deemed to provide the most aesthetically satisfying way of dividing a linear space, or forming the aspect ratio of a rectangle. Many painters, sculptors, architects and even musicians are reputed to have made use of it, as first popularly explained by Luca Pacioli (1445-1517) in his *Divina Proportione* of 1509, and in numerous analytical publications since.* The golden ratio was known to **PYTHAGORAS** and appears first in **EUCLID**, where it is described as the "extreme and mean ratio" in *Book VI* of his *Elements*. The formal geometrical definition of the golden section divides a line so that the ratio of the larger part (ϕ) to the smaller part (1) is equal to the ratio of the whole line ($\phi+1$) to the larger part (ϕ) thus:

$$\phi/1 = (\phi+1)/\phi$$

which can be rearranged to:

$$\phi^2 = \phi+1$$

As any polymathic school-boy or girl can demonstrate, solution of this quadratic equation yields the two possible values for ϕ as the irrational numbers:

$$\phi = (\sqrt{5}\pm1)/2$$

The larger root is usually taken so that:

$\phi = 1.6180339887498948482045868343656381177203091798057628621...$

ϕ, like π and e, is one of those "magic" irrational numbers whose special properties cause surprising recurrences both in mathematics and in nature. In 1608 **KEPLER** showed that the ratio of successive **FIBONACCI NUMBERS** converges on the value of ϕ. It is also favoured by Dame Nature in her phyllotaxy: *e.g.* sunflower heads display spirals of florets whose number, counted respectively clockwise and counterclockwise, converges on the ratio ϕ. Pine cones, pineapples and artichokes also provide perfect fodder for golden numerologists. Golden rectangles, when whirled around, generate a logarithmic spiral whose growth factor is ϕ. The shell of the chambered nautilus (*Nautilus pompilius*) is frequently celebrated as an instance of a logarithmic spiral in nature, but it is not strictly golden. There is a profound connection between ϕ and 5-foldness: our polymathic schoolperson could no doubt also demonstrate that, in a regular pentagon, the ratio of the chord to the edge is ϕ, so it plays a central role in the geometry of **PENROSE TILINGS**. Occultists with a penchant for pentacles and trigonometry may find some diabolical satisfaction in contemplating this exact relationship between **PHI** and the Number of the Beast:

$$\phi = -2 \sin 666°$$

(MW)

* Notably *The Golden Ratio* (2002) of Mario Livio, head of the Science Division at the HUBBLE SPACE TELESCOPE, who examines critically the mystical subculture of "Golden Numerology".

[711] PHILIDOR DEFENCE

Chess opening named after FRANÇOIS ANDRÉ DANICAN PHILIDOR (1726-1795), French composer and champion chess player. His *Analyse du jeu des échecs* (1749) was long considered the standard work on the subject, went through numerous editions, and was translated into English, Italian and German. Philidor was marooned in London by the outbreak of the French Revolution (he was a proscribed person) and died there. (See also RUY LOPEZ.)

[712] PICKETT'S CHARGE

An incident at the Battle of Gettysburg in the American Civil War. At the end of June 1863 Robert E. Lee crossed the Potomac with 80,000 men and invaded Pennsylvania. The Confederates met the Army of the Potomac under General Meade at Gettysburg. (Gettysburg was an "encounter battle" – that is, neither the time nor the place of the engagement was planned by either side. The two armies simply bumped into each other.) In the two-day engagement that followed (July 2-3) the outcome was still in the balance when, on the second day, Lee ordered one of his divisional commanders, Major-General GEORGE EDWARD PICKETT (1825-1875), to organise a last desperate attempt to break the Union line by an assault on Meade's centre with 10 brigades (some 15,000 men). This involved an advance over half a mile of open ground under concentrated musketry and artillery fire. The Confederates, amazingly, actually succeeded in reaching the Union lines but were unable to hold the position in the face of a counter-attack from Meade's reserves. They fell back. Barely half the attacking force returned to the start line. Gettysburg is generally accounted the turning point in the war. Though after the battle Lee was able to withdraw virtually unopposed, the South never recovered the strategic initiative. Gettysburg, therefore, was the last moment at which, in the event of a victory, the Confederacy might have hoped to end the war on terms. And PICKETT'S CHARGE was the last moment at which the tide of battle might have swung the other way. In which case, it is hardly an exaggeration to say that on success or – as it turned out – failure of the assault depended the whole outcome of the war. Pickett was a West Point graduate who served in the Mexican War and against Indians on the Western frontier before resigning to join the army of the Confederacy. After the war, he was offered a commission by the Khedive of Egypt (Gordon's employer) but turned it down in favour of peaceable employment as an insurance agent in Virginia.

[713] PIERPONT MORGAN LIBRARY

American banker, bibliophile, and art collector **JOHN PIERPONT MORGAN** (1837-1913) amassed during his lifetime an almost unparalleled collection of precious books, manuscripts and art-works. On his death, he left his library and part of his art collection to be administered as a public educational resource. Originally known as the **PIERPONT MORGAN LIBRARY**, it has now been rechristened the **MORGAN LIBRARY AND MUSEUM.** Its premises are on Madison Avenue in New York City. As well as being a generous benefactor to artistic Good Causes such as New York's Metropolitan Museum of Art (see also **LUTTRELL PSALTER**), Morgan was a hugely influential figure in the economic and financial history of the US. He is said to have prevented, almost single-handed, the collapse of America's banking system in 1893 and again in 1907. How he might have coped with the present (2009) chaos – a triumph of greed over prudence – in the world's banking system is an intriguing speculation.

[714] PIKE'S PEAK

The wonderfully-named **ZEBULON MONTGOMERY PIKE** (1779-1813), while still a junior officer in the American army, led two exploring expeditions west of the Mississippi in 1805-6 and 1806-7, which hugely contributed to the mapping of this virtually unknown part of the continent. In the course of his second journey, on November 23 1806, he observed (one is not allowed these days to say "discovered"), in what was to become the State of Colorado, the mountain he called "Highest Peak" and which was subsequently renamed **PIKE'S PEAK** in his honour. He attempted to climb the mountain but failed, driven back by a lack of suitable winter clothing. It was not climbed until 1820. Pike saw action against the British in the War of 1812. In April 1813 he led an attack on the town of York (now Toronto) and was killed by a blow on the head from a flying lump of rock when the retreating garrison blew the magazine. Pike published an account of his explorations in 1810. (Standard ed. by Elliott Coues, 3 vols, N.Y. 1895). The height of Pike's Peak is given as 4301 metres. The 1 is a nice touch.

[715] PIMM'S

An alcoholic drink favoured by, but not confined to, the upper drinking classes of southern England at refined events such as Henley Royal Regatta and Glyndebourne opera. It is the taste of summer, of garden parties, cricket matches and tennis tournaments. Pimm's No.1 was created in the 1840's by **JAMES PIMM** (179[?2]-1866), who ran an oyster bar in the City of London and it was served with the sea food for which the customary accompaniment would have been either stout or a rum-based "house-cup". Pimm's cocktail was based on the newly fashionable gin, mixed with fruit extracts, liqueurs, spices, and bitter herbs, and soon gained in popularity. After Pimm's death the business was acquired by hotel and restaurant owner Horatio David Davies (1842-1912), a future Lord Mayor of London and MP for Chatham. It was Davies who expanded the enterprise to create five Pimms restaurants. By the turn of the nineteenth century Pimm's was being produced for a worldwide market, though the company has never divulged the secret of its recipes. Later additions to the range were versions based on rum, whisky, brandy, etc., each with its own number. But none has outsold the original formula and "Pimm's" *tout court* is universally understood to mean Pimms No. 1. (RS)

[716] PINCHBECK

A variety of brass – an alloy chiefly of 83% copper and 17% zinc – intended to simulate gold. It was used in the 18th century for imitation jewellery, and in the 19th century as an ornamental surround and protection for cased photographic images, such as **DAGUERREOTYPES** and **AMBROTYPES.** The alloy was invented in the early 1700s by **CHRISTOPHER PINCHBECK** (1670-1732) a London clockmaker. Pinchbeck himself never sought to deceive with his "Pinchbeck Metal", as he called it, otherwise known as "poor man's gold", but after his death, as a consequence of unscrupulous jewellers passing off sham articles as real gold, the name fell into disrepute, coming to signify anything **TAWDRY** or counterfeit. (MW)

[717] PITCAIRN ISLAND

In 1766 a two-ship expedition under the command of Captain Samuel Wallis in *Dolphin* left England bound for the South Pacific. The second ship, *Swallow* under Captain Philip Carteret became separated in the Strait of Magellan but continued the cruise which resulted, among other discoveries, in the first sighting of Pitcairn Island by a midshipman named **ROBERT PITCAIRN** (1745?-1770?). Carteret completed his circumnavigation, returning home in 1769. Twenty years later Pitcairn was chosen as a refuge by the *Bounty* mutineers (1789), whose descendants still inhabit the island.

[718] PITMAN SHORTHAND

Script for rapid speech-recording invented by schoolmaster, phonetician and educationalist **ISAAC PITMAN** (1813-1897). He published his *Stenographic Sound Hand* in 1837 and opened a school for teaching his system in Bath. His brother **BENJAMIN PITMAN** (1822-1910) was despatched to the States in 1852 to spread the gospel of "phonography", which he did with conspicuous success, finding time in the meanwhile to invent a relief-printing process and later becoming a teacher at the Cincinnati School of Art. The main rival to Pitman's system was/is that of **JOHN ROBERT GREGG** (1867-1948). Gregg was born in Ireland and emigrated to the States in 1893. He founded schools for teaching shorthand in Britain and America. The forms of **GREGG SHORTHAND**, being largely based on curves, are said by adepts to flow more easily from the secretary's pencil than the jerkier forms of Pitman's system. Pitman users, naturally, deny this. Shorthand was an indispensable item of office equipment until the advent, in the sixties of the last century, of the dictaphone and its digital successors.

[719] PITOT TUBE

HENRI PITOT (1695-1771) was a French hydraulic engineer who worked on the Canal du Midi, the Languedoc Canal, and on aqueducts at Montpellier and Nîmes. He studied the theory of pumps and hydraulic machinery with a view to improving their efficiency, disproved the prevailing notion that water in a river flows faster as depth increases, and invented the **PITOT TUBE**, an instrument for measuring the rate of flow by measuring the height of a column of water that the pressure exerted by the movement of water would maintain. He was elected to the *Académie des sciences* in 1724. WWII aircraft were fitted with an instrument for measuring airspeed based on the same principle, whose gun-like protruding nozzle was known as the **PITOT HEAD**. Malfunctioning of the aircraft's pitot sensors is thought to have caused the loss of an Air France Airbus off the coast of Brazil in June 2009, which cost the lives of all on board.

[720] PITT-RIVERS MUSEUM

An extraordinary collection of ethnographic and archaeological finds from all over the world donated to Oxford University in 1884. (It shares a building with the University Museum of Natural History – an edifice in the Industrial Early English style, a pleasing blend of Gothic cathedral and Victorian railway station.) The donor was **General AUGUSTUS HENRY LANE FOX PITT-RIVERS** (1827–1900), soldier, landowner, archaeologist, anthropologist and educationalist. The original bequest consisted of approximately 20,000 items and has now grown to half a million. Public education was one of Pitt-Rivers' primary goals. He believed that existing museums confused their roles in research and education, so that most museum displays were simply tedious. His own museum, with its illustrative models, is a cornucopia of delights. The exhibits are arranged thematically, according to how the objects were used, rather than according to their age or place of origin. This layout owes a lot to the theories of General Pitt Rivers himself, who intended his collection to show, via progression in design, the evolution of material culture from the simple to the complex. Though some of his ideas are now outmoded, his thinking on the subject of typology and the idea that objects can be placed in chronological sequence on the basis of slight changes in design, were crucial concepts for archaeology. The thematic arrangement also illustrates the old dictum that "form follows function" by showing how the need for a tool to do a particular job – a fish spear, for example – produces surprisingly similar artefacts in locations and among peoples widely separated in time and space. Perhaps unusually for a professional soldier (Pitt-Rivers had seen active service in the Crimea and retired from the army with the rank of lieutenant-general in 1882, the same year in which he become the first Inspector of Ancient Monuments) he became actively interested in the evolution of culture, inspired by Darwin's *Origin of Species*, published in 1859. He became a field archaeologist in the 1860's, surveying a number of prehistoric forts in southern Ireland, working as a barrow digger in Yorkshire, and excavating hill forts and flint mines on the Sussex Downs. Thanks largely to his insistence on contextual recording, Pitt-Rivers is widely regarded as a founding father of scientific archaeology in this country. By noting the precise position of each find he gave them solid evidential value, and so was among the first practitioners to turn antiquarianism into archaeology. He was particularly fortunate in being the owner of large estates rich in archaeological remains in which to pursue his interests. As part of his legacy, he is remembered as the creator of the Larmer Pleasure Grounds in South Wiltshire, set high on Cranborne Chase, a 12-acre site for picnics, open-air concerts, sporting contests, and similar jollifications. Nowadays the Larmer Tree Gardens are the venue for a summer music festival that attracts bigger crowds with each year that passes. In addition to numerous publications in scientific journals, P-R's writings include his 4-volume *Excavations at Cranborne Chase* (1887-1898) and *The evolution of culture and other essays*, ed. Myres (1906). (RS)

[721] PLANCK'S CONSTANT

It has long been appreciated that matter is not infinitely "smooth", but consists ultimately of atoms. That the same idea must apply to energy came as a shock in 1900: energy, too, is not infinitely subdivisible but comes in tiny packets called quanta. This was established by German theoretical physicist **MAX KARL ERNST PLANCK** (1858-1947), who studied under **KIRCHHOFF** and **VON HELMHOLZ** in Berlin, where he succeeded to the chair of physics (1889-1926). His explanation of "black body radiation" – the frequencies of light energy emitted by a hot object – necessitated that the energy, E, of a quantum of light was proportional to its frequency, f, or symbolically: $E = hf$, where the constant of proportionality, h, is called **PLANCK'S CONSTANT** and is remarkably tiny. (The fact that this defines the smallest possible stepwise change in energy, makes a nonsense of the currently trendy expression "a quantum leap" to describe a huge change.) This innocent-seeming formulation of Planck's quantum theory completely revolutionised physics, and successfully accounted for phenomena that were inexplicable using classical **NEWTONIAN THEORY**, earning Planck the **NOBEL PRIZE** for physics in 1918. (MW)

[722] PLATONIC SOLIDS

These are the regular convex polyhedra, each of which fulfills the criteria that all its faces, vertices, and edges are, respectively, the same, *i.e.* congruent, or indistinguishable. For each solid, all the faces are one kind of regular polygon. It can be proved that the solids satisfying all these requirements are only five in number*:

Numbers of -

Name	Faces	Vertices	Edges	Face type
Tetrahedron	4	4	6	equilateral triangle
Octahedron	8	6	12	equilateral triangle
Cube	6	8	12	square
Icosahedron	20	12	30	equilateral triangle
Dodecahedron	12	20	30	regular pentagon

The numerically-observant reader may have spotted an apparent relationship here: Faces + Vertices = Edges + 2, which is indeed generally true for all convex solids, however irregular, and is known as **EULER'S THEOREM**. These five solids have achieved mystical status: **KEPLER** based his model of the solar system upon them; and they have also been identified with the elements of classical antiquity, fire, air, earth, water, and aether, respectively. Many natural philosophers have remarked upon their occurrence in nature: the forms of crystals, molecules, radiolarian skeletons, pollen grains, and viruses. Elaborations of these solids were used by **BUCKMINSTER FULLER** in his architectural structures. The pre-eminent Greek thinker **PLATO** (*ca.* 429-347 BC), was a pupil of **SOCRATES**, teacher of Aristotle, and founder of the "Academy"**, the Athenian school of philosophy which most profoundly influenced Christian theology and Western thought. Although Plato gets the credit for the five regular solids, three of them were among the secrets previously enjoyed by the **PYTHAGOREAN** brotherhood (*ca.* 580-500 BC), and the remaining two (octahedron and icosahedron) were discoved by Plato's colleague at the Academy, Theaetetus (ca. 414-369 BC). The discovery of the presence of polyhedral stone artefacts in Scotland, strongly suggests that they were also known there in the megalithic era *ca.* 2000 BC. (MW)

* But if the requirement for convexity is lifted, and intersecting or 'dimpled' faces allowed, the four remarkable **KEPLER-POINSOT** star polyhedra must be added to the list.

** Named after a garden on the outskirts of Athens where Plato taught, the garden itself being named after the mythical hero Akademos.

[723] PLIMPTON 322

Unless you belong to the presumably tiny band of people who can read a washing bill in Babylonian cuneiform *and* have a profound knowledge of the early history of mathematics, the words **"PLIMPTON THREE TWO TWO"** are not going to make your pulse beat faster. But to that handful of initiates, it is like "walkies" to a dog. **GEORGE ARTHUR PLIMPTON** (1855-1935), American author and publisher (he headed the firm of Ginn and Company), assembled during his lifetime an important collection of books and manuscripts dealing with the history of education, and which he bequeathed to Columbia University in 1936. No. 322 in the Plimpton collection, a clay tablet with a cuneiform inscription thought to date from about 1800 BC, is the most famous of the many hundreds of known cuneiform tablets dealing with mathematical topics. Though its importance as an indicator of the sophistication of Babylonian mathematics is beyond question, its interpretation is in some respects problematic and so continues to provide ample matter for academic debate. It appears to consist of a table of so-called "Pythagorean numbers" which satisfy the expression $a^2+b^2=c^2$ as in the famous theorem concerning right-angled triangles. But how this list was generated and for what purpose remains a mystery.

[724] PLIMSOLL LINE

It was while working the coal trade in London in the 1850's that **SAMUEL PLIMSOLL** (1824-1898) became aware of the unnecessary dangers incurred by seamen due to the overloading of ships. He was elected to Parliament in 1868 and made it his business to publicise maritime abuses through the publication of a book *Our seamen: an appeal* (1873). The outcome was the passing – over determined obstruction from ship-owning Members – of the Merchant Shipping Act of 1876, which including the stipulation that every ship should be marked by means of a circle with a horizontal line drawn through it to indicate the limit to which it could safely be loaded. This mark became known as the **PLIMSOLL LINE**. Plimsoll's humanitarian concerns were not limited to the hardships faced by sailors: in 1890 he published a "Second appeal" entitled *Cattle ships* to bring public attention to the cruelties and dangers involved in the shipping of live cattle – abuses which today we have still shamefully failed to eradicate. Plimsoll is also remembered in the nickname of a rubber-soled canvas shoe developed by the Liverpool Rubber Company (later acquired by the Dunlop Rubber Company*) in the 1830's. It was intended for beach wear and is supposed to have acquired this name from the fact that if water was allowed to go above the line which marked the junction of sole and upper, the foot got wet. The **PLIMSOLL**'s other names include sand shoe (the original name), sneaker, tennis shoe, gym shoe, and (in Wales) "dap" – an acronym for Dunlop Athletic Plimsolls. Dunlop still make rubber-soled sports shoes but now, inevitably, they are called trainers.

* Founded (1889) as the Dunlop Pneumatic Tyre Co. by the Scotch inventor and veterinary surgeon JOHN BOYD DUNLOP (1840-1921).

[725] PLUTONIUM – see THORIUM

[726] PLYUSHKIN'S SYNDROME – see DIOGENES SYNDROME

[727] POCOCK'S CHARVOLANT

In the annals of chartaetology (the making and flying of kites) the name of GEORGE POCOCK (b. 1796, date of death unknown) has an honoured place as the pioneer of kite traction. In 1826, Pocock, a schoolteacher and amateur inventor living in Bristol, patented a horseless carriage drawn by two kites. This was no mere paper invention. It was actually built – in several versions of different sizes – and actually worked. It was capable of speeds of up to 20 miles per hour, was steered partly by control lines and partly by steerable front wheels, and was equipped with a brake mechanism in the form of an iron bar which could be lowered by a control lever to dig into the ground. Though the **"CHARVOLANT"**, as Pocock called it, had the added advantage that it travelled free on toll roads, tolls being based on the number of horses per vehicle, it was largely thanks to the difficulty of controlling speed and direction that the charvolant failed to replace horse-drawn (let alone steam-driven) vehicles. Pocock publicised his invention in a book entitled *The Aeropleustic Art, or, Navigation in the Air by the use of Kites or Buoyant Sails,* and in the same work suggested other ways in which kite traction might be employed, such as a source of auxiliary power for sailing ships or a means of rescuing people from stranded vessels (*cf.* **MANBY APPARATUS**). There must have been a gene for eccentric inventiveness in the Pocock family since, according to humorist Arthur Marshall, famous for his impersonations of teachers at girls' boarding schools, one Alfred Pocock, a great uncle of cricketer W.G. Grace, was responsible for the invention of a steam-driven **SCHOOLBOY-BEATING MACHINE***. Whether Pocock's ingenious correctional device (it had presets for number and severity of strokes) ever existed outside Arthur Marshall's fertile and mischief-loving brain is a question that would certainly repay investigation, as would (some might say) his machine's re-introduction to our educational system.

* *Whimpering in the Rhododenrons* (1982) p. 127. George Pocock's daughter Martha gave birth to the hairy old ball-walloper of sporting legend Dr. H.M. Grace. Alfred Pocock, if such a person existed, must have been a brother of kite-flying George, but *DNB* has no mention of him.

[728] PODSNAPPERY

MR. PODSNAP, a character in Dickens' *Our Mutual Friend* is presented as a monster of smug, blinkered complacency, "particularly well satisfied with most things, and, above all other things, with himself." Dickens coined the word **"PODSNAPPERY"** to describe Mr P's character and behavioural quirks. The name Podsnap re-occurs in Huxley's *Brave New World* (1932). In the hatcheries where human beings are conceived, grown and "born" *in vitro*, **PODSNAP'S TECHNIQUE** refers to a system the operators have evolved for fertilising the lifetime supply of eggs a woman carries in her ovaries in one fell swoop (after which, of course, reproductive biology need no longer concern her – a great relief, one imagines). The reasons for Huxley's choice of name in this instance is not immediately apparent, but a fair guess would be that it has less to do with Dickens than with shelling peas.

[729] POINCIANA

Poinciana regia (synonyms: *Delonix regia*, *Caesalpina regia*), a beautiful flowering tropical and sub-tropical tree, originally a native of Madagascar. Named after a **M. DE POINCI**, a 17th-century governor of the French Antilles. The song *Poinciana* has become a jazz standard recorded by (among others) Gerry Mulligan and, notably, Ahmad Jamal.

[730] POINSETTIA

Euphorbia pulcherrima or Poinsettia is a deciduous winter-flowering plant, native of Mexico, which appears in large numbers in British houses around Christmas. It is named after, and was first bred as a garden plant by, US diplomat and politician **JOEL ROBERTS POINSETT** (1779-1851). In 1810 Poinsett was posted as special agent to S. America, charged with supporting the local independence movements in Chile and La Plata, and later (1825-1830) served as first US ambassador to Mexico.

[731] POISEUILLE

A unit of fluid dynamic viscosity – that is, measuring the resistance to flow in a liquid or gas, due to its "internal friction". It is proposed – but not yet accepted – for the Système International, with the symbol Pl, and it derives from one **PASCAL** second. It is equal to ten times the old cgs unit of viscosity, the **POISE**. Both units were named for the French physician, **JEAN LOUIS MARIE POISEUILLE** (1799-1869), who was born in Paris and studied at the École Polytechnique. His interest in the flow of human blood through veins – which had been visibly copious in the streets of Paris during recent years (see **GUILLOTINE**) – led him to the concepts of viscosity and the formulation of **POISEUILLE'S LAW**. (MW)

[732] PONTON'S PROCESS

Scottish inventor **MUNGO PONTON** (1802-1880) a farmer's son, trained as a lawyer and was one of the founders of the National Bank of Scotland (1825). Ill-health forced an early retirement and allowed him to devote himself to his scientific interests. In the history of photography he is remembered for his early discovery (1839) that paper coated with a soluble dichromate is light-sensitive, changing colour from yellow to brown and ultimately greenish-blue. This photochemical reaction also involves the sizing agent of the paper – usually gelatin. **PONTON'S PROCESS** is consequently the forerunner of all the dichromated-colloid pigment processes: the carbon or Autotype process of Poitevin, and Swan; the gum bichromate process or Photoaquatint of Maskell and Demachy, and Rouillé-Ladevèse; the Fresson process, derived from Artigue's process and so on. These photographic printing processes are characterised by their "painterly" qualities (*viz.* application of the sensitizer by brush in a wide range of pigment colours) and they tend to be favoured by artists *manqués*, in preference to the merely "mechanical" procedures of conventional photographic printing. (MW)

[733] PONZI SCHEME

Fraudulent investment scheme named after Italian-American swindler and confidence trickster **CARLO PONZI** (1882-1949). Economists, keen to have their arcane mumbo-jumbo mistaken for a science, have preferred to ignore the fact that *Homo economicus*, the basic unit of their study material, is, like every other kind of *Homo*, only partially and intermittently rational,* and for this reason alone no generalisation about economic behaviour can have any predictive value, and no economic forecast is worth its weight in hot air. The Ponzis of this world, on the other hand, are keenly aware of the limits of human rationality, and know exactly how to make it work for them. Reason tells us that when offered a proposition that is too good to be true, it almost certainly isn't true. But the con man knows that this reasonable objection can be all too easily overpowered by another universal human characteristic – greed. However, the mechanics of the Ponzi scheme are far from simple because the operation carries within it the seeds of its own destruction. With cunning diffidence, even a show of reluctance, the Schemer – let's pluck a couple of random initials from the air and call him BM – offers his victim a chance to invest in a deal that will net him (the victim) an improbable amount of interest in an improbably short time. (Some of Ponzi's punters were offered a 100% profit within three months.) Money duly changes hands but is not invested. Instead, part of it goes to pay the investor a dividend, thus reassuring him that the scheme is working as advertised, and the rest goes into BM's Cayman Islands bank account. So far, so good. But in order to keep the scheme going, BM has to continue to enlist new investors, who in turn will have to be paid phoney dividends from the contributions of yet further investors. Growth, therefore, has to be not merely continuous but *exponential*, and it is this ultimately impossible requirement that brings about the scheme's collapse.** BM naturally doesn't want to be around when this happens. So for him, as for any successful Ponzi schemer, timing is everything, and the trick is to judge the exact moment at which to turn mother's picture to the wall and get out of town. If most Ponzi schemers fall at this last fence, the reason is not far to seek – it's our old friend Mr. Greed again.

* See, for example, Charles Mackay's 1842 classic *Extraordinary popular delusions and the madness of crowds*. Or, for something more recent, more technical and even more mouth-fillingly titled: Akerlof and Shiller *Animal spirits: how human psychology drives the economy and why it matters for global capitalism* (2009).

** Arguably, this applies to the economy as a whole. Current orthodoxy apparently regards continuous growth as the sign of a healthy economy. But growth *sine fine*, as the Romans used to say of their empire, growth without limits, is an impossibility in human affairs as in nature and sooner or later, in Yeats's words, "*Things fall apart*".

[734] POOLE'S CAVERN

Originally **POOLE'S HOLE**, this system of limestone caves in the hillside of Grin Low just south of the Derbyshire spa town of Buxton has disclosed evidences of habitation from the Bronze Age, and numerous Roman artefacts. By Victorian times it had become a show-cave, boasting formations of stalagmites, stalactites, and sundry other attractive speleothems. Originally the property of the Dukes of Devonshire, the cavern and its surrounding woodlands are now owned and run as a tourist attraction by the Buxton Civic Association. It is listed as the first of the *Seven Wonders of the Peak*, so named in 1636 by Thomas Hobbes, and described in the work of that name (1683) by Charles Cotton, Isaac Walton's angling oppo. Another visitor was Daniel Defoe who reorded his impression in his *Tour of the whole island of Great Britain* (1725). Nothing is known of the semi-mythical **POOLE** (*ca.* 1440) beyond his status as a reclusive 15th-century outlaw who made the "hole" his lair, sallying forth only to rob the odd passing traveller. He may have been a maverick, or a political refugee, from a good family residing at Poole's Hall in Staffordshire. The geology of Derbyshire is conspicuous for its extensive limestone caves: the most celebrated of them – Peak Cavern in Castleton – was reputed to emit flatulent sounds from its interior, and therefore acquired the dubious eponym of the **DEVIL'S ARSE**; but this name was suppressed in 1880 so as not to offend a visiting Queen Victoria. (MW)

[735] POOR RICHARD'S ALMANACK

Published annually in Philadelphia from 1732 to 1758, *Poor Richard's Almanack* was the work of Boston-born **BENJAMIN FRANKLIN** (1706-1790), author, printer, publisher, inventor, scientist and diplomat, who adopted the pseudonymous persona of **POOR RICHARD** for the purpose. Its contents comprised the usual mixture of astronomical and astrological tables, weather forecasts, and practical advice for farmers and householders, interspersed with useful maxims and homely proverbial sayings couched in language coloured by Franklin's own down-to-earth and slightly cynical wit. It is thanks to the latter element that the *Poor Richard* holds its interest today, while Franklin the scientist is represented in the popular imagination by a man holding the end of a kite string while he waits to get struck by lightning, and Franklin the inventor by the **FRANKLIN STOVE** or "Pennsylvania Fireplace" which heated rooms more efficiently and more cheaply than conventional fireplaces (*cf.* **RUMFORD FIREPLACE**). His role as a diplomat dates from 1757 when Franklin was sent to London to represent the interests of Pennsylvania. From this point he gradually acquired wider responsibilities until he became in effect the semi-official ambassador on this side of the Atlantic for the American colonies. Following the Declaration of Independence, which he helped to draft, Franklin went to France as one of three Colonial Commissioners, charged with negotiating a treaty of friendship between France and the rebel colonies. In France Franklin was a popular and respected figure and extracts from the *Almanack* were published in a French translation under the title *Les maximes du Bonhomme Richard*. When in 1779 the French put the frigate *Duc du Duras* at the disposal of John Paul Jones to sail against British merchant shipping, Jones renamed the ship *Bonhomme Richard* in Franklin's honour. On September 23 1779, Jones attacked a merchant fleet escorted by the British frigate *Serapis* off Flamborough Head. In the famous and hard-fought action which followed, Jones succeeded in boarding and capturing *Serapis* but, shortly after, the badly-damaged *Bonhomme Richard* foundered. The wreck has never been located despite the efforts of author Clive Cussler, who has mounted and led two diving expeditions in search of it. Finding it would be a feather in anyone's cap as the brief but glorious career of the *Bonhomme Richard* has become a symbol of the Americans' struggle to free themselves (slaves excepted) from the tyrant's yoke, and perhaps also a reminder that without French help they might well have failed in the attempt. (See also **OLD MOORE'S ALMANACK, WHITAKER'S ALMANACK**.)

[736] PORTHMADOG – see PORTMADOC

[737] PORTLAND VASE

One of the British Museum's most famous acquisitions and probably the most famous piece of glassware in the world. It was acquired in 1778 and brought to England by Sir William Hamilton who, apart from his duties as ambassador to the court of Naples and husband to Nelson's mistress, was a considerable antiquary. He sold it to a member of the Cavendish-Bentinck family, the **DUKES OF PORTLAND**, and it was the Fourth Duke who deposited it with the BM in 1810 as a permanent loan and whose name is attached to it. It was finally purchased from the Seventh Duke in 1945. The vase is thought to have been made in Rome around 25 BC at a time when the Republic was drawing to a messy close and Augustus was establishing himself as first emperor. The design of white figures on a blue background was achieved by coating the blue vase with a layer of white glass and then cutting away the unwanted portion of the white layer. The perfection of the workmanship and the beauty of the design would make the vase stand out in any company, but did not save it from the attentions of a drunken **HOOLIGAN** named William Lloyd who smashed it to pieces in 1845. It has since been twice restored, the last time in 1987. The vase was at one time on loan to Josiah **WEDGWOOD** who set out to copy it in porcelain and its influence visibly informs much of Wedgwood's work. The scenes depicted on the vase are clearly allegorical, though their meaning is subject to some uncertainty. It seems likely that they represent the abandonment by Mark Antony of his second wife Octavia, sister of Augustus, and his seduction by **CLEOPATRA**. If the interpretation is correct, this transcendently beautiful object was originally intended as a piece of political propaganda.

[738] PORTMADOC

A small seaside town and harbour in north Wales on the Glaslyn Estuary with access to Cardigan Bay. Its name is said to derive from one or both of two sources. (1) **WILLIAM ALEXANDER MADOCKS** (1773-1828), English property developer and MP for Boston in Lincolnshire, who built the harbour wall known locally as The Cob around 1798 and at ruinous expense. (2) **PRINCE MADOC** (or **MADOG**), son of Owain Gwynedd, who made a fictitious voyage from this locality to America in the 12th century. (Since Madoc never returned, the only evidence for his having reached America is the fictitious discovery of a fictitious tribe of Welsh-speaking Indians reported by the (real) Rev. William Jones, who was made captive by them in 1669 and talked his way out in Welsh. He claimed. Which the Indians understood. He claimed.) Madoc's imaginary voyage has done much to enhance the tourist appeal of Portmadoc, but Madocks' cob brought the town more solid advantages when the harbour it formed became the terminus for a number of narrow-gauge railways bringing slate from the quarries of Snowdonia for loading onto ships. The town also housed at one time a shipyard building Welsh topsail schooners. These handsome, sturdy and adaptable vessels, though mainly used for coastal trading, also carried slates to distant destinations in America, Northern Europe and the Mediterranean, returning with cargoes as varied as Newfoundland salt cod and fresh fruit from Greece or the Azores. Portmadoc officially became **PORTHMADOG** in 1974 in line with the place-name-welshification policy then (and still) in force in the Principality. In Madocks' time, it was known simply as Pentre Gwaelod (= "bottom village").

[739] POSTMAN CHEVAL'S IDEAL PALACE

In a cottage garden in the village of Hauterives in the department of Drôme stands one of the most extraordinary buildings in Europe – "Le Palais idéal du facteur Cheval". It is the work of the one-time village postman **JOSEPH FERDINAND CHEVAL** (1836-1924), who dreamed of recreating, in the spot where his fellow villagers would have been growing radishes and peas, a palace from the Arabian Nights. His daily round of some 33 km, traversed on foot, gave him ample opportunity to dream, and each day for 33 years he carried home with him in his pockets interestingly-shaped stones that caught his eye. With these, his "faithful wheelbarrow",* and a great deal of cement, his dream grew into solid reality. It has been compared with the Watts Towers in Los Angeles (which also, coincidentally, took Simon Rodia 33 years to build) but Cheval's palace is less grandiose in scale, though both are clearly concrete expressions of a unique individual imagination. In style and spirit, the palace might best be described as a three-dimensional counterpart to the naive sea-paintings of Cheval's near-contemporary, the Cornish fisherman Alfred Wallis (1855-1942). In 1969, the "Palais Idéal" was accorded the status of a National Monument.

* Set into one of the walls of the building is a plaque recording Cheval's gratitude to "*ma fidèle brouette*", the only companion of his long labour.

[740] POTT'S FRACTURE

Otherwise known as a broken ankle, **POTT'S FRACTURE** denotes a common fracture of one or both of the lower leg-bones just above the ankle. It commemorates the delightfully-named English physician **PERCIVALL POTT** (1714-1788) whose *Some few general remarks on fractures and dislocations* appeared in 1769. His interest in the subject had been aroused by a dangerous leg fracture of his own (though not a Pott's Fracture), caused by a riding accident. He planned and personally supervised its successful reduction, avoiding the necessity of amputation. Pott worked and taught for most of his career at Bart's Hospital, winning an international reputation in his own lifetime. Among his patients were **DOCTOR JOHNSON** and David Garrick, and among his students the famous surgeon and anatomist John Hunter. Pott has an honoured place in the history of health-and-safety legislation. It was he who noted a link between cancer of the scrotum and contact with soot, an observation which led to the passing of the Chimney Sweeper's Act in 1788, the first of numerous subsequent legislative attempts to control the practice of cleaning chimneys by using a small child as a pull-through.

[741] POUBELLE

The French term for a *dustbin, litter bin*, or *waste-paper basket* has, strictly speaking no place in this compilation, since unlike **GUILLOTINE, MONTGOLFIÈRE, MARTINET, MANSARD** and **DAGUERREOTYPE** it has not been admitted to the English lexicon. On the other hand, may we not be allowed to tip our hats to the man who is to municipal refuse collection what Einstein is to physics? In 1884, **EUGÈNE RENÉ POUBELLE** (1831-1907), Prefect of the department of Seine, put his name to a decree aimed at freeing the streets and alleyways of Paris of accumulated noisome debris. The decree stated that, "From now on, household waste will be collected by means of a wooden receptacle lined with tin so as to prevent anything escaping from it." The lining was designed not only to prevent leakage but to eliminate the risk of fire caused by hot ashes, then an important component of household waste. Poubelle's directions made it clear that sorting and recycling were part of the plan, as separate receptacles were to be provided for paper and rags and for glass and china. The scheme met, at first, with considerable opposition from various interested parties such as the sisterhood of Parisian concierges (a pestilential set of bolshy old harridans to this day) who had to see to their management. Household waste of all types was at one time used as agricultural fertiliser and it is said that the wine-growing *terroirs* of Champagne still contain a generous proportion of non-degradable rubbish from Parisian dustbins. A tiny, and one hopes tidy, street in the 16th Parisian *arrondissement* has now been named after Poubelle.

[742] POWDER OF ALGAROTH

VITTORIO ALGAROTTI (1553-1604) was a spagyrist (alchemist) of Verona who established himself in Venice as a Europe-wide purveyor of medicaments, notably his **POWDER OF ALGAROTH** or simply **ALGAROT,** which also rejoiced in the names of "mercurius vitae" and "spirit of philosophical vitriol". It was a purgative much-favoured for the vigor of its emetic action. Chemically it is an oxychloride of antimony, prepared by hydrolysing "butter of antimony" (antimony trichloride), a highly toxic substance. Curiously, in recent years antimony compounds did prove useful chemotherapeutic agents for the treatment of the parasitic disease **BILHARZIA,** so the spagyrists were on to something. (MW)

[743] PRATIA

A genus of some 30 species of southern hemisphere flowering plants named after **CHARLES LOUIS PRAT-BERNON**, a midshipman on board the French corvette *Uranie,* who died at sea shortly after the beginning of her voyage of circumnavigation (1817-1820). The genus was named in his memory by the ship's pharmacist/botanist Charles Gaudichaud-Beaupré (1789-1854) whose own name normally appears in the technical literature of botany abbreviated to "Gaudich." The *Uranie's* mission, under her captain Louis-Claude de Saulces de Freycinet

(1779-1842), was one of scientific exploration and stands comparison with those of Cook and **BOUGAINVILLE**. Freycinet had a clandestine companion on the voyage, his wife Rose, whose account of the voyage survives in her journal and letters. The *Uranie* was wrecked in the **FALKLANDS** on the way home and the voyage was completed in another vessel.

[744] PRINCE RUPERT'S DROPS

Lacrymae vitreae are obtained by dripping molten glass from a height into water to solidify it by rapid cooling into teardrop-shapes with long thin tails, like gigantic glass spermatozoa. The thick end of the drop is robust but is under such high internal strain that snapping the thin tail causes the entire drop to explode into glass powder with a sharp report. The Health & Safety Police have now made a rarity of this "incorrect" parlour entertainment. For a demo see:

http://www.popsci.com/diy/article/2008-06/shattering-strongest-glass

It illustrates the principle of "toughened" glass for windscreens. The drops probably originated in the glass-making workshops of Holland in the mid 17th century, and were called *Larmes Bataviques* in France. They were not invented by Prince Rupert, but introduced by him into England in 1661. The drops were already well-known on the Continent; in 1657 Sir Constantijn **HUYGENS** sent some to Margaret Cavendish* then expatriate in Antwerp: "Your Exellencie hath no cause to apprehend the cracking blow of these innoxious gunnes. If you did, Madam, a servant may hold them close in his fists, and yourselfe can break the little end of their taile without the least danger." **PRINCE RUPERT, COUNT PALATINE OF THE RHINE AND DUKE OF BAVARIA** (1619-1682) was born in Prague, the third son of the Elector Palatine Frederic V and Princess Elizabeth Stuart, daughter of James I. Rupert survived a colourful military career as a leading English cavalry officer, always to be found in the thick of any current fighting, be it the 80 years' war (1568-1648), the 30 years' war (1618-1648), the second (1665-1667) and third (1672-1674) Anglo-Dutch wars, or the English civil war (1642-1651), in which he distinguished himself as the "Mad Cavalier" of the Royalist cause, going into battle accompanied by a mascot in the shape of a white poodle called "Boye", which was widely feared as possessing supernatural powers. Having lost the civil war he took refuge as a Caribbean buccaneer, but after the Restoration he transmogrified into Admiral of the British fleet. In retirement he mellowed into something of an amateur scientist, giving us **PRINCE RUPERT'S METAL** – a version of brass, 75% copper 25 % zinc – and a fair imitation of gold (see **PINCHBECK**). (MW)

* Who, with her husband William, Duke of Newcastle, was renting the Reubens House at the time.

[745] PROJECT MOHOLE – see MOHOROVIČIĆ DISCONTINUITY

[746] PROMETHIUM – see CERIUM

[747] PRUSIK KNOT

The **PRUSIK KNOT**, or more properly **PRUSIK HITCH**, is credited to **DR. KARL PRUSIK** (1896-1961), mountaineer and twice president of the Austrian Alpine Club, who published it in an Austrian mountaineering journal in 1931. It is a means of attaching a loop of cord from the climber's harness to a fixed rope. When under tension, the hitch is immovable, but when the weight is taken off it can be pushed up the rope by hand, enabling the climber to ascend the rope by stages. It is widely used not only by alpinists and cavers but also by tree surgeons and loggers. According to Geoffrey Budworth (*Knots and ropework* 1999), it was originally devised as an emergency repair for broken strings on musical instruments, though the present writer, who has broken a fair few guitar strings in his time, cannot for the life of him understand of what use it would be in these often embarrassing situations. (See also **MATTHEW WALKER**.)

[748] PRZEWALSKI'S HORSE

The wild horse *Equus przewalskii* was discovered by the Russian soldier, geographer, naturalist, and explorer of Siberia and Central Asia **NICOLAI PRZEWALSKI** (1839-1888) in the Altai mountains in the west of Mongolia. This was already the animal's last refuge and it is now on the verge of extinction. The principal remaining breeding reservoir consists of zoo populations. Its close relative the Tarpan (*Equus przewalskii gmelini*) is already extinct, the last specimen having died in captivity in 1919. Przewalski, a tireless traveller, is reported to have covered over 30,000 kilometres in the course of his journeys. His travel narratives have been translated into English, French and German. Also named after him is a Central Asian rodent **PRZEWALSKI'S GERBIL** (*Brachiones przewalskii*). Spellings of Przewalski's name in languages other than Russian vary quite widely.

[749] PSALMANAZAR CONTROVERSY

The *Encyclopaedia Britannica* (11th ed.) rather indulgently calls the Frenchman **GEORGE PSALMANAZAR** (*ca.* 1679-1763), an "adventurer". We would have no hesitation in calling him a con-man. Even his surname, an idiosyncratic spelling of the Biblical name Salmanazar (see **JEROBOAM**) was fraudulent. He impudently imposed upon the learned community of Europe by pretending to be, of all things, a Japanese convert to Christianity. He made his way to London where he published in 1704 a totally spurious *Historical and geographical description of Formosa* (which he had never visited), and managed to persuade the Bishop of London to employ him to translate the Catechism into Japanese (a language of which he had zero knowledge). However, not everyone was as gullible as the good Bishop. Psalmanazar's pretensions were, from the start, viewed with suspicion in some quarters and a lively debate ensued regarding his authenticity or otherwise. He was eventually exposed, made a full confession, and thereafter lived a life which impressed Dr. Johnson by its exemplary piety. His memoirs were published in English in 1764. His real name was never known.

[750] PTOLEMAIC SYSTEM

This is the geocentric cosmology of ancient astronomy, originating with **PLATO** and Aristotle, and famously expounded by the Egyptian astronomer **CLAUDIUS PTOLEMAEUS** (ca. 90-168) of Alexandria in the work the Arabs knew by the name of *Almagest*.* It assumed that the earth lay at the centre of the universe, and that all the celestial bodies revolved around it in eight concentric spherical shells. The apparently irregular motions of the planets were accounted for by a complex system of retrograde epicycles, which would certainly have had **OCCAM** reaching for his razor.** This model held sway among the faithful until the 17th century and, for obvious metaphysical reasons, enjoyed the approval of the Church, notwithstanding the endeavours of **COPERNICUS, GALILEO** and **KEPLER**. Ptolemy was also a geographer; his more useful contribution to human understanding was a map of the world and a system of latitude and longitude. It is therefore appropriate that geocentric cosmology is still a going concern in the realm of astro-navigation, which works on the fundamental axiom that the Sun, Moon, stars and planets all lie on the surface of a globe – the "celestial sphere" – concentric with the earth – the "terrestrial sphere". (MW)

*From the Greek *megistos* = "greatest"

** It was only when **KEPLER** determined that the orbits of the planets were elliptical and not circular that the "epicycles" could be dispensed with.

[751] PULITZER PRIZE

A group of American literary prizes awarded annually to works in several categories, including: fiction, drama, poetry, history, biography and general non-fiction (or journalism). They were founded in 1917 as part of the bequest with which the newspaper proprietor **JOSEPH PULITZER** (1847-1911) established the Columbia University School of Journalism. The terms of the fiction prize, which originally specified that the work should have an American subject, were relaxed in 1932 to allow the award to go to *The Good Earth* by Pearl S Buck and in 1947 to allow collections of short stories as well as novels to be considered. The list of winners reads like a roll of honour of American fiction and includes Edith Wharton, Willa Cather, Eugene O' Neill, John Steinbeck, Robert Frost, Tennessee

Williams, Ernest Hemingway, Arthur Miller and, in 2007, Cormac McCarthy.* The prize currently comprises a gold medal and a cash award of $10,000. Born in Hungary, Pulitzer emigrated to the United States in 1864, served a year in the Union army in the Civil War, and became a journalist on the *Westliche Post*, a German-language newspaper. In 1869 he was elected to the Missouri legislature, where he earned a reputation as a liberal reformer. As an independent minded liberal he believed that a newspaper should actively seek to right injustices so that government could remain small. "More crime, immorality and rascality is prevented by the fear of exposure in the newspapers than by all the laws, morals and statutes ever devised." (If only!) In 1878 he bought the *St. Louis Dispatch* and merged it with the *Post* to make the *St. Louis Post-Dispatch*, which flourished under his owner-editorship. In 1883 he acquired the *New York World* and it was with this paper that he would establish his reputation. Pulitzer's aggressive methods of building up this paper, its Sunday issue, and the *Evening World* (started 1887) included the use of illustrations, news stunts, crusades against corruption, and cartoons, as well as aggressive news coverage. From 1895 onwards he enjoyed a lively battle with the rival newsprint empire of William Randolph Hearst. (RS)

* *Wikipedia* offers a complete list of Pulitzer laureates running to 173 pages.

[752] PURPLE OF CASSIUS

A superb red pigment, stable enough to be fired under a glaze at 1100° CELSIUS and therefore much favoured by ceramicists and stained glass artists. It consists of a dispersion of colloidal (nanoparticle) gold metal in a matrix of tin hydroxide. The name is a misattribution, since neither ANDREAS CASSIUS, father (1605-1673), nor ANDREAS CASSIUS, son (1645-1700?), were actually responsible for its discovery, although the latter did publish an account of it in 1685 in his pamphlet *Concerning Gold*. The first preparation of the pigment can be credited to the Bavarian proto-chemist, Johann Rudolf Glauber (1604-68) – he of the celebrated GLAUBER'S SALT – who, in his first publication, *New Philosophical Furnaces* (1648), described experiments with gold-purple, precipitating it with "liquor of flints" (sodium silicate) and melting it into a red glass. Glauber's major work, *Germany's Prosperity* (1656), clearly describes the precipitation of gold-purple with metallic tin dissolved in hydrochloric acid. The application for staining glass was taken up in 1678 by Johann Kunckel (1630-1703) when he was given charge of a glass factory in Potsdam, but he did not disclose the secret until 1716, rather transparently disguised in alchemical language as *praecipitatio Solis cum Jove* which translates as "the precipitation of the Sun [*i.e.* gold] by means of Jupiter [*i.e.* tin]". By 1719 the pigment was in use for the decoration of the porcelain manufactured at the famous Meissen pottery, and by 1723 the secret had found its way to China, where it was used as a pink colorant for the exquisite *Famille Rose* ware. (MW)

[753] PUSCHKINIA

Genus of hardy bulbs native to a region stretching from Turkey to Afghanistan and including the Lebanon, hence the name *Puschkinia scilloides var. libanotica* or Striped Squill. It is named after the Russian chemist and plant collector COUNT APOLLO APOLLOSOVICH MUSSIN-PUSCHKIN whose 1802 botanising expedition to the Caucasus led to its introduction as a European garden plant (1808).

[754] PYKRETE

The name of GEOFFREY NATHANIEL PYKE (1893-1938), Cambridge-educated British scientist, inventor and, in WWII parlance, "boffin", is preserved in the name given to a composite, shock-resistant substance of his own invention formed by the addition of ice (applied as super-cooled water) to a fibrous substrate such as sawdust or wood shavings. Pyke maintained that objects made of pykrete could be virtually any size or shape and virtually indestructible as long as they were not permitted to melt. Specifically, he proposed the construction of unsinkable aircraft carriers from this material. The germ of the idea came from Pyke's reading that during mountain warfare between the Italians and the Austrians in WWI it was found that ice-caves in which troops took shelter were virtually immune to damage from artillery fire. Pyke's suggestion found favour with the Admiralty, and with Churchill (avid, as ever, for war-winning wheezes), who is said to have tested a sample of pykrete by dropping it in his bathwater and firing a pistol at it. Construction of a prototype pykrete ship was started in Canada but never completed. Pyke was a fervent practitioner of what later became known, thanks to Edward de Bono, as "lateral thinking". He committed suicide in 1948. (See David Lampe *Pyke, the unknown genius* London 1959; John Timpson *Timpson's English eccentrics* London 1991.) Magnus Pyke (1908-1992), another and perhaps better-known eccentric scientist and broadcaster, was Geoffrey Pyke's cousin.

[755] PYRRHIC VICTORY

A victory in which irreparable damage is incurred by the winning side. Rome's piecemeal absorption of the western portion of Alexander's empire (Greece, Asia Minor, Palestine, Egypt) involved war with, amongst others, KING PYRRHUS OF EPIRUS (319-272 BC), who, intending to put a stop to the rise of the Roman upstarts, invaded Italy with a Greek army in 281 BC and, like Hannibal, won battle after battle without achieving final victory. After winning the battle of Asculum in 279, and although his casualties were only half those of his Roman opponents, he is reported to have said, "One more such victory will undo me!" – a recognition both of the Romans' dogged refusal to accept any defeat as final, plus the fact that they had greater reserves of manpower to draw on than did Pyrrhus. After many tough campaigns, Pyrrhus was killed at Argos where, in confused street fighting, it is alleged an old woman felled him with a well-aimed roof-tile, allowing an Argive soldier to finish him off. Pyrrhus was considered in his time to be one of the greatest of military commanders, ranked by Hannibal second only to **ALEXANDER THE GREAT**. (RS)

[756] PYRRHONISM

A form of extreme philosophical scepticism associated with **PYRRHO OF ELIS*** (*ca.* 360-270 BC). Pyrrho held that since final truth is unknowable and final certainty unattainable, and since any proposition can be countered by an opposing proposition of equal validity, the wise course is to refrain from judgement and keep one's mouth shut. Pyrrho started life as a painter before becoming interested in philosophy. He travelled to the East in the train of Alexander the Great and in India came under the influence of the Hindu ascetics whom the Greeks called "gymnosophists" ("naked wise men"). On the return journey he studied under the Magi of Persia and, back in Elis, set up as a jobbing philosopher, earning the admiration and respect of his fellow Eleans. It has to be said that Pyrrho's espousal of Oblomovian ataraxy and resolute non-commitment has an obvious drawback: if, as the Greeks believed, the ultimate purpose of philosophy is to teach men how to live, **PYRRHONISM** is of limited utility since it offers no guidance in the daily business of making decisions. All choices become either impossibly easy or impossibly difficult, depending on which end of the telescope you are looking down. Pyrrho appears to have dodged the question by retreating into eremitic isolation. His distrust of the power of language to resolve philosophical dilemmas carried an echo of his predecessor Heraclitus (*ca.*540-*ca.*480 BC), famous for the dictum "all things flow". Tired of pointing out to his fellow men that one cannot jump into the same river twice, Heraclitus towards the end of his life took to simply standing in the river and silently wagging an admonitory finger at anyone who happened by.

* A city, and district of the same name, in the western Peloponnese.

[757] PYTHAGORAS' THEOREM

That semi-mythical personage Every Schoolboy knows that in a plane right-angled triangle the square on the hypotenuse equals the sum of the squares on the other two sides. Not every schoolboy realises, however, that the man whose name is attached to this luminous formulation is himself a semi-mythical figure about whose life we have precious little reliable information. We can be reasonably confident that **PYTHAGORAS** was born on the island of Samos* around 566 BC and died at the Greek colony of Metapontion near present-day Taranto around 497 BC. Between-times he immersed himself in the study of mathematics, astronomy, music and religion, drawing heavily on Ionian, Jewish, Babylonian and Egyptian learning. He later founded a school at Croton, another Greek colony in southern Italy, where he gathered a group of disciples who formed themselves into a quasi-religious order held together by some fairly peculiar beliefs and practices including a rule of secrecy and a taboo on meat, fish, beans, wine, woollen clothes and shoes. Their main concern was mathematics and in particular the theory of numbers. The connection between religion and mathematics may not be obvious to us but it was very clear to Pythagoras and, indeed, central to his thought and belief. He held that the pursuit of knowledge was as much a spiritual as an intellectual exercise, purifying and redemptive in its effects. This sat well with his fascination with numbers since numbers appear to exhibit what can only be called *behaviour*, suggesting that they have a life, so to speak, independent of human enquiry and on a different, higher plane, so that by our attempting to gain access to their world, we are brought nearer to the gods. It is therefore not surprising that the followers of Pythagoras, the **PYTHAGOREAN BROTHERHOOD**, came increasingly to behave like an occultist religious sect, or that their mathematical theorisings came more to resemble esoteric number-magic than what we would see as rational investigation. Nor is it surprising that later off-centre sects such as the Freemasons and the Rosicrucians claimed to be the inheritors of the Pythagorean mysteries. (See also **EUCLID, HERMETIC TEACHINGS** and **PLATONIC SOLIDS**.)

* There is a town on the south coast of the island named in his honour. But like many Greek towns and villages from Athens downwards it has two names: an official name – in this case *Pythagórion* – and the name everybody uses – in this case *Tigáni*, which means "frying pan".

Q

[758] QUAIN'S DICTIONARY

SIR RICHARD QUAIN (1816-1898) was one of the most influential and best-respected physicians of his day. Born in Ireland, he studied medicine at University College, London, attaining his MD with high honours in 1842. He went from strength to strength in his chosen profession, becoming physician extraordinary to Queen Victoria in 1890 and being awarded his baronetcy in 1891. He is remembered (if only just) eponymously in QUAIN'S FATTY DEGENERATION, a heart condition, and QUAIN'S STETHOMETER, a now obsolete instrument for using chest measurements as a diagnostic tool in cases of suspected TB. His most important and most durable contribution to medicine, however, is undoubtedly the DICTIONARY OF MEDICINE he edited and first published in 1882, and which, through successive editions, became the bible of generations of medical students. An older cousin, Jones Quain, (1796-1865) was the author of an earlier medical work *Quain's elements of anatomy*, while another cousin, also named Richard (1800-1887) was President of the Royal College of Surgeons in 1868 and on his death endowed several professorships (botany, English language and literature, law, physics) through a bequest to University College.

[759] QUECKENSTEDT'S SIGN

A test (now outdated) to determine whether there is a blockage in the flow of cerebrospinal fluid in the spinal canal by applying pressure to the jugular veins. Described by German surgeon HANS HEINRICH GEORG QUECKENSTEDT in 1916. The procedure is also associated with the name of American neurosurgeon BYRON POLK STOOKEY (1887-1966), hence the mouth-filling alternative appellation QUECKENSTEDT-STOOKEY TEST. There is no eponymous recognition for the British anatomist John Hilton (1804-1878) who described the relevant phenomenon in 1863.

[760] QUEENSBERRY RULES

The idea of regulating the sport of pugilism by limiting the range of permissible assaults (no biting, scratching, head-butting, kicks to the groin, etc.) is undoubtedly a tiny step on the road to a better world. On the other hand, JOHN SHOLTO DOUGLAS, 8th Marquess of QUEENSBERRY (1844-1900), under whose patronage the Rules were drawn up in 1867 and after whom they were named, seems to have been a less than likeable person. This may however be a biased judgement derived from the fact that in Queensberry's very public two-round bout with Oscar Wilde over Wilde's friendship with Queensberry's son Lord Alfred Douglas, history has, on the whole, taken Wilde's side. Since Oscar lost massively on points, this might be seen as another example of the British fondness for a plucky loser (see **EDDIE THE EAGLE SYNDROME**).

[761] QUETELET'S BELL CURVE

The astronomer and mathematician **LAMBERT ADOLPHE JACQUES QUETELET** (1796-1874) ought to figure on anybody's list of famous Belgians. Though Director of the Brussels Royal Observatory for most of his working life, his most important contribution to the march of science was in the application of statistical methods to the study of human beings. He measured simple physical characteristics of human groups, height for example, and found that departures from the average showed the same kind of random scatter as bullet holes on a rifle target, and that when plotted as a graph the results formed a **BELL-SHAPED CURVE** (otherwise known as a "normal distribution" or **GAUSSIAN CURVE**). Quetelet's anthropometrical findings were important in the development of actuarial statistics (of life expectancy, for example), becoming an indispensable tool for the insurance industry. At the same time, they were fundamental to the development of sociology and scientific anthropology. Quetelet also made a special study of criminal statistics. Apart from papers on astronomy, geology and climatology, his principal published works are: *Sur l'homme et le développement de ses facultés: essai de physique sociale* (1835); *Du système sociale et les lois qui le régissent* (1848); and *L'anthropométrie, ou mesure des différentes facultés de l'homme* (1871). Also originating with Quetelet is the **QUETELET INDEX** or Body Mass Index (BMI), which divides body mass in (kg) by height (in meters) yielding a figure which, by comparison with a "normal" standard enables doctors to rapidly estimate whether a person is under- or overweight.

[762] QUINCKE'S METHOD

A laboratory technique for determining the magnetic properties of a substance in solution. Its inventor was German physicist **GEORG HERMANN QUINCKE** (1834-1924) who taught at Würzburg and later Heidelberg. His younger brother **HEINRICH IRENAEUS QUINCKE** (1842-1922) made medicine his career and a number of medical conditions and procedures are named after him. Most notably, Quincke recognised and promoted the utility of the lumbar puncture – or **QUINCKE'S PUNCTURE** as it became known – as a diagnostic and therapeutic tool.

[763] QUINQUET – see **ARGAND BURNER**

[764] QUISLING

The Norwegian right-wing soldier and politician VIDKUN QUISLING (1887-1945) formed a pro-German government in Nazi-occupied Norway in WWII and in doing so gave his name to all those persons in occupied countries who willingly and openly supported or collaborated with the invaders or consented to act in official capacities under German oversight. The term quisling, like all terms of opprobrium (or approval) embodies a point of view, so that one man's quisling is another man's loyal ally, just as one man's terrorist is another man's freedom fighter. The Norwegians, however, acknowledged no such subtle distinction in Quisling's case and after the war promptly tried him for high treason and shot him.

[765] QUIVERFULL CHRISTIANS

In Trollope's *The Warden* we meet a downtrodden clergyman by the name of Mr. Quiverful, reduced to penury by the fact that he is evidently one of those chaps whose wife falls pregnant every time he hangs his trousers on the bedpost. The resulting over-supply of children explains Mr. Quiverful's name – a reference to Psalm 127, where we read:

> *Lo, children are an heritage of the Lord, and the fruit of the womb is his reward.*
> *As arrows are in the hand of a mighty man, so are children of the youth.*
> *Happy is the man that hath his quiver full of them.*

Trollope would have been tickled to learn that in the States, where the tree of spiritual belief and practice can produce some very odd fruit, a band of modern Christians calling themselves "THE QUIVERFULLS" take the words of the Psalm very seriously indeed and devote themselves to the business of producing as many children as possible (ten is normal, thirteen not unusual) in order to swell the ranks of footsoldiers in Christ's army. Bearing in mind the falling birth-rates in "advanced" societies, it is permissible to wonder whether the Quiverfull Christians are not at some level motivated by that perennial racist bugbear – the fear of being out-bred and outnumbered by "lesser breeds without the law".

[766] QUONSET HUT – see NISSEN HUT

R

[767] RAFFLES HOTEL

It used to be said that if you spent enough time in the Long Bar of the RAFFLES HOTEL in Singapore, everyone you had ever known would sooner or later stop by. Obviously this was never literally true but it must have been more nearly so in the days when Britain had an Empire and those involved in it, in whatever capacity, could be seen as belonging to a kind of club with a wide and varied, but finite, membership whose avocations kept them continually moving about the world. And it is, of course, to the high days of Empire that the hotel owes its name and fame, and more particularly to **Sir THOMAS STAMFORD RAFFLES** (1781-1826) who was responsible for persuading his employers, the Honourable East India Company, to acquire the island of Singapore in 1819. Raffles entered the Company's service in 1805 and took part in the operations which saw the island of Java wrested from the control of the Dutch. (The Netherlands were at that time under French occupation and therefore considered a hostile power – a situation not unlike that which led to the British attack on the French fleet at Oran in 1940 after the fall of France.) Raffles was appointed governor of Java, where he introduced important administrative reforms while immersing himself in the history, natural history and ethnology of the East Indies, the results being embodied in his *History of Java* (1817). Java was returned to the Dutch in 1815 and Raffles was appointed Governor of Bencoolen (Sumatra). He returned to England in 1824 and Bencoolen was handed over to the Dutch the following year. Tragically, Raffles' vast collection of natural history specimens and all his papers were lost in a shipboard fire on the way home. The original Raffles Hotel, named in honour of the "Founder" of Singapore, was established by a family of Armenian hoteliers in 1887, and flourishes today.

[768] RAGLAN

A type of overcoat made without shoulder seams so that the tops of the sleeves reach as far the neck. Named after **FITZROY JAMES HENRY SOMERSET, 1st Baron RAGLAN** (1785-1855). Raglan served under Wellington in the Peninsula and lost an arm at Waterloo. In 1854 he was given command of the British expeditionary force in the Crimea and was blamed – not entirely fairly – for some of the resulting cock-ups. The fact is that he was too old for the job, and the British army, after a long period of peace, was simply out of practice. In our own time, a time when our armed forces have been committed to not one but two campaigns as ill-conceived, as ill-managed, and as little conducive to the national interest as the *débacle* over which poor Raglan presided, the history of the Crimean campaign should repay study by our national decision-makers.

[769] RAMAN EFFECT

When light is scattered by any transparent substance, most of it bounces off with no change in wavelength – this is called **RAYLEIGH SCATTERING** (see below). But a small proportion of the scattered light gives up a little of its energy to the substance and is therefore scattered with diminished energy – *i.e.* longer wavelength, according to **PLANCK'S LAW**. This effect can be seen if light of a single wavelength (monochromatic light) is used and measured with a spectrometer, which disperses the visible spectrum: extra weak lines are observed, displaced from the strong line of the "exciting" radiation. The **RAMAN EFFECT** was first observed in India by C.V. Raman and K.S. Krishnan in 1928. Later the same year it was independently discovered in the USSR where it is still loyally referred to as the Landsberg-Mandelstam effect. The eminent Indian physicist **CHANDRASEKHARA VENKATA RAMAN** (1888-1970) was born in Tamil Nadu, and became professor at Calcutta University, then Director of the Indian Institute of Science at Bangalore. He was knighted in 1929 and awarded the **NOBEL PRIZE** for physics in 1930. His effect has been developed into the powerful investigative tool of **RAMAN SPECTROSCOPY** for studying the vibration and rotation of molecules, which provides information on their chemical identities, shapes, sizes, and bonding. It's also useful for analysing and identifying – non-invasively – the pigments in precious works of art (see **RECKITT'S BLUE**). (MW)

[770] RASCHIG RINGS – see **MAGNUS' GREEN SALT**

[771] RAYLEIGH SCATTERING

It is obvious that light is scattered by particulate matter – water droplets in a fog, say, or a cloud of smoke, or the fat globules in milk – but it is much less obvious that light is also scattered by a perfectly homogeneous medium such as clear air or water, because the effect is very weak. Nonetheless this **RAYLEIGH SCATTERING** by the molecules of the atmosphere is the reason why the sky is blue and not black: the intensity of scattering is inversely proportional to the fourth power of the wavelength, so favours the shorter wavelengths of light at the blue end of the spectrum. The first person to discover the phenomenon and offer a quantitative physical explanation for it, was English physicist, **JOHN WILLIAM STRUTT, 3rd Baron RAYLEIGH** (1842-1919). He was born in Maldon, Essex, educated at Harrow and Trinity College, Cambridge, where he graduated as Senior Wrangler; from 1879 to 1884 he was the second **CAVENDISH** Professor of Physics at the University, then professor at the Royal Institution (1888-1905) and President of the Royal Society (1905-08). He also made significant contributions to the theory of sound, and shared with Sir William Ramsay (see **TURNBULL'S BLUE**) the discovery of the inert gas argon in 1894. He was awarded the **NOBEL PRIZE** for physics in 1904. (MW)

[772] RÉAUMUR TEMPERATURE SCALE

RENÉ ANTOINE FERCHAULT DE RÉAUMUR (1683-1757) was a French man of science born in La Rochelle. His education brought him to Paris in 1703, where he was elected member of the *Académie des Sciences* in 1708. He had wide-ranging interests in natural history and his publications were prolific and varied, including an analysis of carbon in iron and steel (see **BESSEMER**). In 1731, he proposed, for rather complicated reasons connected with the expansivity of alcohol, a temperature scale having 80 degrees between the fixed points of melting ice (0 °Re) and boiling water (80 °Re). This was deemed by many in Europe to be an improvement on the scale due to **FAHRENHEIT** in 1724, and was widely used until replaced by the **CELSIUS** scale in 1794 by decree of the revolutionary French government. (MW)

[773] REBECCA RIOTS

Economic distress among the poorer classes in south and west Wales in the year 1843 led to serious popular disturbances, which focused at first on a single grievance – toll roads. Toll gates and toll-booths were attacked and destroyed by bands of rioters dressed in many cases and for unknown reasons as women. They called themselves "**REBECCAS**", inspired by a text from *Genesis xxiv. "And they blessed Rebekah and said unto her, Thou art our sister, be thou the mother of thousands of millions, and let thy seed possess the gate of those which hate them."* Emboldened by their early successes, the rioters turned their attention to other grievances and other targets and a general state of mayhem persisted in the region until the Rebeccas were brought to heel by powerful combined detachments of soldiery and London policemen. A commission of enquiry later the same year ruled that the rioters had a real basis for their grievances and the few malefactors who were captured were only lightly punished. It has been surmised that the cross-dressing element in these goings-on may have been an oblique reference to the crowd of Welsh women whose red flannel petticoats and tall black hats caused them to be mistaken for soliders and so allegedly frustrated an imminent French invasion of Pembrokeshire during the Napoleonic wars.

[774] RECHABITES

The Independent Order of Rechabites, founded in England in 1835 and later spreading to Australia and the US, was, and is, a "friendly society" and an offshoot of the temperance movement. The rather odd name, and the fact that the members referred to their local branches as "tents", are explained by a passage in the Book of Jeremiah, chapter 35. Here the gloomy old Prophet relates how he was told by the Lord to conduct a group of people known as Rechabites (*i.e.* the family, clan or tribe of a man called Rechab) to the House of the Lord in Jerusalem and give them wine to drink. On arrival at the venue, the Rechabites jibbed at the proffered refreshments, saying, "*We will drink no wine: for Jonadab the son of Rechab our father commanded us saying, 'Ye shall drink no wine, neither ye nor your sons for ever: neither shall ye build house, nor sow seed, nor plant vineyard, nor have any: but all your days ye shall dwell in tents; that ye may live many days in the land where ye be strangers'.*" Jeremiah goes on to relate (though in a seemingly confused and contradictory manner) how the Lord pronounced his approval of the Rechabites' firm stand, contrasting it with the backsliding ways of certain other parties (un-named) who are promised "all the evil that I [the Lord] have pronounced against them". Like so much of the Old Testament, the narrative is only partly and with difficulty comprehensible to the modern reader, thanks to the passage of time, the devoted but error-prone efforts of copyists and translators, and loss or change of cultural context. One thing, however, is clear: that teetotalism was not the central issue in the confrontation between Jeremiah and the Rechabites. The central issue was the refusal of the Rechabites to abandon a life of nomadic pastoralism for that of settled agriculturalists. But why this was a matter of moment to the Lord, or why Jeremiah thought it worth recording, or why, for that matter, the Rechabites' modern namesakes (for whom the life of nomadic shepherds had no particular attraction) chose them as role models, are questions whose solution one hesitates even to guess at.

[775] RECKITT'S BLUE

Before optical brightening agents were invented, blue pigments were long used as laundry whiteners to offset visually the yellowing of used cotton garments. Also called Blue Bag, Dolly Blue, or Laundry Blue, RECKITT'S BLUE consisted of the pigment ultramarine compacted with sodium bicarbonate, and wrapped in small muslin bags. Other blue pigments were sometimes used (see TURNBULL'S BLUE) but ultramarine was preferred for its non-toxic, non-migratory properties. However, ultramarine is ground *lapis lazuli*, a precious mineral mined only in Afghanistan, so its employment for this everyday purpose only became economically possible with the first production of cheap synthetic ultramarine by French chemist Jean-Baptiste Guimet in 1824, by heating china clay, soda and sulphur. Ultramarine is essentially a sodium aluminosilicate (clay), but with a subtle inclusion of polysulphide anions, S_3^- and S_2^-, that confer the colour (this evidence comes from recent investigations by RAMAN SPECTROSCOPY). Reckitt & Sons began production of the blue in 1852 using imported French ultramarine, but by 1884 the pigment was being manufactured in Hull by Holliday Pigments Ltd. The company was founded by Quaker ISAAC RECKITT (1792-1862) the son of a Lincolnshire farmer, who worked as a miller before purchasing a starch business in 1840 in Hull, which became one of the most successful businesses in the region, making domestic cleaning products for 150 years. Reckitt was a paternalistic employer but allowed no pubs (*cf.* SALTAIRE). What began as a family business expanded around the world: in 1938 there was a merger with J&J Colman Ltd, of mustard fame, to form Reckitt & Colman Ltd. Another merger with a Dutch company in 1999 gave rise to Reckitt Benckiser plc, now one of the largest multinational companies, manufacturing household cleaners and disinfectants. (MW)

[776] REEVES' MUNTJAC

Of the ten muntjac species, two are eponymous, one being that of FEA, and the other being REEVES' MUNTJAC (*Muntiacus reevesii*), which hails originally from Formosa (Taiwan). JOHN REEVES (1774-1856) was an amateur naturalist employed as a tea inspector by the Honourable East India Company in Canton. It is "his" muntjac which has now established itself in the wild in Britain, probably following releases or escapes from the Duke of Bedford's estate at Woburn and/or from Whipsnade Zoo. Reeves has also given his name to a Chinese pheasant, *Syrmaticus reevesii*, and was responsible for a number of garden plant introductions including REEVESIA, a genus of East Asian flowering shrubs, and REEVES' SPIRAEA (*S. cantoniensis*). He used his time in China to put together a remarkable collection of beautiful botanical illustrations commissioned from Chinese artists. These are now in the care of the Royal Horticultural Society..

[777] REHOBOAM – see JEROBOAM

[778] REICH'S ORGONE ACCUMULATOR

Back in the silly sixties a new way was found of achieving the effects claimed over a hundred and fifty years earlier for GRAHAM'S CELESTIAL BED – namely, a revving up of sexual potency (and sexual pleasure) by mechanical means. The idea behind this excellent scheme came from an Austrian-American charlatan named WILHELM REICH (1897-1957), who practised as a psychiatrist and had at one time been a collaborator of Freud (see OEDIPUS COMPLEX). Reich claimed to have discovered a previously unknown form of energy permeating the atmosphere and capable when harnessed and directed of producing remarkable effects on living subjects such as people. This ethereal substance (or essence) he called "orgone". Orgone, as it turned out, could be collected, concentrated and focussed by means of an "ORGONE ACCUMULATOR". Among its other virtues, the accumulator was easy to construct and consisted simply of a box made of alternate layers of metallic and organic material – aluminium foil and wood, for example* – in which a person (or, if suitably proportioned, a number of persons) could sit or lie while the orgone worked its magic on them, producing, in addition to erotic stimulation, such add-on effects as a generalised sense of well-being and a sun-tan. Smaller hand-held versions could be constructed into which various parts of the body needing special attention could be inserted. The present writer is unable to testify from personal experience that the Reichian accumulator actually worked (or didn't work) as advertised. Repeated exhortations to give it a whirl from practising orgone enthusiasts were unable to overcome his native claustrophobia and scepticism.

* A lead-lined wooden coffin might serve. New hope for dead people?

[779] RHIND PAPYRUS

One of the most important of the few surviving texts relating to ancient Egyptian mathematics. It was acquired in Luxor in 1858 by the Scotch antiquarian **ALEXANDER HENRY RHIND** (1833-1863), travelling in Egypt for his health. It is now held by the British Museum who acquired it in 1864 together with another of Rhind's collectables known as the Egyptian Mathematical Leather Roll. The **RHIND PAPYRUS** takes the form of a scroll, at present in two parts. A fragment which would connect the two parts is in New York. It is written in the hieratic (as opposed to hieroglyphic) script, dates to about 1800 BC, and is the work of a scribe named Ahmes or Ahmose, who apparently copied it from earlier, now lost, sources. He heads the text *"Directions for attaining knowledge of all dark things"*. Ahmose sets out solutions to a series of mathematical problems relating to measurement of areas, angles, volumes, and the calculation of fractions. The approach is "semitheoretical, semipractical"*, that is, it presents much, but not all, of its material as solutions to specific problems rather than general rules for solving problems of a certain type. Rhind's was an early voice raised against the destructive plundering of Egypt's archaeological heritage and calling for responsible scientific excavations (*Thebes, its tombs, and their tenants* 1862).

* George Sarton *A history of science* 1952. See also Robins and Shute *The Rhind mathematical papyrus: an ancient Egyptain text*, BM, 1987.

[780] RICHARDSON MEDAL

The **LEWIS FRY RICHARDSON MEDAL** is one of a number of such distinctions in the award of the European Geosciences Union (EGU*) and which are named after predecessors who have made notable contributions to earth sciences (**WEGENER, CASSINI, HUMBOLDT**...) The Richardson Medal honours a remarkable British scientist whose name and work deserve to be more widely known. **LEWIS**

FRY RICHARDSON (1881-1953) was a meteorologist, mathematician, statistician, Quaker and pacifist (not necessarily in that order). Richardson studied mathematical physics at Durham and natural sciences at Cambridge, followed by a doctorate in mathematical psychology at London. In WWI he registered as a conscientious objector but served in France as a member of a Friends Ambulance Unit. Before and after the war he held various posts at the National Physical Laboratory, with the Meteorological Office and elsewhere. He was elected FRS in 1926. As a meteorologist he devoted himself to the application of statistical methods to the problem of weather forecasting, methods which are still in use today though transformed by the huge advances in computational power unavailable to Richardson. In 1940 he retired to pursue his own research interests, which arose directly from his pacifist beliefs. His enquiry into the causes of wars involved once again statistical analysis of quantifiable facts and resulted in two books, published in 1960 after Richardson's death. In *Statistics of deadly quarrels* Richardson collected and analysed in a standard format information on all lethal conflicts throughout the world taking place in the period 1820 to 1949. Factors making for amity or enmity, as well as "ambivalent" factors, were allotted alphabetical designations and violent incidents were grouped according to their magnitude (*i.e.* number of deaths) on a logarithmic scale ranging from 7.3 for WWII to 0.5 for conflicts involving as few as four deaths. Though the number of deaths was the only directly quantifiable element in each case, Richardson was also able to apply mathematical analysis to such aspects of warfare as the frequency with which this or that causative factor appeared to be present, to the duration of conflicts, and to their distribution in a space and time. In *Arms and insecurity* Richardson turned his attention to the arms trade and to arms races. Here quantifiable information, obviously, plays a leading role and Richardson's analysis is more purely mathematical as a result, though psychological factors are given due weight. Much of the text, accordingly, is likely to be inaccessible to non-mathematicians and this may well be the reason for Richardson's researches not being as widely known as they otherwise might be. It also needs to be said that, while complex physical phenomena involving a large number of interacting variables (such as the weather) have proved amenable (though not easily amenable) to mathematical treatment, when human activities are in question, another variable comes into play – the fact that human beings are only partially and intermittently rational. This fact introduces a crippling degree of randomness into the most careful calculations. This can be clearly seen in the field of Games Theory, a branch of mathematics which came into prominence in the decades following WWII through the work of Anatol Rapoport and others as part of the now established academic discipline of Conflict Studies, and which suffers from the disadvantage that in order to produce sensible results, it has to be assumed that both sides in a conflict situation make only rational decisions, while history tells us that this is all too seldom the case.

* Since 2002, the awarding body of this and other medals in related fields is the European Geosciences Union (EGU), formed in 2002 jointly by the European Geophysical Society (EGS) and the European Union of Geosciences (EUG).

[781] RICHTER SCALE

The scale used for measuring the magnitude of earthquakes is named after American seismologist **CHARLES RICHTER** (1900-1985), who is not be be confused with American physicist and Nobel laureate Burton Richter (b. 1931), or with German mineralogist Theodor Richter (1824-1894) after whom the rare mineral **RICHTERITE** (also known as tremolite) is named. Richter's earthquake scale, properly called the Local Magnitude scale, was developed in 1935 while he was working at the California Institute of Technology. Events measuring less than 2 on the scale are imperceptible except to extremely sensitive seismometers. The largest magnitude ever recorded weighed in at 9.5 (Chile 1960), but there is no theoretical upper limit. (*Cf.* **MERCALLI SCALE.**)

[782] RICKETTSIAE

Disease-causing micro-organisms named after American bacteriologist and pathologist **HOWARD TAYLOR RICKETTS** (1871-1910). Rickettsiae have some of the properties of viruses and some of bacteria so may be said to occupy a sort of mid-position in the great chain of being. Rickettsial diseases – which include Rocky Mountain spotted fever, trench fever, Japanese river fever, Q-fever and typhus – can affect both man and other mammals, the usual vector being the bites of ticks, lice or mites. Ricketts, by a horrid irony, died of typhus while investigating an outbreak in Mexico. His memorial is the name – *Rickettsia prowazeki* – bestowed on the causative agent of typhus by Henrique da Rocha Lima in 1916. The second element names another researcher, the Austrian bacteriologist Von Prowazek who, in 1915, likewise fell victim to the disease he was investigating. There is no etymological connection between the name Rickettsiae and "rickets", the common name of a bone disorder caused by vitamin-D deficiency. For rickets, OED has "origin uncertain", (anybody's guess).

[783] RITTER-KELLNER PROCESS – see CASTNER KELLNER CELL

[784] RIZLA

Devotees of the hand-rolled smoke asking at the shop-counter for a packet of "rizzlers" are in most cases unaware that the inscription **RIZLA +** on the packet denotes the paper-making firm **RIZ LA CROIX** founded by Frenchman **FRANÇOIS LA CROIX** in 1736. The company is now a subsidiary of the Imperial Tobacco group. Most French smokers use **JOB** papers made by a firm of specialist paper manufacturers whose name derives from that of **JEAN BARDOU**, a baker of

Perpignan, who first (1838) hit on the notion of selling fag papers in the form of a handy booklet, an idea which proved a runaway success.

[785] ROBINIA

Robinia pseudo-acacia, False Acacia or Locust Tree, is a North American species grown in this country as an ornamental and introduced to Europe in 1636. The genus is named after the French botanist **JEAN ROBIN** (1550-1629) official herbalist to Henri IV (1533-1610), and his son **VESPASIEN** (1579-1660). During his sojourn in America, William Cobbett became enamoured of the False Acacia and advocated its widespread planting in this country to back up England's dwindling reserves of building and ship-building timber. The results, however, were disappointing (especially to Cobbett who had hoped to make his fortune by promoting and selling the trees) and the **ROBINIA**, though a graceful addition to our parks and gardens, especially in its Golden form, never became a serious rival to the English oak.

[786] ROBOROVSKI'S HAMSTER

The world's smallest hamster (it's about as long as your thumb) inhabits the semi-desert regions of Mongolia and Dzungaria. It is named after **Lt. V.I. ROBOROVSKI**, Russian army officer and explorer of Mongolia and Tibet (expeditions 1889-90, 1894), who followed in the footseps of the great **PRZEWALSKI** of the multiple spellings. Like all small mammals, **ROBOROVSKI'S HAMSTER** (*Phodopus roborovskii*) exists in fast-forward mode: it is sexually mature at five weeks and lives for about three years. Among pet owners it has a reputation for aggression and though its diminutive stature means it can't actually chew your arm off, it won't stop it trying.

[787] ROCKWELL HARDNESS SCALE – see BRINNELL SCALE

[788] ROGET'S THESAURUS

As we now know, the Thesaurus is not a carnivorous dinosaur roaming the plains of Panglossia but a form of dictionary. The word is Greek and means "treasury" – something any young Scotsman on the make would make his mummy proud by becoming First Lord of. The treasury or word-hoard compiled (or unlocked) by **PETER MARK ROGET** (1779-1869) and which he published in 1852 under the modest title *Thesaurus of English words and phrases* was an enterprise of considerable intellectual audacity. Roget set himself the task of arranging all the words and word-combinations (phrases) in the English language into groups according to their meaning and connotations, or, as he put it in the introduction to the 1st edition:

"The present Work is intended to supply, with respect to the English language, a desideratum hitherto unsupplied in any language; namely, a collection of the words it contains and of the idiomatic combinations peculiar to it, arranged not in alphabetical order as they are in a dictionary, but according to the *ideas* they express...."

In order to fulfil this ambition and to impose order on the work as a whole, Roget had first to work out a typology of ideas*, a way of arranging and classifying the multitudinous subjects which language is, or may be, used to speak about. The almost casual aplomb with which he achieved this stunningly difficult task is not the least admirable feature of the finished work. Since 1852, successive editions have sold between them tens of millions of copies, and today the *Thesaurus* retains unchallenged its place on any short-list of indispensable reference books. Though Roget is now remembered mainly as a lexicographer, the *Thesaurus* was almost a footnote to the achievements of a busy and varied career. He qualified as a physician in Edinburgh (1798), practiced and lectured in Manchester and London, took part in the government enquiry into London's water-supply (1827-8), invented a new slide rule which earned him his FRS (1815), acted as Secretary to the Royal Society and edited its *Proceedings* (1827-49), and was an active participant in the establishment of London University (1837) – in a word, one more example, if one were needed, of the astonishing energy and capacity for work that the Victorians exhibited in so many fields.

* *Cf.* DEWEY DECIMAL SYSTEM

[789] RÖNTGEN RAYS

WILHELM KONRAD VON RÖNTGEN (1845-1923) was a German physicist born in Lennep in Prussia, who studied at Zürich, and held chairs at Strasbourg (1876), Giessen (1879), Würzburg (1888) and Munich (1899-1919). In 1895 he discovered the penetrating electromagnetic rays of short wavelength (0.01 to 10 nm), which were named eponymously, but which he modestly preferred to call X-rays. While investigating electrical discharges through gases at low pressure in glass tubes (see CROOKES) he observed scintillations on a fluorescent screen external to the tube, and inferred that a penetrating new form of radiation had been generated by the cathode rays impinging on a metal target anode. Röntgen also recorded these X-rays photographically, and thus founded radiography, the sub-science of diagnostic medical imaging. He was awarded the RUMFORD MEDAL in 1896 and the first NOBEL PRIZE for physics in 1901. He is one of the very select band of scientists to achieve the hat trick of winning a NOBEL PRIZE and having both a physical unit and a chemical element named after him (see also CURIE, EINSTEIN, BOHR). The RÖNTGEN OR ROENTGEN is a non-SI unit, abbreviated as R, measuring the ionizing power of X-rays or gamma radiation. It is defined by the electrostatic charge produced in a specified mass of dry air at standard pressure: one roentgen is 258 microcoulombs per kilogram of air. It is useful for measuring the exposure of biological tissues. The synthetic element ROENTGENIUM, atomic number 111 and symbol Rg, was first made in Darmstadt in 1994, in a quantity of a few atoms, so nothing is known about it and it has no uses, and but for Roentgen's name, the IUPAC would have us referring to this element by the barbarous title of "unununium". (MW)

[790] ROSS'S GULL

There are, confusingly, two Polar explorers by the name of Ross, both naval officers. The first is JOHN ROSS (1777-1856), whose abortive search for the N.W. Passage is referred to below (see SABINE'S GULL). The second is JAMES CLARK ROSS (1800-1862). It is after the former that *Rhodostethia rosea**, an old-world gull of the high Arctic, is named. The second Ross, who explored both North and South Polar regions, is remembered in the ROSS SEA in Antarctica, the landward portion of which is covered (for the time being) by the ROSS ICE-SHELF.

* *Rhodostethia* means "pink-breasted" – a lovely epithet that could have come straight out of Homer.

[791] ROTHSCHILD'S NEW GUINEA MARSUPIAL MOUSE

Murexia rothschildi is one of a number of animal species named in honour of banker and zoologist LEONARD WALTER ROTHSCHILD, 2ND BARON ROTHSCHILD (1868-1937). Others include *Mallomys rothschildi* (the New Guinea complex-toothed rat), ROTHSCHILD'S ROCK WALLABY (*Petrogale rothschildi*), and ROTHSCHILD'S GIRAFFE (*Giraffa camelopardis rothschildi*) the rarest of 9 extant subspecies. Rothschild formed an enormous collection of zoological specimens, living and dead, in his home at Tring in Hertfordshire, both the property and the collection later passing by his bequest to the Natural History Museum, London, of which Tring is now an out-station. He was rich enough to permit himself a number of eccentricities. These included keeping kangaroos in his garden and driving about London in a four-wheeled carriage drawn by zebras. (It seems that conspicuous eccentricity is reserved to persons either rich enough not to have to care what people think or so completely destitute as to be beyond caring. By and large, an eccentric lifestyle is a luxury denied the modestly-funded.) Walter Rothschild was the uncle of Dame Miriam Rothschild (1908-2005), another extraordinary member of an extraordinary family – self-taught entomologist, parasitologist and botanist. A woman of wide interests, enormous energy, and not a little of her uncle's tendency to eccentricity, she cut her scientific teeth on cataloguing her father Charles Rothschild's extensive collection of fleas – a subject on which she later became a (if not the) world expert – and once likened the excitement of making a scientific discovery to the experience of smoking cannabis. (See also BALFOUR DECLARATION.)

[792] ROXBURGHE CLUB

JOHN KER, 3rd Duke OF ROXBURGHE (1740-1804) was a noted book-collector who at the time of his death was reputed to own the finest private library in Britain, amounting to some 30,000 volumes. In 1812 the collection was sold at auction and dispersed, but his name and fame survive both in precious volumes from his collection which are now treasured by libraries and collectors the world over, and by the foundation, on the occasion of the sale, of the ROXBURGHE CLUB by a select group of bibliophiles under the secretaryship of Thomas Dibdin (1745-1814), actor, playwright and song-writer. The Club's activities soon extended beyond its original, largely convivial, purposes into publishing, at the members' expense, beautiful editions of rare and interesting books and manuscripts. This it continues to do today and the list of Roxburghe Club publications now amounts to nearly 300 volumes.

[793] ROZIÈRE

JEAN-FRANÇOIS PILÂTRE DE ROZIER (1754-1785) was a French science teacher who made the first free flight in 1783, in a MONTGOLFIÈRE hot-air balloon, accompanied by the Marquis d'Arlandes. Subsequently, de Rozier thought he could combine the best features of the MONTGOLFIÈRE with those of the hydrogen balloon, or CHARLIÈRE, and eliminate the disadvantages of both, by conserving buoyancy and gaining control over altitude. His hybrid aerostatic vessel, christened a ROZIÈRE, consisted of a 7 meter high cylinder, 4 meters in diameter, of hot air maintained by a blazing fire at its base, surmounted by a 10m diameter rubberized globe of hydrogen gas. In view of the combustible nature of hydrogen, there is an obvious design flaw here. On 15th June 1785, de Rozier and Pierre Romain set out from Boulogne in a fatal attempt to cross the English Channel, and so became the first known victims of air-travel (since Icarus, anyway). However, Rozier's design idea was vindicated in the 20th century – but using the inert and non-flammable helium instead of hydrogen. 1978 saw the first crossing of the Atlantic in a modern version of the Rozière. In 1999, the design enabled Bertrand Piccard and Brian Jones to balloon non-stop around the world in 478 hours, and the late-lamented and disappeared Steve Fossett to make the first solo circumnavigation in 2002. (MW)

[794] RUBE GOLDBERG

American cartoonist RUBEN GARRET GOLDBERG (1883-1970) trained as an engineer but quickly found his true métier as a humorous artist and began drawing cartoons for newspapers in his home town of San Francisco and later New York. He created a large number of characters but it was the amazing and absurd inventions of Professor Lucifer Gorgonzola Butts that made Goldberg a national figure and, literally, a figure of speech, whose name is now commonly attached by Americans to any unreliable and unnecessarily complicated machine or system, in exactly the same way as the British use the name of **HEATH ROBINSON**. Goldberg was awarded a **PULITZER PRIZE** in 1948 for his political cartoons.

[795] RUFF'S GUIDE

What **WISDEN** is to cricket, **RUFF'S GUIDE TO THE TURF** is to horse-racing. **WILLIAM RUFF** (1801-1856) was a sporting journalist and widely-respected purveyor of "racing intelligence". With a true journalist's instinct for being first with the news, he adopted carrier pigeons as the fastest method of getting his accounts of race meetings back to the London papers. Ruff's *Guide to the Turf, or Pocket Racing Companion* first appeared in 1843 and remains to this day a trusted source of racing facts, with new editions appearing at regular intervals.

[796] RUHMKORFF COIL

The German instrument-maker **HEINRICH DANIEL RUHMKORFF** (1803-77) was born in Hanover, and settled in Paris in 1839. In 1851, building on **FARADAY**'s 1831 discovery of induced currents and subsequent work by a number of researchers including **MORSE**'s collaborator **JOSEPH HENRY,** he patented a refined version of the induction coil invented by Irish physicist-priest, Nicholas Callan in 1836. The device is a step-up electric transformer with an interrupter to generate high AC voltages from a low voltage DC supply such as a **VOLTA'S** battery or **DANIELL'S CELL**. Besides furnishing whacking great electric sparks for hazardous Victorian parlour amusements, its most important use was to provide the high electric potential needed to operate the gas discharge tubes made by **GEISSLER**, **CROOKES**, and **RÖNTGEN**. It also powered the earliest spark-gap radio transmitter due to **HERTZ** and was the forerunner of the **TESLA COIL**. All in all, a handy bit of kit. (MW)

[797] RUMFORD FIREPLACE

The American physicist and inventor **BENJAMIN THOMPSON, COUNT RUMFORD** (1753-1814) was born in Woburn, Massachussetts and educated partly at Harvard. When the American rebellion broke out, his pro-British sympathies meant he had to leave town on a fast horse, one jump ahead of a group of angry citizens come to tar and feather him. He made his way to Europe where he continued his studies, notably into the subject of heat. As a spin-off from these investigations, he discovered and promoted* a way of constructing or reconstructing fireplaces. His two main innovations were to set the sides of the fireplace ("covings" as he called them) at an oblique angle in order to reflect more heat into the room, and narrowing the throat of the chimney so that it would no longer allow smoke back into the room or, alternatively, empty the room of warmed air which would then necessarily be replaced by cold air from outside. Thompson's title was conferred on him by the Elector of Bavaria who made him a Count of the Holy Roman Empire. The English awarded a knighthood and made him a Fellow of the Royal Society. And the Americans forgave him to the extent of adopting his fireplace design (which rapidly became an accepted standard and was installed in Jefferson's house at Monticello) and by making his birthplace a National Historic Landmark. The **RUMFORD MEDAL**, awarded every two years for outstanding achievement in science was established in 1796 by Rumford's simultaneous gifts of $5,000 to the Royal Society and to the American Academy of Arts and Sciences. Medallists have included **DAVY, FARADAY, PASTEUR, MAXWELL,** Edison and **FERMI**.

*He published papers on the subject in in 1796 and 1798

[798] RUPERT

The use of the word "rupert" by Other Ranks in the army to mean "officer" is probably explained by the conviction among the said Other Ranks that a large proportion of officers actually have been saddled with this name by cruel parents. There is however an alternative – if unsubstantiated – explanation which relates use of the term to the **RUPERT BEAR** trousers worn by officers in some Scottish regiments on formal occasions.

[799] RUSSELL'S PARADOX

In a town, the only barber shaves all and only those men who do not shave themselves. Who shaves the barber? Any attempt to reason an answer to this question leads to self-contradiction (the barber is presumed to be male). This is one simplified version of **RUSSELL'S PARADOX** of 1901 cast into language that ordinary mortals might hope to understand. It stems from Russell's critique of a flaw in the mathematical set theory of Friedrich Frege (1848-1925), concerning whether the set of all sets that are not members of themselves is a member of itself. Russell proposed a resolution of this paradox, based on his Theory of Types, which declares there to be a hierarchy between sentences about individuals, sentences about sets of individuals, and sentences about sets of sets of individuals, etc. What can meaningfully be asserted at one level does not apply at another, so the paradox cannot be formulated, for it will always be formally invalid to count a set as a member of itself. **BERTRAND ARTHUR WILLIAM RUSSELL, 3ʳᴰ Earl RUSSELL** (1872-1970) a Welshman born in Trelleck, Gwent, was brought up by his grandmother owing to the early death of his parents. After a lonely, contemplative childhood he entered Cambridge in 1890 and took a double first in mathematics and philosophy, being elected fellow of Trinity College in 1895. During a long, productive, and often controversial intellectual life, he stood out as the pre-eminent British philosopher and social reformer of the 20th Century. He was a prolific author of popular works on philosophy, religion, social and ethical issues (he was married four times); in all some 70 books too numerous to list here, but the pinnacle of his intellectual achievement was to co-author with Alfred North Whitehead (1861-1947) the seminal academic work *Principia Mathematica* (3 vols., 1910-13): a fully developed formal system for deriving the axioms of mathematics from pure symbolic logic, and arguably the greatest contribution to logic since Aristotle. Russell was elected FRS in 1908. His philosophical development followed the empiricist tradition, influenced by his former pupil Ludwig Wittgenstein, and was centred on linguistic analysis, the theory of descriptions and what he called "logical atomism". Always a committed political activist, Russell became widely known as a conscientious objector during WWI, and was consequently removed from his Trinity College lectureship in 1916, and imprisoned in 1918 for publishing a seditious article, but then reinstated by Trinity in 1919. He also campaigned actively for women's suffrage. He travelled and lectured widely in the Soviet Union and China, and in the USA from 1924-31, inheriting the Earldom from his brother in 1931. More visiting lectureships in the USA followed in 1938-42, where he was sacked by City College, New York as "an enemy of religion and morality" but subsequently won damages for wrongful dismissal. With the rise of Fascism, Russell renounced his pacifist stance in 1939 as the lesser evil in the interests of defeating Hitler. He was honoured, somewhat reluctantly, by King George VI with the Order of Merit in 1949. He delivered the first BBC Reith Lectures the same year, and was awarded the Nobel Prize for literature in 1950. He was a powerful opponent of the Vietnam War. In 1958 he became first President of the Campaign for Nuclear Disarmament and was imprisoned in 1961 for leading a "sit-in" – an act of mass civil disobedience in London's heart of government. MW cherishes the memory of having once been privileged, with many others, to share a cold, hard Whitehall pavement with Bertrand Russell. **RUSSELL'S TEAPOT** refers to his whimsical observation on the statement commonly asserted by theists, that "science cannot disprove the existence of God": neither can science disprove the existence of a teapot in orbit around the Sun. (MW)

[800] RUTHERFORDIUM

Claims for the successful synthesis of element number 104 have been much contested: it has previously been baptised as Dubnium, Unnilquadium, and Kurchatovium, but was again renamed (see **SEABORGIUM**) in 1997 – after international controversy – to celebrate the memory of the pre-eminent experimental physicist who ushered in the atomic age: New Zealander **SIR ERNEST RUTHERFORD** (1871-1937). His list of scientific achievements is stunning: above all, in 1919 he became the first true alchemist by transmuting one element into another – but because he chose to convert nitrogen into oxygen, the enterprise did not make his fortune. In 1902, while at McGill University, he put forward the theory of radioactive disintegration. In 1907 he took the chair of physics at Manchester, and identified the nature of alpha and beta particles (see GEIGER COUNTER). In 1919, while CAVENDISH professor at Cambridge, he provided experimental proof of the structure of the nuclear atom, and in 1920 posited the existence of a neutral fundamental particle, the neutron, which was experimentally proved by James Chadwick in 1932. Rutherford received the NOBEL PRIZE for physics in 1908, was knighted in 1914, and created Baron Rutherford of Nelson (his NZ birthplace) in 1931. Besides the obscure synthetic element no. 104, RUTHERFORDIUM, symbol Rf, his name is commemorated in many prestigious research institutions throughout the world. (MW)

[801] RUY LOPEZ

A classic chess opening named after the Spanish bishop RUY LOPEZ DE SEGURA (*ca.* 1540 – 1580). Lopez was probably the finest chess-player of his age, and author of an early work on chess entitled *Libro de la invención y arte del juego del Axedrez.* There are more than 1000 eponymous chess openings – see WARE'S OPENING.

[802] RYDBERG CONSTANT

This can be thought of as the PIN for the hydrogen atom, a unique number (10967758) that identifies the exact value of hydrogen's internal energy and the precise colour of light it emits, when excited. For the background to this piece of fundamental atomic science, first see BALMER SERIES where you will read how the emission spectrum of atomic H comprises several series of sharp lines with wavelengths that can be related by simple empirical mathematical expressions. In 1888 Swedish physicist JOHANNES ROBERT RYDBERG (1854-1919) of Lund University devised a single overarching formula which accurately provides the wavelengths of all the 50 or so observable lines of the entire H spectrum,* in the ultraviolet, visible and infrared. His simple formula just employs two integers (whole numbers), which are each allowed to run through the values 1,2,3,4,5... etc., to generate the different lines, and are scaled by the RYDBERG CONSTANT which can be measured by spectroscopists with exquisite precision as 10967758 m^{-1} (in SI units of reciprocal meters). BOHR'S theory of the hydrogen atom (1913) explains its line spectra as arising from jumps between quantized states of its internal energy, and Bohr comes up with a theoretical expression for the RYDBERG CONSTANT in terms of known universal physical constants: the charge and mass of the electron and proton, the speed of light and PLANCK'S CONSTANT. When appropriate numerical values for these (determined by totally independent means) are plugged into Bohr's expression for the **RYDBERG CONSTANT** the result that falls out is 10967758 m^{-1}. Getting things like that so accurately correct is very persuasive evidence that atomic science must be on the right track. (MW)

*The Rydberg formula can be used to explain the spectra of elements other than hydrogen, too, with some modification.

S

[803] SABINE'S GULL

Larus sabini is named after the artillery officer **Sir EDWARD SABINE,** FRS (1788-1883) who identified this previously unrecorded species while accompanying as astronomer and naturalist the expedition of **JOHN ROSS** to Baffin Bay in search of the North-West Passage in 1818. The Ross expedition ended in fiasco, but Sabine sailed again to Arctic waters under **EDWARD PARRY** in 1819-20. Subsequently he was appointed scientific adviser to the Admiralty, contributed largely to a systematic world-wide measurement of magnetic inclination as part of a ground-breaking programme of international scientific co-operation organised by **HUMBOLDT**, and carried out two magnetic surveys of the British Isles (1834-6 and 1861).

[804] SACHER TORTE

Viennese chocolate cake involving marmalade, baked to a recipe created by confectioner **FRANZ SACHER** (1806-1907) in 1832. Sacher's son Eduard followed in his father's footsteps and trained as pastrycook and *chocolatier* before establishing the **HOTEL SACHER** in Vienna (1876), where the now trademarked **"ORIGINAL SACHERTORTE"** still figures among the delights on offer to the sweet of tooth. The avidity of the Viennese for sweet cakes and sticky pastries (perhaps owing something to Turkish influence?) is a constant background theme in Frank Tallis's riveting psychological murder mystery *Vienna Blood* (2006).

[805] SADISM

A psychological disorder whereby the sufferer can only achieve sexual gratification through the infliction of pain or humiliation on his/her partner(s). It takes its name from the French pornographer **DONATIEN ALPHONSE FRANÇOIS, Comte DE SADE** (1740-1814), generally referred to as the **MARQUIS DE SADE**. De Sade served as an army officer in the Seven Years' War (1756-1763), narrowly escaped execution following charges of cruelty and unnatural practices, was imprisoned in Vincennes and later in the Bastille (where he turned author and gave expression to his sexual fantasies in a number of well-known fictions*), and ended his miserable life in the lunatic asylum at Charenton. It is fashionable nowadays to idolise this nasty little man as a brave and misunderstood champion of liberty of expression (and, presumably, of behaviour). This is a view that should be received only with the gravest possible reservations. The defining characteristics of pornographic writing (and behaviour) are *infantilism* and *monotony*. Where the last of these is concerned, it is a curious fact that in circumstances where anything and everything is permitted, it turns out that the range of possible activities is actually very limited. Hence the endless and boring repetition of essentially the same sexual scenario. The same observation might be extended in the political sphere to the behaviour of the madder sort of dictator. Here again, the possessor of absolute power is in theory free to do absolutely anything he or she likes. But once total power has been achieved, a drastic failure of imagination sets in, and what they almost invariably end up doing is killing lots of people and indulging in grandiose and tasteless architectural projects by which they hope to give concrete expression to their fantasies of omnipotence.

* *Les 120 journées de Sodome* (1764), *Justine* (1791), *La philosophie dans le boudoir* (1793), *Juliette* (1798), *Les crimes de l'amour* (1800).

[806] SAINT DUNSTAN'S

ST. DUNSTAN (*ca.* 909-988) was an English monk who rose to be Archbishop of Canterbury and an influential adviser to the Saxon kings. Following his canonisation, and until his fame was eclipsed by that of Thomas à Becket, he was England's most popular saint. Among many reforms, he promoted the pursuit of useful trades as a means of self-improvement. He was himself a skilled artist, illuminator and metal worker and is the patron saint of gold- and silversmiths. His saint's day (May 19th – the day of his death) marks the beginning of the year denoted by jewellers' hallmarks. SAINT DUNSTAN'S, a charity devoted to the care of blind and visually impaired ex-service personnel was founded in 1915 to help causalties resulting from the horrors of WWI. On an unserious note, a well-worn anecdote may bear repeating here. It relates how Noel Coward, escorting a young boy down a public street, was confronted by the sight of a pair of copulating dogs. Coward promptly interpreted the event for his young charge: "The little doggy in front has suddenly gone blind, and the little doggy behind is pushing him all the way to Saint Dunstan's."

[807] SAINT GEORGE'S DAY

The English notoriously know so little about their patron saint as to be largely unaware even of the day in the calendar on which he is celebrated. (It's April 23rd.) As regards who he was, ignorance is pretty well general and total. The great Gibbon thought he knew the answer, and in his *Decline and fall of the Roman empire* identifies our patron saint as the notorious GEORGE OF CAPPADOCIA, a crooked purveyor of mouldy bacon to the Byzantine army* – crooked but ambitious, as he somehow later managed, while on the run from the victims of his bacon scam, to get himself appointed archbishop of Alexandria, where he ran his parish like a one-man Mafia. However, after backing the losing side in a bloodily-contested theological controversy, he was dragged by a furious mob from the prison where he had been lodged to answer for his crimes, and lynched with extreme prejudice (361 AD). His corpse was paraded through the streets on a camel and then thrown into the sea. But alas! it now seems that Gibbon's polished barbs were peppering the wrong target, though the now more generally accepted identification of Saint George with a soldier in the Roman army, martyred in 303 AD has no textual evidence to back it. Like most Christian hagiography his story is compounded 99% of creative imagination and 1% of wishful thinking. Apart from his patronage of England, Saint George extends his protection to Bulgaria, farmers**, the Greek army, butchers, shepherds, the Order of the Garter, a Brazilian soccer team, and – for some reason – syphilis.

* Of George's approach to the bacon business, Gibbon remarks: "His employment was mean: he rendered it infamous. He accumulated wealth by the basest arts of fraud and corruption... etc." Gibbon's 2-page summary of George's character and career prior to his canonisation is peppered with words like *notorious, avaricious, servile, impious, tyrannical, vile, pernicious, cruel , odious, and unjust.* No doubt modern taste would consider these usages overly judgemental but I say, "Stick it to him, Mr Gibbon."

** Hence Virgil's "*Georgics*".

[808] SAINT JOHN'S WORT

The medicinal herb *Hypericum perforatum* or **SAINT JOHN'S WORT** flowers in mid-summer and so takes its common name from the feast of **SAINT JOHN THE BAPTIST** (June 24th), which falls three days after the summer solstice and is celebrated as Midsummer Day. On St. John's Eve it used to be the custom to light bonfires and run through them or jump over them.* Many pagan rituals which survived into the Christian era were originally propitiatory or apotropaic in intention and this is especially true of ceremonies marking the solstices and equinoxes. The thinking (perfectly logical) was that when one season ends and another begins, there has to be a moment at which the rules governing the old order no longer obtain and the new order has not yet established itself. This is the moment when spirits of *dis*-order, of malice and evil, seize their chance to make hay, and this is why what we might call "boundary ceremonies" (which would include rituals connected with spatial boundaries) are necessary to counter or avert their influence and prevent mere chaos.

* See for example Laurence Whistler *The English festivals* (1947) and, more exhaustively, Frazer's *Golden Bough.*

[809] SAINT LEGER STAKES

Annual race held (normally) at Doncaster for three-year-old thoroughbreds (*sc.*

horses), and run over a distance of 3,212 yards or a little under two miles. It takes it name from **Col. ANTHONY SAINT LEGER** (1731/2-1786), MP for Grimsby. The first race, for a stake of 25 guineas, was organised by the Marquess of Rockingham on St. Leger's suggestion in 1776 and was run over two miles on Cantley Common, near the present racecourse. Rockingham's nag came in first and St. Leger's second. Today the St. Leger is classed as one of the five British Classic Flat Races, the others being the Two Thousand Guineas and One Thousand Guineas, both held at Newmarket, and the Oaks and **DERBY,** both held at Epsom.

[810] SAINT TIGGYWINKLE'S

The perhaps unserious but absolutely appropriate name for the large and busy wildlife hospital located at Haddenham in Buckinghamshire and originally devoted to caring for sick, injured or orphaned hedgehogs as well as deer, badgers and other wild creatures. It was founded by Sue and Les Stocker and their son Colin in 1978 and named for the eponymous heroine of Beatrix Potter's *Tale of Mrs Tiggywinkle* (1905). All honour to those who devote themselves to the welfare of these innocent sharers of our fields, woods and gardens and helpless victims of far-too-many speeding motorists.

What God abandoned, these defended.

[811] SAINT VALENTINE'S DAY

Scholars inform us that our present Saint Valentine's observances are a dumbed-down and cleaned-up version of the Roman *Lupercalia*, a mid-February fertility festival which featured over-excited young men dashing about lashing maidens and matrons with whips made from the skins of recently-sacrificed goats in order to boost their (the maidens' and matrons') fertility. In a slightly later version it included the drawing of temporary sexual partners by random ballot. This harmless way of letting off erotic steam may well have had the effect, intended or not, of cooling the ardour of the participants for the rest of the year and so reducing the incidence of random copulation and consequent social disharmony. In the Middle Ages, it was believed that the same mid-February date was the occasion for birds to choose their mates for the coming year, a pleasant notion celebrated by Chaucer in a longish dream-poem entitled *The Parlement of foules*. Reminding us that the Lupercalia also heralded the beginning of spring, Chaucer's birds are made to sing (to a French melody, the poet notes) an invocation to Summer which goes:

> *Now welcome Somer, with thy sonne softe,*
> *That hast this wintres weders overshake,*

And driven away the longe nyghtes blake.
Saynt Valentyn, that art ful hy on-lofte,
Thus syngen smale foules for thy sake:
Now welcome Somer, with thy sonne softe,
That hast this wintres weders overshake.

February may seem a little early to be greeting the summer. Possibly Chaucer already had this charming little lyric up his sleeve and this was the best occasion he could find of working it into a poem. Or perhaps in his day the weather got warmer sooner and the nights less "blake". Of SAINT VALENTINE, as usual with the saints of the early Church, we have no reliable information. Given that the compilers of early martyrologies were out to propagate faith rather than facts, this is unsurprising. We don't even know which of four possible Saint Valentines we are honouring by sending each other vaguely lascivious greeting cards from supposedly anonymous admirers – a tradition which has some centuries of antiquity behind it and which helps keep the card publishers in business during the year-long run-up to Christmas.

[812] SAINT VITUS' DANCE

SAINT VITUS DANCE, also known as SYDENHAM'S CHOREA, is a serious disorder of the central nervous system due to streptococcal infection and characterised by involuntary jerking movements on the part of the sufferer. It particularly affects children following rheumatic heart disease. It was first described by the German physician-alchemist Paracelsus, the *nom de guerre* of Theophrastus Bombastus von Hohenheim (1493-1541), but named after the English physician THOMAS SYDENHAM (1624-1688) who described it in a work of 1686. The attribution to SAINT VITUS, a 4th(?)-century Sicilian martyr, patron of actors and dancers, reflects the mediaeval belief that certain saints were particularly likely to intercede on behalf of sufferers from particular diseases. The "dancing" (chorea, from the Greek χορός), in early accounts may well be as much a description of the behaviour of people frightened by an outbreak of the disease as that of people actually afflicted by it, since history offers numerous descriptions of irrational crowd behaviour and mass moral panic in the face of epidemics. These range from Herodotus' account of the Great Plague in Athens during the Peloponnesian War (with people running about the streets and jumping into wells) to Defoe's description of the Great Plague of 1665 in London, via the "Dancing Plague" that ravaged the city of Strasbourg in 1418. Sydenham's Chorea is sometimes referred to as "chorea minor", to distinguish it from HUNTINGTON'S CHOREA or "chorea major".

[813] SALMANAZAR – see JEROBOAM

[814] SALTAIRE

Model village three miles outside Bradford built by SIR TITUS SALT (1803-1876), a local wool-man. The name embodies his own name plus that of the river that runs through the valley. Salt is remembered as having introduced alpaca weaving in Bradford, an enterprise whose success was the foundation of his fortune. In addition he developed improved techniques for weaving fine worsteds at a reasonable price. Like other paternalist philanthropists of his day, Salt was no believer in allowing the workers control over their own destinies, and though a doughty proponent of decent working conditions for the labouring classes, he would have no truck with trade unions. His village was planned with an eye to eliminating opportunities for socialistic goings-on. Drink was outlawed. One feature of Salt's work has a particular modern resonance: Bradford, lying in a hollow surrounded by hills, was a hell of smoking mill-chimneys until well into the 1950s. Salt, as mayor of Bradford, endeavoured to get his fellow mill-owners to install a smoke-reducing device known as the RODDA SMOKE BURNER* in their chimneys and did so in his own mill. He failed, however, to get the rest of the owners to follow suit. Doubtless they had better uses for their brass. Salt's mill today is an art gallery and arts centre which boasts, among other treasures, a fine collection of paintings by David Hockney, local lad made good.

* Best authorial endeavours have failed to elicit an answer to the question "Rodda – who he?" apart from a hint that he may have hailed from Cornwall. Any help from better-informed readers of these pages would be most welcome.

[815] SAM BROWNE

The Sam Browne belt is an item of military equipment, officers for the use of, which consists of a leather belt around the wearer's waist to which is attached a secondary belt that starts at the front, crosses the chest, passes through an epaulette, and descends to meet the waist-belt again at the back. It might at first appear to have no function, but in fact, like many another military institution, it is a fossilised relic of a former necessity – it supports the weight of the officer's sword, which, normally, he has not got. This now-only-occasionally-useful accoutrement is named after its inventor GENERAL SIR SAMUEL JAMES BROWNE, V.C. (1824-1901), who for some forty years fought in, and commanded with credit, numerous Indian campaigns and lively engagements on the North-West Frontier.

[816] SAMARIUM – see CERIUM

[817] SAMSON POST

The term is applied to a strong, upright structural member in a variety of applications: the main roof-supporting members in a mediaeval aisled hall, a part of an oil derrick, a stanchion passing through the decks of a ship, and, in the days of wooden sailing ships, a temporary upright erected on deck to which the tackle for raising the anchor was attached. All uses embody the idea of strength and allude, of course, to the muscular Israelite SAMSON* whose adventures are recounted in *Judges* 13-16. The odd part is that in all engineering contexts the samson post is holding something up, whereas the Samson of the Bible is more widely remembered for pulling things down. Even more puzzling – according to the OED (citing a usage of 1828) – the name was at one time applied to a kind of mouse-trap. Presumably it was so designed as to have the roof of the trap collapse on top of a visiting rodent, after its suspicions had been lulled by engaging it in some form of entertainment or festivity.

* Attempts to visualise what Samson may have looked like inevitably call up the image of Arnold Schwarzenegger, a man once memorably (if unkindly) described as resembling a huge condom filled with walnuts.

[818] SANDEMANIANS

Christian sect founded in Scotland around 1730 by breakaway Presbyterian clergyman John Glas* (1695-1773) and spread by the writings and ministry of his son-in-law ROBERT SANDEMAN (1718-1771). Sandemanian congregations were established in Scotland, England, and America (where Sandeman died), but the number of adherents was never very large. The sect is now reckoned extinct, having died out around 1890. The Sandemanians practised a form of primitive Christianity, imitating as far as they could the lives and habits of the earliest followers of Jesus as recorded in the Gospels. Holy Communion, for example, took the form of a proper communal meal rather than a token sip-and-nibble. Sandeman took an extreme, indeed a revolutionary, position in the old debate regarding Justification by Faith versus Justification by Works. He held that Christ's sacrifice had brought about the salvation of all mankind, regardless of an individual's behaviour or beliefs. A summary of this remarkably humane approach appears on his tombstone, where it is stated, "*That the bare death of Jesus Christ, without a thought or deed on the part of man, is sufficient to present the chief of sinners spotless before Christ.*" Good news indeed, if correct. In its day, the Church numbered two famous persons among its members: the scientist MICHAEL FARADAY, and the anarchist philosopher William Godwin (1756-1836), father of Mary Shelley (see FRANKENSTEIN'S MONSTER).

* Hence the alternative name "GLASITES".

[819] SANDWICH

Britain's only contribution to world cuisine is named after JOHN MONTAGU, 4TH EARL OF SANDWICH (1718-1792). The story of how Sandwich, at the card table, had dinner brought to him between two slices of bread so that he could eat it with one hand and without interrupting play (he once stayed at the table for 24 hours continuously) has a smell of folk etymology about it, though it is accepted by the OED. More certain is the naming of the **SANDWICH ISLANDS** (now Hawaii) in his honour by Cook, thanks to the fact that Sandwich was First Lord of the Admiralty from 1748 to 1782 during the period of Cook's three great voyages. Though early in his career Sandwich made some important naval reforms with the help of Anson,* honour was not much in evidence during his later period of office, which was marked by corruption, incompetence, and jobbery.

* See **WAR OF JENKINS' EAR**

[820] SAPIR-WHORF HYPOTHESIS

In the 1920s and 30s, two American linguists **EDWARD SAPIR** (1884-1939) and his colleague **BENJAMIN LEE WHORF** (1897-1941), promulgated the theory that cognition is in part culturally determined, *i.e.* that the language we speak affects the way we see and understand the world. The idea was not new. Sapir, as an anthropologist as well as a linguist, was clearly influenced by **K.W. HUMBOLDT** (brother of the great naturalist), a strong believer in linguistic determinism, who wrote, "*Man lives in the world about him principally, indeed exclusively, as language presents it to him.*" The idea may be even older, going back to the opening of Saint John's gospel with its implication that the pre-existing Word was the force which brought the World into being. In any case, it is clear that if our perceptions are indeed moulded by the linguistic categories of whatever happens to be our mother tongue, and if these vary from language to language, this has important psychological, philosophical, and scientific implications. It is a relativistic concept which raises in acute form the still-open question of whether it is possible to perceive with perfect objectivity *things-as-they-are*. In addition it is in conflict with the theory later advanced by Noam Chomsky* that the grammatical basis of all languages is universal and innate. Chomsky's thesis, however, has yet to be proved. His argument rests in part on the assertion that it is possible to generate a meaningless but grammatically-correct sentence. This is not as easy as it sounds. The best Chomsky could manage was the twin oxymorons of *Colorless green ideas sleep furiously* – a sentence which would be regarded as perfectly lucid if it had come from a poem by, for example, Dylan Thomas.

* *Syntactic structures* 1957

[821] SAPPHIC STANZA

A classical – originally Greek – stanza (verse) composed of four lines, unrhymed. The first three are of five feet (a foot consisting of two or three syllables, varying in pattern as to stress), and the last of two feet. Each foot of the first three lines is trochaic (a stressed followed by an unstressed syllable TUM-ti) except for the third foot which is dactylic (a stressed syllable followed by two unstressed, TUM-ti-ti). The last line has two feet only, the first dactylic, the second trochaic. This verse form is named after the Greek lyric poet **SAPPHO OF LESBOS** (born *ca.* 650 BC) who used it in some of her poems, though most of her work survives only in fragments recorded by later writers. Among the Greeks, Sappho's reputation rivalled that of Homer. The Latin lyric poets Catullus and Horace both imitated the Sapphic stanza and, though it is not well suited to English verse, versions have been attempted by Thomas Campion (1567-1620) and by poor mad William Cowper* (1731-1800) as well as by the German poet Klopstock (1724-1803). Swinburne's efforts to reproduce the Sapphic metre in English have been hailed** as "daring and brilliant". Thus -

APHRODITE

All the night sleep came not upon my eyelids,
Shed not dew, nor shook nor unclosed a feather,
Yet with lips shut close and with eyes of iron
*   Stood and beheld me.*

Then to me so lying awake a vision
Came without sleep over the seas and touched me,
Softly touched mine eyelids and lips; and I too,
*   Full of the vision,*

Saw the white, implacable Aphrodite,
Saw the hair unbound and the feet unsandalled
Shine as the fire of sunset on western waters;
*   Saw the reluctant*

Feet, the straining plumes of the doves that drew her,
Looking always, looking with necked reverted,
Back to Lesbos, back to the hills whereunder
*   Shone Mitylene.*

For English-speakers, Sappho's shorter poems and fragments should be read in the beautiful translations of Mary Barnard (U. of California Press 1958, still in print).

* The writer and critic Laurence Housman (brother of A.E.) gave it as his opinion that in the late 18th and early 19th centuries the best poets were all insane, and instanced Cowper, Clare, Blake and Christopher Smart. An exaggeration near enough the truth to be considered seriously.

** *Encyclopaedia Britannica* 11th ed.

[822] SARIN

Form of nerve gas developed during WWII by scientists working for the German chemical giant IG Farben. It was amazingly effective. Distributed in aerosol form, it was found that a single drop on the unprotected skin of an experimental subject (apes were used, among others) could cause incapacity and death in almost no time at all. Sarin was the brain-child of a chemist named GERHARD SCHRADER who in 1936 created the first organo-phosphorus agent, originally intended for use as an insecticide. The military authorities were quick to recognise its potential as a homicide and the next step was a chemical warfare agent code-named "Tabun", of which SARIN was an improved version. The name is an acronym composed of the last-name initials of Schrader, his head of department Otto Ambros, and two army officers involved in the project. With the end of the war, the Allies spirited away some of the German chemists involved in the nerve-agent programme to continue working in Canada, the US and Britain. The outcome was a further-improved version of Sarin, allotted the NATO codename VX, which it was hoped in some quarters might replace the atom bomb as the weapon of choice for mass extinctions. It has not yet been used in this role, though it is widely believed that VX, along with other agents, was used in the Halabja Kurdish massacre of 1988.* How Saddam Hussein obtained these weapons is not known, though a cynic might note that at that time Saddam was America's good buddy, and that to help out in the aftermath of the atrocity, the Americans attempted to spread the story that it had been perpetrated by the Iranians (also no friends to the Kurds). Efforts have been made to introduce an international ban on the production and use of lethal chemical weapons, and some rather half-hearted agreements have been reached, but the status even of these is now moot, given America's declaration that it is not bound by international law or treaty obligations. So it goes.

* As well as by members of a group of Japanese religious nutters known as Aum Shinrikyo in the Tokyo subway in 1995

[823] SAUSSUREA

Genus of some 300 species of mostly alpine plants belonging to the family Asteraceae, some grown as garden plants. *Saussurea lappa*, a native of the Himalayas, has a long history of medicinal use and is currently being investigated as a potential anti-carcinogen. The genus is named after NICOLAS THÉODORE DE SAUSSURE (1767-1845), who first investigated the chemistry of plant physiology (respiration, photo-synthesis), and held the chair of mineralogy and zoology at Geneva from 1802. He belonged to a veritable dynasty of French-Swiss scientists and academics which recalls the no less remarkable CASSINI dynasty in France and which included Nicolas de Saussure (1709-1790), agronomist and viticulturalist; his son Horace Bénédict de Saussure (1740-1799), geologist and physician, father of N.T. de Saussure, the first traveller to ascend Mont Blanc, and the author of *Voyages dans les Alpes* (8 vols. 1779-1796); Henri de Saussure (1829-1905), grandson of Horace Bénédict, entomologist who studied and collected in Central America; and, not least, Ferdinand de Saussure (1857-1913), son of Henri, father of Structural Linguistics. *Saussurea* is also the title of the journal of the Geneva Botanical Society.

[824] SAXOPHONE

The saxophone is one of the few musical instruments named after its inventor*. Instrument maker ANTOINE JOSEPH "ADOLPHE" SAX (1814-1894) was born at Dinant in Belgium but spent most of his working life in Paris. He combined mechanical ability and a scientific understanding of acoustics with a flair for self-promotion. In 1845 he patented an instrument he called the "saxhorn" and a family of cylinder instruments called "saxotrombas", before registering the SAXOPHONE in 1846. This was a single-reed instrument with a clarinet mouthpiece, a brass body, and a conical bore, wide at the bottom and narrowing towards the top. The originality of Sax's invention lay in his discovery that the timbre of the instrument depended not on the material of which it was made (in this case, metal) but on the proportions of the tube within which the air vibrates. The saxophone as it now exists is not a single instrument but a family of 12 instruments, differing in size and register and ranging from the sopranino at the top end to the contrabass at the very bottom. The saxophone soon found a place in military bands where it forms a kind of bridge between the reed and brass sections, and in the latter part of the 19th century began to feature in the symphonic works of many composers, especially French. Sax won the support of no lesser personages than Hector Berlioz and Giacomo Rossini (he of the TOURNEDOS) in his struggles with detractors and envious instrument-makers who continuously harassed him with court cases challenging the priority of his invention or the value of his instruments. Today there are many saxophone quartets, emulating the string quartet, which they are able to do because, like the family of bowed string instruments, the saxophone family exhibits homogeneity of timbre among its various members as well as outstanding fluency and expressiveness. It is perhaps the latter quality which has made the saxophone a mainstay of jazz music. Players like Johnny Hodges, Coleman Hawkins, Lester Young, the great Charlie Parker, and John Coltrane were able to make their unique contributions to our musical heritage in large measure because of the way Sax's instruments can be made to "talk" with such a personal voice, and explains why any musician worth his salt can tell you after a few bars which of any one of the 30 best sax players in the world is playing. (PP)

* But see also MOOG SYNTHESISER, THEREMIN, SOUSAPHONE.

[825] SCHECHTMANITE

It was always thought by crystallographers, for as long as their science has existed (something over 300 years), that Dame Nature had totally anathematized periodic 5-fold symmetry in crystals as a geometrical impossibility (see **PENROSE TILING**). Then in 1984 Israeli physicist **DR DANY SCHECHTMAN** working at the US National Bureau of Standards prepared an alloy of aluminium and manganese, since honorifically named **SCHECHTMANITE**, that gave an X-ray diffraction pattern displaying five-fold symmetry. A paradigm shift for the crystallographers! This is now regarded as an example of the so-called *quasicrystalline* state of matter, intermediate between a fully-ordered crystal and a completely amorphous glass, or supercooled liquid. (MW)

[826] SCHEELE'S GREEN

This fine apple-green pigment, discovered in 1778, became popular in the Victorian period, especially for decorative wallpapers and textiles, along with several similar greens accorded the names of Brunswick, Emerald, Paris, Schweinfurth, and Vienna. These fell from favour because they all contain a cumulative poison, copper arsenite. What's worse, mildew growing on wallpaper coloured with Scheele's green etc., can emit a deadly arsenical vapour, called **GOSIO GAS**. Since the 1960s, when radioactivation analysis of Napoleon Bonaparte's hair detected significant amounts of arsenic, there has been debate concerning the cause of his death, which terminated his 6-year exile on St. Helena in 1821. His diagnosed gastric cancer may have been exacerbated by arsenic poisoning – accidental, or, according to conspiracy theorists, not. A specimen of contemporary wallpaper from Longwood House, Napoleon's dwelling on St. Helena, came to light in 1980, and was found to contain some **SCHEELE'S GREEN**. The debate continues. **CARL WILHELM SCHEELE** (1742-1786) was a Swedish chemist, born in Pomerania (then a Swedish province), who worked as a pharmacist in Stockholm, Uppsala and Köping. He made numerous significant chemical discoveries, some of a life-threatening nature, including chlorine, hydrogen fluoride, hydrogen sulphide and hydrogen cyanide. It is a tribute to his manipulative skills that he survived these innovations even to the age of 43, but the circumstances of his premature death do suggest accidental poisoning. (MW)

[827] SCHEELITE

Most naturally occurring minerals are named either like geological strata after the/a place where they occur (Andesite, Bauxite, Iceland spar, Vesuvianite, etc.) or after some property they possess (bloodstone, magnetite, meerschaum, nephrite, etc.) A few however, are named after persons, usually their discoverers or describers. Such a one is **SCHEELITE** named after the Swedish chemist **CARL**

WILHELM SCHEELE (see **SCHEELE'S GREEN**). Other examples are: **ANDRADITE** (Brazilian statesman and mineralogist **JOSÉ BONIFACIO DE ANDRADA E SILVA** 1763-1838); **BORNITE** (Transylvanian mineralogist and metallurgist **IGNAZ von BORN** 1742-1791); **BRAUNITE** (German archaeologist and homeopath **AUGUST EMIL BRAUN** 1809-1856); **CORDIERITE** (French geologist and mineralogist **LOUIS CORDIER** 1777-1861); **GADOLINITE** (Finnish chemist and mineralogist **JOHAN GADOLIN** 1760-1852, who also gave his name to the metal **GADOLINIUM**); **HEULANDITE** (named after the English mineral collector **HENRY HEULAND** in 1822); **HUMITE** (geologist and MP **Sir ABRAHAM HUME** 1749-1838, who donated his collection of precious stones to the Cambridge University Museum); **MORGANITE** (American banker and art collector **JOHN PIERPONT MORGAN** 1837-1913); **UVAROVITE** (Russian statesman, scholar and educationalist **Count SERGEI S. UVAROV** 1785-1855); **WITHERITE** (English physician, botanist and mineralogist **WILLIAM WITHERING** 1741-1799, more generally known as the man who introduced digitalis into the British pharmacopeia); **ZIN(C)KENITE** (German mineralogist **J.K.L. ZINCKEN** 1790-1862); **ZOISITE** (Slovenian aristocrat **Baron SIGISMOND ZOIS VON EDOLSTEIN** 1747-1819). It is curious and perhaps significant that most of these persons were contemporaries or near-contemporaries. (See also **DOLOMITE** and **DIOGENITE**.)

[828] SCHRÖDINGER'S CAT

Austrian physicist **ERWIN RUDOLF JOSEF ALEXANDER SCHRÖDINGER** (1887-1961) is famous for his contributions to quantum mechanics, an area of scientific knowledge (and uncertainty) which includes something called the Theory of Superposition. To make sense of this one has to imagine that when a quantum mechanic is considering some entity, let's say an electron, she cannot consider it as being in only one state. Instead, it has a number of possible states, over which it is "smeared". Only when the mechanic actually tries to measure it does its state become definite. (This is not easy to get one's head round, but if it were otherwise, it wouldn't be quantum mechanics.) One consequence is that if electrons are kept in the subatomic equivalent of a sealed box, they are nevertheless "to some extent" outside the box too. Weird – though we use devices every day which take advantage of this behaviour in an electronic component called a tunnel diode (a.k.a. **ESAKI DIODE***). To clarify this particular concept, Schrödinger offered one of those "thought experiments" beloved of theoretical physicists. The setup is a cat in a pretty well-sealed box (Erwin apparently forgot the cat would need to breathe). Also in the box (i.e. hidden from any observer) is a devilish device worthy of a Bond scenario: a tiny piece of some radioactive material, a geiger counter, some electronics, a solenoid-actuated hammer, and a vial of hydrocyanic acid, the Poisoner's Friend. If one of the radioactive nuclei should decay, it will emit a particle which the geiger counter will register, triggering the electronics which will activate the solenoid which will trip the hammer which will shatter the vial which will release the cyanide which will kill the cat. But radioactive decay is a notoriously stochastic kind of thing – you can't know when it's going to happen. So, if we do not actually open the box we have to consider the state of the cat as being both alive and dead, it is "distributed between the states of life and death". It is probably fair to ask why Erwin had to dream up such a macabre and elaborate scenario. Why not just have a box with two compartments, and a trap door between? Let's say there's food in one part, water in the other. The cat could be in either part, so its state must be distributed between "in compartment A" and "in compartment B". And to save extra work, let's use the same box we had MAXWELL'S DEMON in before, only make the trap door a bit bigger. (PP)

* After Japanese physicist LEO ESAKI (b. 1925), NOBEL PRIZE 1973.

[829] SCHRÖDINGER'S WAVE EQUATION

The first task of any atomic theory is to account for the properties of the hydrogen atom, the simplest of the chemical elements, having only one electron "orbiting" a positively charged nucleus. BOHR tried to do this by classical NEWTONIAN mechanics and ended up with a fudge. So Austrian physicist ERWIN SCHRÖDINGER (1887-1961) of Vienna, invoked the wavelike nature of the electron (see DE BROGLIE) to achieve a more consistent picture of the hydrogen atom by means of wave mechanics, which employs the HAMILTONIAN operator. He satisfactorily calculated the energy states of the hydrogen atom, and the quantum properties (see PLANCK) of the electron in the hydrogen atom that fell out of this theory quite prettily explain the structure of the periodic table of the elements (see MENDELEEV). Schrödinger shared the 1933 NOBEL PRIZE for physics with DIRAC. He spent the war years in Ireland as Professor at the Dublin Institute for Advanced Studies – one way, perhaps, of resolving the horrible moral dilemma that faced some other scientists in Nazi-dominated Europe. (MW)

[830] SCOPES MONKEY TRIAL

In 1925 the American Civil Liberties Union decided to test the validity of the so-called Butler Act,* a law recently passed by the State of Tennessee forbidding the teaching of Darwinian evolution in its public schools. A group of local notables from the town of Dayton volunteered to back the scheme on the grounds that the ensuing publicity would be good for business, and JOHN THOMAS SCOPES (1900-1970) undertook the role of guinea pig. Scopes was a high school football coach who had once substituted for the school's science teacher, on which occasion he believed (his memory on the point was hazy) he had used an evolutionary tree to illustrate the descent of Man. Scopes was duly indicted. His students, on Scopes' urging, testified against him, and after an eight-day trial and nine-minutes of jury deliberation, Scopes was found guilty and fined $100. On appeal the judgment was set aside on a technicality. This rather bathetic outcome belied the enormous interest the trial had aroused. Major national figures in the forms of William Jennings Bryan for the prosecution and Clarence Darrow for the defence made the occasion a clash of titans. The formidable H.L. Mencken covered the trial for the *American Mercury* of which he was founder and editor, and the progress of the case was reported on radio (a first). Quite apart from complex judicial and constitutional issues raised by the case, on both sides there were those who had hoped to see in the trial a decisive encounter between truth and error. But inevitably they were disappointed. Clearly, the opposition between faith and reason is not something that can be resolved in a court of law. In the end the trial changed no-one's mind and served only to inflame the argument, and the truth or otherwise of Darwinian evolution remains (inexplicably) a lively issue in America today. And even in this country, where philosophical debate comes a very poor second to football and binge-drinking, there are still some persons on both sides for whom a question that for most of us was decisively settled a hundred and fifty years ago is still, apparently, worth arguing about (see **DARWINISM**). For other than legal specialists, the 1955 play *Inherit the Wind* by Jerome Lawrence and Robert Edwin Lee, together with its successive film adaptations, remains the account of the Monkey Trial which has made the widest and most lasting impression on the popular imagination.

* Named after its originator, Tennessee State Representative John Washington Butler (1875-1952).

[831] SCOVILLE TEST

A means of allotting a numerical value to the pepperiness of different kinds of chili pepper. It is the brainchild of American chemist **WILBUR SCOVILLE** (1865-1942), an employee of Parke Davis Pharmaceuticals, who unveiled it in 1912 in the *Journal of the American Pharmacists' Association*. It is an organoleptic test (i.e. dependent on human taste buds), each candidate vegetable being rated by a panel of qualified tasters – "qualified", presumably, meaning persons whose taste buds haven't yet undergone total burnout. The ingredient which causes the impression of heat in the mouth is a compound called *capsiacin*, and pure capsiacin tops the scale at 15-16 million SHU (Scoville Heat Units). At the other end, rated zero, is the familiar bell pepper. The hottest pepper, by a comfortable margin is found to be an Indian entrant known as Naga Jolokia which scores a respectable 1 million. The Jalapeño pepper, for comparison, though reckoned a sure-fire gringo-killer in Mexico, rates a mere 8 thousand SHU. An alternative, more hi-tech, and probably more reliable means of rating the heat of peppers is by the **GILLETT METHOD** which uses high-performance liquid chromotography to measure their capsiacin content.

[832] SCROOGE

When, on account of a fancied similiarity to the hero(?) of Dickens' *Christmas Carol* we describe a selfish, and avaricious person as "a **SCROOGE**", this is not, strictly speaking, a case of *eponymy* but of the even grander-sounding *antonomasia*, defined by the *OED* as "the use of a proper name to express a general idea, as in calling a wise judge *a Daniel.*" Dickens provides a number of common examples (Fagin, Pecksniff, Uriah Heep, Mr Pickwick...) and many others are drawn either from Shakespeare (Hamlet, Falstaff, Romeo...) or the Bible (Samson, Goliath, Herod, **JEZEBEL**, Judas, Magdalene...). This is as it should be, given that the Bible, Shakespeare and Dickens are the three legs on which our shared national literary culture stands. So if a time comes when these allusive usages are no longer understood by the general populace, we should start worrying, if we haven't already done so.

[833] SEA AREA FITZROY

The sea area previously known as Finisterre and familiar to all listeners to BBC shipping forecasts underwent a name change in February 2002 and was henceforth to be known as **FITZROY** after **ADMIRAL ROBERT FITZROY** (1805-1865), naval hydrographer and meteorologist. The change of name was due to an agreement between the Atlantic-coast nations Britain, France, Spain, Portugal and Morocco to co-ordinate shipping areas and their names. As the Spanish also had a sea area they called Finisterre, they were allowed to keep it and Britain bowed out gracefully. It was Fitzroy who, as commander of the *Beagle*, ferried **DARWIN** about the world on his 5-year epoch-making voyage of scientific discovery (1831-1836). As head of the Meteorological Department from 1854, Fitzroy instituted a national system of storm warnings – effectively the first weather forecasts. Fitzroy's name is also commemorated in the cheap and serviceable **FITZROY BAROMETER** which he designed. (See also **FITZROYA**.)

[834] SEABORGIUM

Bestowing a name on a newly man-made chemical element is in the gift of the makers, but it must be ratified by that stern body, the International Union of Pure and Applied Chemistry (IUPAC). Since this "Big Science" game began in the 1950s, the elemental manufacture has taken the form of a three-cornered contest: between Lawrence Berkeley National Laboratory in California, USA (see **LAWRENCIUM**), the Joint Institute for Nuclear Research at Dubna in Russia (see **RUTHERFORDIUM**), and the Institute for Heavy Ion Research in Darmstadt, Germany (see **MEITNERIUM**). Each institute boasts hugely expensive machines (cyclotrons and linear accelerators) capable of smashing atoms together with the unparalleled violence needed to fuse their nuclei and bring about the nucleosynthesis of yet heavier atoms.* Needless to say, the novel claims, and consequent names for these new elements have often proved contentious (see **GHIORSIUM**), requiring the adjudication of IUPAC committees over many years. Customarily, the naming had been posthumous (**FERMI** and **EINSTEIN** were elementally honoured in their lifetimes, but only in secret), but in 1974 **SEABORGIUM,** element number 106 and symbol Sg, was the first to celebrate publicly a living person,** although the name was only ratified reluctantly by IUPAC in 1997. **GLENN THEODORE SEABORG** (1912-1999) was born in Michigan and moved in his youth to California, where he received his education at UCLA. He obtained his PhD in 1937 at the University of California, Berkeley, where he remained to teach and research, becoming the leading chemist of the element nucleosynthesis team at LBNL. With ten new transuranic elements under his belt, he was the successful contender for the 1951 Nobel Prize in chemistry. Also deeply involved in science politics, he was Chairman of the US Atomic Energy Commission for ten years, and acted as Advisor to ten Presidents. His outstanding career in nuclear chemistry inevitably drew him into the development of nuclear weapons during the Manhattan Project; the opprobrium now attaching to this history is somewhat offset by his powerful advocacy of treaties for nuclear non-proliferation and the ban on nuclear testing. Some of Seaborg's radio-isotopes have found beneficial use in "nuclear medicine". (MW)

*In some instances no more than two or three atoms of the new elements have been made, possessing lifetimes shorter than a second. Classicists who may be unmoved by the exquisiteness of the nuclear physics involved, will probably recall the words of Horace: *Parturiunt montes, nascetur ridiculus mus* ("The labouring mountain gives birth to a silly mouse.")

There is a case for arguing that **SAMARIUM was the first element conferring this distinction.

[835] SECCOTINE

Trade name for a form of liquid fish glue invented in Germany in the late 19th century and widely used by woodworkers and others until the advent of modern synthetic adhesives. The name has been appropriated for a cartoon character who appears in the Franco-Belgian children's comic series *Spirou et Fantasio*. (It might be permissible to insert here a word of commendation for the French-language children's comics *Spirou* and *Pilote*, whose content and production values make *The Beano* and its congeners look like what they are – trash.)

[836] SELENIUM – see TITANIUM

[837] SELOUS' ZEBRA

FREDERICK COURTENEY SELOUS, DSO (1851-1917) is among the best known of a generation of Englishmen in Africa whose passion for hunting co-existed with a naturalist's fascination for the wildlife around them. It is therefore not unfitting that Selous (pronounced *sell-oo*), explorer, imperialist, ivory trader, hunter and soldier, should have not one but two creatures named after him: "his" zebra (*Equus burchelli selousi*) and a MEERKAT (*Paracynictis selousi*). The young Rider Haggard met Selous in South Africa in the 1870's and the meeting must have made a deep impression as Selous subsequently appears in the guise of Allan Quartermain, one of the heroes (the other being a Zulu named Umslopagaas) of several of Haggard's African adventure stories, notably *King Solomon's Mines*. Thus it is not only naturalists who owe a debt to Selous, but also that generation of boys fortunate enough to have been brought up on the novels of Rider Haggard, John Buchan, Warwick Deeping and Dornford Yates. Selous was killed in East Africa in 1917 fighting the forces led by the brilliant German guerrilla leader Paul von Lettow-Vorbeck. He published a number of accounts of his African experiences, including: *Travel and adventure in S.E. Africa* (1893) and *African nature notes and reminiscences* (1908).

[838] SEQUOIA NATIONAL PARK

The park, in the Sierra Nevada mountains of California, established in 1890, is named after a person only, so to speak, at one remove. Its name derives from that of the trees it was set up to protect from the attentions of the logging industry: *Sequoia sempervirens* or Coast Redwood, the world's tallest tree; and *Sequoiadenron giganteum* also called Big Tree or Giant Redwood, (or in England WELLINGTONIA), the world's largest living organism by volume. Some of these trees are thought to be as much as three thousand years old. The trees, in turn, were named in honour of the half-Cherokee scholar SEQUOYAH (*ca.* 1770-1843), also known as George Guess or Gist. He is best remembered for his invention of the so-called Cherokee alphabet designed to give written expression to his maternal language. It was not, strictly, an alphabet but a syllabary. Of its 86 characters, 26 were the letters of the English alphabet and the rest of Sequoyah's own devising. He was not actually literate in English, and the English letters he used had no relation to their English sounds. For example, W represented the sound "la" and S the sound "du". Cherokee belongs to the Iroquoian language family, which has ten other members.

[839] SEWARD'S FOLLY

American statesman WILLIAM HENRY SEWARD (1801-1872) served as Secretary of State under Presidents Lincoln and Johnson. He was a doughty supporter of the abolitionist cause as he was of American expansionism. In 1867, the Russians renewed negotiations for the sale of Alaska which had been interrupted by the Civil War and it was Seward who clinched the deal, increasing the area of the United States by an area twice that of Texas for a price of something under 2 cents an acre. The treaty passed the Senate by one vote but the public was underwhelmed by the acquisition of what was widely seen as an expanse of barren and unprofitable wilderness. Alaska was scathingly referred to in the press by such terms as "Seward's Ice-box" and **"SEWARD'S FOLLY"** and declared fit for no purpose except as a playground for polar bears. The discovery of gold in the Yukon in the 1890's changed some people's minds*. The formal handover took place on October 18, 1867, since celebrated as "Alaska Day", in addition to which the Alaskans celebrate "Seward's Day" on the last Monday of March.

* The geo-strategic importance of Alaska to the United States looks likely to be enormously enhanced if and when the melting of the Arctic sea-ice opens a navigable "North-West Passage" between the North Atlantic and the Pacific. This will not, however, be good news for the polar bears, or for relations between the US and Canada. (It is a fair bet that in ten years' time the geopolitical fun and games already under way in the Arctic will be absorbing as much of the Great Powers' attention as is now being lavished on the Middle East.)

[840] SHERMAN TANK

The main tank used by US (and, thanks to lend-lease, Allied) forces in WWII was the M4 medium tank named after Civil War General **WILLIAM TECUMSEH SHERMAN** (1820-1891). When the American forces in North Africa first encountered Rommel's Panzers in the debacle at Kasserine Pass in February 1943, it rapidly became clear that the **SHERMAN** was no match for the German tanks and anti-tank artillery, being both outgunned and too-lightly armoured.* A series of modifications improved their performance and the updated Sherman was still in service at the time of the Korean War (1950-1953).

* "The Shermans fought well, but they had a tendency to catch fire from even glancing hits (earning them the derisive nickname of 'Ronsons')". Saul David *Military blunders* London 1997)

[841] SHRAPNEL

As early as the 15th century, it was realised that for destroying human beings (as opposed to fortifications) solid shot fired from cannon was less effective than lots of small projectiles from the same source which, by scattering on arrival, could cause more widespread damage. Hence the appearance of **"LANGRIDGE"** shot (bits of scrap metal loaded either loose or in some kind of frangible container,* "case" shot (cages or canisters filled with musket balls), etc. The projectile developed from 1784 onwards by artillery officer **HENRY SHRAPNEL** (1761-1842) was of the last type but with refinements. Ordinary case shot merely broke up on impact. Shrapnel's consisted of a hollow metal sphere packed with a mixture of musket balls and gunpowder, fused to burst on reaching the target. Shrapnel's invention had nearly three times the range of its predecessors and proved its worth in the Peninsula and at Waterloo as well as in later conflicts. Its weak point was the difficulty in timing the fuse correctly. In the 20th century with the arrival of rifled artillery, the shrapnel shell more usually consisted of a bursting charge inside a steel projectile designed to shatter into jagged fragments which have greater trauma-producing potential than nice smooth musket balls.

* The etymology of "langridge" (sometimes spelt "langrage") is unknown. It has the look of a personal name, but if it is, that person remains to be identified.

[842] SIDCOT SUIT

A one piece, wool-lined, leather flying suit dating from about 1916 and intended to protect WWI pilots against the freezing temperatures of open cockpits and high altitudes. Its designer was the Australian **FREDERICK SIDNEY COTTON** (1894-1969) himself a pilot. He was, in addition, a pioneer of aerial photography, especially for military purposes, and all-round colourful character of the buccaneering variety. The Sidcot suit was still in service in WWII, as was Sidcot himself, who developed high-speed, high-level stereoscopic photo-reconnaissance for the RAF using specially-adapted (and unarmed) Mosquitoes. Restless after the war, Sidcot turned his hand to a number of enterprises including gun-running but died in poverty. (See also **FOURCADE'S STEREOGONIOMETER**.)

[843] SIDE-BURNS

Strips of facial hair worn forward of the ears, usually by men, and known in England as "side-boards". The word is a metathesised form of their original name "burnsides", so called in honour of those affected by **AMBROSE EVERETT BURNSIDE** (1824-1881) a Union General in the American Civil War. A recent and excellent film about that war* was roughly handled by some critics on the grounds that the beards of the senior officers looked patently false. However, photographs of the participants taken during the war by the great Mathew Brady and others reveal a wild profusion of whiskers, astonishing in their variousness, which in some cases actually do look as though they had been put together on a mad whim using handfuls of material collected from the floor of a busy barber's shop.

* *Gettysburg* dir. Ronald F. Maxwell, 1993.

[844] SIEMENS

The SI unit of electrical conductance (or "admittance" in alternating current circuits). It is accorded the symbol, S, and is the inverse of electrical resistance (or impedance) and therefore measured in reciprocal **OHMS**, Φ^{-1}. The use of the word "mho" for this unit has been mercifully discontinued. **ERNST WERNER VON SIEMENS** (1816-1892) was a German electrical engineer, born in Hanover, who became a Prussian artillery officer. He developed a system of electric telegraphy and its attendant equipment and instrumentation, became a significant industrialist, and discovered the electrically insulating properties of gutta-percha, which were no doubt essential to his survival. (MW)

[845] SIEVERT

An SI unit that measures the "effective" dose of ionizing radiation received by a living organism, human or otherwise. It has the symbol Sv, and is defined by the actual radiation dose absorbed, measured in GRAYS, multiplied by a "quality factor" which is larger, the more damaging the nature of the radiation. Thus the effective dose of alpha radiation is 20 times that of a comparable amount of beta or gamma radiation. The unit is named for the Swedish medical physicist ROLF MAXIMILIAN SIEVERT (1896-1966), who was born in Stockholm, and worked at the Karolinska Institute to measure and standardize the radiation doses used to treat cancer by radiotherapy. (MW)

[846] SILHOUETTE

There is no firm general agreement as to how the name of ETIENNE DE SILHOUETTE (1709-1767), who, under the patronage of Madame de Pompadour, was appointed Finance Minister to Louis XV of France in 1759, became attached to a way of making shadow portraits. Some say it was his miserly approach to money (compared with sculpture or painting in oils, the silhouette was a cheap way of procuring a likeness of yourself or your loved ones). Others affirm that it was Silhouette's own proficiency in this form of portraiture, which he was said to engage in as a pastime. Yet others, including the great Littré, affirm that he actually invented the technique. All, any, or none may be correct.

[847] SIMONY

In the *Acts of the Apostles* (Ch. 8) we read how a Samarian wizard named Simon, known to history as SIMON MAGUS, offered money to Peter to be let in on the secret of curing the lame, the halt, etc. by the laying-on of hands. He was sent off with a flea in his ear. God's gifts, he was told sternly, are not for sale. It is on account of this incident that in the Middle Ages the widespread practice of selling ecclesiastical preferments was known as SIMONY, and condemned as a mortal sin. Simoniacs, a group which notoriously included several Popes, were placed by Dante in the eighth circle of Hell. The attribution is a little strange since Simon's offence lay not in selling that which belongs to God but in attempting to buy it. Be that as it may, simony, along with the sale of indulgences, invariably came high on the list of grievances put forward against the Church by groups such as the Lollards who wished – like all Christian break-away groups – to cleanse the Church of corruption and return to a purer and simpler form of religion.

Nowadays, one feels a twinge of sympathy for these impulses when obliged to buy a ticket in order to enter an English cathedral. How long before indulgences are being sold out of those same ticket-offices?

[848] SKINNER BOX

Otherwise known as the "operant conditioning chamber". A device invented by American experimental psychologist BURRHUS FREDERIC SKINNER (1904-1990), arch-apostle of the school of psychology known as Behaviourism (or Behaviorism). The SKINNER BOX is a sort of mini-lab, a controlled environment in which the behaviour of experimental animals – usually rats or pigeons – can be analysed and the rate of learning, induced by "reinforcement" (*i.e.* rewards and punishments), can be measured. It may be regarded as a refinement of the techniques pioneered by the Russian psychologist Ivan Petrovich Pavlov (see PAVLOV'S DOGS). Skinner's wide-ranging interests and fertile creative imagination led him to consider how these techniques might be applied to human learning and – by a further extension – to the management of human behaviour and thus to the design of human societies. The product of this line of thought was *Walden Two* (1948), an account in the form of a novel of what Skinner imagined a rationally organised human society might be like. It therefore has its place alongside More's *Utopia* (1516, 1556) and Samuel Butler's *Erewhon* (1872). The *New Yorker* called it "extremely interesting". The *New York Times* called it "alluring, sinister and appalling".

[849] SKINNER'S HORSE

An Indian army cavalry unit whose origins can be traced back to the Second Maratha War of 1803-1805. When the French-trained Maratha forces were decisively beaten at the Battle of Delhi (1803) by those of General Gerard Lake, Lake was offered and accepted the services of a number of troops who had been fighting for the opposite side and had decided to switch their allegiance. They were allowed to choose their own commander and chose JAMES SKINNER (1778-1841) an experienced soldier who had led them in previous encounters until dismissed by the French general Perron on account of his mixed (Scottish/Rajput) blood. SKINNER'S HORSE as they became known, distinguished themselves in further campaigns in Hindustan, the Punjab, the North-West Frontier, Afghanistan and, in WWI, in France and Flanders. (A further mark of distinction was the bright yellow coats of the troopers, a colour found in no other formation of the British or any colonial army and one which earned them the soubriquet "Yellow Boys".) In 1899 they acquired the subsidiary title of The 1st Duke of York's Own Cavalry in honour of their then Colonel-in-Chief. The regiment was mechanised in 1939. In WWII it acted as reconnaissance regiment to the 5th Indian division which fought in Eritrea, the Western Desert and Burma. Skinner's Horse still has its place as an armoured regiment in the post-independence Indian Army and is the senior formation of those making up the President's Bodyguard. Skinner's career brought him both wealth and fame. With his money he built a mosque, a temple and a Christian church in Delhi (in the last of which he was buried with great ceremony). His military skills earned him the name Sikander Sahib among his men (after Alexander the Great) and – after it was long denied him on account of his Eurasian origins – the rank of Lieutenant Colonel in the British Army (1827). He was, besides, a scholar who wrote in classical Persian on the history of Hindustan. *Skinner's Horse* is the title of a 1979 novel by Philip Mason, a leading authority on India under the Raj.

[850] SMITHSONIAN INSTITUTION

JAMES SMITHSON (1765-1829), was an illegitimate son of the Duke of Northumberland, a distinguished student of chemistry and mineralogy, Fellow of the Royal Society (1786), and a man of republican sympathies. Dying without issue, he bequeathed £100,000 to the United States of America to fund an establishment for the "increase and diffusion of knowledge". The outcome was the Smithsonian Institution, inaugurated by Act of Congress in 1846 and now generally regarded as the American equivalent in functions and prestige of the British Museum. The original collections, largely in the fields of science, natural history, and art, have grown to the point where today the Smithsonian comprises 19 museums, 8 educational and research centres, and a zoo, mostly sited in Washington D.C. Funding is partly from government, partly from endowments, and partly from commercial activities. The Smithsonian's first Secretary and Director was **JOSEPH HENRY** (1797-1878), collaborator of **SAMUEL MORSE**.

[851] SNELL'S LAW

Quantifies the phenomenon of *refraction* of a ray of light as it is deflected on passing from one medium to another – see **FERMAT'S PRINCIPLE OF LEAST TIME** and **ABBE'S REFRACTOMETER.** If the ray's angle of incidence is i and that of the refracted ray is r, then **SNELL'S LAW** states that the ratio sin i/sin r is equal to the ratio of the velocities of light in the two media, or to the inverse ratio of their indices of refraction. It underpins the entire sub-science of geometric optics. Dutch mathematician and astronomer **WILLEBRORD VAN ROYEN SNELL** (1580-1626) was born in Leiden and studied law at the University, but succeeded his father as professor of mathematics there in 1613. His publication *Eratosthenes Batavus** (1617) introduced the use of triangulation in surveying, and explored methods of measuring the earth which have proved fundamental to geodesy. He developed his law of refraction in 1621, although it remained unpublished until **CHRISTIAAN HUYGENS** included it, bearing Snell's name, in his *Traité de la Lumière* of 1678. However, Snell was not the original discoverer: he was antedated as early as 984 by Arab scholar **IBN SAHL** (*ca.* 940-1000) in his *On Burning Mirrors and Lenses*, then again in 1602 by English astronomer and mathematician, Thomas Harriot (1560-1621), and finally the law was independently re-invented in 1637 by **RENÉ DESCARTES** in *Discours sur la mèthode*. The French refer to it as "la loi de Descartes". Naturally. (MW)

* *i.e. "The Dutch Eratosthenes"* after the 3rd century BC Greek polymath who, by practical experiment, first determined (pretty accurately) the circumference of the globe.

[852] SNELLEN CHART

Everyone who's ever had an eye test knows what a **SNELLEN CHART** is, even if they couldn't put a name to it. The printed card (or illuminated screen) bearing a series of letters of decreasing size which the examinee is called on to read is the invention of Dutch ophthalmologist **HERMANN SNELLEN** (1834-1908) and dates from 1862. Anyone who has had his or her visual acuity tested in this way is probably familiar with the odd psychological phenomenon associated with it whereby one attempts to *guess* the illegible letters as if in the belief that there was some advantage in persuading the optician that one's sight was better than it actually is.

[853] SNOW'S MAP

Dr JOHN SNOW (1813-1858) was the first English medical practitioner to introduce diethylether as an anaesthetic – already pioneered in America – into British medical practice.* But he is perhaps more usually remembered for his proving by experiment that the infective agent in the murderous cholera epidemics which afflicted English cities in the 19th century was not, as was generally believed, toxic air but water contaminated with sewage. During the 1854 cholera epidemic, Snow made a house-to-house survey of a badly affected area of South London, which led him to the conclusion that the infection was water-borne, since affected households were getting their water from one source and unaffected ones from another. He then transferred his attention to another focus of infection, Broad Street in Soho. He obtained permission to remove the handle of the pump from which the inhabitants of the neighbourhood were getting their drinking water, and cases declined dramatically. Subsequently Snow published his findings in the form of a **MAP** on which he plotted instances of infection in the Broad Street neighbourhood against proximity to the pump. This map has been called "one of the most famous documents in the history of science".** Needless to say, the authorities ignored Snow's discovery and continued faithful to the "bad air" theory. Thus it is now difficult to be sure whether it was the filthy condition of London's water supply, or the filthy smell of a city which had become a single huge cesspool, which led to the construction of an effective sewage-disposal and water-supply system in the 1860's and 70's.

* See his *Chloroform and other anaesthetics* 1858.

** Helen Epstein reviewing Steven Johnson's *The ghost map* ('New York Review of Books' 28.6.07).

[854] SOCRATIC METHOD

The Athenian philosopher SOCRATES was born in 469 or 470 BC and died by compulsory judicial suicide in 399 BC. As a citizen, he took his place in the phalanx and fought in several campaigns including the siege of Potidaea (432-429 BC). His comrades were struck by his courage and his apparent imperviousness to physical hardship – cold, loss of sleep, and the effects of too much wine. In at least one other respect he was reassuringly human and fallible – he was hen-pecked by his wife Xanthippe, a notorious shrew. In the Greek world philosophy was a trade by which a man might make a living if he could attract sufficient students. Socrates operated his own peripatetic school in the streets of Athens and the houses of his disciples, who included notably PLATO and the charming but unreliable Alcibiades. It is from Plato's accounts that we derive our knowledge of Socrates' ideas and his teaching style, though how far these accounts are coloured by Plato's own ideas is matter for scholarly debate. What is clear is that Socrates taught by discussion, and that the structure of the lessons wasn't didactic in the normal sense. His method was to get some unwary companion or disciple to assent to a proposition and then to destroy that proposition not by argument as such, but by means of a series of questions, the answers to which brought out the flaws in the proposition's logic and forced the victim, in effect, to condemn himself out of his own mouth. Such a discussion might have proceeded on something like the following lines.

Socrates: Would you not agree, my dear Isosceles, that blah blah blah?
Isosceles: Yes, of course, Socrates.
Socrates: But surely in that case blah blah blah. Is it not so?
Isosceles: Well, since you put it like that...
Socrates: I do. And is it not also true, therefore, that blah blah blah?
Isosceles: Oh, undoubtedly.
Socrates: So logically it must follow that blah blah blah?
Isosceles: I cannot deny it, Socrates.
Socrates: Then how can you possibly continue to maintain that blah blah blah?
Isosceles: Um... I see now that I was mistaken.
Socrates: So it would seem. Time for lunch, I think.

This may be a dandy debating tactic but it isn't necessarily the way to win friends and influence people. The nineteenth century virtually canonised Socrates, ranking

him only just below Jesus Christ in the hierarchy of diamond geezers. His fellow
Athenians didn't see him like that, and they might almost be forgiven for regarding
Socrates as an annoying little person, too clever by half, whose speciality was
making normally intelligent blokes look stupid. In which case his trial and
execution (on charges of blasphemy and corrupting the young), manages to be
shocking without being altogether surprising.

[855] SOD'S LAW – see MURPHY'S LAW

[856] SOLVAY PROCESS
A successful method for achieving the industrially all-important conversion of
common salt (sodium chloride) into soda (sodium carbonate), without which we
would have no glass, no paper, and – *quel horreur!* – no soap. The SOLVAY PROCESS,
also called the "ammonia-soda" process, is an improvement on its obnoxious and
environmentally unfriendly predecessor, the LEBLANC PROCESS (*q.v.*) which
involved nasties like hydrochloric acid, sulphuric acid and sulphides. The raw
materials for the ammonia-soda process are simply: brine (a strong solution of
salt) and limestone (calcium carbonate); but these won't react directly. The trick is
to:
1. dissolve some ammonia gas in the brine
2. heat the limestone to 1000 Celsius to turn it into calcium oxide (quicklime)
   and carbon dioxide gas
3. dissolve this carbon dioxide gas in the ammoniated brine
4. filter off the precipitate of solid sodium bicarbonate that forms from the
   solution of ammonium chloride
5. roast the sodium bicarbonate to get the desired product: sodium carbonate or
   "soda ash", and carbon dioxide gas, which is recycled...
6. heat the ammonium chloride by-product with the calcium oxide by-product to
   regenerate ammonia gas, which is recycled...
7. leaving only calcium chloride as the final waste product. This is not much use,
   but can be spread on the roads on icy days, or used to keep things dry (it's a
   desiccant).
This procedure is substantially non-polluting, though rather energy-intensive.
Credit for first proposing the chemistry belongs to Harrison G. Dyar and John
Hemming (British Patent, 1838). However the process could only be worked on
a small technical scale until various problems, essentially of engineering rather
than chemistry, were solved in 1861 by ERNEST GASTON JOSEPH SOLVAY (1838-
1932). Born at Rebecq near Brussels, Solvay did not attend university but
worked for his father, a salt-refiner, and for his uncle who managed a gasworks.
He brought his practical experience to bear on the problems and patented a
design for an efficient carbonating tower (and much else). His first full-scale
plant was commissioned at Charleroi in 1865. In 1874 Ludwig Mond acquired

the rights to the process, with John Brunner, and introduced the Solvay technology to Britain, already the world centre for soda production by the **LEBLANC PROCESS**. Competition ensued, with the Leblanc process finally displaced by 1890. Solvay's entrepreneurial skills over the licensing of his patents and his royalties on production made him a very rich man, but also a philanthrope: he endowed the Free University of Brussels generously, and founded in 1911 the prestigious **SOLVAY CONFERENCES** on physics and chemistry which attracted luminaries such as **EINSTEIN, PLANCK, RUTHERFORD, CURIE** and **BOHR**. The **SOLVAY PROCESS** is still responsible today for the manufacture of three quarters of the world's soda: about 6 kilograms per head per annum. (MW)

[857] SOMERVILLE COLLEGE

Founded in 1879 as one of the earliest women's colleges of the University of Oxford, **SOMERVILLE** can boast household names among its alumni, such as: authors Vera Brittain, Dorothy Sayers and Iris Murdoch; politicians Indira Gandhi and Margaret Thatcher; philosopher Mary Midgley, and Nobel Laureate Dorothy Hodgkin (Chemistry 1964).* It was only in 1992 that Somerville first admitted men through its portals (as undergraduates, anyway)**. This prestigious College was named after Scotswoman **MARY SOMERVILLE** née **FAIRFAX** (1780-1872), who was born in Jedburgh, the daughter of Admiral Sir William Fairfax, and brought up in an ethos which deemed a gentlewoman's education to consist in needlework, piano lessons, and the odd watercolour. Nonetheless Mary contrived to teach herself mathematics, sciences and Latin, in the teeth of her father's anxiety that "... *the strain of abstract thought would injure the tender female frame.*" In 1816 she moved from Edinburgh to London with her second husband Dr William Somerville FRS (1771-1860) who, unlike the first, was supportive of her scientific interests, and provided her with an entrée into intellectual society where she could discourse with the leading men of science at home and abroad. Their circle of friends included George **AIRY**, John, William and Caroline **HERSCHEL**, and Charles **BABBAGE**. Caroline Herschel (see **URANUS**) and Mary Somerville shared the distinction of being the first women elected to membership of the Royal Astronomical Society. Mary's mathematical powers enabled her to publish, among several other scholarly works on physical science and geography, *The Mechanism of the Heavens* (1831), a very successful English translation and popular interpretation of *Méchanique Céleste* by Pierre-Simon Laplace. After bearing six children to two husbands – presumably without undue injury to the tender female frame – Mary became a pioneer for the education and emancipation of women; she was the first signatory to John Stuart Mill's petition to parliament for women's suffrage. Sir David **BREWSTER** described her as: "... *certainly the most extraordinary woman in Europe – a mathematician of the very* *first rank with all the gentleness of a woman ... She is also a great natural philosopher and mineralogist."* (MW)

* Member by marriage of a remarkable family which included physician and humanitarian reformer Thomas Hodgkin (1798-1866) of **HODGKIN'S DISEASE**; historian Thomas Hodgkin (1831-1913), author of the magisterial *Italy and her invaders* (1870, 1892-9); and physiologist Sir Alan Hodgkin (1914-1998), also a Nobel laureate (medicine and physiology 1963).

** The last women's college to accept male undergraduates as members was St Hilda's, which held out bravely till 2008.

[858] SORBUS "JOSEPH ROCK"

A type of rowan tree, probably originating in China and commonly planted as an ornamental for its pale gold berries and autumn foliage. The name is that of Austrian-American explorer, ethnologist and botanist **JOSEPH FRANCIS CHARLES ROCK** (1884-1962). In 1920 Rock, by now a naturalised American citizen, was working and teaching as a (largely self-taught) botanist at the College of Hawaii when he was sent by the US Department of Agriculture to Indo-China to collect *chaulmoogra* seeds with a view to establishing a plantation in Hawaii. The oil derived from these seeds had long been used by native practitioners in India and China as a treatment for leprosy (see **HANSEN'S DISEASE**) but it was not until the end of the 19th century that Western doctors working in India became aware of its virtues, there being no other known specific for the treatment of leprosy at this time. "Chaulmoogra" is a Bengali word but the tree is not native to Bengal so there was for some time doubt as to which tree the seeds came from. Eventually the "chaulmoogra tree" was identified as *Hydnocarpus kurzii* (synonym *Taraktogenos kurzii*), a native of Assam and Burma. Rock's travels took him to Yunnan province in South-Western China where he established himself near the town of Lijiang. He subsequently led several botanising expeditions to Tibet, Western China, Annam and Cambodia. Between 1922 and 1935, he undertook an intensive study of the history, culture and language of the Nakhi people inhabiting the Lijiang region, collecting and translating a huge collection of religious texts and compiling a dictionary of the Nakhi language, at the same time making extensive botanical and zoological collections and sending back articles to the *National Geographic Magazine* illustrated with his own photographs.* In 1944 he was evacuated from China but his library and fourteen years' worth of research papers were lost when the ship taking them to the United States was torpedoed by the Japanese (a disaster recalling those visited on **WALLACE** and **RAFFLES**). In 1946 Rock returned to China but was again forced to flee, this time on account of fighting between Nationalists and Communists and the local prevalence of banditry. He returned to America and at the time of his death was Professor of Oriental studies at the University of Hawaii. Meanwhile, chaulmoogra oil, whose success as a leprosy cure had not lived up to its early promise, had been supplanted by sulpha drugs, the first really effective treatment. Apart from his *National Geographic* articles, Rock's principal publications are: *The Ancient Nakhi Kingdom of Southwest China* (1948), and *A Nakhi-English encyclopedic dictionary* (1963). Another foreign resident of Lijiang was Peter Goullart, a refugee from revolutionary Russia, author of a 1955 book on the Nakhi people entitled *Forgotten Kingdom.*

* There is a story that Rock quarrelled with *National Geographic* on account of the magazine's vile habit of editing the prose of individual contributors down to a blandly uniform house style. This may or may not be true. What is certainly true is that Rock was not a blandly uniform sort of person but a highly individual one and in some respects a full blown eccentric.

[859] SOUSAPHONE

Musical instrument of the brass family, nowadays used mainly by marching bands and conspicuous by its high, wide, forward-facing bell. It is said to have been designed by the American composer and bandmaster **JOHN PHILIP SOUSA** (1854-1922), who gave us such stirring marches as *Washington Post* and *Stars and Stripes Forever*, and built for him by Philadelphia instrument-maker J.W. Pepper. The sousaphone is essentially a tuba topologically rearranged to make it easier to carry and to make the sound carry better in the open air. Most are tuned to B-flat and usually have parts written in the bass clef. Modern sousaphones are sometimes built of fibreglass, making them even easier to march about with.

[860] SOYER STOVE

French chef and practical philanthropist **ALEXIS BENOÎT SOYER** (1809-1858) had already made a name for himself in Paris when he fled to England during the 1830 Revolution. In London he rapidly attained the status of England's top kitchen mechanic, working at first in a number of aristocratic households and later at the Reform Club where he was Head Chef from 1837 to 1850. He introduced numerous improvements to kitchen equipment (coolers, adjustable ovens, a portable stove) and specialised in feeding large numbers of people efficiently. During the Irish Famine (1847) he opened a free soup kitchen in Dublin at the request of the British government. His most durable innovation was the **SOYER STOVE,** a mobile field cooker which proved itself during the Crimean War whither Soyer had gone at his own expense in 1855 to advise the military on food preparation and to train army cooks. The stove was adopted by the army and remained in service for the next 120 years. He published a number of books on food and cookery including *Soyer's charitable cookery* (1847), *The pantropheon, a history of food and its preparation* (1853), and *A shilling cookery book for the People* (1855) based on his belief that deep pockets are not a prerequisite for healthy, satisfying and well-cooked meals.

[861] SPARMANNIA

The Swedish naturalist **ANDERS ERIKSON SPARRMAN** (1748-1820) was a pupil of **LINNAEUS** at Uppsala, where he enrolled at the age of 9 and studied medicine and natural history.* In 1765 he voyaged to China as a ship's doctor and in 1772 sailed to the Cape where he had found employment as a tutor. Here he was scooped up by Cook, then beginning his second voyage, to serve as assistant to the expedition's naturalists Georg and Johann Forster. At the end of the 3-year voyage he returned to the Cape, where he practiced medicine and travelled in the interior among the Hottentots and "Caffres". On his return to Sweden in 1776 he was greeted with academic honours and made Keeper of the natural history collections of the Swedish Academy of Sciences. He published an account in Swedish of his voyage with Cook and his travels in Africa, which appeared in an English translation by Georg Forster in 1785 (*A voyage to the Cape of Good Hope...&c.* 2 vols. London 1785). **SPARMANNIA,** a genus of South African trees belonging to the family Tiliaceae (limes) was named by Linnaeus himself after his brilliant pupil. More recently an asteroid (no. 16646) was christened in his honour.**

* Virtually every notable naturalist (botanist, zoologist...) from at least the 16th century until well into the 19th, combined this interest with medical training.

** See http://www.cfa.harvard.edu/iau/lists/MPNames.html for a list of the names of "minor planets".

[862] SPENCER

A tight-fitting, military style, bum-freezer jacket named after **GEORGE JOHN SPENCER, 2nd EARL SPENCER** (1758-1834). Originally a male garment, it had a second incarnation adorning the top portion of fashionable Regency ladies, and later degenerated into a women's knitted vest. Though having a coat named after him earns Earl Spencer a place alongside other aristocratic inspirers of male costume such as Messrs. **CARDIGAN** and **RAGLAN**, he has other and better claims on our notice and respect. Intelligent, highly educated,* a member of Johnson's literary circle and a Fellow of the Royal Society, Spencer played a leading part in the cultural and political life of his country, including a distinguished term as First Lord of the Admiralty from 1784-1801. A noted bibliophile, he put together what was probably the finest private library in Europe, which at the time of his death amounted to some 40,000 volumes including many priceless incunabula. In 1892 it was sold for a quarter of a million pounds to become the core collection of Manchester's **JOHN RYLANDS LIBRARY**.

* One of his tutors was Sir William Jones (1746-1794), the philologist who first recognised the family connection between European and North Indian languages.

[863] SPLATT-WEEDON EFFECT – see CRAPPER

[864] SPOONERISM

A form of fugitive speech defect which consists in unintentionally transposing letters (usually initial consonants) from one word of a phrase to another. Thus "bum rutter" for "rum butter", and so forth. Most people do this occasionally, but **WILLIAM ARCHIBALD SPOONER** (1844-1930), Warden of New College, Oxford, is supposed to have done it more than most and so has given his name to the phenomenon. Many examples of Spooner's gaffes survive and are regularly quoted. As with the sayings attributed to Sam Goldwyn, most of the corpus of original spoonerisms is of suspect authenticity, but a lenient judge might say of it, *"Ce n'est pas vrai, mais c'est bien trouvé"*. A less lenient judge might say they were too good to be true. Spooner was an albino and had particularly poor eyesight, but neither of these is a likely explanation of the reverend and learned gentleman's linguistic lapses. Nor do they explain another of Spooner's pecularities – "physical" spoonerisms, such as the occasion on which, having spilt some salt on a table-cloth, Spooner proceeded to pour wine on it. In 1977 Sir William Hayter, a later Warden of New College, published a biography of his predecessor, entitled simply *Spooner*.

[865] STAKHANOVITE

One who follows the example of **ALEXEY GRIGORYEVICH STAKHANOV** (1906-1977) in increasing industrial output to an exceptional extent and thereby gaining special awards. Stakhanov became a role model and a lauded hero of the Soviet Union during the Stalinist period (*cf.* **LYSENKO**). He was a coal miner who began working in a mine called "Tsentralnaya-Irmino" in Kadiyevka (Donbass). In 1933, Stakhanov was made a jackhammer operator. In 1935, he took a local course in mining. On 31 August, it was reported that he had mined a record 102 tons of coal in 5 hours and 45 minutes (14 times his quota). On 18 September, Stakhanov was reported to have set a new record by mining 227 tons of coal in a single shift. The Stakhanovite movement was kicked into action during the second 5-year plan in 1935. The Soviet authorities claimed that this movement had caused a significant increase in labour productivity. It was reported that during the first 5-year plan (1929-1932) industrial labour productivity increased by 41%. During the second 5-year plan (1933-1937) it reportedly increased by 82%. It was convenient for the Soviet authorities that this superman should come along when he did. Despite suspicions, it was only in 1985 that the full extent of the deceit was revealed as a cunning ploy of Soviet propaganda. The *New York Times* printed a story reporting that though Stakhanov had indeed succeeded in his feat, it was only because the Communist Party had pre-arranged the event as a way of boosting public morale, with many other miners working to help Stakhanov beat the mining record. The paper quoted the chief of the mine's Party Committee, Konstantin G. Petrov, as saying that "I suppose Stakhanov need not have been the first... It could have been anybody else. In the final analysis it was not the individual face-worker who determined whether the attempt to break the record would succeed, but the new system of coal extraction." In 1988 Pravda exposed the falsifications, revealing that Stakhanov used a number of helpers on support works, while the throughput was tallied for him alone. Nevertheless the state rewarded Stakhanov with two Orders of Lenin, Order of the Red Banner, and numerous medals. The last Sunday of August was designated "Coal Miner's Day", also apparently in his honour. The patriotic Stakhanovite slogan "I resolve to overfulfill my work norms" might with advantage be applied to all those workers in the UK's state-supervised service sector who today labour under a heavy load of government "targets". Even better, they might say, "Stuff your targets." (RS)

[866] STALIN ORGAN – see KATYUSHA

[867] STANLEY KNIFE

Hand-held cutting tool with a disposable blade, also known as a "utility knife". The name, which in this country has become generic for all knives of this kind, is that of the STANLEY WORKS, now a world-famous American tool-making company incorporating Black & Decker, founded in 1920 by the merger of two companies founded in 1843 and 1857 respectively by two American industrialists FREDERICK TRENT STANLEY (1802-1883) and his cousin HENRY STANLEY. What we call a "stanley knife", the Americans call a "box-cutter" – a name that has acquired sinister overtones since its employment as a weapon by the 9/11 hijackers. The tool-making Stanleys are not to be confused with another pair of ingenious entrepreneurs – brothers in this case – FRANCIS EDGAR STANLEY (1849-1918) and FREELAN O. STANLEY (1849-1940), inventors and manufacturers of the "STANLEY STEAMER", an effective and popular steam-powered automobile, whose day may well come again.

[868] STANLEY STEAMER – see STANLEY KNIFE

[869] STARK-EINSTEIN LAW

One of the four laws of photochemistry (curiously, all four are joint eponymies: for the other three, see BEER-LAMBERT LAW, BUNSEN-ROSCOE LAW and GROTTHUSS-DRAPER LAW). It dates from 1912 and posits an equivalence betweeen the quantity of light absorbed and the amount of substance chemically transformed: *one photon must be absorbed for each molecule of substance that reacts.* This amounts to little more than a statement of good book-keeping at the quantum-molecular level: "Everyone a coconut!" But it is not always true: sometimes light provokes a "chain reaction", and sometimes the effect of the light is thwarted by a "back-reaction". German physicist JOHANNES STARK (1874-1957) was born in Schickenhof, educated at Munich University, and after research in several German universities became professor of physics at Würtzburg. He won the Nobel prize for physics in 1919 for his discovery of the splitting of spectral lines in an electric field – known as the STARK EFFECT (see also ZEEMAN EFFECT). However, his distinction in experimental physics was not matched by the ethical quality of his politics: during the Third Reich he acted as a conspicuous Nazi propagandist, denouncing the "Jewish physics" of EINSTEIN and HEISENBERG (who wasn't Jewish) in the SS Newspaper *Das Schwartze Korps*. In 1947 a denazification court sentenced him to four years imprisonment. Ironically, it was "Jewish physics" that ultimately built the atomic bomb. It's a further irony that, in this photochemical law, STARK'S name is indissolubly wedded to that of his primary hate-object, ALBERT EINSTEIN, who is justly celebrated elsewhere in this volume. (MW)

[870] STAUNTONIA

Genus of 16 evergreen flowering shrubs native to S.E. Asia and Japan. Named after Sir GEORGE LEONARD STAUNTON (1737-1801), who combined the careers of physician and diplomatist. In 1792 Staunton was appointed second-in-command of an embassy to China led by his friend Lord Macartney (1737-1806). The mission was an embarrassing failure, thanks to the inability of the Chinese to understand the concept of nations negotiating as equals, and Macartney's inability to understand that this was the problem. (The fertile Chinese mind has been responsible for many useful inventions, but international diplomacy isn't one of them.) However, Staunton made good use of the opportunities the trip afforded for making botanical collections, while his son George Thomas Staunton (1781-1859), the future sinologist, who accompanied the mission as Macartney's page, taught himself Chinese, the only member of the mission to do so. Staunton's *Authentic account of an embassy from the king of Great Britain to the emperor of China* was published in 2 volumes in 1797 with a second edition the following year.

[871] STEINER SCHOOLS

Scattered around the world there are well over two thousand schools and kindergartens dedicated to the teaching methods and educational philosophy of Austrian philosopher and educationalist RUDOLPH STEINER (1861-1925). The curriculum of these schools, also known as WALDORF SCHOOLS (see ASTORIA) is partly governed by Steiner's belief that the education of a child should recapitulate the cultural evolution of the human race. So the children, like mediaeval monks, hand-write and illustrate their own school books before they are introduced to printed texts, and woodwork lessons begin with axes, chisels and hammers before moving on to more technically sophisticated tools like saws, planes and twist drills. Creativity, which Steiner believed went hand-in-hand with spiritual development, is emphasised at all stages through painting, sculpture, music, drama and eurhythmics. Steiner was one of those rare beings – men who think things out for themselves, and like all such he flirted continually with the danger of appearing, or actually becoming, a crank. He studied mathematics, physics and philosophy at Vienna before moving to Rostock, where he gained his doctorate in philosophy. While still a student, he was appointed scientific editor of a new edition of Goethe's writings, and later worked, by invitation, on the Goethe archives at Weimar. Around 1900 Steiner became involved in Theosophy, an ersatz religion which sought to combine eastern and western spirituality on a pick-and-mix basis, and though he soon broke with the Theosophists to follow his own path, he retained an interest in the esoteric and in eastern religions. His own philosophic system he called Anthroposophy, founding his Anthroposophical Society in 1923, with its headquarters in Switzerland (see **GOETHEANUM**). The repertory of Steiner's published works (books and lectures) is enormous, running to over 300 volumes and reflecting both the breadth of Steiner's interests and the depth of his intellectual engagement.

[872] STELLER'S SEA-COW

Rhytina stelleri (alternatively *Rhytina gigas*) no longer exists, having been hunted to extinction in recent times. It is, or rather was, the largest of the Sirenians, a relative of the Manatee and Dugong, found in the waters around the Bering Strait. It takes its name from its discoverer **GEORG WILHELM STELLER** (1709-1746), German physician, botanist and zoologist attached to the St. Petersburg Academy of Sciences. In 1738 Steller sailed as naturalist with Bering's second Kamchatka expedition and accompanied Bering to Alaska where he described several species of otherwise unrecorded North American birds and mammals. Bering died on the journey home as, two years later after further explorations in Kamchatka, did Steller. His journals, however, got back to the Academy and were published by **PALLAS**, a countryman of Steller's and his successor as a scientist in the Russian service. Named after Steller, apart from the late Sea-Cow, are: **STELLER'S EIDER** (*Polysticta stelleri*); **STELLER'S JAY** (*Cyanocitta stelleri*); **STELLER'S SEA-EAGLE** (*Haliaeetus pelagicus*); **STELLER'S SEA-LION** (*Eumetopias jubatus*); **STELLERA** a genus (10 species) of Asian perennial herbs and shrubs of which one *Stellera chamaejasme* is grown as a garden plant; and two other plants – *Cryptochiton stelleri* and *Artemisia stelleriana*. Not a bad score-card.

[873] STEN GUN

9-mm British sub-machine gun in service from 1941 until the 1960's. The name is acronymic, formed from the initials of its designers, **MAJOR REGINALD SHEPHERD** and **HAROLD TURPIN** plus the first two letters of the **ENFIELD** Small Arms Factory.* It was supplied to British commandos in WWII and to resistance groups throughout Europe, and saw service in the de-colonisation conflicts which followed, as well as in Korea. Notoriously, the sten was a dangerous weapon in the sense that it was liable to go off if you just looked at it sideways, but on the plus side it was incredibly cheap to produce, two-and-sixpence a throw (12.5 pee) being a commonly-cited figure. (See also **OWEN GUN, TOMMY GUN**.)

* The same two letters, -EN, form part of the name of another long-serving British infantry weapon, the bren light machine gun. In this case, the first two letters signify the town of Brno in Czechoslovakia where the weapon was designed and produced in the 1930's before being adopted and adapted by the British armed forces.

[874] STETSON

Takes its name from the hatter **JOHN B. STETSON** (1830-1906) who first produced it. The firm is still in business, trading under the slogan "Legendary hats since 1865".The stetson is favoured in the westerly parts of the U.S., mainly by men, but more especially by Men. It is headgear, rather than any other item of male attire, that tells us the most about what kind of person the wearer imagines himself to be.

[875] STEVEN(S)GRAPH

A small, machine-woven silk picture, very often of hunting scenes, named after British weaver **THOMAS STEVENS** (1828-1888).

[876] STIGLER'S LAW

In 1980, **STEPHEN MACK STIGLER** a statistics professor at the University of Chicago, published **STIGLER'S LAW OF EPONYMY** dedicated to the proposition that "*no scientific discovery is named after its original inventor*". This is at best a half-truth, and it hardly needs to be pointed out that almost everybody who has ever given even the most meagre attention to the history of science had already made this discovery before Stigler named it. Nevertheless, it does call attention to a common phenomenon of which *What's Who?* furnishes numerous instances.

[877] STILLSON WRENCH

The stillson differs from the **MONKEY WRENCH** in that, while both are adjustable spanners, the stillson can grip curved, unfaceted surfaces while the monkey wrench is adapted to handle different sizes of faceted nuts and bolt-heads. Hence the stillson's alternative title of *pipe wrench*. It was invented in 1869 by **DANIEL C. STILLSON**, an ex-USN fireman who had served in the American Civil War and later joined the Walworth Manufacturing Company (still in existence), which specialised at that time in iron-ware for the heating industry – boilers, radiators and, of course, pipes. On his employers' advice, Stillson registered the design in his own name and by the time of his death had earned nearly $100,000 in royalties.

[878] STIRLING ENGINE

Named after its inventor **ROBERT STIRLING** (1790-1878) Scottish clergyman and scientific instrument maker, who patented it in 1817. Stirling's design has twin cylinders with a piston in each. The first powers the drive shaft and works by the expansion of a pre-heated gas (air in Stirling's original engine, hydrogen in modern versions). The second drives the "regenerator" which sits between the two cylinders and is used to recapture the waste heat, which in a normal petrol or diesel engine would be simply evacuated to atmosphere through the exhaust system, and return it to the working cylinder. Though the Stirling engine can run on almost any fuel and rates high in terms of thermodynamic efficiency, it is comparatively expensive to manufacture as it requires materials resistant to high temperatures. (In early versions, the hot end of the working cylinder tended to burn out in a matter of only months.) In modern applications the Stirling engine has an important role in Air Independent Propulsion (AIP) systems for submarines in both the Swedish and Japanese fleets, enabling underwater endurances of up to 21 days using stored diesel and cryogenic liquid oxygen fuel.

[879] STOKE(S)

C.g.s. unit of kinematic viscosity. It is now obsolete but stands as a reminder of the British mathematician and physicist **SIR GEORGE GABRIEL STOKES** (1819-1903), who served successively as Lucasian professor of mathematics at Cambridge, President of the Royal Society, and MP for Cambridge (1887-1892) – all posts that had been held by Sir Isaac Newton. Stokes didn't, however, quite complete the Newtonian *cursus honorum* as he never got to be Master of the Royal Mint.

[880] STOKES' ASTER

Stokesia laevis (synonym: *Stokesia cyanaea*) is a perennial plant of the daisy family (*Compositae*), native to the south-eastern United States and named after the English botanist **DR. JONATHAN STOKES** (1755-1831). Its lavender, blue, or pink flowers earn it its place as an ornamental in herbaceous borders. In America it is also grown as a commercial oil-seed crop with a number of industrial uses in the manufacture of plastics, varnishes, and adhesives including "superglue".

[881] STOKES MORTAR

The three-inch Stokes mortar was developed for trench warfare in WWI, the steep trajectory characteristic of all mortars making it possible to lob a missile from one trench to another. It was designed in 1915 by **Mr.** (later **Sir**) **WILFRED STOKES** (1860-1927) who worked for Ransome's of Ipswich, the famous agricultural engineers. Though man-portable, it had the hitting-power of a field gun of the same calibre. The Stokes mortar is not to be confused with the 1.75 inch Vickers mortar, an only patchily reliable weapon firing a so-called "toffee-apple" – an unhandy-looking football-sized spherical bomb on a slender stem inserted into the barrel for firing – nor with the 9.45 inch heavy mortar known to its habitués as the "Flying Pig".

[882] STRADIVARIUS

The Latinised name of **ANTONIO STRADIVARI** of Cremona (1644-1737), considered the greatest of all violin makers, and of the instruments he made. On May 16, 2006, Christie's auctioned a Stradivarius called *The Hammer* for a record $3,544,000 – the most paid at public auction for any musical instrument. Stradivari was born in Cremona, possibly serving an apprenticeship as a woodcarver before becoming a pupil of Nicolo Amati. Before 1680 Stradivari probably produced other instruments in addition to violins: harps, lutes, mandolins, guitars, and a *tromba marina*. Not until 1666 did he begin to place his own label on violins of his making, signing them *Antonius Stradivarius Cremonensis Faciebat Anno* [year]. These at first followed the smaller of Amati's models, solidly constructed, with a thick yellow varnish. In 1684 Stradivari began to produce larger models, using a deeper-coloured varnish and experimenting with minute details in the form of the instrument. After 1690 he further refined his style and devised the "Long Strad" design. He is generally considered to have produced his greatest instruments in the period from about 1700 to 1720. His "long" models represent a complete innovation in the proportions of the instrument. He devised the modern form of the violin bridge and set the proportions of the modern violin, with its shallower body yielding a more powerful and penetrating tone than earlier instruments. It was long thought that the secret of Stradivari's acoustically perfect violins lay in their varnish, the formula for which, though much debated, has never been discovered. Recent research, however, has discovered certain factors that influence the beauty of a violin's tone. Among these are the thickness (hence, the vibrational properties) of its wooden top and back plates, the condition of the microscopic pores within the wood of the violin, and lastly the composition of the varnish. Of the 1,100 instruments from the Stradivari family workshop, over 650 still survive. The inspired brilliance of Stradivari's workmanship as an instrument-maker may be considered part and parcel of the great flowering of Northern Italian baroque music which gave us the concertos of Vivaldi, Albinoni and Corelli. (RS)

[883] STUHLMANN'S GOLDEN MOLE

Chrysochloris stuhlmanni is a native of East Africa named after the German traveller and naturalist **Dr. FRANZ STUHLMANN** (d. 1928). Stuhlmann had spent some considerable time in Equatoria (the southern province of the Egyptian Sudan) along with the Governor of the province who called himself Emin Pasha. Emin was another German doctor-naturalist whose real name was Eduard Schnitzer. He and Stuhlmann became friends and when Stuhlmann returned to Germany, he published an account of his travels under the title *Mit Emin Pascha ins Herz von Afrika* (1894). Stuhlmann also edited Emin's diaries in 6 volumes (1916-1927). (See also under **GRANT'S GAZELLE**.)

[884] STURGEON'S LAW – see MURPHY'S LAW

[885] SWAN VESTA – see VESTA

[886] SWAYNE'S DIK-DIK

Africa is particularly rich in animals named after 19th-century European travellers and explorers, who took a great interest in the continent's teeming wildlife while in many cases working hard to reduce its numbers. Among the cloven-footed creatures are several species of dik-dik (a pygmy antelope), and the explorer **Col. HARALD GEORGE CARLOS SWAYNE** (b. 1860) was not the only person to have one named after him (hence, in addition to *Madoqua swaynei,* the dik-diks of Salt, Philip, Günther, Cordeaux, Erlanger, and Kirk). Of one expedition led by Swayne, his second-in command, Frederick Jackson, later reported: "Swayne... neither knew nor cared about anything connected with the safari [*i.e. caravan*]; and though very anxious to get off, had done nothing to expedite it. Big game shooting was an obsession with him, and he could think and talk of nothing else. He had, amongst other rifles, a 4-bore, and with that he would tear about the camp until he was blown, then aim at a leaf or other object, about the height of an elephant's vitals, and shout 'Am I steady, Jackson, am I steady?' The position was hopeless..."* A stuffed specimen of Swayne's dik-dik may be found in the Natural History Museum, S. Kensington. Swayne, to do him justice, later made important explorations in Somaliland.

* *Early days in East Africa* 1930

[887] SYDENHAM'S CHOREA – see SAINT VITUS' DANCE

[888] SYKES-PICOT AGREEMENT

Though WWI saw the destruction of four empires (those of Germany, Austria-Hungary, Russia, and Turkey), imperialist habits of thought and action persisted among the victors, who never doubted their right to re-draw the map of the world as seemed to them best. This was the attitude which underlay the arrangement by which Britain and France decided, in 1916 while the war was still at its height, on the dismemberment of the **OTTOMAN** empire and the redistribution of its territories as "spheres of influence" between the two Powers. The Agreement which resulted (it was a secret understanding which never had the status of a formal treaty) bears the joint names of British scholar, diplomat, soldier, traveller and Near-Eastern specialist **sir MARK SYKES** (1879-1919) and French diplomat **FRANÇOIS GEORGES PICOT** (1870-1951). Though never implemented in its exact original form, the ideas and intentions behind it largely conditioned the post-war re-arrangement of the Middle East (or Near East as it was then known) and to it may be traced virtually everything that has gone wrong in that part of the world since: the ethnic cleansing of Greeks from Anatolia, the division of Cyprus, the Suez Crisis, Kurdish irredentism, the Armenian genocide, the internal disunity of Iraq, Syrian interference in the Lebanon, and, not least, the creation of the state of Israel and the permanent running sore of Israeli-Arab relations. Sykes died in Paris, while attending the Peace Conference, a victim of the "Spanish" flu pandemic which followed close on the heels of WWI and killed more people than the war itself. He was buried in a lead-lined coffin at his family home, Sledmere in East Yorkshire. In 2007 it was proposed to disinter his body to look for DNA traces of the flu virus, the idea being that this might help us prepare for the next outbreak of Mad Duck disease or some other as yet unnamed viral nasty. The grave was duly opened in 2008 and tissue samples removed but we don't yet know with what results.

[889] SYMMES' HOLE

It is often, though not always, possible to make a distinction between theories about the nature of the world which subsequently turn out to be false and the theories of out-and-out cranks which never turn out to be false because their adherents are impervious to rational argument or demonstration. The cosmological notions of **JOHN CLEVES SYMMES, JNR.** (1779-1829) may be said to have a foot in both camps. Symmes believed that the Earth is a hollow sphere. This was not an entirely unreasonable belief in Symmes' day. True, there was no evidence for it, but there was no evidence against it, either. It could conceivably have turned out to be correct.* In our time, however, it would only be possible to hold such a belief in the teeth of the evidence, and the fact that there still are believers in the hollow-earth theory, tells us only what most of us already know – that our species is only partially and intermittently rational (thank God). Symmes, nephew of a prominent jurist of the same name, was a native of New Jersey. He joined the United States army and served with credit on the Canadian frontier in the war of 1812. He left the army with the rank of Captain and set up as an Indian trader on the Mississippi. In 1818 he abandoned his work, his wife, and his ten children, and spent the next 11 years – the rest of his life, in fact – on a gruelling round of lectures, promulgating his startling hypothesis wherever he could find an audience. In its developed form, Symmes' theory envisaged a series of concentric spheres with light and air being delivered through a hole at each pole.** The holes were accessible, Symmes believed, if one could pass beyond the Arctic and Antarctic Circles because beyond these ice-bound regions there was open water stretching to the poles, kept ice-free by heat issuing from the planet's hollow interior. The belief in an open polar sea, based on shaky reports from earlier mariners and explorers, had a long pedigree by Symmes' time and was only finally put to rest when men actually reached the poles in the 20th century and found no open water – and no holes. Another believer in holes-at-the-poles was the extraordinary William Money (1809-1883), Scottish-born naturalist and traveller. Money spent years mapping and making botanical and zoological collections in northern Mexico only to have the entire fruits of his labours, notes and specimens, destroyed during an attack on his camp by American troops. The magnitude of his loss apparently unhinged him. He channelled his energies into founding a new religion, but failing to make any converts, turned instead to pseudo-science. He set up the so-called Moneyan Institute at San Gabriel in California to propagate, among other notions, his theory that an opening in the Arctic ice-cap fed sea-water into a subterranean ocean which stretched as far at the opposite pole and had outlets which fed volcanically-warmed water into the Atlantic. (For Symmes, see Sachs *The Humboldt Current* 2006, and for a fuller account, Paul Collins' excellent compendium of heroic failures *Banvard's Folly* 2001; for hollow-earth theory, see Standish *Hollow Earth* 2006; for the open polar sea, see Wright *Human Nature in Geography* 1966; for Money, see Donaldson *Brewer's Rogues, Villains and Eccentrics* 2002.)

*In his brilliant new book *The Age of Wonder* (2008), Richard Holmes, the biographer of Shelley and Coleridge, raises in passing the question whether our understanding of the history of science is not distorted by an undue concentration on theories which turned out to be right and by ignoring or undervaluing theories which turned out to be wrong. (See pp. 94-95 and especially the footnote p. 95)

** Symmes believed that we we live on the outer surface of the outermost sphere – orthodox enough, up to a point. But other, even nuttier versions of the hollow-earth theory, including one that was popular with the Nazi pseudo-scientists (*cf.* **HÖRBIGER**), had us on the *inside* of the *Hohlkugel* so that in England, for example, we had Australia almost directly overhead – an unnerving prospect.

T

[890] T-34

In many respects, notably simplicity of design and manufacture, and its success in achieving the difficult balance between speed, armour, and hitting power, the Russian T-34 tank is widely considered one of the most effective tank designs of WWII. Though it was the brain-child of an engineer named TSIGANOV who led the design team at the Comintern Factory in Kharkov, the T in T-34 does not commemorate his name but simply means "Tank" and 34 designates the year the prototype went into production. It has been calculated that before, during and after the war, some 70,000 of these weapons were produced in Russian factories.

[891] TALBOT

The Talbot family has the distinction of being able to trace its pedigree back to one of the brutish land-grabbing gangsters who arrived in this country in the train of William of Normandy. It has also the possibly unique distinction of taking its family name from a breed of dog. The TALBOT is, or rather was (it is now extinct except as a charge in heraldry), a Norman breed of hunting dog, perhaps something between a mastiff and a bloodhound, recognisable by its impressive size and speed and by its pure white coat. One Richard, who figures in the Domesday Book, acquired the nickname "Talbot" partly, no doubt, to distinguish him from other brutish land-grabbers with the same given name, and partly as a tribute, one supposes, to some such doggy personal characteristic as, for example, the ability to bring down a deer using nothing but his teeth. This soubriquet he passed on to succeeding generations, among whom were the pioneer photographer WILLIAM HENRY FOX TALBOT (see TALBOTYPE), and the industrialist CHRISTOPHER RICE MANSEL TALBOT (1803-1890) who gave his name to the town of PORT TALBOT in South Wales, thus arguably challenging BEDDGELERT's claim to be the only town in the UK named after a dog. (See also CHATEAU TALBOT.)

[892] TALBOTYPE

WILLIAM HENRY FOX TALBOT (1800-1877) is credited with the invention of photography on paper in 1834, in distinction to DAGUERRE'S independent invention of photography on metal *ca.* 1837. Both men published in 1839 – but Daguerre first. Talbot's original photographic medium, called "photogenic drawing paper", depended on light-sensitive silver chloride precipitated within the fibres of fine writing paper. This was a slow "printing-out" process that required exposures in the camera of about an hour. In 1840 Talbot chanced upon the phenomenon of the latent image in silver iodide and its development by gallic acid. The discovery accelerated his exposures to a minute or less, and photographic portraiture became possible. He modestly named this improved photographic process the *calotype*, from the Greek *kalos* = beautiful, but his supporters re-named it the **TALBOTYPE** to individualise his achievement *vis á vis* his French rival's **DAGUERREOTYPE**. In 1844 Talbot published *The Pencil of Nature*, one of the earliest photographically-illustrated books, demonstrating the usefulness of the negative-positive process on paper. The calotype, patented in 1841, was the forerunner of the successful method of modern photography that lasted until the digital imaging revolution of the 1990s. Talbot was born into a family of landed gentry and inherited the 16th-century Abbey at Lacock in Wiltshire. He was educated at Harrow and read for the Mathematical Tripos at Trinity College, Cambridge. As an archetypal gentleman-scholar of the Victorian era, he was a Fellow of the Royal Society, receiving its **RUMFORD MEDAL** in 1842, and a close colleague of **SIR JOHN HERSCHEL** with whom he collaborated on photographic innovations. He also helped decipher the cuneiform inscriptions at Nineveh. Talbot's legacy of several thousand negatives and prints on paper, recently gifted to the British Library and the National Media Museum, Bradford, constitutes the richest photographic vision we have of the mid-19th century. A **TALBOT** is the name put forward – but not yet approved – for the SI unit of luminous energy, in units of lumen seconds. (At a wavelength of 555 nm, where the human eye is most sensitive, one Talbot = 1.464 milliJoules). (MW)

[893] TAM O'SHANTER

A brimless woollen bobble hat or beret named after the hero of a well-known narrative poem by Robert Burns, *Tam O'Shanter's ride* (1790). In Scotland, Burns is reckoned to be one of that nation's finest poets, the other being William McGonagall (1830-1902).

[894] TANTALUM – see VANADIUM

[895] TANTALUS

In Greek Mythology, accounts differ as to as to whether **TANTALUS** was of divine or mortal parentage (Graves *The Greek Myths* 1955) but there is broad agreement on the nature of his crime and punishment: he laid on a banquet for Zeus and a few other select divinities at which food ran short. Tantalus rose to the occasion. He killed and jointed his son Pelops and served him up as a locally-sourced ragout. The gods easily detected the meat's origin and took a dim view. Tantalus, already in bad odour with the Olympians for imparting their secrets to mortals, was condemned to spend eternity tied to a tree suspended over a lake, tormented by thirst but unable to drink, the water receding from him every time he bent to take a mouthful. In modern usage, a TANTALUS is a lockable holder for spirit decanters, found in the better class of household, where it is deemed necessary to prevent the servants, however thirsty, from taking surreptitious swigs of whisky or cognac when they should, as befits their class and station, be content with beer. The verb "TANTALISE" is first recorded from 1587.

[896] TARTAGLIA'S TRIANGLE – see PASCAL'S TRIANGLE

[897] TARTE TATIN
This popular if somewhat eccentric version of the familiar apple tart was invented (allegedly as the result of a culinary accident) in 1898 by STÉPHANIE TATIN who, with her sister Caroline kept the Hotel Tatin at Lamotte-Beuvron in central France. The memory of Miss Tatin's moment of serendipity is kept alive by an annual festival in the tart's home town and by "La Confrérie des Lichonneux", which roughly translates as "brotherhood of lip-smackers" – one of those quintessentially French gastronomic guilds dedicated to celebrating the virtues of some local edible or drinkable delicacy.

[898] TATTERSALL'S
RICHARD TATTERSALL (1817-1849), bloodstock breeder and auctioneer, was the son of a Yorkshire wool-merchant who, more interested in horses than sheep, started out as stud-groom to the Duke of Kingston and went on to found the firm which bears his name and which has become a central pillar of the British bloodstock industry. He set up in business on rented land at Hyde Park Corner in 1766 and soon attracted wealthy clients by his honesty and business acumen. In 1779 he acquired a stallion named *Highflyer* which carried the bloodlines of all three of the founding British Thoroughbreds, the BYERLEY TURK, the DARLEY ARABIAN and the GODOLPHIN ARABIAN. Thanks largely to *Highflyer's* success as a stud horse and to Tattersall's canny preference for selling his progeny as young stock rather than as racers, he amassed a large enough fortune to build himself a grand house outside Ely, which, giving credit where it was due, he named *Highflyer Hall*.

[899] TAWDRY
Now usually an adjective signifying anything showy but worthless, originally applied to a cheap form of lace. The word is a corruption of SAINT AUDREY (Saint Ethldrida or Ethelreda) the 7th-century patron saint of Ely, where, in the Middle Ages at St. Audrey's fair, cheap but gaudy goods were bought and sold (*cf.*

PINCHBECK). Audrey's claim to sanctity seems to have stemmed largely, if not solely, from her success in maintaining her virginity despite being married. She eventually escaped from her husband with the aid of Saint Wilfrid of York and went on to take the veil and found the great abbey of Ely, her husband, meanwhile, having found a more compliant partner. The Saint's life and miracles are recounted in a late 12th or early 13th-century French verse translation (*La Vie Seinte Audrée*) of an unknown Latin original. Her feast day falls on June 23rd.

[900] TAYLORISM – see THERBLIG

[901] TEDDY BEAR

The **TEDDY BEAR,** ubiquitous toy companion-animal of 20th century children, derives its name from that of American President **THEODORE ROOSEVELT** (1858-1919) who, on a hunting expedition in the swamps of Mississippi in 1902, refused to shoot an old she-bear that had been cornered and tied to a tree. Had he done so, he said, he wouldn't "be able to look my boys in the face again" (though this delicate sentiment didn't stop him shooting a panda on a trip to China). The *Washington Post* made the incident famous with a front-page cartoon in which the artist Clifford Berryman transformed the old bear into a cub. Among the many readers who saw the Berryman cartoon was Russian immigrant Morris Michtom, owner of a small Brooklyn novelty store. Seeing a potential market, Morris had his wife run up a toy bear with movable limbs. When it sold quickly, the Michtoms made others. After obtaining Roosevelt's permission to use the abbreviated form of his Christian name, Michtom closed a distribution deal with a large toy wholesaler. Today, some makes of teddy bear fetch thousands from collectors known as "arctophiles" (Gk. ἄρκτος = bear). The cuddly toy belies the fact that the President was a far from cuddly individual. Despite his owlish appearance he was famous as a model of rough-shooting masculinity and for his rugged "cowboy" image (which Gore Vidal believed to be a cover for latent homosexuality. He called Roosevelt, along with Hemingway, "fat cissies with guns".) (RS)

[902] TEDDY BOY

The **TEDDY BOY** phenomenon which, along with its associated music Rock 'n Roll, involved a considerable section of British youth in the 1950's, took its name (which originated with a *Daily Express* headline) from the "Edwardian" fashions favoured by its adepts and hence from that of **KING EDWARD VII** (reigned 1901-1910). Style-wise, it involved such fancies as long high-necked jackets, sometimes of velvet, or with velvet-trimmed collar and cuffs, lined with floral or bright-coloured materials. Add to this: brocade waistcoat, bootlace or "slim-jim" tie, drainpipe trousers, high-necked loose "Mr B" collar on a white shirt (as worn by jazz musician Billy Eckstein), and suede shoes, previously known as "BKs" (brothel-kreepers). The hair should be worn greased-up and strongly-moulded with a quiff at the front and the side hair combed into a "DA" (duck's arse) at the back, with, as a finishing touch, sideboards of generous length. An alternative style was the "Boston", where the hair was greased straight back and cut square across at the nape. In both cases a comb was a necessary accessory, kept ready to hand. Largely a lower-class phenomenon (middle-class youth in the fifties was into traditional jazz and the Beats), "Ted" fashion influenced to some extent the tailoring of people who ought to have known better (one thinks, for example, of the velvet-collared overcoats sported by persons such as Jeremy Thorpe and Lord Snowdon who, in a generous interpretation, might otherwise be considered gentlemen). (RS)

[903] TEMMINCK'S STINT

Member of the sandpiper family of waders, similar to our native dunlin, but present in Britain only as a migrant. *Calidris temminckii* takes its name from the Dutch zoologist **COENRAAD JACOB TEMMINCK** (1778-1858), the first director of the Leiden Natural History Museum. Though Temminck is mainly remembered as an ornithologist, the large number (over 30) of creatures – birds, reptiles, fish, sharks, and mammals – named after him testify to the regard in which he was held and the authority he wielded.   Among the species that bear his name a special mention must go to **TEMMINCK'S MOLE**, if only because of its wondrous scientific name: *Mogera wogura*.

[904] TESCO

TESCO (or **TESCO'S** in normal English colloquial usage) takes its origin from a market stall in London's East End operated just after the First World War by **JOHN** (formerly **JACOB**) **EDWARD   COHEN** (formerly **KOHEN**) (1898-1979). It is now Britain's largest retail concern and the world's third largest grocery retailer. "Jack" Cohen created the Tesco brand name in 1924 from the initials of a firm of tea merchants with whom he did business, T.E. Stockwell, and the first two letters of his own surname.

[905] TESLA

The **TESLA** is the SI unit used to measure the strength of magnetic fields – strictly, of magnetic flux density. Accorded the symbol T, it is derived from basic SI units as one **VOLT** second per square meter, or as one **NEWTON** per **AMPERE** meter, or as one **WEBER** per square meter: $1\ T = V\ s\ /m^2 = N\ /A\ m\ = Wb\ /m^2$. A magnetic field of one tesla is very strong – as generated by a powerful magnet – and is equal to 10,000 **GAUSS** (*q.v.*), the old cgs unit of magnetic field strength. The Earth's magnetic field is about 50 microteslas. The unit is named after Serbian physicist and electrical engineer, NIKOLA TESLA (1856-1943) who studied at Graz, Prague and Paris. He emigrated to the USA in 1884 and worked briefly for Edison, but after a falling-out he joined the Westinghouse Company, where he developed the first alternating current induction motor in 1888. Most notable of his other inventions is the TESLA COIL, which is a compact electrical induction coil (see RUHMKORFF) for generating very high voltages at high frequencies. Despite revolutionising the electrical industry and unlike Edison, Tesla died in poverty. (MW)

[906] THALES' THEOREM

is a neat example of pure EUCLIDEAN geometry: *any triangle inscribed in a semicircle, with its diameter as one side, is right-angled.* THALES OF MILETUS (*ca.* 624 – *ca.* 545 BC), from Ionia in Asia Minor is traditionally cited as the founder of Greek philosophy, and therefore of ours too. He is also described as the first "scientist" (a word not actually invented until the 1830s AD). He was the first to propose a natural cosmology founded on rational thought, in contrast to the magical myths of religion, and he proposed that water was the primary substance and basis of the universe – which is not so far out, considering how much hydrogen it contains. He was a geometer and astronomer, engineer and statesman, but he left no writings except, perhaps, a nautical star-guide, now lost. He is famous for successfully predicting an eclipse in 585 BC – possibly based on his knowledge of Babylonian astronomy, which had recognised a 19 year cycle in the recurrence of eclipses. BERTRAND RUSSELL is on record as declaring: "Philosophy begins with Thales." (*History of Western Philosophy*, London, Allen & Unwin 1946, p.21) (MW)

[907] THÉNARD'S BLUE

Alias cobalt blue or Gahn's ultramarine*, this pigment is sometimes also identified with azure blue, but that title properly belongs, as its etymology suggests, to genuine ultramarine, the semi-precious mineral *lapis lazuli*. THÉNARD'S BLUE is a permanent pigment and, unlike most other blues, is unaffected by heat, acids, or alkalis. It is commonly seen in "cobalt glass". Chemically it is cobalt aluminate, first prepared in 1799 by French chemist LOUIS JACQUES THÉNARD (1777-1857) who was born at La Louptière, Aube, into humble circumstances. His evident talent attracted the patronage of the notable chemists Antoine François, Comte de Fourcroy (1755-1809) and his doctoral student Louis Nicolas Vauquelin (1763-1829) at the *École Polytechnique*, where Thénard ended up as professor of chemistry. He established a classification of metals according to their resistance to the action of water and oxygen and, together with GAY-LUSSAC was the discoverer of boron (1810). As a great teacher and an important researcher, he influenced scientific education in France and was ennobled Baron by Charles X in 1825. In 1865 his native village recognised its distinguished son by enhancing its name to La Louptière-Thénard. (MW)

* After Swedish chemist, mineralogist and mining engineer, **JOHAN GOTTLIEB GAHN** (1745-1818), who first (1774) isolated the metallic element manganese. His name is given to the mineral **GAHNITE**, a zinc aluminate, discovered in 1807 in a mine at Falun, Sweden, where Gahn had been appointed Assessor of the College of Mines and where he was instrumental in setting up a number of industrial chemical enterprises including a paint factory.

[908] THERBLIG

FRANK BUNKER GILBRETH (1868-1924) pioneered time-and-motion study as a tool of industrial management. Working with his wife **LILLIAN** (1878-1972), and with the aid of motion-picture cameras, he studied and analysed the physical movements performed by workers on production lines, with the aim, naturally, of increasing efficiency/productivity. The word **THERBLIG**, now fallen into disuse, was his coinage and denoted a unit of work-movement. This enabled him to allot numerical values to particular operations and to set standard performance times. See his *Motion study* (1911), and *Applied motion study* (1917). In odd intervals, Frank and Lillian found time to produce twelve children, two of whom, Frank Gilbreth jnr. and his sister Ernestine, co-authored the best-selling book *Cheaper by the dozen* (1948) based on their experience of growing up in the Gilbreth household. An earlier individual ploughing the same furrow as Gilbreth was "efficiency engineer" **FREDERICK WINSLOW TAYLOR** (1856-1915), a native of Pennsylvania who introduced piece-work into the steel mill where he was employed. His methods, based on close observation of the efficiency with which the individual worker performed specific operations and by stressing the importance of choosing the best man for each task, gained ready and wide acceptance and gave birth to the word **TAYLORISM** and its associated verb **TAYLORISE**. (See his *Principles of scientific management* 1911.) For an even earlier example we might cite **MARC ISAMBARD BRUNEL**, father of the more famous Isambard Kingdom, who introduced a production-line system for the manufacture of pulley blocks in HM's shipyards, dividing the process into separate successive operations each performed by a single worker.

[909] THEREMIN

A sound-emitting device best described as the product of miscegenation between a radar set and a musical saw. It bears the name of its inventor, the Russian **LEV SERGEYEVICH TERMEN** *a.k.a.* **LÉON THEREMIN** (1896-1993), who discovered (in 1919) that valves, oscillators, and other electrical bits could be put together to form a machine that would emit weird wailings and whoopings when it detected movement in its vicinity. Though it has yet to replace the musical saw on the concert platform, the THEREMIN remains popular with composers of film music where the script calls for anything that could be described as "unearthly".

[910] THOMAS GRAHAM HOUSE – see GRAHAM'S LAW

[911] THOMSON'S GAZELLE

Gazella thomsoni is named after the explorer, naturalist and geologist JOSEPH THOMSON (1858-1894) who made a number of hazardous and fruitful (scientifically and politically) journeys through various parts of Africa, including one to open up a route between the East Coast and Uganda in 1882-3 during which he traversed the "country of the dreaded Masai" (DNB). Apart from numerous journal articles, his published accounts of his experiences include: *To the Central African lakes and back* (1881), *Through Masai Land* (1885), *Travels in the Atlas and Southern Morocco* (1889), and (a little surprisingly) *Ulu, an African romance*, which he co-authored with a Miss E. Harris-Smith (2 vols. 1888). Though Thomson's name is associated with the "Scramble for Africa", unlike Stanley, whose motto was "Walk loudly and carry a big stick" (and preferably also a MAXIM GUN), Thomson's dealings with the Africans were characterised by negotiation rather than confrontation. His motto was: "He who goes gently goes safely. He who goes safely goes far." But Thomson's far-faring eventually ruined his health and he died while still in his thirties.

[912] THOREAU'S AXE

On any short list of great American books, *Walden* by HENRY DAVID THOREAU (1817-1862) is sure of a place alongside such giants as *Moby Dick* and *Huckleberry Finn*. Its subject, however, is not exactly epic. It is the account of an experiment in self-sufficiency that Thoreau conducted over two years while living in the woods near Concord, Mass., in a cabin he had built with his own hands. His purpose was to prove how simple it is to provide for one's wants when these are divested of all superfluity. He concluded that a man could meet all his *real* needs by six weeks' paid work a year (no problem for Thoreau who claimed to have "as many trades as I have fingers"). Any further exertion, he believed, for the mere purpose of accumulating money – and with it, wants – was time and effort wasted. "I am convinced," he wrote, "both by faith and experience, that to maintain oneself on this earth is not a hardship but a pastime, if we will live simply and wisely." THOREAU'S AXE, accordingly, may be regarded as a variant form of OCCAM'S RAZOR, signifying "the application of the criterion of *need* as a check on the multiplication of *wants*." Thoreau was an independent-minded man, obnoxiously so at times, marching always to a different drummer. Though his philosophy has much about it to admire, its great weakness is that Thoreau was uncomfortable with the notion that Man is a social animal, and that he himself was bound like the rest of us by ties of affection, dependency and obligation.* It is the more astonishing, therefore, that this feisty individualist begins the account of his experiment in self-sufficiency with the following sentence: "*Near the end of March 1845, I borrowed an axe, and went down to the woods by Walden pond.*" Possibly Thoreau realised that there is something more than a touch paradoxical about starting a demonstration of self-reliance by *borrowing* the tool that makes it possible, because he adds, "*The owner of the axe, as he released his hold on it, said that it was the apple of his eye; but I returned it sharper than I received it.*"

* Compare Mrs. Thatcher's notorious saying, "There is no such thing as society, there are only individuals." Against this wicked and offensive doctrine we might set the words of a great English individualist: "*It is nearer the truth to say that society is the only human reality that we know, and that the individual is an abstraction in terms of which, for certain purposes, it is convenient or even indispensable to think. Everything that is knowable or predicable about an individual – such as, for example, his liberty or freedom or rights or happiness – is derived from the society from which we have abstracted him in order to talk about him.*" (Enoch Powell "The paradox of personal liberty" in *Wrestling with the angel* 1957.) No man is an island.

[913] THORIUM, URANIUM, NEPTUNIUM, PLUTONIUM

Among the naturally-occurring, long-lived radioactive elements is THORIUM, atomic number 90, symbol Th, which was discovered by Berzelius in 1828. Its oxide was essential to that brilliant invention, the WELSBACH gas mantle. In modern times THORIUM has become a source of nuclear energy but, despite its attribution to the Norse god of war, THOR, son of Odin, THORIUM cannot be used directly for making nuclear weapons, unlike the elements that follow it. After THORIUM in the Periodic Table there follows protactinium (see MEITNERIUM), then the planetary trio of elements, URANIUM (U), NEPTUNIUM (Np), and PLUTONIUM (Pu), with atomic numbers 92, 93, and 94, respectively. URANIUM occurs naturally in pitchblende, and its discovery is usually credited to Klaproth in 1789, although the use of its oxide to stain glass yellow was known since Roman times. It is now of enormous importance as a nuclear fuel. And bomb material (see GRAHAM'S LAW). URANUS, the primordial father of the twelve TITANS, was castrated by his youngest son and usurper, Cronus, (Kronos in Greek) at the instigation of Uranus's wife, GAIA. The corresponding planet was discovered by Sir William Herschel in 1781, who opted to call it "GEORGE'S STAR" in honour of George III, but this name was not acceptable to the French, hence it became URANUS. The other two elements are relatively short-lived, and not found in nature; they were first made in 1940 at Berkeley, California (see SEABORGIUM) by the bombardment of uranium with neutrons to yield NEPTUNIUM, and with deuterons to give PLUTONIUM. NEPTUNIUM is the first "transuranic" element, named after the familiar Roman sea-god NEPTUNE, counterpart of the Greek Poseidon. The corresponding planet was discovered in 1846 at the position calculated by Urbain Jean Joseph le Verrier (1811-1877) using **NEWTONIAN MECHANICS**, although its existence had been unknowingly recorded previously, as a fixed star, by **GALILEO**. The second transuranic element **PLUTONIUM** is today the icon of mass destruction. It is appropriately named after the minor deity **PLUTO**, a son of Cronus and Rhea, who is also known in Greek mythology as **HADES**, the lord of his eponymous underworld. His planet was discovered in 1930 at Lowell Observatory by Clyde W. Tombaugh, but the name **PLUTO** was suggested for it by eleven-year-old Oxford schoolgirl, Venetia Burney. Like **CERES** it has now, sadly, been downgraded by the International Astronomical Union to the status of "dwarf planet". (MW)

[914] TILLER GIRLS

It was Manchester businessman **JOHN TILLER** (d. 1926) who in the 1880s put together a troupe of female dancers and trained them in the straight-line, high-kicking, precisely-synchronised dance routines with which his name is associated. Tiller's original formation was known as "The Sunbeams" but as their style of dancing grew in popularity, they became the **TILLER GIRLS** and troupes consisting of anything from four to 30 or more performers were going through their paces in musicals, pantomimes, variety shows, and cabarets from Blackpool to the Folies Bergères and as far afield as New York. At the same time, a number of Tiller Schools opened, training female dancers in the Tiller "tap and kick" technique. Following WWII, they declined in popularity and in the 1960's were largely supplanted by dance troupes which allowed a greater degree of freedom to individual performers. However, straight-line precision dancing made an extraordinary comeback in 1994 when "Riverdance" came from nowhere to take the world by storm.

[915] TILLEY LAMP – see WELSBACH MANTLE

[916] TITAN – see IAPETUS

[917] TITANIUM, PALLADIUM, SELENIUM, MERCURY

Immediately preceding **VANADIUM** in the periodic table, at atomic number 22, is **TITANIUM,** symbol Ti, which was discovered in 1791 by a Cornish vicar and amateur chemist, the Reverend William Gregor (1761-1817), in *ilmenite* sand from a nearby riverbed. He named its oxide after the locality, *manaccanite*. In 1795 the element was "rediscovered" in a different mineral, *rutile*, by the celebrated German chemist Martin Heinrich Klaproth (1743-1817) who named it after the **TITANS,** the race of twelve deities fathered by the primordial sky-god, **URANUS** on the "Earth Mother", **GAIA** (see **IAPETUS**). Pure metallic titanium – mercifully, the proper name *manaccanium* was not adopted – was only extracted in 1910: it is strong, light, and resistant to corrosion, so its alloys are used for airframes.

Titanium dioxide is an important white pigment – appropriately, the Greek word τιταος means "white earth" or "lime". The name of the Greek goddess of wisdom, **PALLAS ATHENA,** was conferred on the newly-discovered, second-largest asteroid, **PALLAS,** in 1802, and almost immediately thereafter on another new transition element, the noble metal **PALLADIUM,** with atomic number 46 and symbol Pd. This was extracted from platinum ores in 1803 by William Hyde Wollaston (1766-1828), and used in dentistry, surgical instruments, and the photographic **PALLADIOTYPE** process. The moon-goddess of Greek mythology **SELENE** was a second-generation **TITAN,** a daughter of Hyperion, and gives her name to the only eponymous non-metallic element, **SELENIUM,** atomic number 34, symbol Se, discovered in 1817 by Jöns Jakob Berzelius (1779-1848), one of the fathers of modern chemistry (see **CERIUM** and **THORIUM**). Selenium falls in the same periodic group 6 as sulphur, and closely resembles it. Our lunar probes have returned with rock specimens revealing the bad news that there is disappointingly little selenium on the moon. **MERCURY,** the winged messenger of the Roman gods, known as Hermes in the Greek pantheon, lends his name to the last of the transition metals, and the only metallic element that is molten at room temperature, atomic number 80, symbol Hg for *hydrargyrum,* the Greek for "water-silver", also known as "quicksilver" (quick = "living", as in "the q. and the dead"). A favourite material of the alchemists, the liquid metal has found a number of uses, particularly for scientific instruments (see **TORRICELLI**). Mercury is used in the extraction of gold and silver, because it is capable of dissolving other metals. Such alloys are called amalgams, and that with silver and tin has been long used for dental treatment, but the toxicity of mercury – its vapour can induce neurological disorders – has made its applications controversial today. (MW)

[918] TITIAN RED

A brownish-orange colour close to Venetian red (*a.k.a.* English red), burnt Sienna, or terra cotta; this does not appear to be a single identifiable pigment, but it is well-established in the vocabulary of colour. It may be seen in paintings by the Pre-Raphaelite Brotherhood of the red-headed beauties who appealed so much to their tastes, but its original attribution lies in the depiction of the red hair of his well-endowed female subjects by **TIZIANO VECELLIO** (*ca.*1488-1576), the leading painter of the 16th century Venetian school of the Italian Renaissance, who signed himself **TITIAN.*** He was born in Pieve di Cadore, in the Veneto. He was apprenticed to Giovanni Bellini, then became an assistant to Giorgione, and in a full life accomplished about one hundred major easel paintings. It is said that, towards the end, he laid down his brush with the words, "I think I am beginning to learn something about painting." (MW)

* There is no truth in the rumour that a National Gallery curator has been heard pleading "We must have more Titians".

[919] TOBY JUG

Ceramic jug in the form of a seated human figure, developed and popularised by Staffordshire makers in the mid-eighteenth century. The origin of the name is commonly traced to the character **SIR TOBY BELCH** in Shakespeare's *Twelfth Night*. But given that the typical Toby jug more commonly depicts a character in 18th-century dress and wearing a tricorn hat, an attribution to **UNCLE TOBY** in Sterne's *Tristram Shandy* of 1760 might be a better guess.

[920] TOMMY GUN

The world's first hand-held machine gun without which, as every cinema-goer knows, any self-respecting Chicago gangster of the 1920's would be considered improperly dressed. It is named after its inventor, **JOHN TALIAFERRO THOMPSON** (1860-1940), an American army officer and ordnance specialist. During service in WWI, Thompson dreamed of a quick-firing, short-range infantry weapon that could be used in clearing enemy trenches – what he called a "trench broom". In civilian life after the war, he perfected his design in partnership with a naval officer John Blish, who had invented a new form of breech-block mechanism that caught Thompson's fancy. They patented the weapon in 1920 and, with no war in prospect, marketed it to civilian law-enforcement agencies. In WWII, the weapon came into its own and was manufactured in huge numbers for the American and British armed forces. It was produced in a number of versions, fitted with either a 50- or 100-round drum magazine or with a 20- or 30-round straight ("stick") magazine. As the gun's rate of fire was 700 (or in some models 1000) rounds per minute, one supposes that brisk and frequent reloading would have been in order whenever any serious trench-sweeping was called for.

[921] TORR

EVANGELISTA TORRICELLI (1608-47) was an Italian mathematician and natural philosopher who, in 1641, became the amanuensis of **GALILEO GALILEI** during the last months of Galileo's life, which were spent under house-arrest thanks to Papal condemnation of his theories. On Galileo's death, Torricelli was invited by the Grand Duke Ferdinand II de Medici to succeed him as professor of mathematics at the University of Pisa. Experience with lift-pumps had shown that the pressure of the atmosphere could only support a column of water about 10 meters high. Torricelli used a column of mercury (which has 14 times the density of water) in a vertical glass tube, about a meter long, sealed at the top end, and found the height of the mercury column supported was 760 mm – the empty space above it is a **TORRICELLIAN VACUUM.** Thus he invented the first mercury barometer in 1643, which became an important and commonplace instrument for three centuries, until mercury was deemed unacceptable in an average domestic environment. The contraction, **TORR** is a non-metric unit of pressure, corresponding to 1/760 of an atmosphere, or the pressure exerted by a column of mercury 1 mm high; one torr is equal to 133 **PASCALS**, the SI unit of pressure. (MW)

[922] TOURETTE'S SYNDROME

An inherited neurological disorder which manifests itself in childhood by "motor tics" (sudden involuntary movements) and sometimes, though less commonly, by sudden and inappropriate utterances of obscene or offensive remarks. In most cases symptoms abate with the onset of adulthood. The disease was first fully described in 1885 by French physician **GEORGES ALBERT ÉDOUARD BRUTUS GILLES DE LA TOURETTE** (1859-1904) and named after him by his superior, Dr. Jean-Martin Charcot (1825-1893), father of the polar explorer and oceanographer Jean Charcot (1867-1936). Nowadays, Tourette's syndrome is sometimes invoked, along with "hyper-activity", by distraught parents to explain the disruptive or unruly behaviour of children who, perhaps, are simply the victims of poor diet and/or poor parenting, or, even more simply, evil little bastards (see **PELAGIAN HERESY**). (Note: A recent American study* finds a statistical link between Attention Deficit Hyperactivity Disorder (ADHD) and organophosphate residues in food, particularly fruit and vegetables. Organophosphates are neurotoxins, originally intended as chemical weapons, now used as pesticides.)
* Reuters report May 17, 2110.

[923] TOURNEDOS ROSSINI

A nourishing snack that anyone who has ready to hand bread, butter, foie gras (duck or goose), fillet of beef, garlic, olive oil, sliced truffles, port, brandy, veal stock and madeira can whip up in minutes. It was named in honour of the Italian composer **GIOACCHINO ANTONIO ROSSINI** (1792-1868) by its inventor Casimir Moisson of the Maison Dorée restaurant, one of Rossini's favourite French hangouts. A notorious foodie, Rossini was on first-name terms with every top kitchen mechanic in Europe, wrote arias for Carême who paid him in pâté, and composed musical *bonnes bouches* named after food items (radishes, anchovies, figs, etc.). Also named in Rossini's honour are dishes (chicken, eggs, sole) involving **ROSSINI SAUCE** made with foie gras and truffles. Tournedos Rossini is not be confused with **CHATEAUBRIAND STEAK**, the recipe for which is positively ascetic by comparison.

[924] TOURNEFORTIA

JOSEPH PITTON DE TOURNEFORT (1656-1708), professor of botany at the Jardin des Plantes, Paris, was commissioned by the King to travel around Europe making collections. He subsequently spent three years (1700-1702) in Greece and Asia Minor, taking with him Claude Aubriet (see **AUBRIETIA**) as illustrator. On his return he published an account of his travels, *Relation d'un voyage au Levant* (1717) and subsequently taught medicine at the Collège de France. He is remembered as a systematising botanist. He classified flowers according to a single character – the number and form of the petals.* This was a step forward from earlier systems which considered a mixed bag of characters but it led to unacceptable simplifications and unlikely pairings. Even so, he may be considered as having in some sense prepared the ground for **LINNAEUS** and was the first person to nail the concept of *genus* to an acceptable definition.** **TOURNEFORTIA,** the genus which (thanks to Linnaeus) bears his name, includes three species of tender flowering shrubs usually found as greenhouse plants.

* *Elemens de botanique* 1684

** *Institutiones rei herbariae*, 3 vols, 1700

[925] TRADESCANTIA

In the history of British horticulture, the two **TRADESCANTS**, father and son, both named John, enjoy a special, almost a hallowed status. Tradescant père (d. ?1637), who had travelled to the Low Countries, Muscovy and the Barbary coast in the employ of various dignitaries, is famous for the establishment of the first English "physic garden" in South Lambeth, and under Charles I enjoyed the post of Keeper of His Majesty's Gardens, Vines and Silkworms. He brought back from his travels not only seeds and plants but also natural history specimens and ethnographical objects which formed the basis of his "Cabinet of Curiosities" and constituted the first museum in this country open to the public. His son (1608-1662), also a traveller and plantsman, inherited the post and the collections, which he enriched with plants from America. On his death, he bequeathed the now famous *Museum Tradescantianum* to Elias Ashmole (see **ASHMOLEAN MUSEUM**) who in turn presented it to the University of Oxford. The genus **TRADESCANTIA,** named after the elder Tradescant, comprises over 60 species of both tender and hardy perennials native to North and South America. The Tradescants' introductions include the Lilac, the Acacia, the Occidental Plane (a parent of the London Plane), and the "Algier apricot".

[926] TRAJAN'S COLUMN

The column, completed in 113 AD was erected in the then recently-completed Forum of Trajan in Rome by order of the Senate. It commemorates the victorious campaigns of the **EMPEROR TRAJAN** against the Dacians (101-106 AD), which it portrays in a spiral arrangement of sculpted scenes in low relief covering the 98-foot high shaft. If unwound from the column, the illustrative sculptures would form a band some 600 feet in length. The structure is hollow and contains a spiral staircase leading to a viewing platform at the top. The shaft is topped by an incongruous statue of St. Peter placed there in 1588 by order of Pope Sixtus V, which replaces one of the Emperor himself. The conquest of Dacia gave the Roman Empire the only addition to its territory lying on the north bank of the Danube and may be said to represent the high-water-mark of Rome's expansionist phase. The column's importance to historians lies in the fact that it is the principal (almost the only) iconographical source we have for the weapons, uniforms and tactics of the Roman army of this period.

[927] TRILBY – see FEDORA

[928] TROILISM
Sometimes wrongly but understandably known as *triolism*, **TROILISM** is a form of sexual activity involving three persons, one of whom is a spectator. It takes its name from Shakespeare's *Troilus and Cressida*, in which **TROILUS** witnesses his fickle mistress Cressida in amorous discourse with the Greek Diomede (Act V, Scene ii). The same play features a character named **PANDARUS**, politely described as a go-between or match-maker but, if spades are to be called spades, a pimp, from whose name we derive the noun and verb **PANDER**.

[929] TRUMAN DOCTRINE
On March 12th 1947, Roosevelt's successor **PRESIDENT HARRY S. TRUMAN** (1884–1972), in a speech to both houses of Congress, asked them to support a policy of material aid to countries in danger of domination by "totalitarian regimes" (in this instance, Greece and Turkey). He stated that, "*One of the primary objectives of the foreign policy of the United States is the creation of conditions in which we and other nations will be able to work out a way of life free of coercion. This was a fundamental issue in the war with Germany and Japan. Our victory was won over countries which sought to impose their will, and their way of life, upon other nations.*" At first blush, these are sentiments with which few would quarrel.* Though it would be interesting to know how many of Truman's audience asked themselves how this policy might be carried into effect otherwise than by imposing America's will and way of life on other nations. Whatever the case, in the half century and more that followed Truman's declaration of intent, America has pursued a consistent policy of generous support for some of the vilest dictatorships the planet has to offer, plus interventions, overt or covert, in country after country to frustrate the emergence of anything that might be or become a democracy. All of which may incline future historians to take a distinctly nuanced view of America's willingness or ability to keep the implicit promise that Truman made on her behalf.

* Presidential addresses designed to be (a) stirring, and (b) memorable are inevitably going to be

judged against the very high standard set by Lincoln's Gettysburg address, perfect of its kind and a worthy successor to Pericles' famous elegy on the Athenian dead in the Peloponnesian War. Kennedy did rather better than Truman in this respect. As witness his justly celebrated inaugural address of January 1961: "*Let every nation know, whether it wishes us well or ill, that we shall pay any price, bear any burden, meet any hardship, support any friend, oppose any foe, in order to assure the survival and the success of liberty...*" &c, &c. Many listeners to President Obama's inaugural address of January 2009 hoped for oratory at least as good, but were disappointed – an augury of further disappointments to follow.

[930] TRUMAN SYNDROME

Television, arguably our most disastrous invention since the aeroplane, has a lot to answer for. Recently, working on the human animal's inexhaustible ability to come up with ever weirder pathological delusions, television has helped to add yet one more identifiable mental aberration to keep psychiatrists in business. Christened **TRUMAN SYNDROME**, it derives its name from a 1998 film entitled *The Truman Show* in which the protagonist, Truman Burbank, is the only man on the planet unaware of the fact that his life is being secretly filmed, second by second, and shown to the world on television. Since the film was first shown, it has emerged that there actually are individuals who believe themselves to be in a similar predicament – *i.e.* that their entire lives are taking place within the context of a so-called "reality" TV show. This offers an interesting example of the extent to which the symptoms of a delusional state may be culturally determined. Fifty years ago sufferers from this class of disorder would probably have been pointing the finger at saucer-borne extra-terrestrials, and five hundred years ago at witchcraft or demonic possession. (See *British Journal of Psychiatry* 2008.193.168 and subsequent correspondence of 8 June 2008.)

[931] TURING MACHINE

ALAN MATHISON TURING (1912-1954), gives his name to the abstract concept of computability evidenced through the test of a process against the ideal computer – the **TURING MACHINE**, designed originally to distinguish mathematical problems not capable of being solved algorithmically (by a process of defined logical steps). He is also the originator (in his 1950 paper *Computing Machinery and Intelligence*) of the concept which became known as the **TURING TEST**. This assesses the ability of a machine to demonstrate "intelligence" by measuring its behaviour against that of a human being in rigorously-controlled circumstances. Inability to distinguish reliably which of the responses emanates from a machine and which from a human being is the criterion for determining whether the machine is exhibiting intelligence. Turing is credited by many authorities with originating the concept of the Stored Program Computer set out in his paper *On Computable Numbers, With an Application to the Entscheidungsproblem* in 1937. He constructed experimental machines operating with **BOOLEAN LOGIC** (the foundation of all digital computers), contributed largely to the wartime activities of the British code-breakers at Bletchley Park and supervised the construction of the ACE computer at the National Physical Laboratory. Never at ease with his homosexual tendencies, he killed himself by taking poison after prosecution for indecency. (GJ)

[932] TURNBULL'S BLUE

This useful artists' colour was long thought to be chemically different from Prussian blue, but MÖSSBAUER SPECTROSCOPY in the 1980s showed the two pigments to be the same substance, ferric ferrocyanide, despite the differing methods of manufacture. Also called Paris blue or Milori blue (after the French chemist), the politically-correct name for Prussian blue in the German-speaking world is *Berlinerblau* – after the place of its first accidental preparation in 1704 (see DIPPEL'S ANIMAL OIL). It does not occur in nature, so has been claimed as the first synthetic pigment, but this title must now be ceded to Egyptian blue. Because Turnbull's blue results from the chemical reaction of cyanides with iron salts, its presence on the walls of suspected gas-chambers has constituted a significant piece of evidence relating to the Holocaust. Messrs. J.M. & W. TURNBULL were a firm of dyers and colour manufacturers in the Scottish town of Haddington in East Lothian during the 18th – 19th centuries. Sir William Ramsay (who otherwise would not get a look-in here) recalls in his Nobel Prize address of 1904 that his great grandfather, also William and a chemist, collaborated with Turnbull's in the first production of their eponymous blue. (MW)

[933] TURNER PRIZE

A bisected cow in formalin; a squalid unmade bed; a shed reconstructed as a boat; paintings embellished with elephant dung; a house filled with cement; these were some of the shortlisted entries for this most prestigious prize in British contemporary visual art. The competition for the TURNER PRIZE never fails to excite high public indignation, for obvious reasons in view of the huge sums paid to purchase the winning works by the likes of Damien Hirst and Tracey Emin. It was set up in 1984 to reward visual artists under the age of 50, but suffered some early vicissitudes of sponsorship. However, in 1991 it was secured by TV's Channel 4 with a doubled cash prize of £20,000. The event is hosted by the Tate Gallery* in the name of England's premier painter of Romantic landscapes and seascapes, JOSEPH MALLORD WILLIAM TURNER (1775-1851), who entered the Royal Academy of Arts school at the tender age of 14, and was exhibiting within a year. Initially a topographical watercolorist of delicacy and charm, in 1796 he began to take to oils, influenced by Claude, TITIAN and Poussin, and his subtly nuanced sense of light and theatrical use of vivid colour identify him as a forerunner of Impressionism. He was championed by John Ruskin in *Modern*

Painters, 1843. Turner conducted an intensely private life, remaining unmarried but not without mistresses, and living frequently in London taverns. He bequeathed 300 paintings and 20,000 watercolours to the nation but, in contravention of his wishes, his work has become somewhat dispersed between our great galleries. The commemorative **TURNER MEDAL** is in the gift of the Royal Academy of Arts. (MW)

* MW will never forget his first visit to the Tate, and observing that it contained an office labelled *Head Attendant*.

[934] TYNDALL EFFECT

When light is shone through a homogeneous liquid, very little is scattered by the molecules and the beam is generally imperceptible when viewed at right angles (see **RAYLEIGH SCATTERING**). If the liquid has a colloid in suspension, however, the light is strongly scattered by the sub-microscopic particles and the beam is visible as a **TYNDALL CONE** of bluish light as it passes through the suspension. **JOHN TYNDALL** (1820-1893) was born in Leighlinbridge, County Carlow, Ireland, son of a shoemaker who claimed descent from William Tyndale, the translator of the English Bible. After various employments including a spell with the Ordnance Survey, he enrolled at the University of Marburg in 1848 to study chemistry under **ROBERT BUNSEN** and physics under Hermann Knoblauch. He returned to England in 1851, a well-trained experimental scientist, was elected FRS in 1852, and performed distinguished work in magnetism which met with the approval of **MICHAEL FARADAY**, who supported his appointment in 1853 as professor of natural science at the Royal Institution. Tyndall's work on the absorption of radiant heat by water vapour constituted the first experimental proof of the suspected atmospheric "Greenhouse Effect". In his addresses and essays *Fragments of Science* (1871) he was a voice for rationality in an era of supernaturalism. A enthusiastic mountaineer, Tyndall made the first ascent of the Weisshorn and contributed to *Glaciers of the Alps*, published in 1860. He died of an overdose of the sleeping draught chloral hydrate administered by his wife – but mistakenly, it seems. (MW)

U

[936] UPCHER'S WARBLER

In the world of the twitcher, it is the warblers that separate the men from the boys. There are some sixty species of Old World warblers, and the differences in outward appearance between species are in many cases almost invisible. **UPCHER'S WARBLER** (*Hippolais languida*) breeds in semi-desert regions from Turkey and the Eastern Mediterranean to Pakistan. It was described in 1864 by Henry Baker Tristram (1822-1906), traveller and naturalist, and a canon of Durham Cathedral. He named it *Hippolais upcheri* in honour of his friend **HENRY MORRIS UPCHER**, and though *upcheri* has since become *languida*, Upcher's is still the accepted common name. Tristram's published works include *The natural history of the Bible* (1867) and *The flora and fauna of Palestine* (1884).

[937] URANIUM – see THORIUM

[938] URANUS

The planet **URANUS**, third largest planet in the Solar System and named after the sky god of the Greeks, was discovered in 1781 by **WILLIAM HERSCHEL** (1738-1822), a German immigrant who at the time was earning his living as a musician and music teacher in Bath and in his spare time pursuing, with the aid of his sister Caroline* and his own home-made telescopes, a passion for astronomy. Herschel was not at first sure what he had discovered. The idea of a new planet was so far from anyone's mind that Herschel originally assumed that he had spotted a comet. But calculation of its orbit made it impossible that it could be anything but a planet. The discovery caused immense excitement in scientific circles, tempered by the difficult mental adjustment to a sudden doubling in size of the solar system (Uranus being twice as far from the Sun as is Saturn). The question arose: What to name it? Herschel, backed by **JOSEPH BANKS** as President of the Royal Society, favoured *Georgium Sidus* (**GEORGE'S STAR**) in honour of his fellow-Hanoverian George III. The French, generously, suggested naming it after Herschel himself. It was left to the German astronomer **CARL BODE** (1747-1826) to make the logical suggestion of *Uranus*, thereby incorporating it into the planetary family of Greco-Roman deities. Remarkably, and to Bode's (one supposes) delight, the distance of Uranus from the sun fitted the formula which is the basis of **BODE'S LAW**, though the next planet to be discovered (Neptune, 1846) unkindly threw a spanner in the works. Uranus has the peculiarity that its axis of rotation lies almost in the same plane as its orbit. In other words, it is rolling round the Sun on its side. Each circuit of the Sun takes 84 years. This means that Uranus has not yet been scrutinised by modern instruments for the whole of a Uranian year and, as a result, much remains to be learned about its seasonal variations and their causes.

* **CAROLINE HERSCHEL** (1750-1848), trained by her brother in his rigorous observational technique, established in later life a solid reputation among Europe's scientific community as an astronomer in her own right. She was responsible for the discovery of no fewer than 8 comets, she revised and updated Flamsteed's star catalogue, and published *A catalogue of the Nebulae* which included no fewer than 17 of which she was herself the discoverer. She more than earned her place in that special galaxy of female scientific luminaries of the period alongside such figures as the mathematician Ada Lovelace (see **BABBAGE** and **ADA**) and **MARY SOMERVILLE**.

[939] UREY-MILLER EXPERIMENT

The origin of life on Earth is an interesting question, except to those unfortunate believers in the literal truth of Genesis, who are convinced of God's act of creation in 4004 BC.* The **UREY-MILLER EXPERIMENT** of 1952 was designed to test the 1920s hypothesis of Alexandr Oparin and J.B.S. Haldane that organic compounds could have been synthesised from inorganic precursors in the likely conditions prevailing on early Planet Earth: the experimenters mixed together the gases thought to constitute Earth's reducing atmosphere about 4 billion years ago – methane, ammonia, and hydrogen – over circulating water vapour; they also passed electric sparks through it to simulate lightning. Although nothing actually crawled out of the "primordial slime" left in their flasks, they did reap a rich harvest of complex organic molecules in the resulting brew – a broth of amino acids, sugars, nucleotides like adenine, and lipids – providing many of the molecular building blocks needed to make a living cell. And that took only a week, in a flask. Given half a billion years and all the waters of Planet Earth, it's not so surprising that a primitive cell arose spontaneously and multiplied: following that, it was uphill all the way with **DARWINISM,** given the occasional meteoritic hiatus which switched the flow of mainstream evolution. Against this plausible scenario, the Creationists' standard argument is the improbability of a tornado sweeping through a junkyard causing the accidental assembly of a Boeing 747. False analogy! As every chemist knows, chemistry isn't random. It's perfectly within the Laws of Thermodynamics, and the specificity of chemical reactions, that complex molecules are favoured for "spontaneous self-assembly" from simpler precursors. Leave the Creationists to their junkyard. In the real world, beautiful complexity is emerging all the time. American physical chemist **HAROLD UREY** (1893-1981) was born in Walkerton, Indiana, graduated at Montana, and obtained his Ph.D. under **G.N. LEWIS** at Berkeley, California. He worked with **BOHR** in Copenhagen, then became professor of chemistry at Columbia, where he made his most notable discovery in 1931, the heavy isotope of hydrogen, deuterium, and received the Nobel prize for chemistry in 1934. Urey's team contributed to the study of isotope separation for the Manhattan Project. Post-war he held chairs at Chicago (1945-52) and later at San Diego, California. American chemist, **STANLEY LLOYD MILLER** (1930-2007) was born in Oakland, California, where he graduated at the University. He performed his famous experiment in 1952 while a Ph.D. student of Urey's at the University of Chicago. He then returned to an academic career in California, devoting much of his research to elaborations of his experiment, with different starting materials and conditions. Despite this initial success in tackling the question, the precise mechanism for the origin of life presently remains obscure. (MW)

* This must have come as quite a surprise to the Sumerians, who were busy building a civilization at the time.

[940] UVAROVITE – see SCHEELITE

[941] UZI

"**UZI**" was the nickname of **UZIEL GAL** (1923-2003) born **GOTTHARD GLASS** in Weimar, Germany. The machine gun he invented bears his name, though against his wishes. His weapon design, which has gone through many iterations since its inception in 1951, proved to be robust, cheap to manufacture, safe and easy-to-use, being capable of firing 600 rounds/minute full-auto in single-handed operation. The Mini-UZI is capable of firing at approximately 16 rounds/second; whilst the Micro-UZI is a semi-automatic pistol which at 1250 rounds/minute will empty its 20-round mgazine in under one second and is normally set to operate in semi-automatic mode only. UZIs in their various guises are estimated to have earned over \$2 billion for Israeli coffers – possibly assisted by product placement in a number of films and by the attempted assassination of Ronald Reagan on 30 March 1981. Film-goers will not fail to have noted that the Hollywood version of the UZI is apparently capable of continuous firing for minutes at a time and only runs out of ammo when the plot requires it. (GJ)

V

[942] VALLETTA

The capital of Malta commemorates its founder JEHAN PARISOT DE LA VALETTE (1494-1568), Grand Master of the military-religious order known as the Knights of Saint John or Knights Hospitallers. The knights had been successively expelled from Jerusalem, where the order was founded in 1099 for the care and protection of Christian pilgrims, and in 1522 from Rhodes, where they had subsequently made their headquarters. This brought them to Malta in 1530. Here in 1565, under La Valette's leadership, and although outnumbered by five or six to one, they defended the island against a Turkish invading force in an action which unquestionably deserves the title "heroic". The defenders came from all over Europe to rally round their chief, though only one English Knight was present, Oliver Starkey. When the Turks eventually lifted the siege and departed, La Valette signified the Order's intention to stay put by commencing the building of the town which is today Valletta. The Knights governed the island until once more displaced, this time by the arch-upsetter Napoleon in 1798. An eyewitness account of La Valette's defence published in 1568 by Francisco Balbi di Correggio, an Italian soldier of fortune who took part in the fighting, has been published in an English version by historian Ernle Bradford, who also authored the standard modern account *Malta – the Great Siege* (1961). A second heroic defence of Malta, this time against the German air force in WWII, earned the entire island the award of the George Cross, the highest civilian award for valour.

[943] VAN ALLEN BELTS

Two areas with a high density of energetic particles emanating from the "solar wind" which are trapped by the earth's magnetic field and which encircle the planet above the equator, one at a height of 1,000-5,000 km and the second at around 20,000 km. They were discovered by, and named after, American physicist JAMES ALFRED VAN ALLEN (1914-2006), war-time inventor of the proximity fuse for anti-aircraft artillery. After the war, Van Allen, who had a long-standing interest in cosmic ray research, was involved in research into the upper atmosphere and beyond, using at first German V-2 rockets surplus to military requirements following the end of hostilities.

[944] VAN DE GRAAFF GENERATOR

A machine for producing huge charges of static electricity: it consists of a vertical insulating tower containing a motorized continuous rubber belt, brushed to produce an electrostatic charge which accumulates on a hollow metal sphere topping the whole apparatus. The potential builds up to several million volts, and its discharge is used for studies of artificial lightning and atom-smashing by particle accelerators. **ROBERT JEMISON VAN DE GRAAFF** (1901-1967) was an American physicist born in Tuscaloosa, Alabama, of Dutch descent. He took his DPhil at Oxford in 1928, and went on to chairs at Princeton, where he developed his first high voltage generator in 1929, and MIT in 1931 where he remained until 1960. **VAN DER GRAAF GENERATOR** is a deviant spelling of this title signifying something completely different: a progressive English rock band formed in 1967 at the University of Manchester (where the Physics Department has a **VAN DE GRAAFF GENERATOR.**) It is believed that the misspelling was accidental. (MW)

[945] VAN DER WAALS EQUATION

This is a refinement of the simple equations governing "perfect" gases (see **BOYLE'S LAW** and **CHARLES'S LAW**) in an attempt to describe the pressure/volume/temperature relationships of real gases, whose behaviour is always "non-ideal" or "imperfect". **VAN DER WAALS EQUATION** provides what the physical chemist calls "an equation of state" for gases and liquids: it takes account of the weak attractive forces between molecules – called **VAN DER WAALS FORCES** – and the fact that molecules must occupy a finite volume, so fluids are not infinitely compressible (*i.e.* a molecule has a **VAN DER WAALS RADIUS**). Without such forces, gases would never liquefy or solidify. The man whose name has been attached to these important physico-chemical concepts was the Dutch physicist **JOHANNES DIDERIK VAN DER WAALS** (1837-1923), who put forward his eponymous equation in 1873 in his doctoral thesis at the University of Leiden. He subsequently became professor at the new University of Amsterdam in 1877, and received the **NOBEL PRIZE** for physics in 1910. (MW)

[946] VAN DIEMEN'S LAND

The former name of Tasmania, given it in 1642 by its Dutch discoverer Abel Jans Tasman (1603-c.1659) in honour of his patron, the Dutch governor general of Batavia (Dutch East Indies), **ANTHONY VAN DIEMEN** (1593-1645). Following bankruptcy as an Amsterdam businessman, van Diemen had gone to the Netherlands East Indies in 1618 in the employ of the Dutch East India Company (*Vereenigde Oost-Indische Compagnie* or V.O.C.) but under the assumed name of Thonis Meeuwisz of Utrecht, to bypass the rules against employing bankrupts. He then rose through the ranks and as Governor General oversaw the Company's period of greatest expansion taking in Malacca, part of Ceylon, and Formosa. Tasman explored the Indian Ocean, the waters around Australia, and New

Zealand, and in 1643 Tonga and Fiji. The island which bears his name was discovered by Tasman in 1642 and was visited by Capt. Cook in 1777. (Though Tasman and earlier Dutch navigators like Jacobsen and Houtman had partially elucidated the shape of the Australian continent, it was left to Cook to finally ascertain that it was not part of a larger landmass which early geographers had supposed must exist in the southern hemisphere to balance the continents of the north.) The island was used as a penal colony between 1803-53, and was then renamed after its discoverer in order to rid it of dark associations with bushrangers, convicts and the evils of forced transportation. It became a state of the British Commonwealth in 1901. The last of its Tasmanian aborigines died in 1876, hunted to extinction. The name VAN DIEMEN'S LAND lives on in folk song (see, for example, the versions by Shirley Collins or Steeleye Span) and in many literary references. Tasmania boasts two carnivorous marsupials: the so-called Tasmanian Devil (*Sarcophilus harrisi*) and the nearly-extinct Thylacine or Tasmanian Tiger (*Thylacinus cynocephalus*). (RS)

[947] VAN DYKE BROWN

This rather grungy artists' colour is derived from natural sources as a somewhat variable mix containing the minerals, haematite (iron(III) oxide), pyrolusite (manganese dioxide) and lignite (fossilized humic acid) in various proportions. The pigment is named after the celebrated Flemish master SIR ANTHONY VAN DYCK (1599-1641) who was born in Antwerp. His precocious talent soon made him assistant to Peter Paul Rubens. On a brief visit to England he executed a portrait of James I. After six years in Italy (1621-27) painting religious subjects, he returned to Antwerp, then to England in 1632 to be knighted by Charles I, becoming "painter-in-ordinary". His flair for subtly flattering the character of his courtly sitters set the tone of British portraiture for the next 150 years. VAN DYKE BROWN is also the name of an alternative photographic printing process based on the light sensitivity of ammonium iron(III) citrate. Plain artists' paper is hand-coated with a solution of this salt mixed with silver nitrate and tartaric acid: exposure to UV-containing light through a negative causes photo-reduction of the iron(III) to iron(II), which then reduces the silver salt to finely-divided silver metal, which constitutes the final brown image of nanoparticle silver. The print is washed in water to remove excess chemicals. This process was re-discovered in the 1890s but originates from one called *argentotype* in 1842 by its inventor, SIR JOHN HERSCHEL. A latter-day improved version (1991) by the present author is called *argyrotype*. (MW)

[948] VANADIUM, NIOBIUM, TANTALUM

A number of the chemical elements in the Periodic Table are named after gods and goddesses of classical mythology – Greek, Roman, and Norse (since the Scandinavian countries have produced some very distinguished chemists). The claims for precedence over these chemical discoveries often prove as contentious as the doings of the gods they celebrate. VANADIUM, having atomic number 23 and symbol V, was first discovered in 1801 by Spanish mineralogist Andrés Manuel del Rio (1764-1849), while working in Mexico City. He named it *erythronium*. Mistakenly, he was persuaded to withdraw his claim, allowing the element to be rediscovered in 1831 by Swedish chemist Nils Gabriel Selfström (1787-1845). The richness and variety of colours displayed by its compounds led him to name it after VANADIS, the old Norse name for the goddess of beauty, Freyja, (who gives us Friday), the wife of Odin, finally deserted by her consort because she loved finery better than she loved him. VANADIUM is used as a steel additive, and its pentoxide is an important catalyst. The humble sea squirt *ascidium* owes its existence to vanadium as the respiratory oxygen-carrier in its blood, instead of Dame Nature's usual metal, iron. Vanadium's confusing congeners in Group 5a of the transition metal block of the Periodic Table are, appropriately, NIOBIUM and TANTALUM. NIOBIUM has atomic number 41, symbol Nb, and was identified in 1801 as a new element by English chemist Charles Hatchett (1765-1847) in a mineral, columbite, sent to the British Museum in 1753 (the year of its establishment) by John Winthrop (1714-1779), American astronomer, physicist and mathematician. This origin explains Hatchett's original naming of the new element *columbium*, symbol Cb, after the alternative name for America: Columbia. However, the element was – due to chemical confusion with similar members of its group – "rediscovered" in 1844 by German chemist, Heinrich Rose (1795-1864), who proposed the classical name of NIOBIUM. The mortal daughter of TANTALUS (see below), the unfortunate NIOBE, had fourteen children who were all slaughtered by jealous gods, who then transmogrified the weeping NIOBE into a stone waterfall. Following a century of wrangling, the International Union of Pure and Applied Chemistry in 1950 finally came down in favour of niobium in preference to columbium. The metal is used as an alloying agent in steels and non-ferrous metals and American manufacturers and metallurgists (not chemists) still call it columbium. TANTALUM, atomic number 73, symbol Ta, was discovered in 1802 by another Swedish chemist, Anders Gustav Ekeberg (1767-1813), but the metal was not produced until 1903: it is hard, dense, and refractory, with wide industrial uses. Because it is non-irritant to the human system and immune to attack, even by bodily fluids, it now finds important applications for surgically-implanted devices. TANTALUS, the mythical King of Phrygia, was a son of Zeus and a wealthy nymph. He unwisely stole ambrosia from Olympus and revealed the secrets of the gods to men, so was condemned to stand up to his chin in water which, whenever he attempted to drink it, receded – whence our verb *tantalise*. Ekeberg saw this, apparently, as an allusion to the reluctance of tantalum to dissolve in acids. The CUP OF TANTALUS, possibly invented by PYTHAGORAS, may

be bought in any tourist shop on the Greek island of Samos. If over-generously
filled, it swiftly syphons its contents onto the floor – a sure winner at parties.
(MW)

[949] VARROA

VARROA DESTRUCTOR is a mite that lives parasitically on the haemolymph (*i.e.* what
passes for blood) of the honey bee *Apis mellifera*. It attacks larva, pupa and adult
bee indiscriminately and, living up to its name, can bring about the total destruction
of an entire host colony. It is thought to have originated in Japan and Korea but
has recently spread world-wide and constitutes a serious economic danger since
we depend on bees not only for honey but also for the indispensable function of
pollinating our other food crops. It borrows its name from the Roman polymath
MARCUS TERENTIUS VARRO (116-27 BC). Varro, considered the most learned
Roman of his day, was involved in – and survived – the bloody chaos that marked
the end of the Roman republic. Of his published writings, however, little has
survived, the main exception being his *De re rustica*, a treatise on agriculture and
country living.* Varro is credited in some quarters with having prefigured the
germ theory of disease-causation as he warns against frequenting marshy places
where a person may be invaded by invisibly small creatures which will make him
ill. As with all such instances of apparent scientific clairvoyance, what is – or
rather would be – interesting about this statement is not the fact of his having said
it, but his reasons for doing so. In other words, are we looking at a rational if
precocious hypothesis or a lucky guess?

* Fragments of his work on the Latin language have also come down to us. In them we find the first
known use of the word "vernacular", which Varro defines as "the language of slaves and peasants".
(Graves and Hodge *The Reader over your Shoulder* 1944.)

[950] VAUCANSON'S DUCK

JACQUES VAUCANSON (1709-1778) was born into a poor family in Grenoble and
studied for the priesthood. During his novitiate he amused himself by constructing
mechanical automata which he imprudently showed to a passing dignitary of his
Order and, as a result, was promptly shown the door after being ordered to
destroy his creations. He made his way to Paris where he found wealthy patrons
and was able to pursue his interests in anatomy and mechanical engineering. The
exhibition of his uncannily lifelike robotic androids "The flute player" and the
"The Provençal shepherd" brought him to public notice, and in 1740 he was given
the post of Inspector of Manufactures with the mission to effect the technical
improvement of the French silk industry. This led to the creation of the first fully
automated loom,* later perfected by **JACQUARD** , as well as pioneering work in the
design of machine tools. In 1746 he was admitted to the *Académie des Sciences* and

added a "*de*" to his name. He continued to work at improving the mechanisation of industrial processes until his death at Grenoble as the result of injuries caused by a fall. Though not the most useful of Vaucanson's inventions, probably the best known is his **DIGESTING DUCK** (a.k.a. **DEFECATING DUCK**), exhibited in 1739. This extraordinary creation was designed to mimic as accurately as possible the anatomy and physiology of a living creature. It was equipped with a beating heart and was able to quack, flap its wings, walk, take in food, digest it, pass it through its intestines, and expel the waste through an anal sphincter. (The digestion process was actually a fudge. The grain it ate remained in the stomach and the waste consisted of pre-prepared pellets of supposedly fecal matter.) All the internal processes were visible through a window in the side of the machine. Unfortunately for posterity, Vaucanson sold all his automata in 1743 and none have survived, though a reconstructed version of his loom can be seen in the Paris *Conservatoire National des Arts et Métiers*, and a replica of the duck, constructed by a clockmaker of Chambéry, is on display in the *Musée des Automates* in Grenoble. (See also **MASON-DIXON LINE**).

[951] VENN DIAGRAM

A means of illustrating in graphic form through intersecting geometric shapes (usually circles or ovals) the relationships (in terms of shared or differing characteristics) between members of different sets or categories. The method can be useful in a wide variety of disciplines, but mainly in the realms of mathematics, statistics and logic. It is named after **JOHN VENN** (1834-1923) who taught logic at Cambridge from 1862 to 1892, though a similar technique had been used by both Leibniz and **EULER**. Venn was an ordained clergyman but in 1883 he renounced his preferment under the provisions of the 1870 Clerical Disabilities Act on grounds of conscience. In the same year he was made a Fellow of the Royal Society. His works include *The logic of chance* (1866) and *Symbolic logic* (1881), as well as works on the history of the University. Venn was a noted hill-climber, botanist and amateur engineer (he designed and built an effective machine for bowling cricket balls). A memorial stained-glass window in the Hall of Gonville and Caius College, of which Venn was a Fellow, features three coloured circles arranged as a Venn Diagram.

[952] VENTURI EFFECT

A physical observation of fluid (*i.e.* gas or liquid) flow through a constricted region of a tube, in which the pressure exerted by the fluid is found to be *less* than that in the wider region. This somewhat counter-intuitive finding can be explained by Bernouilli's principle which derives from the law of conservation of energy. A **VENTURI PUMP** is a laboratory filter pump, producing a vacuum by the flow of water. Application of the **VENTURI EFFECT** is encountered domestically in "atomizer" sprays to disperse perfume, deodorant, or paint. **GIOVANNI BATTISTA VENTURI** (1746-1822) was born in Bibbiano, Italy, and trained as a priest but – to the enduring benefit of humanity – instead became professor of geometry and philosophy in 1774, then of physics in 1776, at the University of Modena. Something of an *uomo universale* himself, Giambattista deserves great credit for his recognition of the then little-known manuscript scientific works of **LEONARDO DA VINCI** and their compilation in his publication of 1797, *Essai sur les ouvrages physico-mathématiques de Léonard da Vinci.* (MW)

[953] VERNIER SCALE

Before the digitronic revolution provided us with numerical displays on every conceivable item of measuring equipment, *real* scientists, engineeers, surveyors, and navigators had to read the finely-divided scales calibrating their various instruments with a precision limited by their visual acuity and the spacing of the engraved subdivisions. The supplementary **VERNIER SCALE,** invented in 1631, was arranged to slide parallel to the main scale and was so graduated as to enable an extra significant figure to be read off in measuring the basic unit (inch, centimetre, degree, etc.). This ultimately improved the precision by a factor of ten in all manner of instruments: navigational quadrants, sextants, theodolites, barometers, callipers, spectroscopes, *etc.* **PIERRE VERNIER** (1584-1638) was a French instrument-maker and military engineer, born and bred in Ornans near Besançon in Franche-Comté, where he commanded the Castle until the end of his life. In 1631 he published the description of his new measuring device in a work entitled *Construction, usage et propriétés du quadrant nouveau de mathématiques.* For over a century following, however, Vernier's invention was still referred to as a **NONIUS**, after Portugese mathematician **PETER NONIUS** (1502-1578), or Pedro Nuñez, Cosmographer Royal to King John III of Portugal, who had previously devised an improved, but more cumbersome, quadrant in 1542. The name of **VERNIER** was rescued from anonymity, for posterity and for France, by astronomer Joseph Jérôme Le Français de Lalande (1732-1807) in his *Traité d'astronomie* of 1764. (MW)

[954] VERY PISTOL

EDWARD WILSON VERY (1847-1910) was not the inventor of the **VERY PISTOL:** he actually invented in 1877 the signalling flares (**VERY LIGHTS**) which had a major impact on night-signalling, initially in the American Navy (in which he served from 1867 to 1885 as an ordnance expert, finally making Admiral). A wide variety of applications for his coloured flares was opened up by projecting them from a hand-held pistol, which Very adopted from original designs of Benjamin Franklin

Coston and his son, whose ideas were discredited through the lobbying of a jealous Mrs Coston (wife & mother), thus enabling Very to get the credit for the whole package. (GJ)

[955] VESTA
An early name for a small match of wood or wax tipped with an incendiary mixture which could be ignited by friction on any abrasive surface: "strike anywhere" matches were also known as LUCIFERS and CONGREVES, representing an improvement on DOBEREINER'S LAMP (*q.v.*) to light your fag.* The original wax-stemmed VESTA was invented and patented by William Newton in 1832. The best-selling commercial brand SWAN VESTAS are still a household item today. VESTA, daughter of SATURN, was the Roman goddess of the hearth and household. She was worshipped at a round temple in the Forum containing, instead of a statue, a constantly burning fire; her shrine was tended by the six VESTAL VIRGINS – a role with an appointment for 30 years. Any Vestal discovered to be unchaste was entombed alive. The name of VESTA was also taken in 1807 for the brightest of the asteroids, a 500 km chunk of basaltic rock (see DIOGENITE), discovered by HEINRICH WILHELM OLBERS, the fourth asteroid to be found after CERES (see CERIUM), PALLAS and JUNO. The first twenty or so asteroids were dignified with the names of female goddesses of the Greek and Roman pantheon, but subsequently their number outgrew the capacity of classical celestial nomenclature, with the consequence that recent discoveries have descended to *Mr Spock* and *James Bond* (see also SPARRMANNIA). (MW)

* NB, American speakers: this is British slang for "cigarette".

[956] VICKERS HARDNESS SCALE – See BRINNELL SCALE

[957] VICTORIA
'Twere tedious to enumerate every entity named in honour of the Widow of Windsor, but in the interests of fair play we might consider a representative sample. Ignoring several thousand "Queen Vic" pubs and assorted tracts of Canada and Australia, let's start with that splendid confection the VICTORIA SPONGE. The ingredients, (flour, butter, sugar and eggs) are those of the basic sponge recipe. The Victoria is distinguished from other sponge cakes merely by the absence of icing and its filling of jam and cream. It owes its name to nothing more substantial than the fact that Our Dear Queen fancied (they say) a bit of sponge cake with her tea. LAKE VICTORIA, on the other hand, one of the world's largest bodies of fresh water, is a geographical feature of major historical importance thanks to the part it played in the search for the sources of the Nile, and its concomitant, the colonisation of Central and East Africa. It owes its name to the first European to visit it, John Hanning Speke (1827-1864). It is now shared

roughly half-and-half between Tanzania and Uganda, with a little corner allotted to Kenya. Moving south on the map, we come to the VICTORIA FALLS, "discovered"* and named by David Livingstone in 1855. Their importance is mainly scenic, though as a barrier to navigation it is the largest of its kind anywhere in the world. Size is also a factor in the case of the VICTORIA WATER-LILY, native to the Amazon, which has floating leaves up to 3 metres in diameter. Its orginal name *Victoria regia* has now been superseded by the appellation *Victoria amazonica*. And last, as a nod to the carriage-trade, we have THE VICTORIA, an elegant 4-wheeled conveyance of French design introduced into this country in the 1860's and re-named after you-know-who.

* Note the quotation marks, pretty much *de rigueur* these days.

[958] VIRGILIAN METRE

The metric form chosen by the Latin poet PUBLIUS VIRGILIUS MARO (70-19 BC) for the *Aeneid*, his epic poem about the founding of Rome, was the dactylic hexameter, the usual choice for heroic poetry in both Greek and Latin. A hexameter is a line containing six feet (a "foot" being roughly equivalent to a "bar" in music). The dactylic foot, from the Greek δάκτυλος meaning "finger", is composed of a long syllable followed by two short syllables (or in English, where it is accentuation not length that counts, a stressed syllable followed by two unstressed syllables). Feet consisting of two long/stressed syllables and known as "spondees" are counted as having the same value as a dactyl. Thus the line of doggerel that English schoolboys used to learn to represent the Virgilian hexameter was:

> 1   2   3   4   5   6
> *Down in a/ deep dark/ hole sat an/ old cow/ munching a /beanstalk*

In English verse, the more usual choice for heroic poetry is the iambic pentameter, a five-foot line in which each foot consists of a short/unstressed syllable followed by a long/stressed syllable. Thus Milton in *Paradise lost*:

> *Of Man's first disobedience and the fruit*
> *Of that forbidden tree whose mortal taste*
> *Brought death into the world....*

Or Pope in his mock epic *The rape of the lock*:

> *And now, unveil'd, the toilet stands display'd,*
> *Each silver vase in mystic order laid.*

This was also the metre preferred by Shakespeare for his plays:

> *And all our yesterdays have lighted fools*
> *The way to dusty death....*

(See also **ALEXANDRINE**)

[959] VITRUVIAN MAN

The famous drawing *Demonstration of the Geometrical Design of the Human Body, based on Vitruvius* by **LEONARDO DA VINCI** (1452-1519) is now in the *Accademia*, Venice. An adult male stands with arms outstretched horizontally to fit into a square which he just touches with fingertips, feet and head; overlaid is the same figure in a spread-eagled posture, legs astride and arms raised, inscribed in a circle centred on the man's navel. This conformity of ideal human proportions with basic geometric figures was first described by the most authoritative classical source on architectural design, **MARCUS VITRUVIUS POLLIO** (*ca.*80–*ca.*15 BC), a Roman architect and military engineer, in the service of Emperor Augustus, specialising in projectile weapons such as the ballista. He authored the ten volume work *De Architectura* (*ca.* 27 BC) which comprises the only surviving record of the architecture of clasical antiquity and greatly influenced Renaissance architects, *e.g.* Alberti, Palladio, and evidently, Leonardo. (MW)

[960] VOLCKRINGER PATTERNS

When botanical specimens are pressed between paper sheets for a time, they sometimes impart a sepia stain to the paper, rendering an image of the plant outline and some internal detail. These **VOLCKRINGER PATTERNS** resemble photograms made by contact-printing. The stain is thought to be due to acids exuded by plant decay causing degradation of the cellulose or lignin in the paper. The phenomenon has been likened to that seen on the egregious Shroud of Turin, by French pharmacist **Dr. JEAN VOLCKRINGER,** who published this explanation for the Shroud's image in 1942, supposing lactic acid in human sweat to be the cause. One of the several rival camps of sindonology still upholds this view, whilst another argues, less plausibly, that the Shroud bears a photographic self-portrait by **LEONARDO DA VINCI.** Who really cares how it was faked? The Shroud has always been, and remains, a reliable money-spinner for the Church. (MW)

[961] VOLT

COUNT ALESSANDRO GIUSEPPE ANASTASIO VOLTA (1745-1827) was born in Como, Italy, and became professor of natural philosophy at Pavia from 1774-1804.

Having contributed to the study of static electricity by the invention of the electrophorus and the electroscope, his greatest achievement was the invention of the electric battery. Called **VOLTA'S PILE**, it consisted of a column of alternating metallic discs of zinc and silver, interspersed by cloths dampened with a saline solution. This provided a consistent flow of electricity, in contrast to the sudden jolts delivered by electrostatic machines, enabling Volta to develop the theory of current electricity – then called **VOLTAIC ELECTRICITY** or **VOLTAISM**. He used his battery to discover the electrolysis of water – its decomposition into hydrogen and oxygen gases (see **DAVY** and **FARADAY**). The **VOLT** is the SI unit of electrical potential difference (see **AMPÈRE, COULOMB,** and **OHM**): one volt represents a potential energy of one **JOULE** per **COULOMB** of charge. (MW)

[962] VON THÜNEN'S ISOLATED STATE

JOHANN HEINRICH VON THÜNEN (1783-1850) was a mathematically-minded North German landowner with an estate at Tellow in Mecklenburg, who made an important contribution to economic theory by his successful search for a rational method of determining land-values, or what he called "locational rent". He achieved this by means of what today would be called a thought experiment, which he published in 1826 in a work entitled *The isolated state*. The "state" in question was actually an idealised and deliberately over-simplified model of the relations between a city (the market) and the agricultural enterprises which sustain it. The basis of the model was the removal from it of all variables except distance. He imagined a region with the city at its centre surrounded by agricultural land of equal productivity in every part and itself surrounded by wilderness which precluded contact with any other region. There were no geographical features, and no roads. In diagrammatic form this resulted in a figure resembling an archery target, a series of concentric rings around the city. The first ring was devoted to dairying and market gardening, whose products being perishable needed to be nearest to the market. Next came woodland, supplying timber and fuel, crops that are heavy and bulky and whose transport cost would therefore be high (Von Thünen's Germany was then still in a pre-industrial age when wood was the main fuel). Beyond the woodland zone was an extensive region producing grain and other field crops. The outermost ring was devoted to raising sheep and cattle, which could reach the market under their own power. Beyond that again, nothing but wilderness. The model also presupposed (like modern Games Theory) an ability and a willingness on the part of the "players" to make rational calculations – in this case as to the profitability of a given crop at a given distance from the city. Von Thünen was then able to show that correct answers could be obtained by the application of a simple formula: $R = Y(P-C) - YDT$ where R is the rentable value of the land, Y is yield per unit of area, P the market price of the crop, C the farmer's production costs, D distance from the market, and T the transport cost.

In simple terms, the formula shows that, as profitability decreases with distance from the market, land values fall *pari passu*. It shows, in other words, the point at which profitability becomes marginal. Von Thünen's model can be applied, with suitable adjustment, to individual farms, since no farmer would have any difficulty in recognising that the value of any given piece of his land will vary with distance from the farmstead, taking into account the number of times it needs to be visited. In later life, Von Thünen turned his attention to a theory of wages, the results of which were published in 1850.

[963] VRIESIA
A genus of 190 species of bromeliads, native to the Caribbean and the tropical regions of South and Central America. Named after the Dutch botanist and physician **WILLEM HENDRIK DE VRIESE** (1806-1862). They require high temperature and high humidity and are grown in this country only as hothouse plants.

[964] VULCANISATION
Name given to a technique discovered in 1840 by American inventor Charles Goodyear (1800-1860) for hardening raw rubber by heating it with sulphur. The resultant material retains the resilience of rubber but without the tackiness which otherwise limits its utility. The name derives from the Roman god **VULCAN**, the lame husband of Venus and counterpart of the Greek god Hephaistos who presided over metal-working (and, of course, volcanoes) and who should also be the god of medical prosthetics since, following a spat with Zeus, Hephaistos was heaved bodily out of Olympus and landed on the island of Lemnos, breaking both his legs in the fall. After this he could only get about on special golden leg-supports he designed, made and fitted himself. The name has also been more recently given to a number of entities including the **AVRO VULCAN** delta-winged bomber in service with the RAF from 1953 to 1984, and to the planet **VULCAN** hypothesised to exist between Mercury and the Sun by the French mathematician Urbain Le Verrier in 1859 to account for perturbations in the orbit of Mercury. He was wrong about this but he correctly predicted the existence of the planet Neptune. (For rubber, see also **DUNLOP TYRE, PLIMSOLL, WELLINGTON BOOT.**)

W

[965] WADE BRIDGE

The town of Wadebridge in Cornwall derives its name from the Anglo-Saxon word *ge-wæd* (ford), plus the later addition of *brycg* (bridge) – presumably a later addition to the town's civic amenities. Scotland, however, has some 40 "Wade bridges" which derive their title from an entirely different source – the activities of GENERAL GEORGE WADE (1673-1748), English soldier and military engineer who between 1726 and 1737 planned and built a 250-mile network of roads connecting Lowland Scotland with the Eastern and Central Highlands. These roads, essentially military in intention (they were put to good use by both sides in the 1745 uprising), were the first properly engineered and metalled roads to be constructed anywhere in Britain since the Roman conquest some seventeen hundred years earlier. Of the bridges which formed an essential element in Wade's road system, the most famous is the beautiful bridge at Aberfeldy. Designed by William Adam*, it was begun and finished in a single year, and was the first bridge over the Tay, Scotland's longest river. Wade was largely responsible for a moderate and sensible pacification policy following the suppression of the 1715 rebellion. Among other measures, he instituted local militias or "watches" of loyal Highlanders, and these companies were later formed into a regiment, the Black Watch. The importance of the part played by the warlike talents of the Highlanders in Britain's subsequent military history can hardly be over-stressed.

* William Adam (1689-1748), Scotland's leading architect of the period and father of architects John, Robert and James and so of the "Adam style".

[966] WADE-GILES TRANSLITERATION

A recent book* on Chinese maritime explorations in the fifteenth century gets through 649 pages without once mentioning the name of the famous Chinese admiral Cheng Ho, the guiding spirit of the entire enterprise. It does, however, have quite a lot to say about the achievements of one Zheng He, who turns out to be the same bloke under what looks at first sight like a pseudonym. The explanation (which also explains why, for instance, Pekin has suddenly become Beijing) lies in the change from the previously standard Wade-Giles system for romanising Mandarin Chinese script to the (new! improved!) Hanyu Pinyin system adopted in 1979 by the Chinese People's Republic and subsequently by the International Organisation for Standardisation (ISO-7089-1991). Wade-Giles was the joint creation of two British scholars **Sir THOMAS WADE** (1818-1895) and

HERBERT ALLEN GILES (1845-1935). Wade, a former diplomat, was professor of Chinese at Cambridge, and Giles, also of the diplomatic service, succeeded him in the chair. The romanisation system which bears their joint names was originally developed by Wade and revised by Giles. It is still in use in Taiwan.

* Gavin Menzies *1421: the year China discovered the world* 2002.

[967] WALDO

Though it appears not to have achieved general currency, the term **WALDO** is found in science fiction of the fifties and sixties to describe remote-controlled or prosthetic mechanical manipulators and force-multipliers. It derives from the name **WALDO FARTHINGWAITE-JONES,** the title character of a 1942 story by **ROBERT HEINLEIN** (1907-1988) about a man born severely physically disabled who overcomes his disability by the application of his own genius for mechanical invention. Heinlein's imaginative creation preceded by some years the real-life design and construction of devices such as he had described. The ultimate fictional waldo might be the cargo-handling machine into which Sigourney Weaver inserts herself in order to battle the monster in the 1979 film *Alien*. (For Heinlein, see also **MURPHY'S LAW**.)

[968] WALDORF SCHOOLS – See STEINER SCHOOLS and ASTORIA

[969] WALDSEEMÜLLER MAP

The German geographer and cartographer **MARTIN WALDSEEMÜLLER*** (1470-1521) was born at Radolfzell in Baden. He worked with a group of geographers and scholars at Saint-Dié near Strasbourg, collating the results of new discoveries and explorations and integrating them with the maps derived from the work of Alexandrian astronomer and geographer **PTOLEMY****, the accepted authority on the shape of the world since the publication of his *Geography* in 150 AD. In 1507, Waldseemüller created a world map in 12 large sheets (together they measure 4 ½ x 8 feet), printed from woodcuts, which is remarkable for two unique features: it is the first known map to show an ocean separating America from Asia; and it is the first map on which **AMERICA** is so-named – in honour, as Waldseemüller stated, of the Florentine **AMERIGO VESPUCCI** (1454-1512), whose four voyages elicited the shape of South America's eastern seabord from the Caribbean to the Straits of Magellan. A thousand copies of the map were printed but only one complete copy survives. This was recently purchased from its owner, a German princeling, by the Library of Congress, where it is on permanent display. Waldseemüller contributed a supplement of 20 new woodcut maps to the 27 Ptolemaic maps in Johannes Schott's edition of Ptolemy, printed in Strasbourg in 1520. Of this edition, Tovey (*Maps and their makers* 6th ed. London 1978) remarks, "The greatly increased number of 'modern maps' makes this in effect the first modern atlas", though other authorities incline to credit the "first modern atlas" to the *Theatrum orbis terrarum* published in 1570 by the Flemish cartographer Abraham Ortelius. (See also: Stetoff *The British Library companion to maps and mapmaking* 1995; Johnson *America explored* NY 1995.)

* Latinised as ILACOMILUS

** See PTOLEMAIC SYSTEM

[970] WALLACE LINE

The naturalist ALFRED RUSSEL WALLACE (1823-1913), who formulated, independently of Darwin, a theory of evolution by natural selection, made his first scientific explorations in South America in company with Henry Walter Bates. On the return journey, Wallace lost four years' worth of collections and notes when his ship caught fire and had to be abandoned. He was still able, however, to publish an account of his journey in *Travels on the Amazon and Rio Negro* (1853). In 1854 he set off for the East Indies and it was here that he observed what appeared to be a clear division between the avifauna of Bali and the neighbouring island of Lombok. As a result, Wallace posited two separate zoogeographical regions, Oriental and Australian, the latter taking in Australia, New Guinea and Tasmania. On the map, the WALLACE LINE starts between Lombok and Bali in the south and runs roughly north, separating Borneo from Sulawesi. Later biogeographers have posited a "mixing zone" between the two regions comprising the islands between Java and New Guinea and christened it "Wallacea". Wallace's later writings include *The Malay Archipelago* (1869), *Contributions to the theory of natural selection* (1870) and *The geographical distribution of animals* (1876). In 1890, appropriately, Wallace was the Royal Society's first DARWIN MEDALLIST.

[971] WALLACE SWORD

The sword supposedly wielded by WILLIAM WALLACE (1270?-1305), the hero who fought – and died a cruel death – for Scotch independence, is regarded in Scotland as a national treasure and invested with huge symbolic significance. The attribution of the sword – an impressive artifact if only for its size – to Wallace is shaky and might tempt an unkind critic to lump it together with other 19th-century tartanesque inventions. The same critic might even go so far as to point out that in general type the sword looks surprisingly like one of the oversize cabbage-cutters sported by the *landsknechts* in 16th century Germany.

[972] WANKEL ENGINE

A type of internal combustion engine in which the usual piston-and-cylinder arrangement is replaced by one which does away with the reciprocating motion of the piston and substitutes a rotating block. In section the block is shaped as a triangle with curved sides and the elliptical cylinder within which it revolves is shaped so as to form two gas-tight sections when mated with the curves in the block. The design was the invention of German engineer **FELIX WANKEL** (1902-1988). A working prototype was produced in 1956/7 but attempts to fit Wankel engines to production models of motor-cars initially encountered considerable problems caused by the difficulty in maintaining a gas-tight seal between the points of the revolving block (which naturally tend to wear down) and the sides of the combustion chamber. New materials have overcome this difficulty, and the engine is used to power the Mazda Rx8 sports car. However, the Wankel engine, though it produces lots of power from a small cubic capacity, is not as fuel-efficient as other car engines. Wankel worked as a consultant for a number of automotive-engineering firms and, despite a disagreement with the Nazi régime which earned him a spell in prison, did important war-work. He was entirely self-taught, having neither attended a university nor served an apprenticeship (a thing unheard-of in Germany). He was awarded an honorary engineering doctorate in 1969 plus numerous other distinctions. Wankel was known as a compassionate humanitarian who campaigned against the use of animals in scientific experiments. He is said never to have held a driving licence.

[973] WAR OF JENKINS' EAR

War between Britain and Spain which lasted from 1739 until 1748, merging into the War of the Austrian Succession when Spain was joined by France, and concluding with the Treaty of Utrecht. The nominal *casus belli* was the cutting off of an ear belonging to a certain **Captain ROBERT JENKINS** by Spanish *guarda-costas* at Havana. Underlying this act of unlicensed ototomy were grievances between English merchants and the Spanish colonial authorities concerning an agreement known as the "*asiento*" by which the British South Sea Company was accorded a monopoly in the supply of slaves to the Spanish possessions in North America. Also involved were disputes over the borders of Georgia and Carolina. One vaguely positive – and certainly memorable – incident of the war was the four-year circumnavigation of a squadron under Commodore (later Lord) Anson sent to harry Spanish possessions in South America and the Pacific. Anson, in spite of disasters to some of his ships and the loss of many of his men through sickness, performed his mission with dogged energy and returned home in his one remaining vessel *Centurion* a rich man, thanks to his capture of a Spanish treasure ship *Nuestra Señora de Covadonga* off the Philippines. He was later instrumental, as a Lord of the Admiralty from 1745 until his death in 1762, in combating corruption and inefficiency in the Navy – problems from which he and his crews had been the sufferers (see also **SANDWICH**). The standard first-hand account of Anson's voyage is that compiled by Richard Walter, chaplain in *Centurion* (numerous eds. from 1748 onward).

[974] WARDIAN CASE

A glass-sided, airtight container used by botanists, plant-collectors and agronomists for the transport of living specimens. It was the invention, in 1833, of English botanist and horticulturalist **NATHANIEL BAGSHAW WARD** (1791-1868). In the Victorian home, the **WARDIAN CASE** found employment for the display of living ferns, *etc.*, in an environment protected from the indoor pollution caused by coal fires, gas-lighting and cigar-smoking.

[975] WARE'S OPENING

While the begetter of this modest tome has claimed several personal eponymies with **JONES, JONES VECTOR, JONES REDUCTOR, JONES NUMBER** and **JONESTOWN**, his co-author has found only this one sad instance of like distinction. The **WARE OPENING** is widely acknowledged to be the worst of the 20 possible first moves in the game of chess. Algebraically: 1. a4, or in more colourful notation: 1. P-QR4. Almost any response by Black can put White at a disadvantage. Incredibly, there is also a **WARE DEFENCE** and even **WARE'S GAMBIT**, but the less said of these the better. American tournament chess-player **PRESTON WARE JNR.** (1821-1890), of Wrentham, Massachusetts, was noted for his unorthodox openings, which generally did him little good.* He created a scandal during the American Chess Congress of 1880 by accepting a $20 bribe from an opponent called Grundy who was desperate to win the prize money, for agreeing to play for a draw; but, as Ware later protested (in public, surprisingly): "...when we began to play I moved back and forth as agreed, and after I had done so, perhaps three or four times, I observed that he was making desperate efforts to win, and finally did so, perpetrating an infamous fraud upon me." This occasioned the wry press comment, "Ware's avowal of his right to sell a game in a tourney was a novelty in chess ethics... Ware's veracity has not been questioned, only his obliquity of moral vision." Amen to that. (MW)

* Though on one memorable occasion at the Second International Chess Tournament in Vienna in 1882, he did beat the World Champion, Wilhelm Steinitz, in a marathon game lasting 113 moves. Not with Ware's opening, however.

[976] WARNERKE'S SENSITOMETER

A sensitometer is an instrument for assessing the light-sensitivity or "speed" of photographic materials: plates, film and papers. The first such serviceable device was invented in 1880 by **LEON WARNERKE** (1837-1900?) a Russian civil engineer who settled in London in 1870, where he established a private photographic laboratory and acquired the reputation of a respected Fellow of the Royal Photographic Society. As recipient of the RPS Progress Medal in 1881, his innovations in photographic practice included: the invention of stripping film in

1881, and roll film in 1875, long before George Eastman's more widely recognised achievement, and – significantly – a photogravure system for intaglio etching of copper plates. WARNERKE'S application of these reprographic techniques was seemingly unsuccessful commercially, but his skills brought hidden benefits: his *alter ego* specialised in counterfeiting banknotes – chiefly Russian roubles and other Eastern European currencies (he had founded a photographic factory in St. Petersburg). His true name (spellings vary) was Vladislav Malakhovskii, and he is now acknowledged as one of the most successful forgers of the 19th Century. He was never brought to book for his crimes, but retired to Geneva and is suspected also of faking his own death there, to escape arrest. (MW)

[977] WATSONIA

HEWETT COTTERELL WATSON (1804-1881) was a botanist who inaugurated the first systematic, co-operative, survey of plant distribution in the British Isles. To this end he divided the country (including Ireland) into areas of equal size based on county boundaries, the larger counties being divided into two, three, or in the case of Yorkshire four, "vice-counties". To each vice-county is appointed an honorary Recorder (a respected local botanist, amateur or professional) whose job it is to maintain a regularly updated register of the wild plants growing in his or her area. Today the register is maintained by the Botanical Society of the British Isles (BSBI) which has its headquarters at the Natural History Museum, London, and which named its journal *WATSONIA* (founded 1949) in Watson's honour. Also bearing his name is the genus WATSONIA comprising some 50 species of flowering bulbs of the lily family, native to South Africa. (See also HOUSTON'S WHITEBEAM.)

[978] WATT

The Scots engineer and inventor, JAMES WATT (1736-1819), was born at Greenock on the Firth of Clyde, the son of a Presbyterian shipwright. His talents for mathematics and instrument-making were initially thwarted, but finally recognised by the eminent chemist, Professor Joseph Black, the discoverer of "latent heat", and Watt was employed to set up a workshop at the University of Glasgow in 1758. Becoming interested in steam, he saw ways of improving on NEWCOMEN'S ENGINE in 1763, which eventually led to a successful partnership with Birmingham ironmaster, Matthew Boulton in 1774, to manufacture and refine the steam engines which energised the Industrial Revolution. Watt successfully converted the reciprocating action of the piston into rotatory power, which brought the steam engine out of the mines, as a simple pump, and installed it in factories, ships, and railway locomotives.* A WATT, symbol W, is the familiar SI unit of power – the rate of doing work, or the rate of delivering or using energy – and is equal to one **JOULE** per second. It applies to all forms of energy – mechanical, electromagnetic, thermal, luminous, and chemical. (MW)

* Among Watt's innovations was the **WATT'S LINKAGE,** an arrangement of jointed rods to minimise the lateral displacement of the rod which connects the rocker arm of a beam engine to its piston and cylinder. The same principle is applied by car manfacturers in an arrangement of rods forming part of the rear suspension system and designed to prevent the axle moving sideways relative to the body of the car. (*Cf.* **CARDAN JOINT**)

[979] WBC HIVE

Form of beehive named after **WILLIAM BROUGHTON CARR**, editor of the *Bee Journal and Record*, who published the design in 1890. It was double-walled, the outer wall consisting of successive layers of removable "lifts" with the sloped sides which gave the WBC hive its familiar zig-zag profile. It has now been largely superseded among British beekeepers by the National Hive, plainly rectangular in form, consisting of a brood box surmounted by a stack of "supers" in which honey is made and stored. The number of supers is determined by the volume of storage space the bees require, depending on the season and the amount of food available.

[980] WEBB-ELLIS CUP

Trophy presented to the winner of the Rugby World Cup since 1987. It commemorates the alleged inventor of rugby football, **WILLIAM WEBB-ELLIS** (1806-1872), who, as a schoolboy at Rugby, "first took the ball in his arms and ran with it". The Webb-Ellis myth has been thoroughly explored and as thoroughly exploded. It is not backed by any first hand-evidence or any word on the subject from Ellis himself. The son of a cavalry officer killed at Albuera in 1811, Ellis became an Anglican clergyman and died in the south of France where his grave at Menton is cared for by French "*rugbymen*". It's worth noting that many of the regional forms of football still current in Britain in the 19th century had a very long history (originating perhaps as ritual contests over tribal boundaries) and involved getting the ball to the enemy's goal by any means short of tanks and artillery. Rules were either flexible (as was the case at Rugby School) or non-existent, and football as then played tended to resemble nothing so much as a game of *bush-kazi*, only with a ball instead of a dead goat.

[981] WEBER

The SI unit of magnetic flux, symbol Wb, has units of **TESLAS** times area in square meters: $T\ m^2$. A flux change of one **WEBER** per second induces an electromotive force of one **VOLT** in a circuit of one turn. **WILHELM EDUARD**

WEBER (1804-1891), the brother of physiologist **ERNST HEINRICH WEBER**, was a German physicist, who became professor at Halle, then Göttingen (1831) and Leipzig. He is chiefly remembered for his contributions to magnetism, including an atlas of geomagnetism (see also **SABINE'S GULL**). (MW)

[982] WEBER-FECHNER LAW

German physician **ERNST HEINRICH WEBER** (1795-1878), brother of physicist Wilhelm Eduard Weber, pioneered the quantitative study of human perceptual responses to external stimuli. With later embellishments from **GUSTAV THEODOR FECHNER** (1801-1887), he is remembered in the **WEBER-FECHNER LAW** of psychophysics, which may be summed up as: "The intensity of sensation is proportional to the logarithm of the stimulus." This appears to hold good, at least for vision (our sense of relative brightness), skin-sensitivity, and hearing (the logarithmic decibel scale). Thus, enhancing one's kicks follows a law of diminishing returns. (MW)

[983] WEDGWOOD

This English family name has come to define the highly characteristic stoneware produced by the dynastic firm of **JOSIAH WEDGWOOD AND SONS** founded in 1759. The Company first marketed a "creamware" product, patented and renamed as "Queens Ware" in 1765 thanks to the patronage of Queen Charlotte; but their best-known line is blue jasperware (1775) named for its resemblance to jasper – a hard, dense, opaque variety of quartz.* Wedgwood's characteristic decoration uses motifs of neoclassical style, often medallion-like, in white bas-relief against an unglazed pastel-coloured base of jasperware. Over 3000 pigment tests by Wedgwood yielded several base colours, but the preferred **WEDGWOOD BLUE** has now passed into the vocabulary of colour to designate a light, slightly greyish blue.** (See also the **PORTLAND VASE**, which was successfully copied by Wedgwood.) **JOSIAH WEDGWOOD I** (1730-1795) was born in Burslem, Staffordshire and apprenticed at the age of ten to his eldest brother. Benefiting from an association with the renowned potter, Thomas Whieldon, he became a master-potter, chemist, and pioneer founder of the modern ceramics industry. His eldest son, **JOSIAH WEDGWOOD II** (1769-1843) inherited the family business, and his daughter Susannah (1765-1817) became the mother of **CHARLES DARWIN** who also married a Wedgwood cousin, Emma, daughter of Josiah II. The youngest son, Tom Wedgwood (1771-1805) anticipated the invention of photography by making contact images on paper and white leather impregnated with silver nitrate, as reported by **HUMPHRY DAVY** in the *Proceedings of the Royal Institution* for 1802, 37 years before **TALBOT**'s announcement of his discovery. (MW)

* Not named after any person called "Jasper", but a derivative (via Greek and Latin) of a Semitic word meaning "speckled stone".

** **WEDGWOOD BLUE** is also the title of an exhibition of work by celebrated American colour photographer, William Eggleston, consisting of 50 photographs of the sky.

[984] WEGENER INSTITUTE

The **ALFRED WEGENER INSTITUTE FOR POLAR AND MARINE RESEARCH,** founded in 1980, has its headquarters at Bremerhaven in Germany. It takes its name from German meteorologist and geophysicist **ALFRED LOTHAR WEGENER** (1880-1930) who put forward the theory of continental drift in a 1912 paper entitled "Die Entstehung der Kontinente". As Wegener was unable to suggest a credible mechanism for sending entire continents steering randomly about the globe like vast slow-moving dodgem cars, his ideas were greeted with deep scepticism or even derision. It wasn't until the 1960's that better understanding of crustal processes and the new science of plate tectonics confirmed Wegener's theory, an outcome he unfortunately did not live to see. The Institute that bears his name is a member of the Helmholtz Association of German research centres and is funded by grants from federal and state governments. In 2009, in concert with India's National Institute of Oceanography, the Wegener Institute carried out a risky-sounding geo-engineering experiment in the Antarctic to test the idea that marine algae could be used as a mechanism for removing carbon dioxide from the atmosphere (see **EHUX**). A sizeable area of the Antarctic Ocean was seeded with a fertiliser (iron sulphate) aimed at stimulating algal growth – in which it succeeded, but only to see the extra growth promptly devoured by microscopic shrimp-like zooplankton. This was perhaps fortunate as an alternative outcome might have been to convert the entire ocean to an algal soup. (*Le Monde Diplomatique* Dec. 2009, p.15)

[985] WEIGELA

A genus of a dozen or so species of flowering deciduous shrubs native to eastern Asia. (Sometimes spelt **WEIGELIA** – and easier to pronounce in that form.) It is named after **CHRISTIAN EHRENFRIED WEIGEL** (1748-1831), who taught chemistry, pharmacy, botany and mineralogy at the University of Greifswald in northern Germany, near the present Polish border. In 1808 he was appointed personal physician to the Swedish royal family. Weigel was the inventor of a piece of chemical apparatus known as the contra-flow condenser, later improved by, and named after, **LIEBIG**.

[986] WEIL'S DISEASE

Properly known as *Leptospirosis* and more colourfully as "rat-catchers' yellows" (jaundice is frequently present). A nasty zoonotic disease caused by a spirochaete of the genus *Leptospira*. It affects a wide range of animals including dogs and farm animals, and transmission to humans is commonly through water contaminated by the urine of infected species, particularly rats – whence the common name – the bacterium gaining access through open wounds or via the mucous membranes or the eyes. Moral: don't swim where rats swim. The condition was first described in 1886 by German physician ADOLF WEIL (1848-1916) though the causative micro-organism was not identified until 1907 by two Japanese researchers Inada and Ito. Treatment is by antibiotics and prophylaxis by vaccination.

[987] WELLINGTON BOMBER

The VICKERS WELLINGTON was a mainstay of RAF Bomber Command throughout World War II. It was named after ARTHUR WELLESLEY, 1ST DUKE OF WELLINGTON (1769-1852), Britain's greatest soldier, and produced by Vickers Aircraft Engineering of Weybridge in Surrey. The first model (of many later variations and adaptations) had its maiden flight in 1936. Though the work of Vickers' head of design R.K. Pierson, it is inevitably associated also with the name of Barnes Wallis (1887-1979) of "bouncing bomb" fame, another of Vickers' designers, since the Wellington's fuselage was constructed on a lattice principle (the "geodesic" system later popularised by BUCKMINSTER FULLER) combining strength with lightness that Wallis had pioneered for airship construction (notably the successful R100 – not to be confused with the ill-fated R101*). The aircraft's nickname "Wimpy" is a reference to the "Popeye" cartoon character J. WELLINGTON WIMPY (see WIMPY BAR). The last Wellington built, one of only 2 known survivors, may be seen at the Royal Air Force Museum in London. The other is at the Brooklands motor and aviation museum in Surrey.

* In the sixties an attempt was made to interest Wallis in a proposed new generation of monocoque cargo airships but his fertile brain was busy elsewhere – with plans for a rocket-powered plane that would deliver passengers to Australia in a matter of minutes, but which has not yet left the drawing board – though still considered a viable proposition.

[988] WELLINGTON BOOT

Named after the tall boot favoured by the DUKE OF WELLINGTON (see above), after whom were also named a WWII bomber, a town in New Zealand, a way of cooking beef *en croûte*, and the WELLINGTONIA, a large tree (see below). The boot, originally of leather* was made of rubber following the discovery of the VULCANISATION process which enormously increased the range of objects and materials that could be made from raw rubber. This represented an enormous contribution to the comfort and health of all those forced to walk or work in wet and muddy places. It was, in, fact, the world's first waterproof footwear. In a peculiarly English fashion, however, this massively useful invention was adapted to the special requirements of the English class system with the appearance around the 1960s of the "green wellie" (preferably with pointless buckles on the sides) which neatly separated the landowning classes from the mere clodhoppers in their black wellies. And even the latter were subject to a further nice distinction thanks to the navvies' habit of turning down the tops of their boots, something the honest English farm-worker would never dream of doing.

* While fighting the French in Spain, Wellington still found time to issue detailed instructions to his London bootmaker on the exact design of his personal footwear.

[989] WELLINGTONIA

In 1853 Scotch plantsman John D. Matthew began to cultivate in this country seeds he had collected in California of the Giant Redwood or Big Tree, reckoned the world's largest living creature in terms of volume. In the same year it was named *Wellingtonia gigantea* by botanist John Lindley (1779-1865) in memory of the DUKE OF WELLINGTON who had died the year before. Unfortunately it turned out that the name was invalid as the generic name *Wellingtonia* had already been allotted to another plant of an unrelated family, *W. amottiana*. A similar fate befell a patriotic American attempt to christen it *Washingtonia californica* in 1854, as *Washingtonia* had already been bestowed on a genus of palm trees. The matter was not settled until 1939 when the name *Sequoiadendron giganteum* was proposed by American botanist John T. Bucholz, who also pointed out that the Giant Redwood differed sufficiently from the Coast Redwood (*Sequoia sempervirens*) to justify allotting it to a separate, monospecific genus. Despite these ups and downs, and despite accusations of cultural imperialism, the name "WELLINGTONIA" persists as a common name in Britain. Specimens may be seen at Kew, at Westonbirt Arboretum (Glos.), and at the Iron Duke's country seat, Stratfield Saye in Hampshire (planted in 1857). The tallest wellingtonia in Britain is said to be at Benmore in Scotland. (See also, SEQUOIA NATIONAL PARK.)

[990] WELSBACH GAS MANTLE

The coal gas flame is an efficient source of heat, but not of light (see BUNSEN BURNER). Before the distribution of generated electricity, our homes and streets had to be illuminated by candles, oil lamps, or gas flames. The latter would have been ineffectual but for the fact that certain metallic oxides, when heated to incandescence, depart markedly from the ideal behaviour of a "black body" radiator (see KIRCHHOFF'S LAW), and efficiently transform the flame's heat into bright white light. The "limelight" of the theatre in the 1820s is an example (lime is calcium oxide), but was impractical domestically. The Austrian nobleman and scientist-inventor, KARL AUER, FREIHERR VON WELSBACH (1858-1929), studied at the University of Vienna then obtained his doctorate under BUNSEN at Heidelberg, where he was responsible for identifying two of the rare earth elements, neodymium and praseodymium (see GADOLINIUM). In 1890 he discovered that a mixture of the oxides of THORIUM and CERIUM, in the ratio 99:1, was a most effective thermo-luminescent material. He capitalized on this commercially by ingeniously weaving the oxides with fabric threads into a hood-like mesh which sat over the burning gas-jet. This fragile lacework constituted the WELSBACH INCANDESCENT GAS MANTLE. It is still employed today in the "Tilley Storm Lamp" for outdoor enthusiasts as well as the wonderful "Aladdin" lamp (embodying an ARGAND BURNER) for indoor use. The Tilley Lamp may also be used indoors but the hissing noise it makes can be annoying. In 1903 Auer won a patent for the lighter "flint", consisting of 70% CERIUM and the rest iron. Quite a bright spark. (MW)

[991] WHEATSTONE BRIDGE

A device for measuring the electrical resistance of a circuit, named after its originator, the English physicist sir CHARLES WHEATSTONE (1802-1873). Wheatstone also invented the telegraph, pipping MORSE at the post, as well as an improved electrical generator. Wheatstone's bridge continues to prove its utility as the basis of a widely-used device for measuring strain in metal structures. And another of Wheatstone's inventions (or perhaps in this case we should say "wheezes") is a continuing source of harmless pleasure: to Wheatstone belongs the credit for the only musical instrument invented in this country – the concertina. Though it doesn't bear his name, this may be just as well. One can only with difficulty imagine one jolly sailor saying to another, "Give us a tune on your wheatstonium, Jack."

[992] WHITAKER'S ALMANACK

London publisher and bookseller JOSEPH WHITAKER (1820-1895) published his first almanac (that for 1869) in 1868. Almanacs, because they are based on astronomical data which cannot be reliably calculated more than a year in advance (see LAGRANGIAN POINTS), are published annually. *Whitaker's*, is a compendium of miscellaneous information with a solid reputation for the reliability of its facts and the width of its coverage, and remains today one of the most resorted-to single-volume reference sources for writers, broadcasters and journalists.

[993] WHITEHEAD TORPEDO

Lancashire-born ROBERT WHITEHEAD (1823-1905) stamped his mark on the development of the torpedo as a weapon which brought revolutionary change to naval warfare. After an engineering apprenticeship in Manchester, he became the manager of an Austrian engineering company in Fiume where he interested himself in the idea of setting off explosive charges under a vessel's waterline, but using underwater self-propelled vehicles to deliver the explosive rather than varieties of (frequently heroically-delivered) mine which were the fashion of the time. After numerous experiments and tests, he developed "The Secret" – a unique method of controlling the depth of the torpedo using a hydrostat/pendulum accurate to within about six inches. With the adoption (in 1895) of Ludwig Obry's gyroscope for azimuth control, contra-rotating propellers and a 3-cylinder Vee compressed-air engine, the basic features of the Whitehead torpedo were defined and incorporated in torpedoes up to the end of the nineteenth century. Whitehead was successful in developing, producing and selling his torpedoes to a long list of Navy customers, some of whom had tried with little success to develop their own designs. In 1871, the Admiralty purchased rights to his early designs and set up their own manufacturing facilities whilst Whitehead continued to sell his products worldwide. Demands for performance improvements drove the development of engines and saw the introduction of the heated or steam Torpedo which burned internal fuel to boost engine power. Whilst the Royal Navy originally envisaged using torpedoes mainly as surface-ship weapons, varieties were developed for submarine and aircraft launching. With the twentieth century development of the torpedo as a formidable underwater guided missile, it is remarkable that the Mark 8 Whitehead torpedo of mid-1930s vintage was used in anger by the Royal Navy nuclear submarine *Conqueror* as recently as 2 May 1982, a testament to the engineering brilliance of Robert Whitehead (see GENERAL BELGRANO). (GJ)

[994] WHITWORTH THREAD

These are engineering standards for screw thread, defining its angle, pitch and depth, for various diameters, using a British Imperial measure – inches. They comprise the British Standard Whitworth (BSW), British Standard Cycle (BSC), British Standard Fine (BSF) and British Association (BA) threads. All are merely relics of those heady days when Imperial mensuration spanned the World, now condemned to obsolescence by the Metric takeover and the *Système International*. Possibly the last survival is the tripod bush in the base of your camera, which is still 1/4 inch BSW.* The standards were proposed in 1841 by SIR JOSEPH WHITWORTH (1803-1887) who was born in Stockport, served an apprenticeship and worked as a mechanic on precision machine tools to become an outstandingly innovative engineer and one of Manchester's most worthy entrepreneurial sons. Under a commission from the War Department for an improved replacement for the LEE-ENFIELD RIFLE, he designed the WHITWORTH RIFLE. Though superior in accuracy, it was rejected by the British Government on the grounds of cost, but was adopted by the French army, and thence found its way into the hands of some Confederate forces of the American Civil War, who became known as **WHITWORTH SHARPSHOOTERS**. In 1867 Whitworth's engineering firm merged with that of engineer and armaments manufacturer Sir William Armstrong to become Armstrong Whitworth, and in 1927 a further merger gave birth to the firm of Vickers Armstrong. Whitworth supported the foundation of the Manchester Mechanics' Institute, later to become the University of Manchester Institute of Science and Technology (UMIST – see **OWENS COLLEGE**), and as a consequence of his bequests he is commemorated by the names of some important buildings around the University campus: the **WHITWORTH HALL**, the **WHITWORTH ART GALLERY**, and the student accommodation at **WHITWORTH PARK**. (MW)

* It is probably safe to assume that American Fine (AF) is still in use across The Pond. Check with your "Snap-on" dealer.

[995] WIGNER ENERGY

An early design of nuclear reactor, which probably gave rise to the popular name of "pile", uses blocks of graphite (rather like coke brickettes) to slow down the flux of neutrons causing the chain reaction. The internal structure of this graphite "moderator" suffers strain under the continuous neutron bombardment, building up a store of **WIGNER ENERGY** which, if inadvertently released, causes a sudden and dangerous temperature rise in the reactor core. This caused the fire in Windscale Pile 1 in 1957, which released 20,000 **CURIES** of radioactivity into the surrounding Cumbrian environment. It was not, however, the cause of the much worse disaster at the Chernobyl nuclear power plant ("the world's first coal-fired nuclear reactor") in 1986. The mathematical physicist **EUGENE PAUL WIGNER** (1902-1995), was the first to identify this problem. He was born to a Jewish family in Budapest, Austria-Hungary, studied at the Technische Hochschule, Berlin, and became a US citizen in 1937, working on the Manhattan Project (the construction of the first atomic bomb) at the University of Chicago during WWII (see **FERMI**). Besides the more pragmatic issues of nuclear reactor design, he was a profound theoretician, receiving the 1963 **NOBEL PRIZE** for physics, while professor at Princeton University, for his application of symmetry principles to quantum mechanics. (MW)

[996] WILLIAMS PEAR – See: BARTLETT PEAR

[997] WILSON CLOUD CHAMBER

Scots physicist **CHARLES THOMSON REES WILSON** (1869-1959) was born in Glencorse, near Edinburgh and educated at the Universities of Manchester, and Cambridge, where he pursued his academic career (FRS 1900), becoming reader in electrical meteorology (1919-1925) and Jacksonian professor of natural philosophy (1925-34). He studied atmospheric electricity and shared with **ARTHUR COMPTON** the Nobel prize for physics in 1927. In 1894 he invented the **WILSON CLOUD CHAMBER**, which became an important apparatus for physics to detect ionizing radiation. This is the principle of its operation: moisture-laden air in a closed vessel is forced to expand, cooling it suddenly (see **JOULE-THOMPSON EFFECT**), and causing super-saturation with water vapour, which is ready to condense on any foreign "nuclei" as tiny water droplets – a cloud, visible through the chamber's glass window. When energetic alpha or beta particles from radioactive decay, or cosmic rays, pass through the chamber, they leave a wake of charged ions in the air, promoting the condensation of "vapour trails", which map their tracks and behaviour. For instance, their deflection by electric and magnetic fields enables the particles' electric charges and masses to be determined. The cloud chamber was superseded in the 1960s by the bubble chamber, using liquid hydrogen. (MW)

[998] WILSON'S DISEASE

A rare, inherited, and dangerous metabolic disorder whereby the body is unable to excrete copper. The consequent toxic build-up shows itself in damage to various organs but notably to the central nervous system and to the liver. The condition was first described in 1854 by the German physician Friedrich Theodor Frerichs (1819-1855) but it was the British neurologist **SAMUEL ALEXANDER KINNIER WILSON** (1878-1937) who first detected the relationship between damage to the liver and damage to the putamen (a structure at the base of the brain). A similar condition, also caused by a recessive gene, occurs in Bedlington terriers.

[999] WIMPY BAR

Before ever Macdonald's golden arches came to beautify our townscapes, the concept of a chain of cheap and nasty restaurants with a hamburger-based menu was already up and running in this country. The Wimpy brand was created by Chicagoan Eddie Gold in the 1930s and named in honour of Popeye's burger-loving friend **J. WELLINGTON WIMPY**, an association it shares with the **WELLINGTON BOMBER**. The establishment of the Wimpy brand in Britain is due to the firm of J.J. Lyons who in the mid-50s managed to create a chain of restaurants with a truly disgusting menu and a decor that had that special kind of ketchup-stained formica seediness which is so English and so characteristic of the period.

[1000] WINCHESTER '73

OLIVER FISHER WINCHESTER (1810-1880) was a successful New England shirt manufacturer who turned to making rifles and pistols under patents owned by

Henry, Wesson, Spencer and others, and calling his firm the Winchester Repeating Arms Company. The Winchester repeater with its tubular magazine and underarm lever action embodied one improvement of Winchester's own, the gated slot in the body through which the magazine could be rapidly replenished. Among its advantages was the fact that it was chambered to accept common calibres of pistol ammunition. Later models were designed by Browning, Goering's favourite gunsmith. The weapon as owned and operated by James Stewart in Anthony Mann's splendid 1950 movie *Winchester '73* wasn't the only "gun that won the West". This enterprise required a multiplicity of firearms ranging from the Hawken rifle, through the Colt six-shooter, to the gigantic and terrifying Sharps buffalo gun, aided, of course, by epidemic measles and the Hereford cow. Nor was it only the West that the Winchester won. Stanley carried one of these weapons on his fateful Congo expedition of 1874-7. The Arab merchant known as Tippu Tib,* describes in his autobiography, the impression made by Stanley's Winchester on people who themselves were armed with so-called Tower muskets, a hundred years out of date:

> A month passed there until one afternoon Stanley appeared. We greeted him, welcomed him and gave him a house. The following morning we went to see him and he showed us a gun, telling us, "From this gun fifteen bullets come out!". Now we knew of no such gun firing fifteen rounds, neither knew of one nor had seen such. I asked him, "From a single barrel?" He said they came from a single barrel. So I asked him to fire it so that we could see. But he said we should produce a fee of twenty to thirty dollars for firing it once. In my heart I thought he was lying. A single-barrelled gun: the second I thought was a cleaning-rod! I said to him, "Over in Rumami there's a bow which takes twenty arrows. When you fire, all twenty fly together. And each arrow kills a man." At that he went outside and fired twelve rounds. Then he took a pistol and fired six rounds. He came back and sat down on the verandah. We were amazed. I asked him how he loaded the bullets and he showed me.**

After Winchester's death, his widow Sarah moved to California and began to build a house in what is today Silicon Valley. Through an informant in the spirit world she learned that the angry shades of dead and dispossessed Indians, including those killed by her husband's rifles, were out to get her but could not act until the house was finished. She launched accordingly into a programme of non-stop construction so that by the time of her death the house covered six acres of ground.

* Tippu Tib was the nickname of Hamed bin Mohammed el Murjebi, a Coast Arab, descendant of Omani traders, who built a virtual empire in East Africa based on the traffic in slaves and ivory. His

sphere of action stretched from Zanzibar to the upper Congo and might well eventually have reached the Atlantic had not its expansion been halted by the Belgians (brought there by Stanley) pushing up-river from the west.

** *Maisha ya Hamed bin Muhammad yaani TippuTip*, tr. Whiteley 1958, 1959 (original in Swahili).

[1001] WISDEN

Compendium of cricket facts and figures, published annually. It first appeared in 1864 on the initiative of cricketer turned publisher **JOHN WISDEN** (1826-1884) and was entitled *The Cricketer's Almanac*. The full modern title is *Wisden Cricketers' Almanac*.

[1002] WITCH OF AGNESI

belies her name. She is no witch, but a piece of mathematics: an algebraic cubic equation that defines a geometric curve which can drape itself elegantly and asymptotically over any circle. It is a bell-shaped curve with a very wide "mouth". It was published by the most famous female mathematician since Hypatia (5th century AD), **MARIA GAËTANA AGNESI** (1718-1799), who was born in Milan, the eldest of 21 children sired by a wealthy businessman in the course of his three marriages. Maria proved to be a child prodigy. Her father sought to exploit her polymathic talents and forbade her from entering a convent, as she wished, but did supply her with able tutors. She devoted herself to private study and published the first mathematical work by a woman: *Instituzioni analitiche ad uso della gioventù italiana* (1748). In 1750 Pope Benedict XIV offered her an Honorary Chair of Mathematics at the University of Bologna, but she preferred to retire into the religious and contemplative life. After the death of her father in 1752, she devoted herself and her wealth to charitable works as directress of the Hospice Trivulzio in Milan, where she also ended her days, in poverty. The misnomer **WITCH OF AGNESI** came about through a mistranslation. The curve had been studied in 1703 by Fr. Luigi Guido Grandi (1671-1742) who, in his commentary on Galileo of 1718, coined for it the name *la versiera* (Ital: "the turning one", supposedly from the Latin, *versoria:* "a rope that turns a sail"). Maria Agnesi also referred to the curve as *la versiera* in her treatise of 1748, but when this was translated into English by the Lucasian professor of Mathematics at Cambridge, John Colson (1680-1760),* he misread *la versiera* for *l'aversiera* (Ital: "she-devil" or "**WITCH**") and so the curve became known thereafter in English. (MW)

* Who taught himself Italian near the end of his life specifically for that purpose. His translation was published posthumously in 1801. NB: Some of the published explanations for the "Witch" seem as erroneous in their etymology as the original mistake (see **MUPHRY'S LAW**).

[1003] WITHERITE – see SCHEELITE

[1004] WOLCOTT CAMERA

A novel design of camera using a concave mirror, rather than a lens, as the imaging element. It has the advantage of a large effective aperture, and consequently short exposures. Moreover, the primary image has the correct handedness, which is important for daguerreotypes which are otherwise left-right reversed in a lens-based camera obscura. The disadvantage of the optical configuration is that the plate, which can only be very small, tends to obscure the aperture. American daguerreotypist **ALEXANDER SIMON WOLCOTT** (1804-1844) opened the first photographic portrait studio, a "Daguerrean Parlor", in New York City in 1840 and in the same year was granted the first photographic patent in the USA for his camera design. It was licensed to Richard Beard (1801-1885) when he opened his celebrated daguerreotype studio in London in 1841. Concave mirrors were used recently for imaging by British artist David Hockney, as described in his *Secret Knowledge* (2001), to illustrate his theory that a number of notable "old master" painters may have employed such optical devices to assist their picture-making. (MW)

[1005] WOLFRAM

Wolfram is the German word for the metallic element tungsten, atomic number 74, symbol W, adjacent to **TANTALUM** in the Periodic Table. Though it is a German personal name, no one knows after which Wolfram, if any, the metal is named, or who it was named by, or why, or when. Perhaps it should be considered a German equivalent of a name like "blue john" (a form of fluorspar found only in Derbyshire), which no one supposes is actually named after a person called John. *Uncle Tungsten* (1971) is an autobiographical memoir of a "chemical boyhood" by the psychiatrist Oliver Sacks. Recommended reading.

[1006] WOLFRAM'S SYNDROME

A rare genetic disorder of the central nervous system named after a **Dr. WOLFRAM** who first descibed it in 1938. Also known as DIDMOAD Syndrome (Diabetes Insipidus and Diabetes Mellitus with Optic Atrophy and Deafness). The aetiologly involves a protein christened **WOLFRAMIN**. There is no known treatment. The average life-expectancy of sufferers is 30 years.

[1007] WOODBURYTYPE

This photomechanical printing process, patented in 1864, produces beautiful monochrome images, usually of a rich purplish-brown, with a truly continuous tone, unlike the grain of a photogravure or the dot screen of a half-tone print. The picture densities depend on the thickness of the pigmented gelatin, so

WOODBURYTYPES show a luminous tonality and a perceptible bas-relief effect. A photographic negative was first printed onto dichromated gelatin, which hardened in light, and this relief positive was then embossed into a lead mould in a hydraulic press, to make the intaglio printing plate; woodburytypes therefore tend to be small. Also known as *photoglypty* or, in France, *Goupil gravure*, the process was much used from 1865 to *ca.* 1900 for art reproductions and high-quality book illustrations. Its inventor, **WALTER BENTLEY WOODBURY** (1834-1885) was born in Manchester, England. In 1852 he gave up his engineering apprenticeship and travelled to Australia to seek his fortune in the goldfields – unsuccessfully. After a stint at Melbourne waterworks, where he became a professional photographer, he travelled to the Dutch East Indies in 1857, forming a business partnership with expatriate photographer, James Page, and making many photographs in Java. Ill-health forced his return to England in 1863, where he devoted the rest of his life, tenaciously, to improving photographic processes and apparatus. In spite of taking out some twenty patents, he died impoverished. (MW)

[1008] WOOLTON PIE

Though during WWII the population of Britain never starved, food had to be rationed and opportunities for making a pig of oneself were limited. As a result we were, so it is said, physically fitter (and leaner – like whippets, one supposes) by the end of the war than is generally the case in the pampered and overfed present. Vegetables, briefly excepting onions, were not "on points" (*i.e.* rationed), thanks largely to the successful "Dig for Victory" campaign and to the activities of the "War Ag.", a government department which undertook the cultivation of under-producing land. Meanwhile, the Ministry of Food headed by **FREDERICK MARQUIS, LORD WOOLTON** (1883-1964) loudly sang the praises of the potato and the carrot in the hope of reconciling a population among whom vegetarianism was virtually unheard-of to the unavailability of meat. As a contribution to the campaign, the Savoy Hotel came up with a nourishing confection of root vegetables and oatmeal under a pastry crust which was promptly baptised **WOOLTON PIE**. It is noteworthy that the pie was supposed to be served with a brown gravy *as if* it were a meat pie.

[1009] WURLITZER

Most people on hearing the word "Wurlitzer" will (if the word means anything at all to them) mentally, and automatically, add the epithet "mighty", and into their minds will spring a picture of the instrument in question rising majestically from its subterranean lair in some cavernous Gaumont or Odeon cinema with Reginald Dixon at the console letting rip a thunderous rendition of "I'm forever blowing bubbles". The theatre organ, of which the **MIGHTY WURLITZER** is the ackowledged *ne plus ultra*, was originally designed to supply the musical accompaniment to silent movies but with the advent of the "talkies" shifted its ground and became an extra attraction or diversion to fill the intervals in the cinema's programme. This splendid beast, however, was very far from being the only instrument designed or sold by the Wurlitzer Company, which made or dealt in a wide variety of instruments from harps and guitars to juke boxes and electric pianos, while a separate branch of the firm dealt internationally in rare stringed instruments. The Wurlitzer family firm was founded by **FRANZ RUDOLPH WURLITZER** (1831-1914) in 1853, based originally in Cincinatti and later moving to Chicago. It ceased trading in the 1980's when it was bought out by the Baldwin Piano Company, a subsidiary of the Gibson Guitar Corporation. A list of surviving cinema organs in the UK made by Wurlitzer and others is held by the Cinema Organ Society (www.cinema-organs.uk)

Y

[1010] YABLOCHKOV CANDLE

An electric carbon arc lamp. The two electrodes are small parallel blocks of carbon separated by a thin layer of insulating plaster. When the arc is struck at one exposed end it burns away steadily, consuming the plaster, making this a more convenient configuration than the original design of carbon arc which called for continual adjustment of the positions of the electrodes. It was the brainchild of Russian electrical engineer **PAVEL NIKOLAYEVICH YABLOCHKOV** (1847-1894) who was born in Serdobsky, and studied at the Technical Galvanic School in St. Petersburg. He invented his arc light in 1876 and went to Paris to develop it commercially: **YABLOCHKOV CANDLES** were soon being used to light the Magasins du Louvre in 1877 and the Avenue de l'Opera for the Paris Exposition of 1878. The success of this improved form of electric lighting at the time caused a serious drop in the value of gas company shares. (MW)

[1011] YAGI ARRAY

A type of aerial known as an "end-fire array" characterised by its capacity for precise directionality, transmitting and/or receiving along an axis determined by the alignment of its parts, of which there are three: a dipole active element, director passive elements and a rear reflector. The dipole is an active element split into electrically separated aligned halves, each connected to one conductor of the feeder connecting the antenna to the receiver/transmitter. A "director" is an element of similar size to the whole dipole, where one or more placed in front of the dipole increases the sensititivity ("focus") of the array to the wanted signal frequency and improves rejection of off-axis signals. Element length & spacing are proportional to the wavelength of the wanted signal (higher frequency/shorter wavelength = shorter elements, more closely spaced), the dipole commonly being half the wavelength of the wanted signal. The Yagi antenna array was invented in 1926 by Shintaro Uda of Tohoku University, Japan working with **HIDETSUGU YAGI** (1886-1976) of the same university. Yagi's name is the one commonly attached to the device since he was the first to publish a description in English, but in the interests of credit-where-it-is-due, it is sometimes referred to as a Yagi-Uda antenna. The main uses of Yagi aerials are in television, direction-finding, and radio astronomy. They were widely used in WWII in airborne radars. (Ironically, Yagi arrays were incorporated into the two atom bombs dropped on Japan in WWII as part of their height measurement instrumentation.) Unlike mobile phones, which need omni-directional antennas (since you don't want to have to point your mobile directly at the fixed cell antenna),Yagi arrays are perfect for (*e.g.*) terrestrial television reception, where neither transmitter nor receiver are mobile. They are also much favoured by the "ham" (amateur radio) fraternity. (gj)

[1012] YALE LOCK

The pin-tumbler cylinder lock, to give it is proper title, was developed in the 1860's by American locksmith and inventor **LINUS YALE, JR** (1821-1868), basing his design on a prototype constructed by his father. In a Yale lock, the revolving barrel which activates the latch is locked in place by a number of spring-loaded two-part tumblers differing minutely in length. These prevent it from rotating until a key is inserted which raises each tumbler to the exact height needed to free the barrel. The Yale Lock Manufacturing company was established in Stamford, Connecticut by Yale and two partners in 1868, shortly before Yale's untimely death of heart failure. He was a descendant of the same family of Welsh immigrants as **ELIHU YALE**, eponymous benefactor of **YALE UNIVERSITY** (see below).

[1013] YALE UNIVERSITY

One of the oldest* American universities and one of the world's most prestigious, **YALE UNIVERSITY**, located in New Haven, Connecticut, was established by a charter of the State government in 1701 as a college for the education of ministers of religion. It was not until 1718 that the college completed its first building, made possible by the generosity of **ELIHU YALE** (1649-1721). Yale's reward was to have the college named after him. Yale was born in Boston but the family returned to England when he was only three and he never saw America again. On leaving school he obtained a clerk's post at the East India Company's offices in Leadenhall Street and one year later (1671) he was sent to India where he rose to become Governor of the Company's establishment at Fort St. George (Madras). As well as looking after the Company's affairs, he traded on his own account, as was the custom, and so successfully that by the time of his return to England (1699) he had amassed a huge fortune. Yale's benefaction may have been prompted by the fact that his father, a native of Denbighshire, was one of the original settlers of New Haven.

* Precedence in terms of age is contested among various American institutions of higher learning. Yale is generally allowed to be the third oldest, but the number of claimants to the first and second positions make it unlikely that the matter will ever be settled to everyone's satisfaction.

[1014] YANG HUI'S TRIANGLE – see **PASCAL'S TRIANGLE**

[1015] YAPP BINDING

Type of book cover made of limp leather without boards and with rounded corners, which overlaps, and folds down over, the edges of the text block. It is named after (but not invented by) a 19th-century London bookseller **WILLIAM YAPP**, who favoured it as a binding for pocket bibles, presumably because, being soft, it made them more easily pocketable.

[1016] YARBOROUGH

A term understood by players of bridge and whist to describe a hand of 13 cards in which none has a face value higher than 9. It takes its name from **CHARLES ANDERSON WORSLEY, 2ND EARL OF YARBOROUGH** (1809–1897) who is said to have risked a large wager (a thousand to one) on the non-occurrence of such a hand. We do not know if he ever paid out.

[1017] YERSINIA PESTIS

The causative agent of bubonic plague was discovered independently in 1894 by two researchers: the Japanese Shibasabura Kitasato (1852-1931), and the Swiss-born French bacteriologist **ALEXANDRE ÉMILE JEAN YERSIN** (1863-1943). In strict justice, it should be Kitasato's name attached to the organism since his was by a short head the prior discovery, but in the event the honour went to Yersin after a period during which the bacillus was known as *Pasteurella pestis* (still in occasional use). The Pasteur connection (see **PASTEUR INSTITUTES**) relates to the fact that Yersin studied under Pasteur in Paris, and worked at the Pasteur Institute there on diphtheria. He subsequently became inspector of the chain of Pasteur Institutes set up in French Indo-China, where he died. Though Yersin appreciated that there was a connection between rats and humans in plague outbreaks, it fell to another of Pasteur's researchers, Paul-Louis Simond (1858-1947), to isolate the final link in the chain of causation: the rat flea, which transmitted the bacillus when it transferred its attentions from an infected rat to a human host. Flea-borne bubonic plague has to be distinguished from the pneumonic variety carried by air-borne droplets from the coughing of infected persons. For a historical discussion of plague pandemics and an overview of what is known, debatable, or unknown about their nature, origin and spread, see *Plague and the end of Antiquity: the pandemic of 541-750* (ed. Little, CUP/American Academy in Rome, 2008).

[1018] YOUNG'S MODULUS

A measure of the stiffness of an elastic body, akin to the original **HOOKE'S LAW CONSTANT** for stretching springs, but redefined in 1807 by a more general and useful mathematical form, in which the **YOUNG'S MODULUS OF ELASTICITY** (symbol E) of a body is the ratio of the *Stress* (the force exerted per unit area of cross-section) to the *Strain* (the relative extension or contraction produced per unit length). The numerical value of Young's modulus is therefore expressed in PASCALS – the SI unit of pressure. THOMAS YOUNG (1773-1829) was one of the last true polymaths – making original contributions to such disparate fields as physics, physiology, medicine, linguistics and Egyptology. Young was born in Milverton, Somerset, of a Quaker family. He studied medicine in London and Edinburgh, and physics at Göttingen and Cambridge. He was elected FRS in 1794 and appointed professor of natural philosophy at the Royal Institution in 1801. Of independent means thanks to an inheritance, he practiced medicine in London from 1799, becoming physician to St George's Hospital in 1811. In physics, he demonstrated evidence for the wave theory of light, contrary to the prevailing corpuscular theory of NEWTON. He also studied surface tension and liquid capillarity, formulating the YOUNG-LAPLACE EQUATION in 1804. In 1802 he put forward a theory of trichromatic colour vision for the human eye, which was later elaborated in 1850 by HERMANN VON HELMHOLTZ to be known as the YOUNG-HELMHOLTZ theory, which has proved essentially correct. Young wrote extensively on the theory of linguistics and contributed to deciphering the Rosetta Stone and Egyptian hieroglyphs with promising results, though later eclipsed by the success of Champollion's decipherment. Any one of these achievements would have sufficed an ordinary mortal for a lifetime. His memorial plaque was placed in Westminster Abbey close to the burial place of Sir Isaac Newton. (MW)

Z

[1019] ZALUZIANSKYA

Genus of annual and perennial night-flowering plants belonging to the snapdragon family (*scrophulariaceae*) and native to South and East Africa. Also known as "night balsam" or "star balsam". The botanical name is that of Czech physician and botanist **ADAM ZALUZIANSKI,** who noted the hermaphroditic nature of plants' sexual apparatus a hundred and fifty years before **LINNAEUS.** His *Methodus rei herbariae* was published in Prague in 1592.

[1020] ZAMBONI

Anyone who doesn't smile fondly at the mention of the word "zamboni", isn't a fan of ice-hockey. This machine, properly known as an "ice-resurfacer", is manufactured exclusively by the firm of **FRANK J. ZAMBONI & CO,** named for its founder and the inventor (1949) of the device. It has only one function: repairing, by means of a thin layer of new, smooth ice, the scratched-up surface of ice-rinks in intervals between the three twenty-minute "periods" into which a match is divided. In appearance like some large mechanised insect and endowed with something of the same blend of elegance and absurdity we find in ducks, the Zamboni has, like the game it serves, its aficionados who, it seems, take positive pleasure in watching its stately evolutions, perhaps as a relaxing contrast to the hectic high-speed violence of the game itself.

[1021] ZEEMAN EFFECT

In the spectra of light emitted by excited atoms (see **BALMER** and **RYDBERG**) the bright lines of discrete wavelengths are observed to split into multiple components when the emitting substance is placed in a magnetic field. This **ZEEMAN EFFECT** is a useful tool for investigating atomic magnetism: spinning electrons behave like tiny bar magnets (see **PAULI**) and when oriented in an applied magnetic field, take on different energy states which, by **PLANCK'S LAW**, show up as a separation of the spectral lines. Dutch physicist **PIETER ZEEMAN** (1865-1943) was born in Zonnemaire and studied at the University of Leiden under Heike Kamerlingh Onnes (see **DEWAR VESSEL**) and **HENDRIK LORENTZ** (see **FITZGERALD-LORENTZ CONTRACTION**), submitting his doctoral thesis on the Kerr effect in 1893; in 1900 Zeeman became professor of physics at the University of Amsterdam, a successor to **VAN DER WAALS.** He shared the Nobel Prize for physics with Lorentz in 1902. (MW)

[1022] ZEISE'S SALT – see MAGNUS' GREEN SALT

[1023] ZEISS OPTICAL WORKS – see ABBE REFRACTOMETER

[1024] ZENER DIODE

A diode is an electronic device (in these days "solid state", *e.g.* a small chip of doped semiconductor such as silicon or germanium constituting a p-n junction) which allows electric current to flow through it in one direction only, *i.e.* it is a "rectifier" of alternating current. A ZENER DIODE is one which will also allow a current to flow in the *reverse* direction, but only when the applied voltage rises above a certain threshold value called the ZENER VOLTAGE. It is therefore useful as a voltage regulator in circuits and as a surge protector. American theoretical physicist CLARENCE MELVIN ZENER (1905-1993) was born in Indianapolis, obtained his PhD from Harvard and worked for Westinghouse, followed by an academic career in several American universities. (MW)

[1025] ZENO'S PARADOXES

A collection of puzzles attributed to ZENO OF ELEA (*ca.* 490-425 BC), which attempt to demonstrate by means of *reductio ad absurdum* the truth of the metaphysical teachings of Parmenides, of whom Zeno was a student. The two principal theses of Parmenidean metaphysics are as follows: first, there exists only one thing, *i.e.* monism is true; second, all change, particularly change through motion, is illusory. Although it is thought that the paradoxes originally numbered forty in total, only eight survive. Aristotle critically paraphrases four in the *Physics*. Of these the three most recognised are: (1) "The dichotomy". In order to cover any distance an object must first cover half of that distance. However, in order to cover half that object must first cover a quarter, which, in turn, requires that it cover an eighth, and so on *ad infinitum*. Since any distance can be halved, there is no *first* distance the object can cover and thus motion is illusory. (2) "Achilles and the tortoise": this is essentially a variation on (1). Suppose the Greek hero and a tortoise race one another. Suppose further that Achilles grants his opponent a handicap. Zeno maintains that the swifter Achilles will never catch the tortoise, for in order to do so Achilles must first cover half the distance separating them, and then half of the remaining distance and so on *ad infinitum*. (3) "The arrow", which requires that we think of time as composed of consecutive instants. Consider an arrow which appears to be in motion. Now, at each instant, claims Zeno, the arrow is at rest, insofar as it occupies an equal space for the whole of that instant. Because time is composed of nothing but instants, and because in each of these instants the arrow is stationary, the arrow, in fact, does not, and cannot, move. The Achilles heel of Zeno's paradoxes is the assumption that a line (following EUCLID) is made up of consecutive, discrete points and time of discrete moments, whereas the geometrical "point" and the "moment" in time are, in fact, covenient dimensionless abstractions which have no existence in the real world. Aside from the paradoxes little is known of Zeno's philosophy or, indeed, his life. His home town, Elea, was one of the Greek colonies of Southern Italy which made up *Magna Graecia*. Zeno and Parmenides are the most notable alumni of the school of philosophy founded there about 500 BC by Xenophanes of Colophon. (BS)

[1026] ZEPPELIN

The idea of steerable balloons or "dirigibles" (based on the CHARLIÈRE) goes back at least to the early 19th century when English cartoonists imagined the wily Frog-eaters invading our country by just such underhand/overhead methods. But it was to be another century before the internal combustion engine and the availability of light but strong structural materials such as aluminium made these fantasies realisable. And in the event, it wasn't the oily Frogs who violated our skies but the sausage-eating Germans. This was thanks almost entirely to one man, FERDINAND Graf VON ZEPPELIN (1838-1917), a prematurely retired military engineer officer whose contributions to the construction of lighter-than-air vehicles (tubular aluminium framework, porous outer skin, gas stored in separate cells) set the pattern for future development. His first working airship, LZ 1 was built near Friedrichshafen on the Bodensee (Lake Constance) and had her trial flight in July 1900. By the outbreak of WWI Zeppelin was building airships for the German Navy and by 1915 these were capable of reaching the English coast and wreaking havoc on places like Yarmouth, neatly demonstrating a combination of German engineering genius and Hunnish *Schrecklichkeit*.

[1027] ZIEGLER-NATTA CATALYST

At the door of this discovery we may lay the World's superfluity of polythene bags (80 million tonnes per annum). Certain metallic compounds – titanium halides and aluminium alkyls – have been found to catalyse the polymerization of that staple product of the petrocarbon industry, the gas ethene (ethylene) and related olefinic molecules, to make the long carbon chain polymers which our civilization has found so indispensible for carrying away its supermarket purchases, and whose stability will ensure their persistence in our environments for centuries to come. Of course, polythene (correctly polyethene, abbreviated to PE), polypropylene, *et al.*, have many more uses than this. German chemist KARL WALDEMAR ZIEGLER (1898-1973) was born near Kassel, educated at the University of Marburg, and became Director of the Max Planck Institut für Kohlenforschung from 1943-1969. Italian GIULIO NATTA (1903-1979) born at Imperia was educated at the University of Milan and held professorships at Pavia, Rome, Turin, then returned to Milan. The pair were awarded the Nobel Prize for Chemistry in 1963. (MW)

[1028] ZIMMER FRAME

A simple but effective walking aid for the elderly and infirm resembling a cross between a clothes horse and four walking sticks. "Zimmer" is a brand name owned by ZIMMER HOLDINGS INCORPORATED, a US-based multinational maker of orthopaedic implants, prosthetic devices, etc. ZIMMERIT, by contrast, was a hard-setting resin applied to German tanks and armoured vehicles during WWII in order to make an uneven surface which would defeat attempts to attach magnetic mines. It was manufactured by, and named after, a different Zimmer Company, CHEMISCHE WERKE ZIMMER, AG, a Berlin firm specialising in paint manufacture. Finally and for the record (so to speak) THE ZIMMERS is a British pop-group, whose members have an average age of 75 and who are responsible for a hit record entitled *My generation.*

[1029] ZIMMERMANN TELEGRAM

In outline, the story is as follows: (1) In January 1917, before America had entered the war against Germany, the German Foreign Minister ARTHUR ZIMMERMANN (1864-1940) sent a coded telegram to the German ambassador in Mexico inviting the Mexicans, in alliance with Germany, to attack the US. (2) In return for this service, the Mexicans were offered a chunk of US territory in the shape of New Mexico, Texas and Arizona. (3) The telegram was forwarded to Mexico by the Americans who were at the time allowing the Germans, who had no direct telegraphic contact with Mexico, to use their facilities. (4) The Americans refrained from decoding the telegram on the grounds that "gentlemen don't read each other's mail". (5) The British, on the other hand had no such scruples, at least where Germany was concerned. The telegram was intercepted and decoded by Naval Intelligence and its contents passed to the Americans, who proceeded, in March 1917, to publish it. (6) The ensuing brouhaha was of material help to President Wilson in carrying the American public with him when he declared war on Germany a few weeks later. There is, it has to be said, an air of unreality about the whole business. The story reads like the plot of a John Buchan novel or a Hitchcock film. And since fabricating mendacious excuses for going to war is something of an American tradition, while British Intelligence, as shown by the ZINOVIEV LETTER, was (and is) not above fraudulent manipulation of public opinion, it isn't being unduly cynical to suggest that the accepted account of the Zimmermann incident should perhaps be treated with at least a tinge of cautious scepticism. Against this, however, it needs to be pointed out that Zimmermann seems to have been exactly the kind of idiot for whom the idea of bribing Mexico to attack America would appear as a brilliant wheeze, and he is known to have involved himself in other schemes of the same sort aimed at Britain and at Russia. In the latter case these included sending Lenin to Russia in the famous "sealed train" in the hope that he would cause trouble. Zimmermann was likewise involved in Casement's abortive attempt to bring aid to the Irish rebels prior to the Easter Uprising, a plot that was also foiled – with fatal consequences for Casement – by London's interception of German diplomatic correspondence through Washington.*

* Sending Lenin to Russia was a tactic deliberately intended to increase the instability of the system – a risky proceeding at the best of times. However, unlike Casement's mission, it succeeded beyond Zimmermann's wildest dreams, as the Russians would no doubt have agreed when the inheritors of Lenin's revolution stormed into Berlin in the spring of 1945. Evidently Zimmermann had forgotten, if he ever knew, what most of us are supposed to have learned by the age of about 8: that our actions may have the consequences we intend but very seldom *only* the consequences we intend. It seems there are certain groups – politicians, economists, town-planners, military strategists – who find the Law of Unintended Consequences particularly hard to grasp.

[1030] ZIN(C)KENITE – see SCHEELITE

[1031] ZINNIA

This genus of (mainly) Mexican flowering plants was named ZINNIA by LINNAEUS in honour of JOHANN GOTTFRIED ZINN (1727-1759), Bavarian anatomist and botanist. Zinn was Director of the University's Botanic Garden at Göttingen (1753) and Professor at the Faculty of Medicine (1755). Anatomically Zinn is remembered for his studies of the human eye (1765) and in the delightfully-named ZONULE OF ZINN, not a character from *Star wars* but a structure located in the eyeball and also known as the ZINN-HALLER ARTERIAL CIRCLE (*Circulus arteriosus sclerae*). ALBRECHT VON HALLER (1708-1777) taught anatomy and physiology at Göttingen from 1736 to 1753.

[1032] ZINOVIEV LETTER

On October 5 1924, the *Daily Mail* published a letter ostensibly written by GRIGORI ZINOVIEV (1883-1936), Chairman of the Executive Committee of the Communist International (Comintern), and addressed to that organism's British representative Arthur MacManus. The letter urged British comrades to step up agitation, particularly in the armed forces. It came at a time when Ramsay Macdonald's minority Labour government (Britain's first) had formally recognised the infant USSR and was about to conclude a trade agreement with Russia – distressing symptoms in many people's eyes of a sinister bolshevising trend in Labour policies. Four days later MacDonald's government was roundly defeated in a general election and the succeeding Conservative administration repudiated the treaty. Historians are agreed that the letter was a forgery, but exactly where and by whom it was concocted and who engineered the plot to palm it off on the British Public are still matters for speculation and debate. The British secret services were certainly involved, and the Foreign Office probably, but the details remain unclear despite the best efforts of generations of researchers. Whether Lord Northcliffe, who at that time owned and managed the *Daily Mail*, was a party to the conspiracy, we do not know.* He may well have believed – and certainly would have wanted to believe – that the letter was genuine. As for the often-repeated assertion that the letter's publication helped towards Labour's election defeat, this logically depends on the unlikely assumption that the readers of a scurrilous fascist-leaning rag like the *Mail* were planning to vote Labour until the letter brought them to their senses. Zinoviev, as a leading player in the Russian Revolution, was inevitably a target for Stalin's murderous paranoia and was duly executed on trumped-up charges in 1936.

* It is a question why Press Barons so regularly turn out to be the kind of people you would set the dogs on if they showed up on your doorstep. The combined virtues of all the newspaper moguls from Gordon Bennet to Robert Maxwell rolled into one probably still wouldn't amount to one decent human being.

[1033] ZOISITE – see SCHEELITE

[1034] ZORN'S LEMMA

The word "lemma", borrowed, for no evident reason, from a classical Greek word (λέμμα) meaning "peel", "skin" or "husk" denotes a particular kind of philosophical or mathematical proposition. That associated with the name of the German-born American mathematician **MAX AUGUST ZORN** (1906-1993) relates to a branch of mathematics known as Set Theory and is sometimes identified with another proposition called the Axiom of Choice. (Caution here! A lemma is not *quite* the same thing as an axiom.) To try and explain exactly what Zorn's Lemma says or means would be a futile undertaking since only a mathematician who already knew what it meant could understand the explanation. And it is a well-established fact that no mathematician, however skilful, can explain Set Theory to a non-mathematician (Molebag's Law of Incommunicability). However, this difficulty did not deter intrepid avant-garde cinéaste Hollis Frampton (1936-1984) from making a film entitled *Zorn's Lemma* in 1970. Though rated as "difficult" it is only 60 minutes in length and so may still tempt the bold enquirer. Finally, and for the record, it should be stated that **ZORN'S LEMUR** (a kind of lemur) and **ZORN'S LEMON** (a kind of fruit) are figments of some joker's imagination and can have no place in any serious work on mathematics or in this dictionary.

[1035] ZOROASTRIANISM

The religion of ancient Persia. It takes its name from **ZOROASTER** (Nietzsche's

Zarathustra) who is thought to have lived about 500 BC. He taught that the world is ruled by two deities of equal power: Ahuramazda (Ormuzd) the god of light, and Ahriman the god of darkness. This dualist view of the human condition, which it must be said has much to recommend it, recurs in a number of Christian heresies such as **MANICHAEISM**. The modern descendants of the Zoroastrians are the Parsees* now found mainly in Western India, whither they fled to escape the advance of militant Islam in the 8th century.** A pleasant legend relates how the refugees applied to a local rajah for permission to settle. He sent back his reply in the form of a bowl brimming with water: no room. They returned the bowl still full of water but now with a large pearl in the bottom – and duly obtained their *permis de séjour*.

* *i.e.* Persians (*cf.* "Farsi")

** There may still be a tiny dualist faction in Persia in the form of the Yezidis of Kurdistan, rumoured to be devil worshippers, though we have little certain information about their beliefs and practices which, according to C.D. Darlington, "they are able to keep secret even from Freya Stark". See also E.G. Browne *A year among the Persians* (1893), and *Encyclopaedia Britannica* (11th ed.)

INDEX OF TOPICS

References are to numbered entries, not pages.

INDEX OF PERSONS

Excludes subjects of headwords.
References are to numbered entries, not pages.